20. $\displaystyle\int \frac{du}{u\sqrt{a+bu}} = \begin{cases} \dfrac{1}{\sqrt{a}}\ln\left|\dfrac{\sqrt{a+bu}-\sqrt{a}}{\sqrt{a+bu}+\sqrt{a}}\right| + C & \text{if } a>0 \\[3mm] \dfrac{2}{\sqrt{-a}}\tan^{-1}\sqrt{\dfrac{a+bu}{-a}} + C & \text{if } a<0 \end{cases}$

22. $\displaystyle\int \frac{\sqrt{a+bu}\,du}{u} = 2\sqrt{a+bu} + a\int \frac{du}{u\sqrt{a+bu}}$

21. $\displaystyle\int \frac{du}{u^n\sqrt{a+bu}} = -\frac{\sqrt{a+bu}}{a(n-1)u^{n-1}} - \frac{b(2n-3)}{2a(n-1)}\int \frac{du}{u^{n-1}\sqrt{a+bu}}$

23. $\displaystyle\int \frac{\sqrt{a+bu}\,du}{u^n} = -\frac{(a+bu)^{3/2}}{a(n-1)u^{n-1}} - \frac{b(2n-5)}{2a(n-1)}\int \frac{\sqrt{a+bu}\,du}{u^{n-1}}$

Forms Containing $a^2 \pm u^2$

24. $\displaystyle\int \frac{du}{a^2+u^2} = \frac{1}{a}\tan^{-1}\frac{u}{a} + C$

25. $\displaystyle\int \frac{du}{a^2-u^2} = \frac{1}{2a}\ln\left|\frac{u+a}{u-a}\right| + C = \begin{cases} \dfrac{1}{a}\tanh^{-1}\dfrac{u}{a} + C & \text{if } |u|<a \\[3mm] \dfrac{1}{a}\coth^{-1}\dfrac{u}{a} + C & \text{if } |u|>a \end{cases}$

26. $\displaystyle\int \frac{du}{u^2-a^2} = \frac{1}{2a}\ln\left|\frac{u-a}{u+a}\right| + C = \begin{cases} -\dfrac{1}{a}\tanh^{-1}\dfrac{u}{a} + C & \text{if } |u|<a \\[3mm] -\dfrac{1}{a}\coth^{-1}\dfrac{u}{a} + C & \text{if } |u|>a \end{cases}$

Forms Containing $\sqrt{u^2 \pm a^2}$

In formulas 27 through 38, we may replace

$\ln(u+\sqrt{u^2+a^2})$ by $\sinh^{-1}\dfrac{u}{a}$

$\ln|u+\sqrt{u^2-a^2}|$ by $\cosh^{-1}\dfrac{u}{a}$

$\ln\left|\dfrac{a+\sqrt{u^2+a^2}}{u}\right|$ by $\sinh^{-1}\dfrac{a}{u}$

27. $\displaystyle\int \frac{du}{\sqrt{u^2\pm a^2}} = \ln|u+\sqrt{u^2\pm a^2}| + C$

28. $\displaystyle\int \sqrt{u^2\pm a^2}\,du = \frac{u}{2}\sqrt{u^2\pm a^2} \pm \frac{a^2}{2}\ln|u+\sqrt{u^2\pm a^2}| + C$

29. $\displaystyle\int u^2\sqrt{u^2\pm a^2}\,du = \frac{u}{8}(2u^2\pm a^2)\sqrt{u^2\pm a^2}$
$\displaystyle\qquad\qquad - \frac{a^4}{8}\ln|u+\sqrt{u^2\pm a^2}| + C$

30. $\displaystyle\int \frac{\sqrt{u^2+a^2}\,du}{u} = \sqrt{u^2+a^2} - a\ln\left|\frac{a+\sqrt{u^2+a^2}}{u}\right| + C$

31. $\displaystyle\int \frac{\sqrt{u^2-a^2}\,du}{u} = \sqrt{u^2-a^2} - a\sec^{-1}\left|\frac{u}{a}\right| + C$

32. $\displaystyle\int \frac{\sqrt{u^2\pm a^2}\,du}{u^2} = -\frac{\sqrt{u^2\pm a^2}}{u} + \ln|u+\sqrt{u^2\pm a^2}| + C$

33. $\displaystyle\int \frac{u^2\,du}{\sqrt{u^2\pm a^2}} = \frac{u}{2}\sqrt{u^2\pm a^2} - \frac{\pm a^2}{2}\ln|u+\sqrt{u^2\pm a^2}| + C$

34. $\displaystyle\int \frac{du}{u\sqrt{u^2+a^2}} = -\frac{1}{a}\ln\left|\frac{a+\sqrt{u^2+a^2}}{u}\right| + C$

35. $\displaystyle\int \frac{du}{u\sqrt{u^2-a^2}} = \frac{1}{a}\sec^{-1}\left|\frac{u}{a}\right| + C$

36. $\displaystyle\int \frac{du}{u^2\sqrt{u^2\pm a^2}} = -\frac{\sqrt{u^2\pm a^2}}{\pm a^2 u} + C$

37. $\displaystyle\int (u^2\pm a^2)^{3/2}\,du = \frac{u}{8}(2u^2\pm 5a^2)\sqrt{u^2\pm a^2}$
$\displaystyle\qquad\qquad + \frac{3a^4}{8}\ln|u+\sqrt{u^2\pm a^2}| + C$

38. $\displaystyle\int \frac{du}{(u^2\pm a^2)^{3/2}} = \frac{u}{\pm a^2\sqrt{u^2\pm a^2}} + C$

Forms Containing $\sqrt{a^2-u^2}$

39. $\displaystyle\int \frac{du}{\sqrt{a^2-u^2}} = \sin^{-1}\frac{u}{a} + C$

40. $\displaystyle\int \sqrt{a^2-u^2}\,du = \frac{u}{2}\sqrt{a^2-u^2} + \frac{a^2}{2}\sin^{-1}\frac{u}{a} + C$

41. $\displaystyle\int u^2\sqrt{a^2-u^2}\,du = \frac{u}{8}(2u^2-a^2)\sqrt{a^2-u^2} + \frac{a^4}{8}\sin^{-1}\frac{u}{a} + C$

42. $\displaystyle\int \frac{\sqrt{a^2-u^2}\,du}{u} = \sqrt{a^2-u^2} - a\ln\left|\frac{a+\sqrt{a^2-u^2}}{u}\right| + C$
$\displaystyle\qquad\qquad = \sqrt{a^2-u^2} - a\cosh^{-1}\frac{a}{u} + C$

43. $\displaystyle\int \frac{\sqrt{a^2-u^2}\,du}{u^2} = -\frac{\sqrt{a^2-u^2}}{u} - \sin^{-1}\frac{u}{a} + C$

(This table is continued on the back endpapers)

THE CALCULUS
WITH ANALYTIC GEOMETRY

THE CALCULUS
WITH ANALYTIC GEOMETRY
third edition

Part II Infinite series, vectors, and functions of several variables

Louis Leithold

UNIVERSITY OF SOUTHERN CALIFORNIA

HARPER & ROW, PUBLISHERS
New York, Evanston, San Francisco, London

To Gordon Marc

Sponsoring Editor: George J. Telecki
Project Editor: Karen A. Judd
Designer: Rita Naughton
Production Supervisor: Francis X. Giordano
Compositor: Progressive Typographers
Printer and Binder: Kingsport Press
Art Studio: J & R Technical Services Inc.
Cover and chapter opening art: "Study Light" by Patrick Caulfield

THE CALCULUS WITH ANALYTIC GEOMETRY, Third Edition
Part II: Infinite Series, Vectors, and Functions of Several Variables.

Copyright © 1968, 1972, 1976 by Louis Leithold

Library of Congress Cataloging in Publication Data
Leithold, Louis.
    The calculus, with analytic geometry.

Includes index.
    CONTENTS: pt. 1.   Functions of one variable,
plane analytic geometry, and infinite series. — pt.
2. Infinite series, vectors, and functions of
several variables.
    1. Calculus. 2. Geometry, Analytic. I. Title.
QA303.L428 1976   515'.15   75-25981
ISBN 0-06-043949-1 (v. 2)

Contents

Preface   *vii*

Chapter 16
INFINITE SERIES
page 659

16.1   Sequences   *660*
16.2   Monotonic and Bounded Sequences   *667*
16.3   Infinite Series of Constant Terms   *673*
16.4   Infinite Series of Positive Terms   *684*
16.5   The Integral Test   *694*
16.6   Infinite Series of Positive and Negative Terms   *697*
16.7   Power Series   *707*
16.8   Differentiation of Power Series   *713*
16.9   Integration of Power Series   *722*
16.10   Taylor Series   *729*
16.11   The Binomial Series   *738*

Chapter 17
VECTORS IN THE PLANE
AND PARAMETRIC
EQUATIONS
page 745

17.1   Vectors in the Plane   *746*
17.2   Properties of Vector Addition and Scalar Multiplication   *751*
17.3   Dot Product   *756*
17.4   Vector-Valued Functions and Parametric Equations   *763*
17.5   Calculus of Vector-Valued Functions   *772*
17.6   Length of Arc   *779*
17.7   Plane Motion   *785*
17.8   The Unit Tangent and Unit Normal Vectors and Arc Length as a Parameter   *792*
17.9   Curvature   *796*
17.10   Tangential and Normal Components of Acceleration   *804*

Chapter 18
VECTORS IN THREE-
DIMENSIONAL SPACE AND
SOLID ANALYTIC
GEOMETRY
page 810

18.1 R^3, The Three-Dimensional Number Space   *811*
18.2   Vectors in Three-Dimensional Space   *818*
18.3   The Dot Product in V_3 *825*
18.4   Planes   *829*
18.5   Lines in R^3 *836*
18.6   Cross Product   *842*
18.7   Cylinders and Surfaces of Revolution   *852*

18.8   Quadric Surfaces   *858*
18.9   Curves in R^3 *864*
18.10 Cylindrical and Spherical Coordinates   *872*

Chapter 19
DIFFERENTIAL CALCULUS
OF FUNCTIONS OF
SEVERAL VARIABLES
page 880

19.1   Functions of More Than One Variable   *881*
19.2   Limits of Functions of More Than One Variable   *889*
19.3   Continuity of Functions of More Than One Variable   *900*
19.4   Partial Derivatives   *905*
19.5   Differentiability and the Total Differential   *913*
19.6   The Chain Rule   *926*
19.7   Higher-Order Partial Derivatives   *934*

Chapter 20
DIRECTIONAL DERIVATIVES,
GRADIENTS, APPLICATIONS
OF PARTIAL DERIVATIVES,
AND LINE INTEGRALS
page 944

20.1   Directional Derivatives and Gradients   *945*
20.2   Tangent Planes and Normals to Surfaces   *953*
20.3   Extrema of Functions of Two Variables   *956*
20.4   Some Applications of Partial Derivatives to Economics   *967*
20.5   Obtaining a Function from Its Gradient   *976*
20.6   Line Integrals   *981*
20.7   Line Integrals Independent of the Path   *989*

Chapter 21
MULTIPLE INTEGRATION
page 1001

21.1   The Double Integral   *1002*
21.2   Evaluation of Double Integrals and Iterated Integrals   *1008*
21.3   Center of Mass and Moments of Inertia   *1016*
21.4   The Double Integral in Polar Coordinates   *1022*
21.5   Area of a Surface   *1028*
21.6   The Triple Integral   *1034*
21.7   The Triple Integral in Cylindrical and Spherical Coordinates   *1039*

APPENDIX
page A-1

Table 1 Powers and Roots   *A-2*
Table 2 Natural Logarithms   *A-3*
Table 3 Exponential Functions   *A-5*
Table 4 Hyperbolic Functions   *A-12*
Table 5 Trigonometric Functions   *A-13*
Table 6 Common Logarithms   *A-14*
Table 7 The Greek Alphabet   *A-16*

ANSWERS TO ODD-NUMBERED EXERCISES   *A-17*

INDEX   *A-25*

Preface

This third edition of THE CALCULUS WITH ANALYTIC GEOMETRY, like the other two, is designed for prospective mathematics majors as well as for students whose primary interest is in engineering, the physical sciences, or nontechnical fields. A knowledge of high-school algebra and geometry is assumed.

The text is available either in one volume or in two parts: Part I consists of the first sixteen chapters, and Part II comprises Chapters 16 through 21 (Chapter 16 on Infinite Series is included in both parts to make the use of the two-volume set more flexible). The material in Part I consists of the differential and integral calculus of functions of a single variable and plane analytic geometry, and it may be covered in a one-year course of nine or ten semester hours or twelve quarter hours. The second part is suitable for a course consisting of five or six semester hours or eight quarter hours. It includes the calculus of several variables and a treatment of vectors in the plane, as well as in three dimensions, with a vector approach to solid analytic geometry.

The objectives of the previous editions have been maintained. I have endeavored to achieve a healthy balance between the presentation of elementary calculus from a rigorous approach and that from the older, intuitive, and computational point of view. Bearing in mind that a textbook should be written for the student, I have attempted to keep the presentation geared to a beginner's experience and maturity and to leave no step unexplained or omitted. I desire that the reader be aware that proofs of theorems are necessary and that these proofs be well motivated and carefully explained so that they are understandable to the student who has achieved an average mastery of the preceding sections of the book. If a theorem is stated without proof, I have generally augmented the discussion by both figures and examples, and in such cases I have always stressed that what is presented is an illustration of the content of the theorem and is not a proof.

Changes in the third edition occur in the first five chapters. The first section of Chapter 1 has been rewritten to give a more detailed exposition of the real-number system. The introduction to analytic geometry in this chapter includes the traditional material on straight lines as well as that of the circle, but a discussion of the parabola is postponed to Chapter 14, The Conic Sections. Functions are now introduced in Chapter 1. I have defined a function as a set of ordered pairs and have used this idea to point up the concept of a function as a correspondence between sets of real numbers.

The treatment of limits and continuity which formerly consisted of ten sections in Chapter 2 is now in two chapters (2 and 4), with the chapter on the derivative placed between them. The concepts of limit and continuity are at the heart of any first course in the calculus. The notion of a limit of a function is first given a step-by-step motivation, which brings the discussion from computing the value of a function near a number, through an intuitive treatment of the limiting process, up to a rigorous epsilon-delta definition. A sequence of examples progressively graded in difficulty is included. All the limit theorems are stated, and some proofs are presented in the text, while other proofs have been outlined in the exercises. In the discussion of continuity, I have used as examples and counterexamples "common, everyday" functions and have avoided those that would have little intuitive meaning.

In Chapter 3, before giving the formal definition of a derivative, I have defined the tangent line to a curve and instantaneous velocity in rectilinear motion in order to demonstrate in advance that the concept of a derivative is of wide application, both geometrical and physical. Theorems on differentiation are proved and illustrated by examples. Application of the derivative to related rates is included.

Additional topics on limits and continuity are given in Chapter 4. Continuity on a closed interval is defined and discussed, followed by the introduction of the Extreme-Value Theorem, which involves such functions. Then the Extreme-Value Theorem is used to find the absolute extrema of functions continuous on a closed interval. Chapter 4 concludes with Rolle's Theorem and the Mean-Value Theorem. Chapter 5 gives additional applications of the derivative, including problems on curve sketching as well as some related to business and economics.

The antiderivative is treated in Chapter 6. I use the term "antidifferentiation" instead of indefinite integration, but the standard notation $\int f(x)\, dx$ is retained so that you are not given a bizarre new notation that would make the reading of standard references difficult. This notation will suggest that some relation must exist between definite integrals, introduced in Chapter 7, and antiderivatives, but I see no harm in this as long as the presentation gives the theoretically proper view of the definite integral as the limit of sums. Exercises involving the evaluation of definite integrals by finding limits of sums are given in Chapter 7 to stress that this is how they are calculated. The introduction of the definite integral follows the definition of the measure of the area under a curve as a limit of sums. Elementary properties of the definite integral are derived and the fundamental theorem of the calculus is proved. It is emphasized that this is a theorem, and an important one, because it provides us with an alternative to computing limits of sums. It is also emphasized that the definite integral is in no sense some special type of antiderivative. In Chapter 8 I have given numerous applications of definite integrals. The presentation highlights not only the manipulative techniques but also the fundamental principles involved. In each application, the definitions of the new terms are intuitively motivated and explained.

The treatment of logarithmic and exponential functions in Chapter 9 is the modern approach. The natural logarithm is defined as an integral, and after the discussion of the inverse of a function, the exponential function is defined as the inverse of the natural logarithmic function. An irrational power of a real number is then defined. The trigonometric functions are defined in Chapter 10 as functions assigning numbers to numbers. The important trigonometric identities are derived and used to obtain the formulas for the derivatives and integrals of these functions. Following are sections on the differentiation and integration of the trigonometric functions as well as of the inverse trigonometric functions.

Chapter 11, on techniques of integration, involves one of the most important computational aspects of the calculus. I have explained the theoretical backgrounds of each different method after an introductory motivation. The mastery of integration techniques depends upon the examples, and I have used as illustrations problems that the student will certainly meet in practice, those which require patience and persistence to solve. The material on the approximation of definite integrals includes the statement of theorems for computing the bounds of the error involved in these approximations. The theorems and the problems that go with them, being self-contained, can be omitted from a course if the instructor so wishes.

A self-contained treatment of hyperbolic functions is in Chapter 12. This chapter may be studied immediately following the discussion of the circular trigonometric functions in Chapter 10, if so desired. The geometric interpretation of the hyperbolic functions is postponed until Chapter 17 because it involves the use of parametric equations.

Polar coordinates and some of their applications are given in Chapter 13. In Chapter 14, conics are treated as a unified subject to stress their natural and close relationship to each other. The parabola is discussed in the first two sections. Then equations of the conics in polar coordinates are treated, and the cartesian equations of the ellipse and the hyperbola are derived from the polar equations. The topics of indeterminate forms, improper integrals, and Taylor's formula, and the computational techniques involved, are presented in Chapter 15.

I have attempted in Chapter 16 to give as complete a treatment of infinite series as is feasible in an elementary calculus text. In addition to the customary computational material, I have included the proof of the equivalence of convergence and boundedness of monotonic sequences based on the completeness property of the real numbers and the proofs of the computational processes involving differentiation and integration of power series.

The first five sections of Chapter 17 on vectors in the plane can be taken up after Chapter 5 if it is desired to introduce vectors earlier in the course. The approach to vectors is modern, and it serves both as an introduction to the viewpoint of linear algebra and to that of classical vector analysis. The applications are to physics and geometry. Chapter 18 treats vectors in three-dimensional space, and, if desired, the topics in the first three sections of this chapter may be studied concurrently with the corresponding topics in Chapter 17.

Limits, continuity, and differentiation of functions of several variables are considered in Chapter 19. The discussion and examples are applied mainly to functions of two and three variables; however, statements of most of the definitions and theorems are extended to functions of n variables.

In Chapter 20, a section on directional derivatives and gradients is followed by a section that shows the application of the gradient to finding an equation of the tangent plane to a surface. Applications of partial derivatives to the solution of extrema problems and an introduction to Lagrange multipliers are presented, as well as a section on applications of partial derivatives in economics. Three sections, new in the third edition, are devoted to line integrals and related topics. The double integral of a function of two variables and the triple integral of a function of three variables, along with some applications to physics, engineering, and geometry, are given in Chapter 21.

New to this edition is a short table of integrals appearing on the front and back endpapers. However, as stated in Chapter 11, you are advised to use a table of integrals only after you have mastered integration.

Louis Leithold

ACKNOWLEDGMENTS

Reviewers of *The Calculus with Analytic Geometry*

Professor William D. Bandes, San Diego Mesa College
Professor Archie D. Brock, East Texas State University
Professor Phillip Clarke, Los Angeles Valley College
Professor Reuben W. Farley, Virginia Commonwealth University
Professor Jacob Golightly, Jacksonville University
Professor Robert K. Goodrich, University of Colorado
Professor Albert Herr, Drexel University
Professor James F. Hurley, University of Connecticut
Professor Gordon L. Miller, Wisconsin State University
Professor William W. Mitchell, Jr., Phoenix College
Professor Roger B. Nelsen, Lewis and Clark College
Professor Robert A. Nowlan, Southern Connecticut State College
Sister Madeleine Rose, Holy Names College
Professor George W. Schultz, St. Petersburg Junior College
Professor Donald R. Sherbert, University of Illinois
Professor John Vadney, Fulton-Montgomery Community College
Professor David Whitman, San Diego State College

Production Staff at Harper & Row

George Telecki, Mathematics Editor
Karen Judd, Project Editor
Rita Naughton, Designer

Assistants for Answers to Exercises

Jacqueline Dewar, Loyola Marymount University
Ken Kast, Logicon, Inc.
Jean Kilmer, West Covina Unified School District

Cover and Chapter Opening Artist

Patrick Caulfield, London, England

To these people and to all the users of the first and second editions who have suggested changes, I express my deep appreciation.

L. L.

16

Infinite series

16.1 SEQUENCES   You have undoubtedly encountered sequences of numbers in your previous study of mathematics. For example, the numbers 5, 7, 9, 11, 13, 15
define a sequence. This sequence is said to be *finite* because there is a
first and last number. If the set of numbers which defines a sequence does
not have both a first and last number, the sequence is said to be *infinite*.
For example, the sequence defined by

$$\tfrac{1}{3}, \tfrac{2}{5}, \tfrac{3}{7}, \tfrac{4}{9}, \; . \; . \; . \tag{1}$$

is infinite because the three dots with no number following indicate
that there is no last number. We are concerned here with infinite sequences, and when we use the word "sequence" it is understood that
we are referring to an infinite sequence. We define a sequence as a particular kind of function.

16.1.1 Definition   A *sequence* is a function whose domain is the set of positive integers.

The numbers in the range of the sequence, which are called the *elements* of the sequence, are restricted to real numbers in this book.

If the nth element is given by $f(n)$, then the sequence is the set of
ordered pairs of the form $(n, f(n))$, where n is a positive integer.

- ILLUSTRATION 1: If $f(n) = n/(2n + 1)$, then

$$f(1) = \tfrac{1}{3} \qquad f(2) = \tfrac{2}{5} \qquad f(3) = \tfrac{3}{7} \qquad f(4) = \tfrac{4}{9}$$

and so on. We see that the range of f consists of the elements of sequence
(1). Some of the ordered pairs in the sequence f are $(1, \tfrac{1}{3})$, $(2, \tfrac{2}{5})$, $(3, \tfrac{3}{7})$,
$(4, \tfrac{4}{9})$, and $(5, \tfrac{5}{11})$. A sketch of the graph of this sequence is shown in
Fig. 16.1.1. •

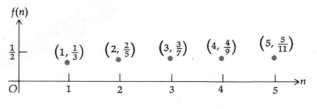

Figure 16.1.1

Usually the nth element $f(n)$ of the sequence is stated when the elements are listed in order. Thus, for the elements of sequence (1) we would
write

$$\frac{1}{3}, \frac{2}{5}, \frac{3}{7}, \frac{4}{9}, \; . \; . \; . \; , \frac{n}{2n + 1}, \; . \; . \; .$$

Because the domain of every sequence is the same, we can use the
notation $\{f(n)\}$ to denote a sequence. So the sequence (1) can be denoted

by $\{n/(2n+1)\}$. We also use the subscript notation $\{a_n\}$ to denote the sequence for which $f(n) = a_n$.

You should distinguish between the elements of a sequence and the sequence itself, as shown in the following illustration.

● ILLUSTRATION 2: The sequence $\{1/n\}$ has as its elements the reciprocals of the positive integers

$$1, \frac{1}{2}, \frac{1}{3}, \frac{1}{4}, \cdots, \frac{1}{n}, \cdots \tag{2}$$

The sequence for which

$$f(n) = \begin{cases} 1 & \text{if } n \text{ is odd} \\ \dfrac{2}{n+2} & \text{if } n \text{ is even} \end{cases}$$

has as its elements

$$1, \tfrac{1}{2}, 1, \tfrac{1}{3}, 1, \tfrac{1}{4}, \cdots \tag{3}$$

The elements of sequences (2) and (3) are the same; however, the sequences are different. Sketches of the graphs of sequences (2) and (3) are shown in Figs. 16.1.2 and 16.1.3, respectively.   ●

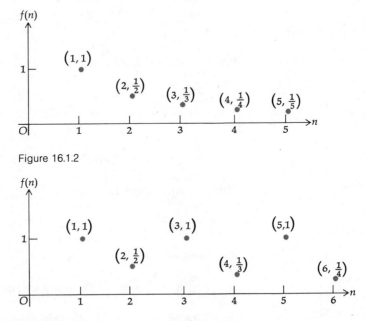

Figure 16.1.2

Figure 16.1.3

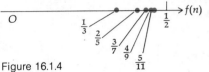

Figure 16.1.4

We now plot on a horizontal axis the points corresponding to successive elements of a sequence. This is done in Fig. 16.1.4 for sequence (1) which is $\{n/(2n+1)\}$. We see that the successive elements of the sequence get closer and closer to $\frac{1}{2}$, even though no element in the sequence has the value $\frac{1}{2}$. Intuitively we see that the element will be as close to $\frac{1}{2}$ as we please by taking the number of the element sufficiently large. Or stating this another way, we can make $|n/(2n+1) - \frac{1}{2}|$ less than any given ϵ by taking n large enough. Because of this we state that the limit of the sequence $\{n/(2n+1)\}$ is $\frac{1}{2}$.

In general, if there is a number L such that $|a_n - L|$ is arbitrarily small for n sufficiently large, we say the sequence $\{a_n\}$ has the limit L. Following is the precise definition of the limit of a sequence.

16.1.2 Definition   A sequence $\{a_n\}$ is said to have the limit L if for every $\epsilon > 0$ there exists a number $N > 0$ such that $|a_n - L| < \epsilon$ for every integer $n > N$; and we write

$$\lim_{n \to +\infty} a_n = L$$

EXAMPLE 1: Use Definition 16.1.2 to prove that the sequence

$$\left\{ \frac{n}{2n+1} \right\}$$

has the limit $\frac{1}{2}$.

SOLUTION: We must show that for any $\epsilon > 0$ there exists a number $N > 0$ such that

$$\left| \frac{n}{2n+1} - \frac{1}{2} \right| < \epsilon \qquad \text{for every integer } n > N$$

$$\left| \frac{n}{2n+1} - \frac{1}{2} \right| = \left| \frac{2n - 2n - 1}{2(2n+1)} \right| = \left| \frac{-1}{4n+2} \right| = \frac{1}{4n+2}$$

Hence, we must find a number $N > 0$ such that

$$\frac{1}{4n+2} < \epsilon \qquad \text{for every integer } n > N$$

But

$$\frac{1}{4n+2} < \epsilon \quad \text{is equivalent to} \quad 2n + 1 > \frac{1}{2\epsilon}$$

which is equivalent to

$$n > \frac{1 - 2\epsilon}{4\epsilon}$$

So it follows that

$$\left| \frac{n}{2n+1} - \frac{1}{2} \right| < \epsilon \qquad \text{for every integer } n > \frac{1 - 2\epsilon}{4\epsilon}$$

Therefore, if $N = (1 - 2\epsilon)/4\epsilon$, Definition 16.1.2 holds.
In particular, if $\epsilon = \frac{1}{8}$, $N = (1 - \frac{1}{4})/\frac{1}{2} = \frac{3}{2}$. So

$$\left| \frac{n}{2n+1} - \frac{1}{2} \right| < \frac{1}{8} \qquad \text{for every integer } n > \frac{3}{2}$$

For instance, if $n = 4$,

$$\left| \frac{n}{2n+1} - \frac{1}{2} \right| = \left| \frac{4}{9} - \frac{1}{2} \right| = \left| \frac{-1}{18} \right| = \frac{1}{18} < \frac{1}{8}$$

• ILLUSTRATION 3: Consider the sequence $\{(-1)^{n+1}/n\}$. Note that the nth element of this sequence is $(-1)^{n+1}/n$ and $(-1)^{n+1}$ is equal to $+1$ when n is odd and to -1 when n is even. Hence, the elements of the sequence can be written

$$1, -\frac{1}{2}, \frac{1}{3}, -\frac{1}{4}, \frac{1}{5}, \cdots, \frac{(-1)^{n+1}}{n}, \cdots$$

In Fig. 16.1.5 are plotted points corresponding to successive elements of this sequence. In the figure, $a_1 = 1$, $a_2 = -\frac{1}{2}$, $a_3 = \frac{1}{3}$, $a_4 = -\frac{1}{4}$, $a_5 = \frac{1}{5}$, $a_6 = -\frac{1}{6}$, $a_7 = \frac{1}{7}$, $a_8 = -\frac{1}{8}$, $a_9 = \frac{1}{9}$, $a_{10} = -\frac{1}{10}$. The limit of the sequence is 0 and the elements oscillate about 0. •

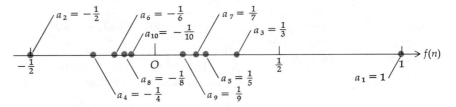

Figure 16.1.5

Compare Definition 16.1.2 with Definition 4.1.1 of the limit of $f(x)$ as x increases without bound. The two definitions are almost identical; however, when we state that $\lim\limits_{x \to +\infty} f(x) = L$, the function f is defined for all real numbers greater than some real number R, while when we consider $\lim\limits_{n \to +\infty} a_n$, n is restricted to positive integers. We have, however, the following theorem which follows immediately from Definition 4.1.1.

16.1.3 Theorem   If $\lim\limits_{x \to +\infty} f(x) = L$, and f is defined for every positive integer, then also $\lim\limits_{n \to +\infty} f(n) = L$ when n is any positive integer.

The proof is left as an exercise (see Exercise 20).

• ILLUSTRATION 4: We verify Theorem 16.1.3 for the sequence of Example 1. For that sequence $f(n) = n/(2n+1)$. Hence, $f(x) = x/(2x+1)$ and

$$\lim_{x \to +\infty} \frac{x}{2x+1} = \lim_{x \to +\infty} \frac{1}{2 + \dfrac{1}{x}} = \frac{1}{2}$$

It follows then from Theorem 16.1.3 that $\lim\limits_{n \to +\infty} f(n) = \frac{1}{2}$ when n is any positive integer. This agrees with the solution of Example 1. ●

16.1.4 Definition If a sequence $\{a_n\}$ has a limit, the sequence is said to be *convergent,* and we say that a_n *converges* to that limit. If the sequence is not convergent, it is said to be *divergent.*

EXAMPLE 2: Determine if the sequence

$$\left\{\frac{4n^2}{2n^2 + 1}\right\}$$

is convergent or divergent.

SOLUTION: We wish to determine if $\lim\limits_{n \to +\infty} 4n^2/(2n^2 + 1)$ exists. Let $f(x) = 4x^2/(2x^2 + 1)$ and investigate $\lim\limits_{x \to +\infty} f(x)$.

$$\lim_{x \to +\infty} \frac{4x^2}{2x^2 + 1} = \lim_{x \to +\infty} \frac{4}{2 + \dfrac{1}{x^2}} = 2$$

Therefore, by Theorem 16.1.3, $\lim\limits_{n \to +\infty} f(n) = 2$. We conclude that the given sequence is convergent and that $4n^2/(2n^2 + 1)$ converges to 2.

EXAMPLE 3: Prove that if $|r| < 1$, the sequence $\{r^n\}$ is convergent and that r^n converges to zero.

SOLUTION: First of all, if $r = 0$, the sequence is $\{0\}$ and $\lim\limits_{x \to +\infty} 0 = 0$. Hence, the sequence is convergent and the nth element converges to zero.

If $0 < |r| < 1$, we consider the function f defined by $f(x) = r^x$, where x is any positive number, and show that $\lim\limits_{x \to +\infty} r^x = 0$. Then from Theorem 16.1.3 it will follow that $\lim\limits_{n \to +\infty} r^n = 0$ when n is any positive integer.

To prove that $\lim\limits_{x \to +\infty} r^x = 0$ $(0 < |r| < 1)$, we shall show that for any $\epsilon > 0$ there exists a number $N > 0$ such that

$$|r^x - 0| < \epsilon \qquad \text{whenever } x > N \tag{4}$$

Statement (4) is equivalent to

$$|r|^x < \epsilon \qquad \text{whenever } x > N$$

which is true if and only if

$$\ln |r|^x < \ln \epsilon \qquad \text{whenever } x > N$$

or, equivalently,

$$x \ln |r| < \ln \epsilon \qquad \text{whenever } x > N \tag{5}$$

Because $0 < |r| < 1$, $\ln |r| < 0$. Thus, (5) is equivalent to

$$x > \frac{\ln \epsilon}{\ln |r|} \qquad \text{whenever } x > N$$

Therefore, if we take $N = \ln \epsilon/\ln |r|$, we may conclude (4). Consequently, $\lim\limits_{x \to +\infty} r^x = 0$, and so $\lim\limits_{n \to +\infty} r^n = 0$ if n is any positive integer. Hence, by Definitions 16.1.2 and 16.1.4, $\{r^n\}$ is convergent and r^n converges to zero.

EXAMPLE 4:   Determine if the sequence $\{(-1)^n + 1\}$ is convergent or divergent.

SOLUTION: The elements of this sequence are 0, 2, 0, 2, 0, 2, . . . , $(-1)^n + 1$, ... Because $a_n = 0$ if n is odd, and $a_n = 2$ if n is even, it appears that the sequence is divergent. To prove this, let us assume that the sequence is convergent and show that this assumption leads to a contradiction. If the sequence has the limit L, then by Definition 16.1.2, for every $\epsilon > 0$ there exists a number $N > 0$ such that $|a_n - L| < \epsilon$ for every integer $n > N$. In particular, when $\epsilon = \frac{1}{2}$, there exists a number $N > 0$ such that

$$|a_n - L| < \tfrac{1}{2} \quad \text{for every integer } n > N$$

or, equivalently,

$$-\tfrac{1}{2} < a_n - L < \tfrac{1}{2} \quad \text{for every integer } n > N \tag{6}$$

Because $a_n = 0$ if n is odd and $a_n = 2$ if n is even, it follows from (6) that

$$-\tfrac{1}{2} < -L < \tfrac{1}{2} \quad \text{and} \quad -\tfrac{1}{2} < 2 - L < \tfrac{1}{2}$$

But if $-L > -\tfrac{1}{2}$, then $2 - L > \tfrac{3}{2}$; hence, $2 - L$ cannot be less than $\tfrac{1}{2}$. So we have a contradiction, and therefore the given sequence is divergent.

EXAMPLE 5:   Determine if the sequence

$$\left\{ n \sin \frac{\pi}{n} \right\}$$

is convergent or divergent.

SOLUTION: We wish to determine if $\lim\limits_{n \to +\infty} n \sin(\pi/n)$ exists. Let $f(x) = x \sin(\pi/x)$ and investigate $\lim\limits_{x \to +\infty} f(x)$. Because $f(x)$ can be written as $[\sin(\pi/x)]/(1/x)$ and $\lim\limits_{x \to +\infty} \sin(\pi/x) = 0$ and $\lim\limits_{x \to +\infty} (1/x) = 0$, we can apply L'Hôpital's rule and obtain

$$\lim_{x \to +\infty} f(x) = \lim_{x \to +\infty} \frac{-\dfrac{\pi}{x^2} \cos \dfrac{\pi}{x}}{-\dfrac{1}{x^2}} = \lim_{x \to +\infty} \pi \cos \frac{\pi}{x} = \pi$$

Therefore, $\lim\limits_{n \to +\infty} f(n) = \pi$ when n is a positive integer. So the given sequence is convergent and $n \sin(\pi/n)$ converges to π.

We have limit theorems for sequences, which are analogous to limit theorems for functions given in Chapter 2. We state these theorems by using the terminology of sequences. The proofs are omitted because they are almost identical to the proofs of the corresponding theorems given in Chapter 2.

16.1.5 Theorem   If $\{a_n\}$ and $\{b_n\}$ are convergent sequences and c is a constant, then

(i) the constant sequence $\{c\}$ has c as its limit;

(ii) $\lim\limits_{n \to +\infty} ca_n = c \lim\limits_{n \to +\infty} a_n$;

(iii) $\lim\limits_{n \to +\infty} (a_n \pm b_n) = \lim\limits_{n \to +\infty} a_n \pm \lim\limits_{n \to +\infty} b_n$;

(iv) $\lim_{n\to+\infty} a_n b_n = (\lim_{n\to+\infty} a_n)(\lim_{n\to+\infty} b_n);$

(v) $\lim_{n\to+\infty} \dfrac{a_n}{b_n} = \dfrac{\lim_{n\to+\infty} a_n}{\lim_{n\to+\infty} b_n}$ if $\lim_{n\to+\infty} b_n \neq 0.$

EXAMPLE 6:   Use Theorem 16.1.5 to prove that the sequence

$$\left\{ \frac{n^2}{2n+1} \sin \frac{\pi}{n} \right\}$$

is convergent and find the limit of the sequence.

SOLUTION:

$$\frac{n^2}{2n+1} \sin \frac{\pi}{n} = \frac{n}{2n+1} \cdot n \sin \frac{\pi}{n}$$

In Example 1 we showed that the sequence $\{n/(2n+1)\}$ is convergent and $\lim_{n\to+\infty} [n/(2n+1)] = \frac{1}{2}$. In Example 5 we showed that the sequence $\{n \sin(\pi/n)\}$ is convergent and $\lim_{n\to+\infty} [n \sin(\pi/n)] = \pi$. Hence, by Theorem 16.1.5(iv),

$$\lim_{n\to+\infty} \left[\frac{n}{2n+1} \cdot n \sin \frac{\pi}{n} \right] = \lim_{n\to+\infty} \frac{n}{2n+1} \cdot \lim_{n\to+\infty} n \sin \frac{\pi}{n} = \frac{1}{2} \cdot \pi$$

Thus, the given sequence is convergent, and its limit is $\frac{1}{2}\pi$.

Exercises 16.1

In Exercises 1 through 4, use Definition 16.1.2 to prove that the given sequence has the limit L.

1. $\left\{ \dfrac{3}{n-1} \right\}$; $L = 0$

2. $\left\{ \dfrac{1}{\sqrt{n}} \right\}$; $L = 0$

3. $\left\{ \dfrac{8n}{2n+3} \right\}$; $L = 4$

4. $\left\{ \dfrac{5-n}{2+3n} \right\}$; $L = -\frac{1}{3}$

In Exercises 5 through 19, determine if the sequence is convergent or divergent. If the sequence converges, find its limit.

5. $\left\{ \dfrac{n+1}{2n-1} \right\}$

6. $\left\{ \dfrac{2n^2+1}{3n^2-n} \right\}$

7. $\left\{ \dfrac{n^2+1}{n} \right\}$

8. $\left\{ \dfrac{3n^3+1}{2n^2+n} \right\}$

9. $\left\{ \dfrac{\ln n}{n^2} \right\}$

10. $\left\{ \dfrac{e^n}{n} \right\}$

11. $\{\tanh n\}$

12. $\left\{ \dfrac{\log_b n}{n} \right\}$, $b > 1$

13. $\left\{ \dfrac{n}{n+1} \sin \dfrac{n\pi}{2} \right\}$

14. $\left\{ \dfrac{\sinh n}{\sin n} \right\}$

15. $\left\{ \dfrac{1}{\sqrt{n^2+1}-n} \right\}$

16. $\{\sqrt{n+1} - \sqrt{n}\}$

17. $\left\{ \left(1 + \dfrac{1}{3n}\right)^n \right\}$

18. $\left\{ \left(1 + \dfrac{2}{n}\right)^n \right\}$

(HINT: Use $\lim_{x\to 0} (1+x)^{1/x} = e$.)

See Hint for Exercise 17.

19. $\{r^{1/n}\}$ and $r > 0$. (HINT: Consider two cases: $r \le 1$ and $r > 1$.)

20. Prove Theorem 16.1.3.

21. Prove that if $|r| < 1$, the sequence $\{nr^n\}$ is convergent and nr^n converges to zero.

22. Prove that if the sequence $\{a_n\}$ is convergent and $\lim_{n \to +\infty} a_n = L$, then the sequence $\{|a_n|\}$ is also convergent and $\lim_{n \to +\infty} |a_n| = |L|$.

23. Prove that if the sequence $\{a_n\}$ is convergent and $\lim_{n \to +\infty} a_n = L$, then the sequence $\{a_n^2\}$ is also convergent and $\lim_{n \to +\infty} a_n^2 = L^2$.

24. Prove that if the sequence $\{a_n\}$ converges, then $\lim_{n \to +\infty} a_n$ is unique. (HINT: Assume that $\lim_{n \to +\infty} a_n$ has two different values, L and M, and show that this is impossible by taking $\epsilon = \frac{1}{2}|L - M|$ in Definition 16.1.2.)

16.2 MONOTONIC AND BOUNDED SEQUENCES

We shall be concerned with certain kinds of sequences which are given special names.

16.2.1 Definition   A sequence $\{a_n\}$ is said to be

  (i) *increasing* if $a_n \leq a_{n+1}$ for all n;
  (ii) *decreasing* if $a_n \geq a_{n+1}$ for all n.

If a sequence is increasing or if it is decreasing, it is called *monotonic*.

Note that if $a_n < a_{n+1}$ (a special case of $a_n \leq a_{n+1}$), we have a *strictly increasing* sequence; if $a_n > a_{n+1}$, we have a *strictly decreasing* sequence.

EXAMPLE 1:   For each of the following sequences determine if it is increasing, decreasing, or not monotonic:

  (a) $\{n/(2n + 1)\}$
  (b) $\{1/n\}$
  (c) $\{(-1)^{n+1}/n\}$

SOLUTION: (a) The elements of the sequence can be written

$$\frac{1}{3}, \frac{2}{5}, \frac{3}{7}, \frac{4}{9}, \cdots, \frac{n}{2n + 1}, \frac{n + 1}{2n + 3}, \cdots$$

Note that a_{n+1} is obtained from a_n by replacing n by $n + 1$. Therefore, because $a_n = n/(2n + 1)$,

$$a_{n+1} = \frac{n + 1}{2(n + 1) + 1} = \frac{n + 1}{2n + 3}$$

Looking at the first four elements of the sequence, we see that the elements increase as n increases. Thus, we suspect in general that

$$\frac{n}{2n + 1} \leq \frac{n + 1}{2n + 3} \tag{1}$$

Inequality (1) can be verified if we find an equivalent inequality which we know is valid. Multiplying each member of inequality (1) by $(2n + 1)(2n + 3)$, we obtain

$$n(2n + 3) \leq (n + 1)(2n + 1) \tag{2}$$

Inequality (2) is equivalent to inequality (1) because (1) may be obtained from (2) by dividing each member by $(2n + 1)(2n + 3)$. Inequality (2) is equivalent to

$$2n^2 + 3n \leq 2n^2 + 3n + 1 \tag{3}$$

Inequality (3) obviously holds because the right member is 1 greater than the left member. Therefore, inequality (1) holds and so the given sequence is increasing.

(b) The elements of the sequence can be written

$$1, \frac{1}{2}, \frac{1}{3}, \frac{1}{4}, \cdots, \frac{1}{n}, \frac{1}{n+1}, \cdots$$

Because

$$\frac{1}{n} > \frac{1}{n+1}$$

for all n, the sequence is decreasing.

(c) The elements of the sequence can be written

$$1, -\frac{1}{2}, \frac{1}{3}, -\frac{1}{4}, \cdots, \frac{(-1)^{n+1}}{n}, \frac{(-1)^{n+2}}{n+1}, \cdots$$

$a_1 = 1$ and $a_2 = -\frac{1}{2}$, and so $a_1 > a_2$. But $a_3 = \frac{1}{3}$, and so $a_2 < a_3$. In a more general sense, consider three consecutive elements $a_n = (-1)^{n+1}/n$, $a_{n+1} = (-1)^{n+2}/(n+1)$, and $a_{n+2} = (-1)^{n+3}/(n+2)$. If n is odd, $a_n > a_{n+1}$ and $a_{n+1} < a_{n+2}$, and if n is even, $a_n < a_{n+1}$ and $a_{n+1} > a_{n+2}$. Hence, the sequence is neither increasing nor decreasing and so is not monotonic.

16.2.2 Definition The number C is called a *lower bound* of the sequence $\{a_n\}$ if $C \leq a_n$ for all positive integers n, and the number D is called an *upper bound* of the sequence $\{a_n\}$ if $a_n \leq D$ for all positive integers n.

• ILLUSTRATION 1: The number zero is a lower bound of the sequence $\{n/(2n + 1)\}$ whose elements are

$$\frac{1}{3}, \frac{2}{5}, \frac{3}{7}, \frac{4}{9}, \cdots, \frac{n}{2n+1}, \cdots$$

Another lower bound of this sequence is $\frac{1}{3}$. Actually any number which is less than or equal to $\frac{1}{3}$ is a lower bound of this sequence.   •

• ILLUSTRATION 2: For the sequence $\{1/n\}$ whose elements are

$$1, \frac{1}{2}, \frac{1}{3}, \frac{1}{4}, \cdots, \frac{1}{n}, \cdots$$

1 is an upper bound; 26 is also an upper bound. Any number which is greater than or equal to 1 is an upper bound of this sequence, and any nonpositive number will serve as a lower bound.   •

From Illustrations 1 and 2, we see that a sequence may have many upper and lower bounds.

16.2.3 Definition   If A is a lower bound of a sequence $\{a_n\}$ and if A has the property that for every lower bound C of $\{a_n\}$, $C \leq A$, then A is called the *greatest lower bound* of the sequence. Similarly, if B is an upper bound of a sequence $\{a_n\}$ and if B has the property that for every upper bound D of $\{a_n\}$, $B \leq D$, then B is called the *least upper bound* of the sequence.

• ILLUSTRATION 3: For the sequence $\{n/(2n+1)\}$ of Illustration 1, the greatest lower bound is $\frac{1}{3}$ because every lower bound of the sequence is less than or equal to $\frac{1}{3}$. Furthermore,

$$\frac{n}{2n+1} = \frac{1}{2 + \dfrac{1}{n}} < \frac{1}{2}$$

for all n, and $\frac{1}{2}$ is the least upper bound of the sequence.

In Illustration 2, we have the sequence $\{1/n\}$ whose least upper bound is 1 because every upper bound of the sequence is greater than or equal to 1. The greatest lower bound of this sequence is 0.   •

16.2.4 Definition   A sequence $\{a_n\}$ is said to be *bounded* if and only if it has an upper bound and a lower bound.

Because the sequence $\{1/n\}$ has an upper bound and a lower bound, it is bounded. This sequence is also a decreasing sequence and hence is a bounded monotonic sequence. There is a theorem (16.2.6) that guarantees that a bounded monotonic sequence is convergent. In particular, the sequence $\{1/n\}$ is convergent because $\lim_{n \to +\infty} (1/n) = 0$. The sequence $\{n\}$ whose elements are

$$1, 2, 3, \ldots, n, \ldots$$

is monotonic (because it is increasing) but is not bounded (because there is no upper bound). It is not convergent because $\lim_{n \to +\infty} n = +\infty$.

For the proof of Theorem 16.2.6 we need a very important property of the real-number system which we now state.

16.2.5 The Axiom of Completeness   Every nonempty set of real numbers which has a lower bound has a greatest lower bound. Also, every set of real numbers which has an upper bound has a least upper bound.

The axiom of completeness together with the field axioms (1.1.5 through 1.1.11) and the axiom of order (1.1.14) completely describe the real-number system. Actually, the second sentence in our statement of the axiom of completeness is unnecessary because it can be proved from the first sentence. It is included in the axiom here to expedite the discussion.

Suppose that $\{a_n\}$ is an increasing sequence that is bounded. Let D be an upper bound of the sequence. Then if the points corresponding to successive elements of the sequence are plotted on a horizontal axis, these points will all lie to the left of the point corresponding to the number D. Furthermore, because the sequence is increasing, each point will be either to the right of or coincide with the preceding point. See Fig. 16.2.1. Hence, as n increases, the elements increase toward D. Intuitively it appears that the sequence $\{a_n\}$ has a limit which is either D or some number less than D. This is indeed the case and is proved in the following theorem.

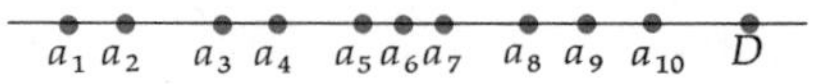

Figure 16.2.1

16.2.6 Theorem   A bounded monotonic sequence is convergent.

PROOF: We prove the theorem for the case when the monotonic sequence is increasing. Let the sequence be $\{a_n\}$.

Because $\{a_n\}$ is bounded, there is an upper bound for the sequence. By the axiom of completeness (16.2.5), $\{a_n\}$ has a least upper bound, which we call B. Then if ϵ is a positive number, $B - \epsilon$ cannot be an upper bound of the sequence because $B - \epsilon < B$ and B is the least upper bound of the sequence. So for some positive integer N

$$B - \epsilon < a_N \tag{4}$$

Because B is the least upper bound of $\{a_n\}$, by Definition 16.2.2 it follows that

$$a_n \leq B \qquad \text{for every positive integer } n \tag{5}$$

Because $\{a_n\}$ is an increasing sequence, we have from Definition 16.2.1(i)

$$a_n \leq a_{n+1} \qquad \text{for every positive integer } n$$

and so

$$a_N \leq a_n \qquad \text{whenever } n \geq N \tag{6}$$

From (4), (5), and (6), it follows that

$$B - \epsilon < a_N \leq a_n \leq B < B + \epsilon \qquad \text{whenever } n \geq N$$

from which we get

$$B - \epsilon < a_n < B + \epsilon \qquad \text{whenever } n \geq N$$

or, equivalently,

$$-\epsilon < a_n - B < \epsilon \qquad \text{whenever } n \geq N$$

which can be written as

$$|a_n - B| < \epsilon \qquad \text{whenever } n \geq N \tag{7}$$

But by Definition 16.1.2, (7) is the condition that $\lim\limits_{n \to +\infty} a_n = B$. Therefore, the sequence $\{a_n\}$ is convergent.

To prove the theorem when $\{a_n\}$ is a decreasing sequence, we consider the sequence $\{-a_n\}$, which will be increasing, and apply the above results. We leave it as an exercise to fill in the steps (see Exercise 13). ■

Theorem 16.2.6 states that if $\{a_n\}$ is a bounded monotonic sequence, there exists a number L such that $\lim\limits_{n \to +\infty} a_n = L$, but it does not state how to find L. For this reason, Theorem 16.2.6 is called an *existence theorem*. Many important concepts in mathematics are based on existence theorems. In particular, there are many sequences for which we cannot find the limit by direct use of the definition or by using limit theorems, but the knowledge that such a limit exists can be of great value to a mathematician.

In the proof of Theorem 16.2.6 we saw that the limit of the bounded increasing sequence is the least upper bound B of the sequence. Hence, if D is an upper bound of the sequence, $\lim\limits_{n \to +\infty} a_n = B \le D$. We have, then, the following theorem.

16.2.7 Theorem   Let $\{a_n\}$ be an increasing sequence, and suppose that D is an upper bound of this sequence. Then $\{a_n\}$ is convergent and

$$\lim_{n \to +\infty} a_n \le D$$

In proving Theorem 16.2.6 for the case when the bounded monotonic sequence is decreasing, the limit of the sequence is the greatest lower bound. The following theorem follows in a way similar to that of Theorem 16.2.7.

16.2.8 Theorem   Let $\{a_n\}$ be a decreasing sequence, and suppose that C is a lower bound of this sequence. Then $\{a_n\}$ is convergent and

$$\lim_{n \to +\infty} a_n \ge C$$

EXAMPLE 2:   Use Theorem 16.2.6 to prove that the sequence

$$\left\{ \frac{2^n}{n!} \right\}$$

is convergent.

SOLUTION: The elements of the given sequence are

$$\frac{2^1}{1!}, \frac{2^2}{2!}, \frac{2^3}{3!}, \frac{2^4}{4!}, \cdot \cdot \cdot, \frac{2^n}{n!}, \frac{2^{n+1}}{(n+1)!}, \cdot \cdot \cdot$$

$1! = 1,\ 2! = 1 \cdot 2 = 2,\ 3! = 1 \cdot 2 \cdot 3 = 6,\ 4! = 1 \cdot 2 \cdot 3 \cdot 4 = 24$. Hence, the elements of the sequence can be written as

$$2, 2, \frac{4}{3}, \frac{2}{3}, \cdot \cdot \cdot, \frac{2^n}{n!}, \frac{2^{n+1}}{(n+1)!}, \cdot \cdot \cdot$$

We see, then, that $a_1 = a_2 > a_3 > a_4$, and so the given sequence may be decreasing. We must check to see if $a_n \geq a_{n+1}$; that is, we must determine if

$$\frac{2^n}{n!} \geq \frac{2^{n+1}}{(n+1)!} \tag{8}$$

which is equivalent to

$$2^n(n+1)! \geq 2^{n+1}n!$$

which is equivalent to

$$2^n n!(n+1) \geq 2 \cdot 2^n n!$$

which is equivalent to

$$n+1 \geq 2 \tag{9}$$

When $n = 1$, inequality (9) becomes $2 = 2$, and (9) obviously holds when $n > 2$. Because inequality (8) is equivalent to (9), it follows that the given sequence is decreasing and hence monotonic. An upper bound for the given sequence is 2, and a lower bound is 0. Therefore, the sequence is bounded.

The sequence $\{2^n/n!\}$ is therefore a bounded monotonic sequence, and by Theorem 16.2.6 it is convergent.

Theorem 16.2.6 states that a sufficient condition for a monotonic sequence to be convergent is that it be bounded. This is also a necessary condition and is given in the following theorem.

16.2.9 Theorem   A convergent monotonic sequence is bounded.

PROOF: We prove the theorem for the case when the monotonic sequence is increasing. Let the sequence be $\{a_n\}$.

To prove that $\{a_n\}$ is bounded we must show that it has a lower bound and an upper bound. Because $\{a_n\}$ is an increasing sequence, its first element serves as a lower bound. We must now find an upper bound.

Because $\{a_n\}$ is convergent, the sequence has a limit; call this limit L. Therefore, $\lim\limits_{n \to +\infty} a_n = L$, and so by Definition 16.1.2, for any $\epsilon > 0$ there exists a number $N > 0$ such that

$$|a_n - L| < \epsilon \qquad \text{for every positive integer } n > N$$

or, equivalently,

$$-\epsilon < a_n - L < \epsilon \qquad \text{whenever } n > N$$

or, equivalently,

$$L - \epsilon < a_n < L + \epsilon \qquad \text{whenever } n > N$$

Because $\{a_n\}$ is increasing, we conclude that

$$a_n < L + \epsilon \qquad \text{for all positive integers } n$$

Therefore, $L + \epsilon$ will serve as an upper bound of the sequence $\{a_n\}$.

To prove the theorem when $\{a_n\}$ is a decreasing sequence we do as suggested in the proof of Theorem 16.2.6: Consider the sequence $\{-a_n\}$, which will be increasing, and apply the above results. You are asked to do this proof in Exercise 14. ∎

Exercises 16.2

In Exercises 1 through 12, determine if the given sequence is increasing, decreasing, or not monotonic.

1. $\left\{\dfrac{3n-1}{4n+5}\right\}$ 2. $\{\sin n\pi\}$ 3. $\left\{\dfrac{1}{n+\sin n^2}\right\}$

4. $\left\{\dfrac{2^n}{1+2^n}\right\}$ 5. $\left\{\dfrac{5^n}{1+5^{2n}}\right\}$ 6. $\left\{\dfrac{n^3-1}{n}\right\}$

7. $\left\{\dfrac{n!}{3^n}\right\}$ 8. $\left\{\dfrac{n}{2^n}\right\}$ 9. $\left\{\dfrac{n^n}{n!}\right\}$

10. $\{n^2+(-1)^n n\}$ 11. $\left\{\dfrac{n!}{1\cdot3\cdot5\cdot\ldots\cdot(2n-1)}\right\}$ 12. $\left\{\dfrac{1\cdot3\cdot5\cdot\ldots\cdot(2n-1)}{2^n\cdot n!}\right\}$

13. Use the fact that Theorem 16.2.6 holds for an increasing sequence to prove that the theorem holds when $\{a_n\}$ is a decreasing sequence. (HINT: Consider the sequence $\{-a_n\}$.)

14. Prove Theorem 16.2.9 when $\{a_n\}$ is a decreasing sequence by a method similar to that used in Exercise 13.

In Exercises 15 through 21, prove that the given sequence is convergent by using Theorem 16.2.6.

15. The sequence of Exercise 1.   16. The sequence of Exercise 4.

17. The sequence of Exercise 5.   18. The sequence of Exercise 8.

19. The sequence of Exercise 11.   20. The sequence of Exercise 12.

21. $\left\{\dfrac{n^2}{2^n}\right\}$

16.3 INFINITE SERIES OF CONSTANT TERMS

The familiar operation of addition applies only to a finite set of numbers. We now wish to extend addition to infinitely many numbers and to define what we mean by such a sum. To carry this out we deal with a limiting process by considering sequences.

16.3.1 Definition If $\{u_n\}$ is a sequence and

$$s_n = \sum_{i=1}^{n} u_i = u_1 + u_2 + u_3 + \cdots + u_n$$

then the sequence $\{s_n\}$ is called an *infinite series*.

The numbers $u_1, u_2, u_3, \ldots$ are called the *terms* of the infinite series. We use the following symbolism to denote an infinite series:

$$\sum_{n=1}^{+\infty} u_n = u_1 + u_2 + u_3 + \cdots + u_n + \cdots \tag{1}$$

Given the infinite series denoted by (1), $s_1 = u_1$, $s_2 = u_1 + u_2$, $s_3 = u_1 + u_2 + u_3$, and in general

$$s_k = \sum_{i=1}^{k} u_i = u_1 + u_2 + u_3 + \cdots + u_k \tag{2}$$

where s_k, defined by (2), is called the kth *partial sum* of the given series, and the sequence $\{s_n\}$ is a sequence of partial sums.

Because $s_{n-1} = u_1 + u_2 + \cdots + u_{n-1}$ and $s_n = u_1 + u_2 + \cdots + u_{n-1} + u_n$, we have the formula

$$s_n = s_{n-1} + u_n \tag{3}$$

EXAMPLE 1: Given the infinite series

$$\sum_{n=1}^{+\infty} u_n = \sum_{n=1}^{+\infty} \frac{1}{n(n+1)}$$

find the first four elements of the sequence of partial sums $\{s_n\}$, and find a formula for s_n in terms of n.

SOLUTION: Applying formula (3), we get

$$s_1 = u_1 = \frac{1}{1 \cdot 2} = \frac{1}{2}$$

$$s_2 = s_1 + u_2 = \frac{1}{2} + \frac{1}{2 \cdot 3} = \frac{2}{3}$$

$$s_3 = s_2 + u_3 = \frac{2}{3} + \frac{1}{3 \cdot 4} = \frac{3}{4}$$

$$s_4 = s_3 + u_4 = \frac{3}{4} + \frac{1}{4 \cdot 5} = \frac{4}{5}$$

By partial fractions, we see that

$$u_k = \frac{1}{k(k+1)} = \frac{1}{k} - \frac{1}{k+1}$$

Therefore,

$$u_1 = 1 - \frac{1}{2}, \; u_2 = \frac{1}{2} - \frac{1}{3}, \; u_3 = \frac{1}{3} - \frac{1}{4}, \cdots, u_{n-1} = \frac{1}{n-1} - \frac{1}{n}, \; u_n = \frac{1}{n} - \frac{1}{n+1}$$

Thus, because $s_n = u_1 + u_2 + \cdots + u_{n-1} + u_n$, we have

$$s_n = \left(1 - \frac{1}{2}\right) + \left(\frac{1}{2} - \frac{1}{3}\right) + \left(\frac{1}{3} - \frac{1}{4}\right) + \cdots + \left(\frac{1}{n-1} - \frac{1}{n}\right) + \left(\frac{1}{n} - \frac{1}{n+1}\right)$$

Upon removing parentheses and combining terms, we obtain

$$s_n = 1 - \frac{1}{n+1} = \frac{n}{n+1}$$

Taking $n = 1, 2, 3$, and 4, we see that our previous results agree.

Note that the method of solution of the above example applies only to a special case. In general, it is not possible to obtain such an expression for s_n.

We now define what we mean by the "sum" of an infinite series.

16.3.2 Definition Let $\sum\limits_{n=1}^{+\infty} u_n$ be a given infinite series, and let $\{s_n\}$ be the sequence of partial sums defining this infinite series. Then if $\lim\limits_{n \to +\infty} s_n$ exists and is equal to S, we say that the given series is *convergent* and that S is the *sum* of the given infinite series. If $\lim\limits_{n \to +\infty} s_n$ does not exist, the series is said to be *divergent* and the series does not have a sum.

Essentially Definition 16.3.2 states that an infinite series is convergent if and only if the corresponding sequence of partial sums is convergent.

If an infinite series has a sum S, we also say that the series converges to S.

Observe that the sum of a convergent series is the limit of a sequence of partial sums and is not obtained by ordinary addition. For a convergent series we use the symbolism

$$\sum_{n=1}^{+\infty} a_n$$

to denote both the series and the sum of the series. The use of the same symbol should not be confusing because the correct interpretation is apparent from the context in which it is used.

EXAMPLE 2: Determine if the infinite series of Example 1 has a sum.

SOLUTION: In the solution of Example 1, we showed that the sequence of partial sums for the given series is $\{s_n\} = \{n/(n+1)\}$. Therefore,

$$\lim_{n \to +\infty} s_n = \lim_{n \to +\infty} \frac{n}{n+1} = \lim_{n \to +\infty} \frac{1}{1 + \dfrac{1}{n}} = 1$$

So we conclude that the infinite series has a sum equal to 1. We can write

$$\sum_{n=1}^{+\infty} \frac{1}{n(n+1)} = \frac{1}{2} + \frac{1}{6} + \frac{1}{12} + \frac{1}{20} + \cdots + \frac{1}{n(n+1)} + \cdots = 1$$

As we mentioned above, in most cases it is not possible to obtain an expression for s_n in terms of n, and so we must have other methods for determining whether or not a given infinite series has a sum or, equivalently, whether a given infinite series is convergent or divergent.

16.3.3 Theorem If the infinite series $\sum\limits_{n=1}^{+\infty} u_n$ is convergent, then $\lim\limits_{n \to +\infty} u_n = 0$.

PROOF: Letting $\{s_n\}$ be the sequence of partial sums for the given series, and denoting the sum of the series by S, we have, from Definition 16.3.2, $\lim\limits_{n\to+\infty} s_n = S$. Therefore, for any $\epsilon > 0$ there exists a number $N > 0$ such that $|S - s_n| < \frac{1}{2}\epsilon$ for every integer $n > N$. Also, for these integers $n > N$ we know that $|S - s_{n+1}| < \frac{1}{2}\epsilon$. We have, then,

$$|u_{n+1}| = |s_{n+1} - s_n| = |S - s_n + s_{n+1} - S| \leq |S - s_n| + |s_{n+1} - S|$$

So

$$|u_{n+1}| < \tfrac{1}{2}\epsilon + \tfrac{1}{2}\epsilon = \epsilon \qquad \text{for every integer } n > N$$

Therefore, $\lim\limits_{n\to+\infty} u_n = 0$. ∎

The following theorem is a corollary of the preceding one.

16.3.4 Theorem   If $\lim\limits_{n\to+\infty} u_n \neq 0$, then the series $\sum\limits_{n=1}^{+\infty} u_n$ is divergent.

PROOF: Assume that $\sum\limits_{n=1}^{+\infty} u_n$ is convergent. Then by Theorem 16.3.3 $\lim\limits_{n\to+\infty} u_n = 0$. But this contradicts the hypothesis. Therefore, the series is divergent. ∎

EXAMPLE 3: Prove that the following two series are divergent.

(a) $\sum\limits_{n=1}^{+\infty} \dfrac{n^2 + 1}{n^2}$

$= 2 + \dfrac{5}{4} + \dfrac{10}{9} + \dfrac{17}{16} + \cdots$

(b) $\sum\limits_{n=1}^{+\infty} (-1)^{n+1}3$

$= 3 - 3 + 3 - 3 + \cdots$

SOLUTION: (a) $\lim\limits_{n\to+\infty} u_n = \lim\limits_{n\to+\infty} \dfrac{n^2+1}{n^2}$

$= \lim\limits_{n\to+\infty} \dfrac{1 + \dfrac{1}{n^2}}{1}$

$= 1$

$\neq 0$

Therefore, by Theorem 16.3.4 the series is divergent.
(b) $\lim\limits_{n\to+\infty} u_n = \lim\limits_{n\to+\infty} (-1)^{n+1}3$, which does not exist. Therefore, by Theorem 16.3.4 the series is divergent.

Note that the converse of Theorem 16.3.3 is false. That is, if $\lim\limits_{n\to+\infty} u_n = 0$, it does not follow that the series is necessarily convergent. In other words, it is possible to have a divergent series for which $\lim\limits_{n\to+\infty} u_n = 0$. An example of such a series is the one known as the *harmonic series*, which is

$$\sum_{n=1}^{+\infty} \frac{1}{n} = 1 + \frac{1}{2} + \frac{1}{3} + \frac{1}{4} + \cdots + \frac{1}{n} + \cdots \tag{4}$$

Clearly, $\lim\limits_{n \to +\infty} 1/n = 0$. In Illustration 1 we prove that the harmonic series diverges and we use the following theorem, which states that the difference between two partial sums s_R and s_T of a convergent series can be made as small as we please by taking R and T sufficiently large.

16.3.5 Theorem Let $\{s_n\}$ be the sequence of partial sums for a given convergent series $\sum\limits_{n=1}^{+\infty} u_n$. Then for any $\epsilon > 0$ there exists a number N such that

$$|s_R - s_T| < \epsilon \qquad \text{whenever } R > N \text{ and } T > N$$

PROOF: Because the series $\sum\limits_{n=1}^{+\infty} u_n$ is convergent, call its sum S. Then for any $\epsilon > 0$ there exists an $N > 0$ such that $|S - s_n| < \frac{1}{2}\epsilon$ whenever $n > N$. Therefore, if $R > N$ and $T > N$,

$$|s_R - s_T| = |s_R - S + S - s_T| \leq |s_R - S| + |S - s_T| < \tfrac{1}{2}\epsilon + \tfrac{1}{2}\epsilon$$

So

$$|s_R - s_T| < \epsilon \qquad \text{whenever } R > N \text{ and } T > N \qquad \blacksquare$$

● ILLUSTRATION 1: We prove that the harmonic series (4) is divergent. For this series,

$$s_n = 1 + \frac{1}{2} + \cdots + \frac{1}{n}$$

and

$$s_{2n} = 1 + \frac{1}{2} + \cdots + \frac{1}{n} + \frac{1}{n+1} + \cdots + \frac{1}{2n}$$

So

$$s_{2n} - s_n = \frac{1}{n+1} + \frac{1}{n+2} + \frac{1}{n+3} + \cdots + \frac{1}{2n} \qquad (5)$$

If $n > 1$,

$$\frac{1}{n+1} + \frac{1}{n+2} + \frac{1}{n+3} + \cdots + \frac{1}{2n} > \frac{1}{2n} + \frac{1}{2n} + \frac{1}{2n} + \cdots + \frac{1}{2n} \qquad (6)$$

There are n terms on each side of the inequality sign in (6); so the right side is $n(1/2n) = \frac{1}{2}$. Therefore, from (5) and (6) we have

$$s_{2n} - s_n > \tfrac{1}{2} \qquad \text{whenever } n > 1 \qquad (7)$$

But Theorem 16.3.5 states that if the given series is convergent, then $s_{2n} - s_n$ may be made as small as we please by taking n large enough; that is, if we take $\epsilon = \frac{1}{2}$, there exists an N such that $s_{2n} - s_n < \frac{1}{2}$ whenever $2n > N$ and $n > N$. But this would contradict (7). Therefore, we conclude that the harmonic series is divergent even though $\lim\limits_{n \to +\infty} 1/n = 0$. ●

A *geometric series* is a series of the form

$$\sum_{n=1}^{+\infty} ar^{n-1} = a + ar + ar^2 + \cdots + ar^{n-1} + \cdots \tag{8}$$

The nth partial sum of this series is given by

$$s_n = a(1 + r + r^2 + \cdots + r^{n-1}) \tag{9}$$

From the identity

$$1 - r^n = (1 - r)(1 + r + r^2 + \cdots + r^{n-1})$$

we can write (9) as

$$s_n = \frac{a(1 - r^n)}{1 - r} \quad \text{if } r \neq 1 \tag{10}$$

16.3.6 Theorem   The geometric series converges to the sum $a/(1 - r)$ if $|r| < 1$, and the geometric series diverges if $|r| \geq 1$.

PROOF: In Example 3, Sec. 16.1, we showed that $\lim_{n \to +\infty} r^n = 0$ if $|r| < 1$. Therefore, from (10) we can conclude that if $|r| < 1$,

$$\lim_{n \to +\infty} s_n = \frac{a}{1 - r}$$

So if $|r| < 1$, the geometric series converges, and its sum is $a/(1 - r)$.

If $r = 1$, $s_n = na$. Then $\lim_{n \to +\infty} s_n = +\infty$ if $a > 0$, and $\lim_{n \to +\infty} s_n = -\infty$ if $a < 0$.

If $r = -1$, the geometric series becomes $a - a + a - \cdots + (-1)^{n-1}a + \cdots$; so $s_n = 0$ if n is even, and $s_n = a$ if n is odd. Therefore, $\lim_{n \to +\infty} s_n$ does not exist. Hence, the geometric series diverges when $|r| = 1$.

If $|r| > 1$, $\lim_{n \to +\infty} ar^{n-1} = a \lim_{n \to +\infty} r^{n-1}$. Clearly, $\lim_{n \to +\infty} r^{n-1} \neq 0$ because we can make $|r^{n-1}|$ as large as we please by taking n large enough. Therefore, by Theorem 16.3.4 the series is divergent. This completes the proof.   ■

● ILLUSTRATION 2:

$$\sum_{n=1}^{+\infty} \frac{1}{2^{n-1}} = 1 + \frac{1}{2} + \frac{1}{4} + \frac{1}{8} + \cdots + \frac{1}{2^{n-1}} + \cdots$$

which is the geometric series, with $a = 1$ and $r = \frac{1}{2}$. Therefore, by Theorem 16.3.6 the series is convergent. Because $a/(1 - r) = 1/(1 - \frac{1}{2}) = 2$, the sum of the series is 2.   ●

The following example illustrates how Theorem 16.3.6 can be used to express a nonterminating repeating decimal as a common fraction.

EXAMPLE 4:   Express the decimal 0.3333. . . as a common fraction.

SOLUTION:

$$0.3333. . . = \frac{3}{10} + \frac{3}{100} + \frac{3}{1,000} + \frac{3}{10,000} + \cdots + \frac{3}{10^n} + \cdots$$

We have a geometric series in which $a = \frac{3}{10}$ and $r = \frac{1}{10}$. Because $|r| < 1$, it follows from Theorem 16.3.6 that the series converges and its sum is $a/(1-r)$. Therefore,

$$0.3333. . . = \frac{\frac{3}{10}}{1 - \frac{1}{10}} = \frac{1}{3}$$

The next theorem states that the convergence or divergence of an infinite series is not affected by changing a finite number of terms.

16.3.7 Theorem   If $\displaystyle\sum_{n=1}^{+\infty} a_n$ and $\displaystyle\sum_{n=1}^{+\infty} b_n$ are two infinite series, differing only in their first m terms (i.e., $a_k = b_k$ if $k > m$), then either both series converge or both series diverge.

PROOF: Let $\{s_n\}$ and $\{t_n\}$ be the sequences of partial sums of the series $\displaystyle\sum_{n=1}^{+\infty} a_n$ and $\displaystyle\sum_{n=1}^{+\infty} b_n$, respectively. Then

$$s_n = a_1 + a_2 + \cdots + a_m + a_{m+1} + a_{m+2} + \cdots + a_n$$

and

$$t_n = b_1 + b_2 + \cdots + b_m + b_{m+1} + b_{m+2} + \cdots + b_n$$

Because $a_k = b_k$ if $k > m$, then if $n \geq m$, we have

$$s_n - t_n = (a_1 + a_2 + \cdots + a_m) - (b_1 + b_2 + \cdots + b_m)$$

So

$$s_n - t_n = s_m - t_m \qquad \text{whenever } n \geq m \tag{11}$$

We wish to show that either both $\displaystyle\lim_{n \to +\infty} s_n$ and $\displaystyle\lim_{n \to +\infty} t_n$ exist or do not exist.

Suppose that $\displaystyle\lim_{n \to +\infty} t_n$ exists. Then from Eq. (11) we have

$$s_n = t_n + (s_m - t_m) \qquad \text{whenever } n \geq m$$

and so

$$\lim_{n \to +\infty} s_n = \lim_{n \to +\infty} t_n + (s_m - t_m)$$

Hence, when $\displaystyle\lim_{n \to +\infty} t_n$ exists, $\displaystyle\lim_{n \to +\infty} s_n$ also exists and both series converge.

Now suppose that $\lim\limits_{n \to +\infty} t_n$ does not exist and $\lim\limits_{n \to +\infty} s_n$ exists. From Eq. (11) we have

$$t_n = s_n + (t_m - s_m) \qquad \text{whenever } n \geq m$$

Because $\lim\limits_{n \to +\infty} s_n$ exists, it follows that

$$\lim_{n \to +\infty} t_n = \lim_{n \to +\infty} s_n + (t_m - s_m)$$

and so $\lim\limits_{n \to +\infty} t_n$ has to exist, which is a contradiction. Hence, if $\lim\limits_{n \to +\infty} t_n$ does not exist, then $\lim\limits_{n \to +\infty} s_n$ does not exist, and both series diverge. ∎

EXAMPLE 5: Determine whether the infinite series

$$\sum_{n=1}^{+\infty} \frac{1}{n+4}$$

is convergent or divergent.

SOLUTION: The given series is

$$\frac{1}{5} + \frac{1}{6} + \frac{1}{7} + \cdots + \frac{1}{n+4} + \cdots$$

which can be written as

$$0 + 0 + 0 + 0 + \frac{1}{5} + \frac{1}{6} + \frac{1}{7} + \cdots + \frac{1}{n} + \cdots \tag{12}$$

Now the harmonic series which is known to be divergent is

$$1 + \frac{1}{2} + \frac{1}{3} + \frac{1}{4} + \frac{1}{5} + \frac{1}{6} + \frac{1}{7} + \cdots + \frac{1}{n} + \cdots \tag{13}$$

Series (12) differs from series (13) only in the first four terms. Hence, by Theorem 16.3.7, series (12) is also divergent.

EXAMPLE 6: Determine whether the following infinite series is convergent or divergent:

$$\sum_{n=1}^{+\infty} \frac{\left[\!\left[\cos \dfrac{3}{n} \pi + 2 \right]\!\right]}{3^n}$$

SOLUTION: The given series can be written as

$$\frac{[\![\cos 3\pi + 2]\!]}{3} + \frac{[\![\cos \frac{3}{2}\pi + 2]\!]}{3^2} + \frac{[\![\cos \pi + 2]\!]}{3^3} + \frac{[\![\cos \frac{3}{4}\pi + 2]\!]}{3^4}$$

$$+ \frac{[\![\cos \frac{3}{5}\pi + 2]\!]}{3^5} + \frac{[\![\cos \frac{1}{2}\pi + 2]\!]}{3^6} + \frac{[\![\cos \frac{3}{7}\pi + 2]\!]}{3^7} + \cdots$$

$$= \frac{1}{3} + \frac{2}{3^2} + \frac{1}{3^3} + \frac{1}{3^4} + \frac{1}{3^5} + \frac{2}{3^6} + \frac{2}{3^7} + \frac{2}{3^8} + \cdots \tag{14}$$

Consider the geometric series with $a = \frac{2}{3}$ and $r = \frac{1}{3}$:

$$\frac{2}{3} + \frac{2}{3^2} + \frac{2}{3^3} + \frac{2}{3^4} + \frac{2}{3^5} + \frac{2}{3^6} + \frac{2}{3^7} + \frac{2}{3^8} + \cdots \tag{15}$$

This series is convergent by Theorem 16.3.6. Because series (14) differs from series (15) only in the first five terms, it follows from Theorem 16.3.7 that series (14) is also convergent.

As a consequence of Theorem 16.3.7, for a given infinite series, we can add or subtract a finite number of terms without affecting its convergence or divergence. For instance, in Example 5 the given series may be thought of as being obtained from the harmonic series by subtracting the first four terms. And because the harmonic series is divergent, the given series is divergent. In Example 6, we could consider the convergent geometric series

$$\frac{2}{3^6} + \frac{2}{3^7} + \frac{2}{3^8} + \cdots \tag{16}$$

and obtain the given series (14) by adding five terms. Because series (16) is convergent, it follows that series (14) is convergent.

The following theorem states that if an infinite series is multiplied term by term by a nonzero constant, its convergence or divergence is not affected.

16.3.8 Theorem   Let c be any nonzero constant.

(i) If the series $\displaystyle\sum_{n=1}^{+\infty} u_n$ is convergent and its sum is S, then the series $\displaystyle\sum_{n=1}^{+\infty} cu_n$ is also convergent and its sum is $c \cdot S$.

(ii) If the series $\displaystyle\sum_{n=1}^{+\infty} u_n$ is divergent, then the series $\displaystyle\sum_{n=1}^{+\infty} cu_n$ is also divergent.

PROOF: Let the nth partial sum of the series $\displaystyle\sum_{n=1}^{+\infty} u_n$ be s_n. Therefore, $s_n = u_1 + u_2 + \cdots + u_n$. The nth partial sum of the series $\displaystyle\sum_{n=1}^{+\infty} cu_n$ is $c(u_1 + u_2 + \cdots + u_n) = cs_n$.

PART (i):   If the series $\displaystyle\sum_{n=1}^{+\infty} u_n$ is convergent, then $\displaystyle\lim_{n \to +\infty} s_n$ exists and is S. Therefore,

$$\lim_{n \to +\infty} cs_n = c \lim_{n \to +\infty} s_n = c \cdot S$$

Hence, the series $\displaystyle\sum_{n=1}^{+\infty} cu_n$ is convergent and its sum is $c \cdot S$.

PART (ii):   If the series $\displaystyle\sum_{n=1}^{+\infty} u_n$ is divergent, then $\displaystyle\lim_{n \to +\infty} s_n$ does not exist. Now suppose that the series $\displaystyle\sum_{n=1}^{+\infty} cu_n$ is convergent. Then $\displaystyle\lim_{n \to +\infty} cs_n$ exists. But $s_n = cs_n/c$, and so

$$\lim_{n \to +\infty} s_n = \lim_{n \to +\infty} \frac{1}{c} (cs_n) = \frac{1}{c} \lim_{n \to +\infty} cs_n$$

Thus, $\lim\limits_{n \to +\infty} s_n$ must exist, which is a contradiction. Therefore, the series $\sum\limits_{n=1}^{+\infty} cu_n$ is divergent.   ∎

EXAMPLE 7:   Determine whether the infinite series

$$\sum_{n=1}^{+\infty} \frac{1}{4n}$$

is convergent or divergent.

SOLUTION: $\sum\limits_{n=1}^{+\infty} \dfrac{1}{4n} = \dfrac{1}{4} + \dfrac{1}{8} + \dfrac{1}{12} + \dfrac{1}{16} + \cdots + \dfrac{1}{4n} + \cdots$

Because $\sum\limits_{n=1}^{+\infty} 1/n$ is the harmonic series which is divergent, then by Theorem 16.3.8(ii) with $c = \tfrac{1}{4}$, the given series is divergent.

Note that Theorem 16.3.8(i) is an extension to convergent infinite series of the following property of finite sums:

$$\sum_{k=1}^{n} ca_k = c \sum_{k=1}^{n} a_k$$

Another property of finite sums is

$$\sum_{k=1}^{n} (a_k \pm b_k) = \sum_{k=1}^{n} a_k \pm \sum_{k=1}^{n} b_k$$

and its extension to convergent infinite series is given by the following theorem.

16.3.9 Theorem   If $\sum\limits_{n=1}^{+\infty} a_n$ and $\sum\limits_{n=1}^{+\infty} b_n$ are convergent infinite series whose sums are S and R, respectively, then

(i) $\sum\limits_{n=1}^{+\infty} (a_n + b_n)$ is a convergent series and its sum is $S + R$;

(ii) $\sum\limits_{n=1}^{+\infty} (a_n - b_n)$ is a convergent series and its sum is $S - R$.

The proof of this theorem is left as an exercise (see Exercise 11).
The next theorem is a corollary of the above theorem and is sometimes used to prove that a series is divergent.

16.3.10 Theorem   If the series $\sum\limits_{n=1}^{+\infty} a_n$ is convergent and the series $\sum\limits_{n=1}^{+\infty} b_n$ is divergent, then the series $\sum\limits_{n=1}^{+\infty} (a_n + b_n)$ is divergent.

PROOF: Assume that $\sum\limits_{n=1}^{+\infty} (a_n + b_n)$ is convergent and its sum is S. Let the

sum of the series $\sum\limits_{n=1}^{+\infty} a_n$ be R. Then because

$$\sum_{n=1}^{+\infty} b_n = \sum_{n=1}^{+\infty} [(a_n + b_n) - a_n]$$

it follows from Theorem 16.3.9(ii) that $\sum\limits_{n=1}^{+\infty} b_n$ is convergent and its sum is

$S - R$. But this is a contradiction to the hypothesis that $\sum\limits_{n=1}^{+\infty} b_n$ is divergent.

Hence, $\sum\limits_{n=1}^{+\infty} (a_n + b_n)$ is divergent.   ■

EXAMPLE 8:   Determine whether the infinite series

$$\sum_{n=1}^{+\infty} \left(\frac{1}{4n} + \frac{1}{4^n} \right)$$

is convergent or divergent.

SOLUTION: In Example 7 we proved that the series $\sum\limits_{n=1}^{+\infty} 1/4n$ is divergent.

Because the series $\sum\limits_{n=1}^{+\infty} 1/4^n$ is a geometric series with $|r| = \frac{1}{4} < 1$, it is convergent. Hence, by Theorem 16.3.10 the given series is divergent.

Note that if both series $\sum\limits_{n=1}^{+\infty} a_n$ and $\sum\limits_{n=1}^{+\infty} b_n$ are divergent, the series

$\sum\limits_{n=1}^{+\infty} (a_n + b_n)$ may or may not be convergent. For example, if $a_n = 1/n$ and

$b_n = 1/n$, then $a_n + b_n = 2/n$ and $\sum\limits_{n=1}^{+\infty} 2/n$ is divergent. But if $a_n = 1/n$ and

$b_n = -1/n$, then $a_n + b_n = 0$ and $\sum\limits_{n=1}^{+\infty} 0$ is convergent.

Exercises 16.3

In Exercises 1 through 6, find the first four elements of the sequence of partial sums $\{s_n\}$ and find a formula for s_n in terms of n; also, determine if the infinite series is convergent or divergent, and if it is convergent, find its sum.

1. $\sum\limits_{n=1}^{+\infty} \dfrac{1}{(2n-1)(2n+1)}$

2. $\sum\limits_{n=1}^{+\infty} \dfrac{2}{(4n-3)(4n+1)}$

3. $\sum\limits_{n=1}^{+\infty} \ln \dfrac{n}{n+1}$

4. $\sum\limits_{n=1}^{+\infty} n$

5. $\sum\limits_{n=1}^{+\infty} \dfrac{2n+1}{n^2(n+1)^2}$

6. $\sum\limits_{n=1}^{+\infty} \dfrac{2^{n-1}}{3^n}$

In Exercises 7 through 10, find the infinite series which is the given sequence of partial sums; also determine if the infinite series is convergent or divergent, and if it is convergent, find its sum.

7. $\{s_n\} = \left\{ \dfrac{2n}{3n+1} \right\}$

8. $\{s_n\} = \left\{ \dfrac{n^2}{n+1} \right\}$

9. $\{s_n\} = \left\{ \dfrac{1}{2^n} \right\}$

10. $\{s_n\} = \{3^n\}$

11. Prove Theorem 16.3.9.

In Exercises 12 through 25, write the first four terms of the given infinite series and determine if the series is convergent or divergent. If the series is convergent, find its sum.

12. $\displaystyle\sum_{n=1}^{+\infty} \frac{n}{n+1}$ 13. $\displaystyle\sum_{n=1}^{+\infty} \frac{2n+1}{3n+2}$ 14. $\displaystyle\sum_{n=1}^{+\infty} \frac{2}{3n}$ 15. $\displaystyle\sum_{n=1}^{+\infty} \left(\frac{2}{3}\right)^n$ 16. $\displaystyle\sum_{n=1}^{+\infty} \frac{2}{3^{n-1}}$

17. $\displaystyle\sum_{n=1}^{+\infty} (-1)^{n+1} \frac{3}{2^n}$ 18. $\displaystyle\sum_{n=1}^{+\infty} \ln \frac{1}{n}$ 19. $\displaystyle\sum_{n=1}^{+\infty} e^{-n}$ 20. $\displaystyle\sum_{n=1}^{+\infty} \sin \pi n$ 21. $\displaystyle\sum_{n=1}^{+\infty} \cos \pi n$

22. $\displaystyle\sum_{n=1}^{+\infty} \frac{\sinh n}{n}$ 23. $\displaystyle\sum_{n=1}^{+\infty} (2^{-n} + 3^{-n})$ 24. $\displaystyle\sum_{n=1}^{+\infty} [1 + (-1)^n]$ 25. $\displaystyle\sum_{n=1}^{+\infty} \left(\frac{1}{2n} - \frac{1}{3n}\right)$

In Exercises 26 through 29, express the given nonterminating repeating decimal as a common fraction.

26. 0.27 27 27 . . .   27. 1.234 234 234 . . .

28. 2.045 45 45 . . .   29. 0.4653 4653 4653 . . .

30. A ball is dropped from a height of 12 ft. Each time it strikes the ground, it bounces back to a height of three-fourths the distance from which it fell. Find the total distance traveled by the ball before it comes to rest.

16.4 INFINITE SERIES OF POSITIVE TERMS

If all the terms of an infinite series are positive, the sequence of partial sums is increasing. Thus, the following theorem follows immediately from Theorems 16.2.6 and 16.2.9.

16.4.1 Theorem   An infinite series of positive terms is convergent if and only if its sequence of partial sums has an upper bound.

PROOF: For an infinite series of positive terms, the sequence of partial sums has a lower bound of 0. If the sequence of partial sums also has an upper bound, it is bounded. Furthermore, the sequence of partial sums of an infinite series of positive terms is increasing. It follows then from Theorem 16.2.6 that the sequence of partial sums is convergent, and therefore the infinite series is convergent.

Suppose now that an infinite series of positive terms is convergent. Then the sequence of partial sums is also convergent. It follows from Theorem 16.2.9 that the sequence of partial sums is bounded and so it has an upper bound.   ∎

EXAMPLE 1:   Prove that the series

$$\sum_{n=1}^{+\infty} \frac{1}{n!}$$

is convergent by using Theorem 16.4.1.

SOLUTION: We must find an upper bound for the sequence of partial sums of the series $\displaystyle\sum_{n=1}^{+\infty} 1/n!$.

$$s_1 = 1, \quad s_2 = 1 + \frac{1}{1 \cdot 2}, \quad s_3 = 1 + \frac{1}{1 \cdot 2} + \frac{1}{1 \cdot 2 \cdot 3},$$

$$s_4 = 1 + \frac{1}{1 \cdot 2} + \frac{1}{1 \cdot 2 \cdot 3} + \frac{1}{1 \cdot 2 \cdot 3 \cdot 4}, \cdots,$$

$$s_n = 1 + \frac{1}{1 \cdot 2} + \frac{1}{1 \cdot 2 \cdot 3} + \frac{1}{1 \cdot 2 \cdot 3 \cdot 4} + \cdots + \frac{1}{1 \cdot 2 \cdot 3 \cdot \ldots \cdot n} \quad (1)$$

Now consider the first n terms of the geometric series with $a = 1$ and $r = \frac{1}{2}$:

$$\sum_{k=1}^{n} \frac{1}{2^{k-1}} = 1 + \frac{1}{2} + \frac{1}{2^2} + \frac{1}{2^3} + \cdots + \frac{1}{2^{n-1}} \quad (2)$$

By Theorem 16.3.6 the geometric series with $a = 1$ and $r = \frac{1}{2}$ has the sum $a/(1 - r) = 1/(1 - \frac{1}{2}) = 2$. Hence, summation (2) is less than 2. Observe that each term of summation (1) is less than or equal to the corresponding term of summation (2); that is,

$$\frac{1}{k!} \le \frac{1}{2^{k-1}}$$

This is true because $k! = 1 \cdot 2 \cdot 3 \cdot \ldots \cdot k$, which in addition to the factor 1 contains $k - 1$ factors each greater than or equal to 2. Hence,

$$s_n = \sum_{k=1}^{n} \frac{1}{k!} \le \sum_{k=1}^{n} \frac{1}{2^{k-1}} < 2$$

From the above we see that s_n has an upper bound of 2. Therefore, by Theorem 16.4.1 the given series is convergent.

In the above example the terms of the given series were compared with those of a known convergent series. This is a particular case of the following theorem known as the *comparison test*.

16.4.2 Theorem
Comparison Test

Let the series $\sum\limits_{n=1}^{+\infty} u_n$ be a series of positive terms.

(i) If $\sum\limits_{n=1}^{+\infty} v_n$ is a series of positive terms which is known to be convergent, and $u_n \le v_n$ for all positive integers n, then $\sum\limits_{n=1}^{+\infty} u_n$ is convergent.

(ii) If $\sum\limits_{n=1}^{+\infty} w_n$ is a series of positive terms which is known to be divergent, and $u_n \ge w_n$ for all positive integers n, then $\sum\limits_{n=1}^{+\infty} u_n$ is divergent.

PROOF OF (i): Let $\{s_n\}$ be the sequence of partial sums for the series $\sum\limits_{n=1}^{+\infty} u_n$ and $\{t_n\}$ be the sequence of partial sums for the series $\sum\limits_{n=1}^{+\infty} v_n$. Because $\sum\limits_{n=1}^{+\infty} v_n$ is a series of positive terms which is convergent, it follows from Theorem 16.4.1 that the sequence $\{t_n\}$ has an upper bound; call it B. Because $u_n \leq v_n$ for all positive integers n, we can conclude that $s_n \leq t_n \leq B$ for all positive integers n. Therefore, B is an upper bound of the sequence $\{s_n\}$. And because the terms of the series $\sum\limits_{n=1}^{+\infty} u_n$ are all positive, it follows from Theorem 16.4.1 that $\sum\limits_{n=1}^{+\infty} u_n$ is convergent.

PROOF OF (ii): Assume that $\sum\limits_{n=1}^{+\infty} u_n$ is convergent. Then because both $\sum\limits_{n=1}^{+\infty} u_n$ and $\sum\limits_{n=1}^{+\infty} w_n$ are infinite series of positive terms and $w_n \leq u_n$ for all positive integers n, it follows from part (i) that $\sum\limits_{n=1}^{+\infty} w_n$ is convergent. However, this contradicts the hypothesis, and so our assumption is false. Therefore, $\sum\limits_{n=1}^{+\infty} u_n$ is divergent. ∎

As we stated in Sec. 16.3, as a result of Theorem 16.3.7, the convergence or divergence of an infinite series is not affected by discarding a finite number of terms. Therefore, when applying the comparison test, if $u_i \leq v_i$ or $u_i \geq w_i$ when $i > m$, the test is valid regardless of how the first m terms of the two series compare.

EXAMPLE 2: Determine whether the infinite series

$$\sum_{n=1}^{+\infty} \frac{4}{3^n + 1}$$

is convergent or divergent.

SOLUTION: The given series is

$$\frac{4}{4} + \frac{4}{10} + \frac{4}{28} + \frac{4}{82} + \cdots + \frac{4}{3^n + 1} + \cdots$$

Comparing the nth term of this series with the nth term of the convergent geometric series

$$\frac{4}{3} + \frac{4}{9} + \frac{4}{27} + \frac{4}{81} + \cdots + \frac{4}{3^n} + \cdots \qquad r = \frac{1}{3} < 1$$

we have

$$\frac{4}{3^n + 1} < \frac{4}{3^n}$$

for every positive integer n. Therefore, by the comparison test, Theorem 16.4.2(i), the given series is convergent.

EXAMPLE 3: Determine whether the infinite series

$$\sum_{n=1}^{+\infty} \frac{1}{\sqrt{n}}$$

is convergent or divergent.

SOLUTION: The given series is

$$\sum_{n=1}^{+\infty} \frac{1}{\sqrt{n}} = \frac{1}{\sqrt{1}} + \frac{1}{\sqrt{2}} + \frac{1}{\sqrt{3}} + \cdots + \frac{1}{\sqrt{n}} + \cdots$$

Comparing the nth term of this series with the nth term of the divergent harmonic series, we have

$$\frac{1}{\sqrt{n}} \geq \frac{1}{n} \qquad \text{for every positive integer } n$$

So by Theorem 16.4.2(ii) the given series $\sum_{n=1}^{+\infty} 1/\sqrt{n}$ is divergent.

The following theorem, known as the *limit comparison test*, is a consequence of Theorem 16.4.2 and is often easier to apply.

16.4.3 Theorem
Limit Comparison Test

Let $\sum_{n=1}^{+\infty} u_n$ and $\sum_{n=1}^{+\infty} v_n$ be two series of positive terms.

(i) If $\lim_{n \to +\infty} (u_n/v_n) = c > 0$, then the two series either both converge or both diverge.

(ii) If $\lim_{n \to +\infty} (u_n/v_n) = 0$, and if $\sum_{n=1}^{+\infty} v_n$ converges, then $\sum_{n=1}^{+\infty} u_n$ converges.

(iii) If $\lim_{n \to +\infty} (u_n/v_n) = +\infty$, and if $\sum_{n=1}^{+\infty} v_n$ diverges, then $\sum_{n=1}^{+\infty} u_n$ diverges.

PROOF OF (i): Because $\lim_{n \to +\infty} (u_n/v_n) = c$, it follows that there exists an $N > 0$ such that

$$\left| \frac{u_n}{v_n} - c \right| < \frac{c}{2} \qquad \text{for all } n > N$$

or, equivalently,

$$-\frac{c}{2} < \frac{u_n}{v_n} - c < \frac{c}{2} \qquad \text{for all } n > N$$

or, equivalently,

$$\frac{c}{2} < \frac{u_n}{v_n} < \frac{3c}{2} \qquad \text{for all } n > N \tag{3}$$

From the right-hand inequality (3) we get

$$u_n < \tfrac{3}{2} c v_n \tag{4}$$

If $\displaystyle\sum_{n=1}^{+\infty} v_n$ is convergent, so is $\displaystyle\sum_{n=1}^{+\infty} \tfrac{3}{2}cv_n$. It follows from inequality (4) and

the comparison test that $\displaystyle\sum_{n=1}^{+\infty} u_n$ is convergent.

From the left-hand inequality (3) we get

$$v_n < \frac{2}{c}\, u_n \tag{5}$$

If $\displaystyle\sum_{n=1}^{+\infty} u_n$ is convergent, so is $\displaystyle\sum_{n=1}^{+\infty} \frac{2}{c}\, u_n$. From inequality (5) and the compari-

son test it follows that $\displaystyle\sum_{n=1}^{+\infty} v_n$ is convergent.

If $\displaystyle\sum_{n=1}^{+\infty} v_n$ is divergent, we can show that $\displaystyle\sum_{n=1}^{+\infty} u_n$ is divergent by assum-

ing that $\displaystyle\sum_{n=1}^{+\infty} u_n$ is convergent and getting a contradiction by applying in-

equality (5) and the comparison test.

In a similar manner, if $\displaystyle\sum_{n=1}^{+\infty} u_n$ is divergent, it follows that $\displaystyle\sum_{n=1}^{+\infty} v_n$ is di-

vergent because a contradiction is obtained from inequality (4) and the

comparison test if $\displaystyle\sum_{n=1}^{+\infty} v_n$ is assumed to be convergent.

We have therefore proved part (i). The proofs of parts (ii) and (iii)
are left as exercises (see Exercises 19 and 20).   ■

A word of caution is in order regarding part (ii) of Theorem 16.4.3.
Note that when $\displaystyle\lim_{n \to +\infty} (u_n/v_n) = 0$, the divergence of the series $\displaystyle\sum_{n=1}^{+\infty} v_n$ does

not imply that the series $\displaystyle\sum_{n=1}^{+\infty} u_n$ diverges.

EXAMPLE 4:   Solve Example 2 by using the limit comparison test.

SOLUTION: Let u_n be the nth term of the given series $\displaystyle\sum_{n=1}^{+\infty} 4/(3^n + 1)$ and

v_n be the nth term of the convergent geometric series $\displaystyle\sum_{n=1}^{+\infty} 4/3^n$. Therefore,

$$\lim_{n \to +\infty} \frac{u_n}{v_n} = \lim_{n \to +\infty} \frac{\dfrac{4}{3^n + 1}}{\dfrac{4}{3^n}}$$

$$= \lim_{n \to +\infty} \frac{3^n}{3^n + 1}$$

$$= \lim_{n \to +\infty} \frac{1}{1 + 3^{-n}}$$

$$= 1$$

Hence, by part (i) of the limit comparison test, it follows that the given series is convergent.

EXAMPLE 5: Solve Example 3 by using the limit comparison test.

SOLUTION: Let u_n be the nth term of the given series $\sum\limits_{n=1}^{+\infty} 1/\sqrt{n}$ and v_n be the nth term of the divergent harmonic series. Then

$$\lim_{n\to+\infty} \frac{u_n}{v_n} = \lim_{n\to+\infty} \frac{\dfrac{1}{\sqrt{n}}}{\dfrac{1}{n}} = \lim_{n\to+\infty} \sqrt{n} = +\infty$$

Therefore, by part (iii) of the limit comparison test, we conclude that the given series is divergent.

EXAMPLE 6: Determine whether the series

$$\sum_{n=1}^{+\infty} \frac{n^3}{n!}$$

is convergent or divergent.

SOLUTION: In Example 1, we proved that the series $\sum\limits_{n=1}^{+\infty} 1/n!$ is convergent. Using the limit comparison test with $u_n = n^3/n!$ and $v_n = 1/n!$, we have

$$\lim_{n\to+\infty} \frac{u_n}{v_n} = \lim_{n\to+\infty} \frac{\dfrac{n^3}{n!}}{\dfrac{1}{n!}} = \lim_{n\to+\infty} n^3 = +\infty$$

Part (iii) of the limit comparison test is not applicable because $\sum\limits_{n=1}^{+\infty} v_n$ converges. However, there is a way that we can use the limit comparison test. The given series can be written as

$$\frac{1^3}{1!} + \frac{2^3}{2!} + \frac{3^3}{3!} + \frac{4^3}{4!} + \frac{5^3}{5!} + \cdots + \frac{n^3}{n!} + \cdots$$

Because Theorem 16.3.7 allows us to subtract a finite number of terms without affecting the behavior (convergence or divergence) of a series, we discard the first three terms and obtain

$$\frac{4^3}{4!} + \frac{5^3}{5!} + \frac{6^3}{6!} + \cdots + \frac{(n+3)^3}{(n+3)!} + \cdots$$

Now letting $u_n = (n+3)^3/(n+3)!$ and, as before, letting $v_n = 1/n!$, we have

$$\lim_{n\to+\infty} \frac{u_n}{v_n} = \lim_{n\to+\infty} \frac{\dfrac{(n+3)^3}{(n+3)!}}{\dfrac{1}{n!}}$$

$$= \lim_{n\to+\infty} \frac{(n+3)^3 n!}{(n+3)!}$$

$$= \lim_{n \to +\infty} \frac{(n+3)^3 n!}{n!(n+1)(n+2)(n+3)}$$

$$= \lim_{n \to +\infty} \frac{(n+3)^2}{(n+1)(n+2)}$$

$$= \lim_{n \to +\infty} \frac{n^2 + 6n + 9}{n^2 + 3n + 2}$$

$$= \lim_{n \to +\infty} \frac{1 + \dfrac{6}{n} + \dfrac{9}{n^2}}{1 + \dfrac{3}{n} + \dfrac{2}{n^2}}$$

$$= 1$$

It follows from part (i) of the Limit Comparison Test that the given series is convergent.

● ILLUSTRATION 1: Consider the geometric series

$$1 + \frac{1}{2} + \frac{1}{4} + \frac{1}{8} + \frac{1}{16} + \frac{1}{32} + \cdots + \frac{1}{2^{n-1}} + \cdots \tag{6}$$

which converges to 2 as shown in Illustration 2 of Sec. 16.3. Regrouping the terms of this series, we have

$$\left(1 + \frac{1}{2}\right) + \left(\frac{1}{4} + \frac{1}{8}\right) + \left(\frac{1}{16} + \frac{1}{32}\right) + \cdots + \left(\frac{1}{4^{n-1}} + \frac{1}{2 \cdot 4^{n-1}}\right) + \cdots$$

which is the series

$$\frac{3}{2} + \frac{3}{8} + \frac{3}{32} + \cdots + \frac{3}{2 \cdot 4^{n-1}} + \cdots \tag{7}$$

Series (7) is the geometric series with $a = \frac{3}{2}$ and $r = \frac{1}{4}$. Thus, by Theorem 16.3.6 it is convergent, and its sum is

$$\frac{a}{1-r} = \frac{\frac{3}{2}}{1 - \frac{1}{4}} = 2$$

We see, then, that series (7), which is obtained from the convergent series (6) by regrouping the terms, is also convergent. Its sum is the same as that of series (6). ●

Illustration 1 gives a particular case of the following theorem.

16.4.4 Theorem   If $\displaystyle\sum_{n=1}^{+\infty} u_n$ is a given convergent series of positive terms, its terms can be grouped in any manner, and the resulting series also will be convergent and will have the same sum as the given series.

PROOF: Let $\{s_n\}$ be the sequence of partial sums for the given convergent series of positive terms. Then $\lim\limits_{n\to+\infty} s_n$ exists; let this limit be S. Consider a series $\sum\limits_{n=1}^{+\infty} v_n$ whose terms are obtained by grouping the terms of $\sum\limits_{n=1}^{+\infty} u_n$ in some manner. For example, $\sum\limits_{n=1}^{+\infty} v_n$ may be the series

$$u_1 + (u_2 + u_3) + (u_4 + u_5 + u_6) + (u_7 + u_8 + u_9 + u_{10}) + \cdots$$

or it may be the series

$$(u_1 + u_2) + (u_3 + u_4) + (u_5 + u_6) + (u_7 + u_8) + \cdots$$

and so forth. Let $\{t_m\}$ be the sequence of partial sums for the series $\sum\limits_{n=1}^{+\infty} v_n$.

Each partial sum of the sequence $\{t_m\}$ is also a partial sum of the sequence $\{s_n\}$. Therefore, as m increases without bound, so does n. Because $\lim\limits_{n\to+\infty} s_n = S$, we conclude that $\lim\limits_{m\to+\infty} t_m = S$. This proves the theorem.   ■

Theorem 16.4.4 and the next theorem state properties of the sum of a convergent series of positive terms that are similar to properties that hold for the sum of a finite number of terms.

16.4.5 Theorem   If $\sum\limits_{n=1}^{+\infty} u_n$ is a given convergent series of positive terms, the order of the terms can be rearranged, and the resulting series also will be convergent and will have the same sum as the given series.

PROOF: Let $\{s_n\}$ be the sequence of partial sums for the given convergent series of positive terms, and let $\lim\limits_{n\to+\infty} s_n = S$. Let $\sum\limits_{n=1}^{+\infty} v_n$ be a series formed by rearranging the order of the terms of $\sum\limits_{n=1}^{+\infty} u_n$. For example, $\sum\limits_{n=1}^{+\infty} v_n$ may be the series

$$u_4 + u_3 + u_7 + u_1 + u_9 + u_5 + \cdots$$

Let $\{t_n\}$ be the sequence of partial sums for the series $\sum\limits_{n=1}^{+\infty} v_n$. Each partial sum of the sequence $\{t_n\}$ will be less than S because it is the sum of n terms of the infinite series $\sum\limits_{n=1}^{+\infty} u_n$. Therefore, S is an upper bound of the sequence $\{t_n\}$. Furthermore, because all the terms of the series $\sum\limits_{n=1}^{+\infty} v_n$ are positive, $\{t_n\}$ is a monotonic increasing sequence. Hence, by Theorem 16.2.7 the sequence $\{t_n\}$ is convergent, and $\lim\limits_{n\to+\infty} t_n = T \leq S$. Now because the given series $\sum\limits_{n=1}^{+\infty} u_n$ can be obtained from the series $\sum\limits_{n=1}^{+\infty} v_n$ by rearranging the order of the terms, we can use the same argument and conclude that $S \leq T$. If both inequalities, $T \leq S$ and $S \leq T$, must hold, it follows that $S = T$. This proves the theorem. ∎

A series which is often used in the comparison test is the one known as the *p series*, or the *hyperharmonic series*. It is

$$\frac{1}{1^p} + \frac{1}{2^p} + \frac{1}{3^p} + \cdots + \frac{1}{n^p} + \cdots \qquad \text{where } p \text{ is a constant} \qquad (8)$$

In the following illustration we prove that the p series diverges if $p \leq 1$ and converges if $p > 1$.

● ILLUSTRATION 2: If $p = 1$, the p series is the harmonic series, which diverges. If $p < 1$, then $n^p \leq n$, and so

$$\frac{1}{n^p} \geq \frac{1}{n} \qquad \text{for every positive integer } n$$

Hence, by Theorem 16.4.2(ii) the p series is divergent if $p < 1$.

If $p > 1$, we group the terms as follows:

$$\frac{1}{1^p} + \left(\frac{1}{2^p} + \frac{1}{3^p}\right) + \left(\frac{1}{4^p} + \frac{1}{5^p} + \frac{1}{6^p} + \frac{1}{7^p}\right) + \left(\frac{1}{8^p} + \frac{1}{9^p} + \cdots + \frac{1}{15^p}\right) + \cdots \qquad (9)$$

Consider the series

$$\frac{1}{1^p} + \frac{2}{2^p} + \frac{4}{4^p} + \frac{8}{8^p} + \cdots + \frac{2^{n-1}}{(2^{n-1})^p} + \cdots \qquad (10)$$

This is a geometric series whose ratio is $2/2^p = 1/2^{p-1}$, which is a positive number less than 1. Hence, series (10) is convergent. Rewriting the terms of series (10), we get

$$\frac{1}{1^p} + \left(\frac{1}{2^p} + \frac{1}{2^p}\right) + \left(\frac{1}{4^p} + \frac{1}{4^p} + \frac{1}{4^p} + \frac{1}{4^p}\right) + \left(\frac{1}{8^p} + \frac{1}{8^p} + \cdots + \frac{1}{8^p}\right) + \cdots \qquad (11)$$

Comparing series (9) and series (11), we see that the group of terms in each set of parentheses after the first group is less in sum for (9) than it is for (11). Therefore, by the comparison test, series (9) is convergent. Because (9) is merely a regrouping of the terms of the p series when $p > 1$, we conclude from Theorem 16.4.4 that the p series is convergent if $p > 1$. ●

Note that the series in Example 3 is the p series where $p = \frac{1}{2} < 1$; therefore, it is divergent.

EXAMPLE 7:   Determine whether the infinite series

$$\sum_{n=1}^{+\infty} \frac{1}{(n^2 + 2)^{1/3}}$$

is convergent or divergent.

SOLUTION: Because for large values of n the number $n^2 + 2$ is close to the number n^2, so is the number $1/(n^2 + 2)^{1/3}$ close to the number $1/n^{2/3}$. The series $\sum_{n=1}^{+\infty} 1/n^{2/3}$ is divergent because it is the p series with $p = \frac{2}{3} < 1$.

Using the limit comparison test with $u_n = 1/(n^2 + 2)^{1/3}$ and $v_n = 1/n^{2/3}$, we have

$$\lim_{n \to +\infty} \frac{u_n}{v_n} = \lim_{n \to +\infty} \frac{\dfrac{1}{(n^2 + 2)^{1/3}}}{\dfrac{1}{n^{2/3}}}$$

$$= \lim_{n \to +\infty} \frac{n^{2/3}}{(n^2 + 2)^{1/3}}$$

$$= \lim_{n \to +\infty} \left(\frac{n^2}{n^2 + 2}\right)^{1/3}$$

$$= \lim_{n \to +\infty} \left(\frac{1}{1 + \dfrac{2}{n^2}}\right)^{1/3}$$

$$= 1$$

Therefore, the given series is divergent.

Exercises 16.4

In Exercises 1 through 18, determine if the given series is convergent or divergent.

1. $\sum_{n=1}^{+\infty} \dfrac{1}{n2^n}$

2. $\sum_{n=1}^{+\infty} \dfrac{1}{\sqrt{2n + 1}}$

3. $\sum_{n=1}^{+\infty} \dfrac{1}{n^n}$

4. $\sum_{n=1}^{+\infty} \dfrac{n^2}{4n^3 + 1}$

5. $\sum_{n=1}^{+\infty} \dfrac{1}{\sqrt{n^2 + 4n}}$

6. $\sum_{n=1}^{+\infty} \dfrac{|\sin n|}{n^2}$

7. $\sum_{n=1}^{+\infty} \dfrac{n!}{(n + 2)!}$

8. $\sum_{n=1}^{+\infty} \dfrac{1}{\sqrt{n^3 + 1}}$

9. $\sum_{n=1}^{+\infty} \dfrac{n}{5n^2 + 3}$

10. $\sum_{n=1}^{+\infty} \sin \dfrac{1}{n}$

11. $\sum_{n=1}^{+\infty} \dfrac{n!}{(2n)!}$

12. $\sum_{n=1}^{+\infty} \dfrac{2^n}{n!}$

13. $\sum_{n=1}^{+\infty} \dfrac{|\csc n|}{\sqrt{n}}$

14. $\sum_{n=1}^{+\infty} \dfrac{1}{n + \sqrt{n}}$

15. $\sum_{n=2}^{+\infty} \dfrac{1}{n\sqrt{n^2 - 1}}$

16. $\sum_{n=1}^{+\infty} \dfrac{1}{(n + 2)(n + 4)}$

17. $\sum_{n=1}^{+\infty} \dfrac{\ln n}{n^2 + 2}$

18. $\sum_{n=1}^{+\infty} \dfrac{1}{3^n - \cos n}$

19. Prove Theorem 16.4.3(ii).

20. Prove Theorem 16.4.3(iii).

21. If $\displaystyle\sum_{n=1}^{+\infty} a_n$ and $\displaystyle\sum_{n=1}^{+\infty} b_n$ are two convergent series of positive terms, use the Limit Comparison Test to prove that the series $\displaystyle\sum_{n=1}^{+\infty} a_n b_n$ is also convergent.

22. Suppose f is a function such that $f(n) > 0$ for n any positive integer. Furthermore, suppose that if p is any positive number $\displaystyle\lim_{n \to +\infty} n^p f(n)$ exists and is positive. Prove that the series $\displaystyle\sum_{n=1}^{+\infty} f(n)$ is convergent if $p > 1$ and divergent if $0 < p \le 1$.

16.5 THE INTEGRAL TEST   The theorem known as the *integral test* makes use of the theory of improper integrals to test an infinite series of positive terms for convergence.

16.5.1 Theorem   Let f be a function which is continuous, decreasing, and positive valued
Integral Test   for all $x \ge 1$. Then the infinite series

$$\sum_{n=1}^{+\infty} f(n) = f(1) + f(2) + f(3) + \cdots + f(n) + \cdots$$

is convergent if the improper integral

$$\int_{1}^{+\infty} f(x)\ dx$$

exists, and it is divergent if the improper integral increases without bound.

PROOF: If i is a positive integer, by the mean-value theorem for integrals (7.5.2) there exists a number X such that $i - 1 \le X \le i$ and

$$\int_{i-1}^{i} f(x)\ dx = f(X) \cdot 1 \tag{1}$$

Because f is a decreasing function,

$$f(i-1) \ge f(X) \ge f(i)$$

and so from (1) we have

$$f(i-1) \ge \int_{i-1}^{i} f(x)\ dx \ge f(i)$$

Therefore, if n is any positive integer,

$$\sum_{i=2}^{n} f(i-1) \ge \sum_{i=2}^{n} \int_{i-1}^{i} f(x)\ dx \ge \sum_{i=2}^{n} f(i)$$

or, equivalently,

$$\sum_{i=1}^{n-1} f(i) \ge \int_{1}^{n} f(x)\ dx \ge \sum_{i=1}^{n} f(i) - f(1) \tag{2}$$

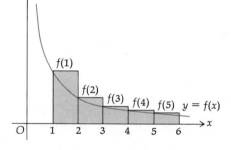

Figure 16.5.1

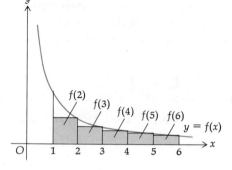

Figure 16.5.2

Figures 16.5.1 and 16.5.2 show the geometric interpretation of the above discussion for $n = 6$. In Fig. 16.5.1, we have a sketch of the graph of a function f satisfying the hypothesis. The sum of the measures of the areas of the shaded rectangles is $f(1) + f(2) + f(3) + f(4) + f(5)$, which is the left member of inequality (2) when $n = 6$. Clearly, the sum of the measures of the areas of these rectangles is greater than the measure of the area given by the definite integral when $n = 6$. In Fig. 16.5.2 the sum of the measures of the areas of the shaded rectangles is $f(2) + f(3) + f(4) + f(5) + f(6)$, which is the right member of the inequality (2) when $n = 6$. This sum is less than the value of the definite integral when $n = 6$.

If the given improper integral exists, let L be its value. Then

$$\int_1^n f(x) \ dx \le L \tag{3}$$

From the second and third members of the inequality (2) and from (3) we obtain

$$\sum_{i=1}^n f(i) \le f(1) + \int_1^n f(x) \ dx \le f(1) + L \tag{4}$$

Consider now the infinite series $\sum_{n=1}^{+\infty} f(n)$. Let the sequence of partial sums of this series be $\{s_n\}$, where $s_n = \sum_{i=1}^n f(i)$. From (4) we see that $\{s_n\}$ has an upper bound of $f(1) + L$. Hence, by Theorem 16.4.1 we conclude that $\sum_{n=1}^{+\infty} f(n)$ is convergent.

Suppose that the given improper integral increases without bound. From (2) we have

$$\sum_{i=1}^{n-1} f(i) \ge \int_1^n f(x) \ dx$$

for all positive integers n. Thus, $\sum_{i=1}^{n-1} f(i)$ must also increase without bound as $n \to +\infty$. Therefore, $\lim_{n \to +\infty} s_n = \lim_{n \to +\infty} \sum_{i=1}^n f(i) = +\infty$. Hence, $\sum_{n=1}^{+\infty} f(n)$ is divergent. ∎

EXAMPLE 1: Use the integral test to show that the p series diverges if $p \le 1$ and converges if $p > 1$.

SOLUTION: The p series is $\sum_{n=1}^{+\infty} 1/n^p$. The function f, defined by $f(x) = 1/x^p$, satisfies the hypothesis of Theorem 16.5.1. Thus, considering the improper integral, we have

$$\int_1^{+\infty} \frac{dx}{x^p} = \lim_{b \to +\infty} \int_1^b \frac{dx}{x^p}$$

If $p = 1$, the above integral gives

$$\lim_{b \to +\infty} \ln x \Big]_1^b = \lim_{b \to +\infty} \ln b = +\infty$$

If $p \neq 1$, the integral gives

$$\lim_{b \to +\infty} \frac{x^{1-p}}{1-p} \Big]_1^b = \lim_{b \to +\infty} \frac{b^{1-p} - 1}{1-p}$$

This limit is $+\infty$ when $p < 1$; it is $-1/(1-p)$ if $p > 1$. Therefore, by the integral test, it follows that the p series converges for $p > 1$ and diverges for $p \leq 1$.

EXAMPLE 2: Determine if the infinite series

$$\sum_{n=1}^{+\infty} ne^{-n}$$

is convergent or divergent.

SOLUTION: Letting $f(x) = xe^{-x}$, we see that f is continuous, decreasing, and positive valued for $x \geq 1$; thus, the hypothesis of the integral test is satisfied. Using integration by parts, we have $\int xe^{-x}\, dx = -e^{-x}(x+1) + C$. Hence,

$$\int_1^{+\infty} xe^{-x}\, dx = \lim_{b \to +\infty} \left[-e^{-x}(x+1) \right]_1^b = \lim_{b \to +\infty} \left[-\frac{b+1}{e^b} + \frac{2}{e} \right]$$

Because $\lim_{b \to +\infty} (b+1) = +\infty$ and $\lim_{b \to +\infty} e^b = +\infty$, we can use L'Hôpital's rule and obtain

$$\lim_{b \to +\infty} \frac{b+1}{e^b} = \lim_{b \to +\infty} \frac{1}{e^b} = 0$$

Therefore,

$$\int_1^{+\infty} xe^{-x}\, dx = \frac{2}{e}$$

and so the given series is convergent.

EXAMPLE 3: Determine if the series

$$\sum_{n=1}^{+\infty} \frac{1}{(n+1)\sqrt{\ln(n+1)}}$$

is convergent or divergent.

SOLUTION: The function f defined by $f(x) = 1/(x+1)\sqrt{\ln(x+1)}$ is continuous, decreasing, and positive valued for $x \geq 1$; hence, the integral test can be applied.

$$\int_1^{+\infty} \frac{dx}{(x+1)\sqrt{\ln(x+1)}} = \lim_{b \to +\infty} \int_1^b [\ln(x+1)]^{-1/2} \frac{dx}{x+1}$$

$$= \lim_{b \to +\infty} \left[2\sqrt{\ln(x+1)} \right]_1^b$$

$$= \lim_{b \to +\infty} \left[2\sqrt{\ln(b+1)} - 2\sqrt{\ln 2} \right]$$

$$= +\infty$$

We conclude that the given series is divergent.

Exercises 16.5

In Exercises 1 through 12, determine if the given series is convergent or divergent.

1. $\displaystyle\sum_{n=1}^{+\infty} \frac{\ln n}{n}$

2. $\displaystyle\sum_{n=2}^{+\infty} \frac{1}{n \ln n}$

3. $\displaystyle\sum_{n=1}^{+\infty} \frac{\tan^{-1} n}{n^2 + 1}$

4. $\displaystyle\sum_{n=1}^{+\infty} ne^{-n^2}$

5. $\displaystyle\sum_{n=1}^{+\infty} n^2 e^{-n}$

6. $\displaystyle\sum_{n=1}^{+\infty} \cot^{-1} n$

7. $\displaystyle\sum_{n=1}^{+\infty} \operatorname{csch} n$

8. $\displaystyle\sum_{n=1}^{+\infty} \frac{e^{\tan^{-1} n}}{n^2 + 1}$

9. $\displaystyle\sum_{n=1}^{+\infty} \frac{e^{1/n}}{n^2}$

10. $\displaystyle\sum_{n=1}^{+\infty} \operatorname{sech}^2 n$

11. $\displaystyle\sum_{n=1}^{+\infty} \ln\left(\frac{n+3}{n}\right)$

12. $\displaystyle\sum_{n=2}^{+\infty} \frac{1}{n (\ln n)^3}$

13. Prove that the series $\displaystyle\sum_{n=2}^{+\infty} \frac{1}{n(\ln n)^p}$ is convergent if and only if $p > 1$.

14. Prove that the series $\displaystyle\sum_{n=3}^{+\infty} \frac{1}{n(\ln n)[\ln(\ln n)]^p}$ is convergent if and only if $p > 1$.

15. If s_k is the kth partial sum of the harmonic series, prove that

$$\ln(k+1) < s_k < 1 + \ln k$$

(HINT: $\dfrac{1}{m+1} \le \dfrac{1}{x} \le \dfrac{1}{m}$ if $0 < m \le x \le m + 1$

Integrate each member of the inequality from m to $m + 1$; let m take on successively the values $1, 2, \ldots, n - 1$, and add the results.)

16. Use the result of Exercise 15 to estimate the sum $\displaystyle\sum_{m=50}^{100} \frac{1}{m} = \frac{1}{50} + \frac{1}{51} + \cdots + \frac{1}{100}$.

16.6 INFINITE SERIES OF POSITIVE AND NEGATIVE TERMS

In this section we consider infinite series having both positive and negative terms. The first type of such a series which we discuss is one whose terms are alternately positive and negative—an "alternating series."

16.6.1 Definition

If $a_n > 0$ for all positive integers n, then the series

$$\sum_{n=1}^{+\infty} (-1)^{n+1} a_n = a_1 - a_2 + a_3 - a_4 + \cdots + (-1)^{n+1} a_n + \cdots$$

and the series

$$\sum_{n=1}^{+\infty} (-1)^n a_n = -a_1 + a_2 - a_3 + a_4 - \cdots + (-1)^n a_n + \cdots$$

are called *alternating series*.

The following theorem gives a test for the convergence of an alternating series.

16.6.2 Theorem
Alternating-Series Test

If the numbers $u_1, u_2, u_3, \ldots, u_n, \ldots$ are alternately positive and nega-
tive, $|u_{n+1}| < |u_n|$ for all positive integers n, and $\lim\limits_{n \to +\infty} u_n = 0$, then the al-

ternating series $\sum\limits_{n=1}^{+\infty} u_n$ is convergent.

PROOF: We assume that the odd-numbered terms of the given series
are positive and the even-numbered terms are negative. This assumption is not a loss of generality because if this is not the case, then we
consider the series whose first term is u_2 because discarding a finite
number of terms does not affect the convergence of the series. So $u_{2n-1} > 0$
and $u_{2n} < 0$ for every positive integer n. Consider the partial sum

$$s_{2n} = (u_1 + u_2) + (u_3 + u_4) + \cdots + (u_{2n-1} + u_{2n}) \tag{1}$$

The first term of each quantity in parentheses in (1) is positive and the
second term is negative. Because by hypothesis $|u_{n+1}| < |u_n|$, we conclude
that each quantity in parentheses is positive. Therefore,

$$0 < s_2 < s_4 < s_6 < \cdots < s_{2n} < \cdots \tag{2}$$

We also can write s_{2n} as

$$s_{2n} = u_1 + (u_2 + u_3) + (u_4 + u_5) + \cdots + (u_{2n-2} + u_{2n-1}) + u_{2n} \tag{3}$$

Because $|u_{n+1}| < |u_n|$, each quantity in parentheses in (3) is negative and
so also is u_{2n}. Therefore,

$$s_{2n} < u_1 \quad \text{for every positive integer } n \tag{4}$$

From (2) and (4) we have

$$0 < s_{2n} < u_1 \quad \text{for every positive integer } n$$

So the sequence $\{s_{2n}\}$ is bounded. Furthermore, from (2) the sequence
$\{s_{2n}\}$ is monotonic. Therefore, by Theorem 16.2.6 the sequence $\{s_{2n}\}$ is convergent. Let $\lim\limits_{n \to +\infty} s_{2n} = S$, and from Theorem 16.2.7 we know that $S \le u_1$.
Because $s_{2n+1} = s_{2n} + u_{2n+1}$, we have

$$\lim\limits_{n \to +\infty} s_{2n+1} = \lim\limits_{n \to +\infty} s_{2n} + \lim\limits_{n \to +\infty} u_{2n+1}$$

but, by hypothesis, $\lim\limits_{n \to +\infty} u_{2n+1} = 0$, and so $\lim\limits_{n \to +\infty} s_{2n+1} = \lim\limits_{n \to +\infty} s_{2n}$. Therefore,
the sequence of partial sums of the even-numbered terms and the se-
quence of partial sums of the odd-numbered terms have the same limit S.
We now show that $\lim\limits_{n \to +\infty} s_n = S$. Because $\lim\limits_{n \to +\infty} s_{2n} = S$, then for any
$\epsilon > 0$ there exists an integer $N_1 > 0$ such that

$$|s_{2n} - S| < \epsilon \quad \text{whenever } 2n \ge N_1$$

And because $\lim\limits_{n \to +\infty} s_{2n+1} = S$, there exists an integer $N_2 > 0$ such that

$$|s_{2n+1} - S| < \epsilon \quad \text{whenever } 2n + 1 \ge N_2$$

If N is the larger of the two integers N_1 and N_2, it follows that if n is any integer, either odd or even, then

$$|s_n - S| < \epsilon \qquad \text{whenever } n \geq N$$

Therefore, $\lim\limits_{n \to +\infty} s_n = S$, and so the series $\sum\limits_{n=1}^{+\infty} u_n$ is convergent.   ∎

EXAMPLE 1: Prove that the alternating series

$$\sum_{n=1}^{+\infty} \frac{(-1)^{n+1}}{n}$$

is convergent.

SOLUTION: The given series is

$$1 - \frac{1}{2} + \frac{1}{3} - \frac{1}{4} + \cdots + (-1)^{n+1}\frac{1}{n} + (-1)^{n+2}\frac{1}{n+1} + \cdots$$

Because $1/(n+1) < 1/n$ for all positive integers n, and $\lim\limits_{n \to +\infty} (1/n) = 0$, it follows from Theorem 16.6.2 that the given alternating series is convergent.

EXAMPLE 2: Determine if the series

$$\sum_{n=1}^{+\infty} (-1)^n \frac{n+2}{n(n+1)}$$

is convergent or divergent.

SOLUTION: The given series is an alternating series, with

$$u_n = (-1)^n \frac{n+2}{n(n+1)} \quad \text{and} \quad u_{n+1} = (-1)^{n+1}\frac{n+3}{(n+1)(n+2)}$$

$$\lim_{n \to +\infty} \frac{n+2}{n(n+1)} = \lim_{n \to +\infty} \frac{\dfrac{1}{n} + \dfrac{2}{n^2}}{1 + \dfrac{1}{n}} = 0$$

Before we can apply the alternating-series test we must also show that $|u_{n+1}| < |u_n|$ or, equivalently, $|u_{n+1}|/|u_n| < 1$.

$$\frac{|u_{n+1}|}{|u_n|} = \frac{n+3}{(n+1)(n+2)} \cdot \frac{n(n+1)}{n+2} = \frac{n(n+3)}{(n+2)^2} = \frac{n^2 + 3n}{n^2 + 4n + 4} < 1$$

Then it follows from Theorem 16.6.2 that the given series is convergent.

16.6.3 Definition   If an infinite series $\sum\limits_{n=1}^{+\infty} u_n$ is convergent and its sum is S, then the *remainder* obtained by approximating the sum of the series by the kth partial sum s_k is denoted by R_k and

$$R_k = S - s_k$$

16.6.4 Theorem   Suppose $\sum\limits_{n=1}^{+\infty} u_n$ is an alternating series, $|u_{n+1}| < |u_n|$, and $\lim\limits_{n \to +\infty} u_n = 0$.
Then, if R_k is the remainder obtained by approximating the sum of the series by the sum of the first k terms, $|R_k| < |u_{k+1}|$.

PROOF: Assume that the odd-numbered terms of the given series are positive and the even-numbered terms are negative. Then, from (2) in the proof of Theorem 16.6.2, we see that the sequence $\{s_{2n}\}$ is increasing. So if S is the sum of the given series, we have

$$s_{2k} < s_{2k+2} < S \qquad \text{for all } k \geq 1 \tag{5}$$

To show that the sequence $\{s_{2n-1}\}$ is decreasing, we write

$$s_{2n-1} = u_1 + (u_2 + u_3) + (u_4 + u_5) + \cdots + (u_{2n-2} + u_{2n-1}) \tag{6}$$

The first term of each quantity in parentheses in (6) is negative and the second term is positive, and because $|u_{n+1}| < |u_n|$, it follows that each quantity in parentheses is negative. Therefore, because $u_1 > 0$, we conclude that $s_1 > s_3 > s_5 > \cdots > s_{2n-1} > \cdots$; and so the sequence $\{s_{2n-1}\}$ is decreasing. Thus,

$$S < s_{2k+1} < s_{2k-1} \qquad \text{for all } k \geq 1 \tag{7}$$

From (7) we have $S - s_{2k} < s_{2k+1} - s_{2k} = u_{2k+1}$, and from (5) we have $0 < S - s_{2k}$. Therefore,

$$0 < S - s_{2k} < u_{2k+1} \qquad \text{for all } k \geq 1 \tag{8}$$

From (5) we have $-S < -s_{2k}$; hence, $s_{2k-1} - S < s_{2k-1} - s_{2k} = -u_{2k}$. Because from (7) it follows that $0 < s_{2k-1} - S$, we have

$$0 < s_{2k-1} - S < -u_{2k} \qquad \text{for all } k \geq 1 \tag{9}$$

Because from Definition 16.6.3, $R_k = S - s_k$, (8) can be written as $0 < |R_{2k}| < |u_{2k+1}|$ and (9) can be written as $0 < |R_{2k-1}| < |u_{2k}|$. Hence, we have $|R_k| < |u_{k+1}|$ for all $k \geq 1$, and the theorem is proved. ∎

EXAMPLE 3:   A series for computing $\ln(1 - x)$ if x is in the open interval $(-1, 1)$ is

$$\ln(1 - x) = \sum_{n=1}^{+\infty} -\frac{x^n}{n}$$

Find an estimate of the error when the first three terms of this series are used to approximate the value of $\ln 1.1$.

SOLUTION: Using the given series with $x = -0.1$, we get

$$\ln 1.1 = 0.1 - \frac{(0.1)^2}{2} + \frac{(0.1)^3}{3} - \frac{(0.1)^4}{4} + \cdots$$

This series satisfies the conditions of Theorem 16.6.4; so if R_3 is the difference between the actual value of $\ln 1.1$ and the sum of the first three terms, then

$$|R_3| < |u_4| = 0.000025$$

Thus, we know that the sum of the first three terms will yield a value of $\ln 1.1$ accurate at least to four decimal places. Using the first three terms, we get

$$\ln 1.1 \approx 0.0953$$

Associated with each infinite series is the series whose terms are the absolute values of the terms of that series.

16.6.5 Definition   The infinite series $\sum\limits_{n=1}^{+\infty} u_n$ is said to be *absolutely convergent* if the series $\sum\limits_{n=1}^{+\infty} |u_n|$ is convergent.

• ILLUSTRATION 1: Consider the series

$$\sum_{n=1}^{+\infty} (-1)^{n+1}\frac{2}{3^n} = \frac{2}{3} - \frac{2}{3^2} + \frac{2}{3^3} - \frac{2}{3^4} + \cdots + (-1)^{n+1}\frac{2}{3^n} + \cdots \qquad (10)$$

This series will be absolutely convergent if the series

$$\sum_{n=1}^{+\infty} \frac{2}{3^n} = \frac{2}{3} + \frac{2}{3^2} + \frac{2}{3^3} + \frac{2}{3^4} + \cdots + \frac{2}{3^n} + \cdots$$

is convergent. Because this is the geometric series with $r = \frac{1}{3} < 1$, it is convergent. Therefore, series (10) is absolutely convergent.   •

• ILLUSTRATION 2: A convergent series which is not absolutely convergent is the series

$$\sum_{n=1}^{+\infty} \frac{(-1)^{n+1}}{n}$$

In Example 1 we proved that this series is convergent. The series is not absolutely convergent because the series of absolute values is the harmonic series which is divergent.   •

The series of Illustration 2 is an example of a "conditionally convergent" series.

16.6.6 Definition   A series which is convergent, but not absolutely convergent, is said to be *conditionally convergent*.

It is possible, then, for a series to be convergent but not absolutely convergent. If a series is absolutely convergent, it must be convergent, however, and this is given by the next theorem.

16.6.7 Theorem   If the infinite series $\sum\limits_{n=1}^{+\infty} u_n$ is absolutely convergent, it is convergent and

$$\left| \sum_{n=1}^{+\infty} u_n \right| \le \sum_{n=1}^{+\infty} |u_n|$$

PROOF: Consider the three infinite series $\sum\limits_{n=1}^{+\infty} u_n, \sum\limits_{n=1}^{+\infty} |u_n|,$ and $\sum\limits_{n=1}^{+\infty} (u_n + |u_n|),$ and let their sequences of partial sums be $\{s_n\}, \{t_n\},$ and $\{r_n\},$ respectively. For every positive integer n, $u_n + |u_n|$ is either 0 or $2|u_n|$; so we have the inequality

$$0 \le u_n + |u_n| \le 2|u_n| \qquad (11)$$

Because $\displaystyle\sum_{n=1}^{+\infty} |u_n|$ is convergent, it has a sum, which we denote by T.

$\{t_n\}$ is an increasing sequence of positive numbers, and so $t_n \leq T$ for all positive integers n. From (11), it follows that

$$0 \leq r_n \leq 2t_n \leq 2T$$

Therefore, the sequence $\{r_n\}$ has an upper bound of $2T$. Thus, by Theorem 16.4.1 the series $\displaystyle\sum_{n=1}^{+\infty} (u_n + |u_n|)$ is convergent, and we call its sum R. Because from (11), $\{r_n\}$ is an increasing sequence, it may be concluded from Theorem 16.2.7 that $R \leq 2T$.

Each of the series $\displaystyle\sum_{n=1}^{+\infty} (u_n + |u_n|)$ and $\displaystyle\sum_{n=1}^{+\infty} |u_n|$ is convergent; hence, from Theorem 16.3.9 the series

$$\sum_{n=1}^{+\infty} [(u_n + |u_n|) - |u_n|] = \sum_{n=1}^{+\infty} u_n$$

is also convergent.

Let the sum of the series $\displaystyle\sum_{n=1}^{+\infty} u_n$ be S. Then, also from Theorem 16.3.9, $S = R - T$. And because $R \leq 2T$, $S \leq 2T - T = T$.

Because $\displaystyle\sum_{n=1}^{+\infty} u_n$ is convergent and has the sum S, it follows from Theorem 16.3.8 that $\displaystyle\sum_{n=1}^{+\infty} (-u_n)$ is convergent and has the sum $-S$. Because $\displaystyle\sum_{n=1}^{+\infty} |-u_n| = \sum_{n=1}^{+\infty} |u_n| = T$, we can replace $\displaystyle\sum_{n=1}^{+\infty} u_n$ by $\displaystyle\sum_{n=1}^{+\infty} (-u_n)$ in the above discussion and show that $-S \leq T$. Because $S \leq T$ and $-S \leq T$, we have $|S| \leq T$; therefore, $\left| \displaystyle\sum_{n=1}^{+\infty} u_n \right| \leq \displaystyle\sum_{n=1}^{+\infty} |u_n|$, and the theorem is proved. ∎

EXAMPLE 4:   Determine if the series

$$\sum_{n=1}^{+\infty} \frac{\cos \frac{1}{3}n\pi}{n^2}$$

is convergent or divergent.

SOLUTION: Denote the given series by $\displaystyle\sum_{n=1}^{+\infty} u_n$. Therefore,

$$\sum_{n=1}^{+\infty} u_n = \frac{\frac{1}{2}}{1^2} - \frac{\frac{1}{2}}{2^2} - \frac{1}{3^2} - \frac{\frac{1}{2}}{4^2} + \frac{\frac{1}{2}}{5^2} + \frac{1}{6^2} + \frac{\frac{1}{2}}{7^2} - \cdots + \frac{\cos \frac{1}{3}n\pi}{n^2} + \cdots$$

$$= \tfrac{1}{2} - \tfrac{1}{8} - \tfrac{1}{9} - \tfrac{1}{32} + \tfrac{1}{50} + \tfrac{1}{36} + \tfrac{1}{98} - \cdots$$

We have a series of positive and negative terms. We can prove this series is convergent if we can show that it is absolutely convergent.

$$\sum_{n=1}^{+\infty} |u_n| = \sum_{n=1}^{+\infty} \frac{\left| \cos \frac{1}{3}n\pi \right|}{n^2}$$

Because

$$|\cos \tfrac{1}{3} n\pi| \leq 1 \qquad \text{for all } n$$

$$\frac{|\cos \tfrac{1}{3} n\pi|}{n^2} \leq \frac{1}{n^2} \qquad \text{for all positive integers } n$$

The series $\sum\limits_{n=1}^{+\infty} 1/n^2$ is the p series, with $p = 2$, and is therefore convergent.

So by the comparison test $\sum\limits_{n=1}^{+\infty} |u_n|$ is convergent. The given series is there-fore absolutely convergent; hence, by Theorem 16.6.7 it is convergent.

You will note that the terms of the series $\sum\limits_{n=1}^{+\infty} |u_n|$ neither increase monotonically nor decrease monotonically. For example, $|u_4| = \tfrac{1}{32}$, $|u_5| = \tfrac{1}{50}$, $|u_6| = \tfrac{1}{36}$; and so $|u_5| < |u_4|$, but $|u_6| > |u_5|$.

The *ratio test*, given in the next theorem, is used frequently to deter-mine whether a given series is absolutely convergent.

16.6.8 Theorem
Ratio Test

Let $\sum\limits_{n=1}^{+\infty} u_n$ be a given infinite series for which every u_n is nonzero. Then

(i) if $\lim\limits_{n \to +\infty} |u_{n+1}/u_n| = L < 1$, the given series is absolutely convergent;

(ii) if $\lim\limits_{n \to +\infty} |u_{n+1}/u_n| = L > 1$ or if $\lim\limits_{n \to +\infty} |u_{n+1}/u_n| = +\infty$, the series is divergent;

(iii) if $\lim\limits_{n \to +\infty} |u_{n+1}/u_n| = 1$, no conclusion regarding convergence may be made.

PROOF OF (i): We are given that $L < 1$, and let R be a number such that $L < R < 1$. Let $R - L = \epsilon < 1$. Because $\lim\limits_{n \to +\infty} |u_{n+1}/u_n| = L$, there exists an integer $N > 0$ such that

$$\left| \left| \frac{u_{n+1}}{u_n} \right| - L \right| < \epsilon \qquad \text{whenever } n \geq N$$

or, equivalently,

$$0 < \left| \frac{u_{n+1}}{u_n} \right| < L + \epsilon = R \qquad \text{whenever } n \geq N \tag{12}$$

Letting n take on the successive values $N, N + 1, N + 2, \ldots$, and so forth, we obtain from (12)

$$|u_{N+1}| < R|u_N|$$

$$|u_{N+2}| < R|u_{N+1}| < R^2|u_N|$$

$$|u_{N+3}| < R|u_{N+2}| < R^3|u_N|$$

$$\cdot \ \cdot \ \cdot$$

In general, we have

$$|u_{N+k}| < R^k|u_N| \qquad \text{for every positive integer } k \qquad (13)$$

The series

$$\sum_{k=1}^{+\infty} |u_N|R^k = |u_N|R + |u_N|R^2 + \cdot \cdot \cdot + |u_N|R^n + \cdot \cdot \cdot$$

is convergent because it is a geometric series whose ratio is less than 1.

So from (13) and the comparison test, it follows that the series $\sum_{k=1}^{+\infty} |u_{N+k}|$

is convergent. The series $\sum_{k=1}^{+\infty} |u_{N+k}|$ differs from the series $\sum_{n=1}^{+\infty} |u_n|$ in only

the first N terms. Therefore, $\sum_{n=1}^{+\infty} |u_n|$ is convergent, and so the given series

is absolutely convergent.

PROOF OF (ii): If $\lim\limits_{n \to +\infty} |u_{n+1}/u_n| = L > 1$ or $\lim\limits_{n \to +\infty} |u_{n+1}/u_n| = +\infty$, then in either case there is an integer $N > 0$ such that $|u_{n+1}/u_n| > 1$ for all $n \geq N$. Letting n take on the successive values $N, N + 1, N + 2, \ . \ . \ . $, and so on, we obtain

$$|u_{N+1}| > |u_N|$$

$$|u_{N+2}| > |u_{N+1}| > |u_N|$$

$$|u_{N+3}| > |u_{N+2}| > |u_N|$$

$$\cdot \ \cdot \ \cdot$$

So we may conclude that $|u_n| > |u_N|$ for all $n > N$. Hence, $\lim\limits_{n \to +\infty} u_n \neq 0$, and so the given series is divergent.

PROOF OF (iii): If we apply the ratio test to the p series, we have

$$\lim_{n \to +\infty} \left| \frac{u_{n+1}}{u_n} \right| = \lim_{n \to +\infty} \left| \frac{\dfrac{1}{(n + 1)^p}}{\dfrac{1}{n^p}} \right| = \lim_{n \to +\infty} \left| \left(\frac{n}{n + 1} \right)^p \right| = 1$$

Because the p series diverges if $p \leq 1$ and converges if $p > 1$, we have shown that it is possible to have both convergent and divergent series for which we have $\lim\limits_{n \to +\infty} |u_{n+1}/u_n| = 1$. This proves part (iii). ∎

EXAMPLE 5:   Determine if the series

$$\sum_{n=1}^{+\infty} \frac{(-1)^{n+1}n}{2^n}$$

is convergent or divergent.

SOLUTION: $u_n = (-1)^{n+1}n/2^n$ and $u_{n+1} = (-1)^{n+2}(n+1)/2^{n+1}$.

Therefore,

$$\left|\frac{u_{n+1}}{u_n}\right| = \frac{n+1}{2^{n+1}} \cdot \frac{2^n}{n} = \frac{n+1}{2n}$$

So

$$\lim_{n\to+\infty} \left|\frac{u_{n+1}}{u_n}\right| = \lim_{n\to+\infty} \frac{1+\dfrac{1}{n}}{2} = \frac{1}{2} < 1$$

Therefore, by the ratio test, the given series is absolutely convergent and hence, by Theorem 16.6.7, it is convergent.

EXAMPLE 6:   In Example 2, the series

$$\sum_{n=1}^{+\infty} (-1)^n \frac{n+2}{n(n+1)}$$

was shown to be convergent. Is this series absolutely convergent or conditionally convergent?

SOLUTION: To test for absolute convergence we apply the ratio test. In the solution of Example 2 we showed that $|u_{n+1}|/|u_n| = (n^2+3n)/(n^2+4n+4)$. Hence,

$$\lim_{n\to+\infty} \left|\frac{u_{n+1}}{u_n}\right| = \lim_{n\to+\infty} \frac{1+\dfrac{3}{n}}{1+\dfrac{4}{n}+\dfrac{4}{n^2}} = 1$$

So the ratio test fails. Because

$$|u_n| = \frac{n+2}{n(n+1)} = \frac{n+2}{n+1} \cdot \frac{1}{n} > \frac{1}{n}$$

we can apply the comparison test. And because the series $\sum_{n=1}^{+\infty} 1/n$ is the harmonic series, which diverges, we conclude that the series $\sum_{n=1}^{+\infty} |u_n|$ is divergent and hence $\sum_{n=1}^{+\infty} u_n$ is not absolutely convergent. Therefore, the series is conditionally convergent.

It should be noted that the ratio test does not include all possibilities for $\lim_{n\to+\infty} |u_{n+1}/u_n|$ because it is possible that the limit does not exist and is not $+\infty$. The discussion of such cases is beyond the scope of this book.

To conclude the discussion of infinite series of constant terms, we suggest a possible procedure to follow for determining the convergence or divergence of a given series. First of all, if $\lim_{n\to+\infty} u_n \neq 0$, we may conclude that the series is divergent. If $\lim_{n\to+\infty} u_n = 0$ and the series is an alternating series, then try the alternating-series test. If this test is not applicable, try the ratio test. If in applying the ratio test, $L = 1$, then another test must be used. The integral test may work when the ratio test does not; this was shown for the p series. Also, the comparison test can be tried.

Exercises 16.6

In Exercises 1 through 8, determine if the given alternating series is convergent or divergent.

1. $\sum\limits_{n=2}^{+\infty} (-1)^n \dfrac{1}{\ln n}$

2. $\sum\limits_{n=1}^{+\infty} (-1)^{n+1} \sin \dfrac{\pi}{n}$

3. $\sum\limits_{n=1}^{+\infty} (-1)^{n+1} \dfrac{n^2}{n^3 + 2}$

4. $\sum\limits_{n=1}^{+\infty} (-1)^{n+1} \dfrac{\ln n}{n}$

5. $\sum\limits_{n=1}^{+\infty} (-1)^{n+1} \dfrac{\ln n}{n^2}$

6. $\sum\limits_{n=1}^{+\infty} (-1)^n \dfrac{e^n}{n}$

7. $\sum\limits_{n=1}^{+\infty} (-1)^n \dfrac{n}{2^n}$

8. $\sum\limits_{n=1}^{+\infty} (-1)^n \dfrac{\sqrt{n}}{3n - 1}$

In Exercises 9 through 12, find the error if the sum of the first four terms is used as an approximation to the sum of the given infinite series.

9. $\sum\limits_{n=1}^{+\infty} (-1)^{n+1} \dfrac{1}{n}$

10. $\sum\limits_{n=1}^{+\infty} (-1)^n \dfrac{1}{n!}$

11. $\sum\limits_{n=1}^{+\infty} (-1)^{n+1} \dfrac{1}{(2n-1)^2}$

12. $\sum\limits_{n=1}^{+\infty} (-1)^{n+1} \dfrac{1}{n^n}$

In Exercises 13 through 16, find the sum of the given infinite series, accurate to three decimal places.

13. $\sum\limits_{n=1}^{+\infty} (-1)^{n+1} \dfrac{1}{(2n)^3}$

14. $\sum\limits_{n=1}^{+\infty} (-1)^{n+1} \dfrac{1}{(2n)!}$

15. $\sum\limits_{n=1}^{+\infty} (-1)^{n+1} \dfrac{1}{n2^n}$

16. $\sum\limits_{n=1}^{+\infty} (-1)^n \dfrac{1}{(2n+1)^3}$

In Exercises 17 through 28, determine if the given series is absolutely convergent, conditionally convergent, or divergent. Prove your answer.

17. $\sum\limits_{n=1}^{+\infty} (-1)^{n+1} \dfrac{2^n}{n!}$

18. $\sum\limits_{n=1}^{+\infty} (-1)^{n+1} \dfrac{1}{(2n-1)!}$

19. $\sum\limits_{n=1}^{+\infty} \dfrac{n^2}{n!}$

20. $\sum\limits_{n=1}^{+\infty} n \left(\dfrac{2}{3}\right)^n$

21. $\sum\limits_{n=1}^{+\infty} (-1)^n \dfrac{n!}{2^{n+1}}$

22. $\sum\limits_{n=1}^{+\infty} (-1)^{n+1} \dfrac{1}{n(n+2)}$

23. $\sum\limits_{n=1}^{+\infty} (-1)^{n+1} \dfrac{3^n}{n!}$

24. $\sum\limits_{n=1}^{+\infty} (-1)^n \dfrac{n^2+1}{n^3}$

25. $\sum\limits_{n=2}^{+\infty} (-1)^{n+1} \dfrac{1}{n(\ln n)^2}$

26. $\sum\limits_{n=1}^{+\infty} (-1)^n \dfrac{\cos n}{n^2}$

27. $\sum\limits_{n=1}^{+\infty} \dfrac{n^n}{n!}$

28. $\sum\limits_{n=1}^{+\infty} \dfrac{1 \cdot 3 \cdot 5 \cdot \ldots \cdot (2n-1)}{1 \cdot 4 \cdot 7 \cdot \ldots \cdot (3n-2)}$

29. Prove by mathematical induction that $1/n! \le 1/2^{n-1}$.

30. Prove that if $\sum\limits_{n=1}^{+\infty} u_n$ is absolutely convergent and $u_n \ne 0$ for all n, then $\sum\limits_{n=1}^{+\infty} 1/|u_n|$ is divergent.

31. Prove that if $\sum\limits_{n=1}^{+\infty} u_n$ is absolutely convergent, then $\sum\limits_{n=1}^{+\infty} u_n{}^2$ is convergent.

32. Show by means of an example that the converse of Exercise 31 is not true.

16.7 POWER SERIES   We now study an important type of series of variable terms called "power series."

16.7.1 Definition   A *power series* in $(x - a)$ is a series of the form

$$c_0 + c_1(x - a) + c_2(x - a)^2 + \cdots + c_n(x - a)^n + \cdots \tag{1}$$

We use the notation $\sum\limits_{n=0}^{+\infty} c_n(x - a)^n$ to represent series (1). (Note that we take $(x - a)^0 = 1$, even when $x = a$, for convenience in writing the general term.) If x is a particular number, the power series (1) becomes an infinite series of constant terms, as was discussed in previous sections. A special case of (1) is obtained when $a = 0$ and the series becomes a power series in x, which is

$$\sum_{n=0}^{+\infty} c_n x^n = c_0 + c_1 x + c_2 x^2 + \cdots + c_n x^n + \cdots \tag{2}$$

In addition to power series in $(x - a)$ and x, there are power series of the form

$$\sum_{n=0}^{+\infty} c_n[\phi(x)]^n = c_0 + c_1\phi(x) + c_2[\phi(x)]^2 + \cdots + c_n[\phi(x)]^n + \cdots$$

where ϕ is a function of x. Such a series is called a power series in $\phi(x)$. In this book, we are concerned exclusively with power series of the forms (1) and (2), and when we use the term "power series," we mean either of these forms. In discussing the theory of power series, we confine ourselves to series (2). The more general power series (1) can be obtained from (2) by the translation $x = \bar{x} - a$; therefore, our results can be applied to series (1) as well.

In dealing with an infinite series of constant terms, we were concerned with the question of convergence or divergence of the series. In considering a power series, we ask, For what values of x, if any, does the power series converge? For each value of x for which the power series converges, the series represents the number which is the sum of the series. Therefore, we can think of a power series as defining a function. The function f, with function values

$$f(x) = \sum_{n=0}^{+\infty} c_n x^n \tag{3}$$

has as its domain all values of x for which the power series in (3) converges. It is apparent that every power series (2) is convergent for $x = 0$. There are some series (see Example 3) which are convergent for no other value of x, and there are also series which converge for every value of x (see Example 2).

The following three examples illustrate how the ratio test can be used to determine the values of x for which a power series is convergent. Note that when $n!$ is used in representing the nth term of a power series (as in Example 2), we take $0! = 1$ so that the expression for the nth term will hold when $n = 0$.

EXAMPLE 1: Find the values of x for which the power series

$$\sum_{n=1}^{+\infty} (-1)^{n+1} \frac{2^n x^n}{n3^n}$$

is convergent.

SOLUTION: For the given series,

$$u_n = (-1)^{n+1} \frac{2^n x^n}{n3^n} \quad \text{and} \quad u_{n+1} = (-1)^{n+2} \frac{2^{n+1}x^{n+1}}{(n+1)3^{n+1}}$$

So

$$\lim_{n \to +\infty} \left| \frac{u_{n+1}}{u_n} \right| = \lim_{n \to +\infty} \left| \frac{2^{n+1}x^{n+1}}{(n+1)3^{n+1}} \cdot \frac{n3^n}{2^n x^n} \right| = \lim_{n \to +\infty} \frac{2}{3} |x| \frac{n}{n+1} = \frac{2}{3} |x|$$

Therefore, the power series is absolutely convergent when $\frac{2}{3}|x| < 1$ or, equivalently, when $|x| < \frac{3}{2}$. The series is divergent when $\frac{2}{3}|x| > 1$ or, equivalently, when $|x| > \frac{3}{2}$. When $\frac{2}{3}|x| = 1$ (i.e., when $x = \pm\frac{3}{2}$), the ratio test fails. When $x = \frac{3}{2}$, the given power series becomes

$$\frac{1}{1} - \frac{1}{2} + \frac{1}{3} - \frac{1}{4} + \cdots + (-1)^{n+1}\frac{1}{n} + \cdots$$

which is convergent, as was shown in Example 1 of Sec. 16.6. When $x = -\frac{3}{2}$, we have

$$-\frac{1}{1} - \frac{1}{2} - \frac{1}{3} - \frac{1}{4} - \cdots - \frac{1}{n} - \cdots$$

which by Theorem 16.3.8 is divergent. We conclude, then, that the given power series is convergent when $-\frac{3}{2} < x \le \frac{3}{2}$. The series is absolutely convergent when $-\frac{3}{2} < x < \frac{3}{2}$ and is conditionally convergent when $x = \frac{3}{2}$. If $x \le -\frac{3}{2}$ or $x > \frac{3}{2}$, the series is divergent.

EXAMPLE 2: Find the values of x for which the power series

$$\sum_{n=0}^{+\infty} \frac{x^n}{n!}$$

is convergent.

SOLUTION: For the given series, $u_n = x^n/n!$ and $u_{n+1} = x^{n+1}/(n+1)!$. So by applying the ratio test, we have

$$\lim_{n \to +\infty} \left| \frac{u_{n+1}}{u_n} \right| = \lim_{n \to +\infty} \left| \frac{x^{n+1}}{(n+1)!} \cdot \frac{n!}{x^n} \right| = |x| \lim_{n \to +\infty} \frac{1}{n+1} = 0 < 1$$

We conclude that the given power series is absolutely convergent for all values of x.

EXAMPLE 3: Find the values of x for which the power series

$$\sum_{n=0}^{+\infty} n!x^n$$

is convergent.

SOLUTION: For the given series $u_n = n!x^n$ and $u_{n+1} = (n+1)!x^{n+1}$. Applying the ratio test, we have

$$\lim_{n\to+\infty}\left|\frac{u_{n+1}}{u_n}\right| = \lim_{n\to+\infty}\left|\frac{(n+1)!x^{n+1}}{n!x^n}\right|$$

$$= \lim_{n\to+\infty}|(n+1)x|$$

$$= \begin{cases} 0 & \text{if } x = 0 \\ +\infty & \text{if } x \neq 0 \end{cases}$$

It follows that the series is divergent for all values of x except 0.

16.7.2 Theorem If the power series $\sum_{n=0}^{+\infty} c_n x^n$ is convergent for $x = x_1$ ($x_1 \neq 0$), then it is absolutely convergent for all values of x for which $|x| < |x_1|$.

PROOF: If $\sum_{n=0}^{+\infty} c_n x_1{}^n$ is convergent, then $\lim_{n\to+\infty} c_n x_1{}^n = 0$. Therefore, if we take $\epsilon = 1$ in Definition 4.1.1, there exists an integer $N > 0$ such that

$$|c_n x_1{}^n| < 1 \qquad \text{whenever } n \geq N$$

Now if x is any number such that $|x| < |x_1|$, we have

$$|c_n x^n| = \left|c_n x_1{}^n \frac{x^n}{x_1{}^n}\right| = |c_n x_1{}^n|\left|\frac{x}{x_1}\right|^n < \left|\frac{x}{x_1}\right|^n \qquad \text{whenever } n \geq N \qquad (4)$$

The series

$$\sum_{n=N}^{+\infty}\left|\frac{x}{x_1}\right|^n \qquad (5)$$

is convergent because it is a geometric series with $r = |x/x_1| < 1$ (because $|x| < |x_1|$). Comparing the series $\sum_{n=N}^{+\infty}|c_n x^n|$, where $|x| < |x_1|$, with series (5), we see from (4) and the comparison test that $\sum_{n=N}^{+\infty}|c_n x^n|$ is convergent for $|x| < |x_1|$. So the given power series is absolutely convergent for all values of x for which $|x| < |x_1|$. ∎

• **ILLUSTRATION 1:** An illustration of Theorem 16.7.2 is given in Example 1. The power series is convergent for $x = \frac{3}{2}$ and is absolutely convergent for all values of x for which $|x| < \frac{3}{2}$. •

The following theorem is a corollary of Theorem 16.7.2.

16.7.3 Theorem If the power series $\sum_{n=0}^{+\infty} c_n x^n$ is divergent for $x = x_2$, it is divergent for all values of x for which $|x| > |x_2|$.

PROOF: Suppose that the given power series is convergent for some number x for which $|x| > |x_2|$. Then by Theorem 16.7.2 the series must converge when $x = x_2$. However, this contradicts the hypothesis. Therefore, the given power series is divergent for all values of x for which $|x| > |x_2|$. ∎

● ILLUSTRATION 2: To illustrate Theorem 16.7.3 we consider again the power series of Example 1. It is divergent for $x = -\frac{3}{2}$ and is also divergent for all values of x for which $|x| > |-\frac{3}{2}|$. ●

From Theorems 16.7.2 and 16.7.3, we can prove the following important theorem.

16.7.4 Theorem Let $\sum\limits_{n=0}^{+\infty} c_n x^n$ be a given power series. Then exactly one of the following conditions holds:

    (i) the series converges only when $x = 0$;
    (ii) the series is absolutely convergent for all values of x;
    (iii) there exists a number $R > 0$ such that the series is absolutely convergent for all values of x for which $|x| < R$ and is divergent for all values of x for which $|x| > R$.

PROOF: If we replace x by zero in the given power series, we have $c_0 + 0 + 0 + \cdots$, which is obviously convergent. Therefore, every power series of the form $\sum\limits_{n=0}^{+\infty} c_n x^n$ is convergent when $x = 0$. If this is the only value of x for which the series converges, then condition (i) holds.

Suppose that the given series is convergent for $x = x_1$ where $x_1 \neq 0$. Then it follows from Theorem 16.7.2 that the series is absolutely convergent for all values of x for which $|x| < |x_1|$. Now if in addition there is no value of x for which the given series is divergent, we can conclude that the series is absolutely convergent for all values of x. This is condition (ii).

If the given series is convergent for $x = x_1$, where $x_1 \neq 0$, and is divergent for $x = x_2$, where $|x_2| > |x_1|$, it follows from Theorem 16.7.3 that the series is divergent for all values of x for which $|x| > |x_2|$. Hence, $|x_2|$ is an upper bound of the set of values of $|x|$ for which the series is absolutely convergent. Therefore, by the axiom of completeness (16.2.5), this set of numbers has a least upper bound, which is the number R of condition (iii). This proves that exactly one of the three conditions holds. ∎

Theorem 16.7.4(iii) can be illustrated on the number line. See Fig. 16.7.1.

If instead of the power series $\sum\limits_{n=0}^{+\infty} c_n x^n$ we have the series $\sum\limits_{n=0}^{+\infty} c_n (x - a)^n$,

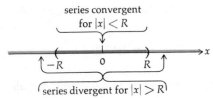

series convergent for $|x| < R$

series divergent for $|x| > R$

Figure 16.7.1

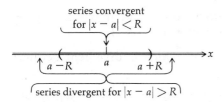

Figure 16.7.2

in conditions (i) and (iii) of Theorem 16.7.4, x is replaced by $x - a$. The conditions become

    (i) the series converges only when $x = a$;
    (iii) there exists a number $R > 0$ such that the series is absolutely convergent for all values of x for which $|x - a| < R$ and is divergent for all values of x for which $|x - a| > R$. (See Fig. 16.7.2 for an illustration of this on the number line.)

The set of all values of x for which a given power series is convergent is called the *interval of convergence* of the power series. The number R of condition (iii) of Theorem 16.7.4 is called the *radius of convergence* of the power series. If condition (i) holds, we take $R = 0$; if condition (ii) holds, we write $R = +\infty$.

● ILLUSTRATION 3: For the power series of Example 1, $R = \frac{3}{2}$ and the interval of convergence is $(-\frac{3}{2}, \frac{3}{2}]$. In Example 2, $R = +\infty$, and we write the interval of convergence as $(-\infty, +\infty)$.   ●

If R is the radius of convergence of the power series $\sum\limits_{n=0}^{+\infty} c_n x^n$, the interval of convergence is one of the following intervals: $(-R, R)$, $[-R, R]$, $(-R, R]$, or $[-R, R)$. For the more general power series $\sum\limits_{n=0}^{+\infty} c_n(x - a)^n$, the interval of convergence is one of the following: $(a - R, a + R)$, $[a - R, a + R]$, $(a - R, a + R]$, or $[a - R, a + R)$.

A given power series defines a function having the interval of convergence as its domain. The most useful method at our disposal for determining the interval of convergence of a power series is the ratio test. However, the ratio test will not reveal anything about the convergence or divergence of the power series at the endpoints of the interval of convergence. At an endpoint, a power series may be either absolutely convergent, conditionally convergent, or divergent. If a power series converges absolutely at one endpoint, it follows from the definition of absolute convergence that the series is absolutely convergent at each endpoint (see Exercise 21). If a power series converges at one endpoint and diverges at the other, the series is conditionally convergent at the endpoint at which it converges (see Exercise 22). There are cases for which the convergence or divergence of a power series at the endpoints cannot be determined by the methods of elementary calculus.

EXAMPLE 4: Determine the interval of convergence of the power series

$$\sum_{n=1}^{+\infty} n(x - 2)^n$$

SOLUTION: The given series is

$$(x - 2) + 2(x - 2)^2 + \cdots + n(x - 2)^n + (n + 1)(x - 2)^{n+1} + \cdots$$

Applying the ratio test, we have

$$\lim_{n \to +\infty} \left| \frac{u_{n+1}}{u_n} \right| = \lim_{n \to +\infty} \left| \frac{(n + 1)(x - 2)^{n+1}}{n(x - 2)^n} \right| = |x - 2| \lim_{n \to +\infty} \frac{n + 1}{n} = |x - 2|$$

The given series then will be absolutely convergent if $|x - 2| < 1$ or, equivalently, $-1 < x - 2 < 1$ or, equivalently, $1 < x < 3$.

When $x = 1$, the series is $\sum_{n=1}^{+\infty} (-1)^n n$, which is divergent because

$\lim_{n \to +\infty} u_n \neq 0$. When $x = 3$, the series is $\sum_{n=1}^{+\infty} n$, which is also divergent because $\lim_{n \to +\infty} u_n \neq 0$. Therefore, the interval of convergence is $(1, 3)$. So the given power series defines a function having the interval $(1, 3)$ as its domain.

EXAMPLE 5: Determine the interval of convergence of the power series

$$\sum_{n=1}^{+\infty} \frac{x^n}{2 + n^2}$$

SOLUTION: The given series is

$$\frac{x}{2 + 1^2} + \frac{x^2}{2 + 2^2} + \frac{x^3}{2 + 3^2} + \cdots + \frac{x^n}{2 + n^2} + \frac{x^{n+1}}{2 + (n + 1)^2} + \cdots$$

Applying the ratio test, we have

$$\lim_{n \to +\infty} \left| \frac{u_{n+1}}{u_n} \right| = \lim_{n \to +\infty} \left| \frac{x^{n+1}}{2 + (n + 1)^2} \cdot \frac{2 + n^2}{x^n} \right| = |x| \lim_{n \to +\infty} \frac{2 + n^2}{2 + n^2 + 2n + 1} = |x|$$

So the given series will be absolutely convergent if $|x| < 1$ or, equivalently, $-1 < x < 1$. When $x = 1$, we have the series

$$\frac{1}{2 + 1^2} + \frac{1}{2 + 2^2} + \frac{1}{2 + 3^2} + \cdots + \frac{1}{2 + n^2} + \cdots$$

Because $1/(2 + n^2) < 1/n^2$ for all positive integers n, and because $\sum_{n=1}^{+\infty} 1/n^2$ is a convergent p series, it follows from the comparison test that the given power series is convergent when $x = 1$. When $x = -1$, we have the series $\sum_{n=1}^{+\infty} (-1)^n/(2 + n^2)$, which is convergent because we have just seen that it is absolutely convergent. Hence, the interval of convergence of the given power series is $[-1, 1]$.

Exercises 16.7

In Exercises 1 through 20, find the interval of convergence of the given power series.

1. $\sum_{n=1}^{+\infty} (-1)^{n+1} \frac{x^{2n-1}}{(2n - 1)!}$

2. $\sum_{n=0}^{+\infty} \frac{x^n}{n + 1}$

3. $\sum_{n=1}^{+\infty} \frac{2^n x^n}{n^2}$

4. $\sum_{n=1}^{+\infty} (-1)^n \frac{x^{2n}}{(2n)!}$

5. $\sum_{n=1}^{+\infty} n! x^n$

6. $\sum_{n=0}^{+\infty} \frac{x^n}{(n + 1)5^n}$

7. $\sum_{n=1}^{+\infty} (-1)^n \frac{x^n}{(2n - 1)3^{2n-1}}$

8. $\sum_{n=1}^{+\infty} (-1)^{n+1} \frac{(n + 1)x}{n!}$

9. $\displaystyle\sum_{n=1}^{+\infty} (-1)^{n+1} \frac{(x-1)^n}{n}$

10. $\displaystyle\sum_{n=1}^{+\infty} \frac{(x+2)^n}{(n+1)2^n}$

11. $\displaystyle\sum_{n=0}^{+\infty} (\sinh 2n)x^n$

12. $\displaystyle\sum_{n=1}^{+\infty} \frac{x^n}{\ln(n+1)}$

13. $\displaystyle\sum_{n=2}^{+\infty} (-1)^{n+1} \frac{x^n}{n(\ln n)^2}$

14. $\displaystyle\sum_{n=1}^{+\infty} \frac{(x+5)^{n-1}}{n^2}$

15. $\displaystyle\sum_{n=1}^{+\infty} \frac{n!x^n}{n^n}$

16. $\displaystyle\sum_{n=1}^{+\infty} \frac{x^n}{n^n}$

17. $\displaystyle\sum_{n=1}^{+\infty} \frac{\ln n(x-5)^n}{n+1}$

18. $\displaystyle\sum_{n=1}^{+\infty} n^n(x-3)^n$

19. $\displaystyle\sum_{n=1}^{+\infty} (-1)^n \frac{1 \cdot 3 \cdot 5 \cdot \ldots \cdot (2n-1)}{2 \cdot 4 \cdot 6 \cdot \ldots \cdot 2n} x^{2n+1}$

20. $\displaystyle\sum_{n=1}^{+\infty} \frac{(-1)^{n+1}1 \cdot 3 \cdot 5 \cdot \ldots \cdot (2n-1)}{2 \cdot 4 \cdot 6 \cdot \ldots \cdot 2n} x^n$

21. Prove that if a power series converges absolutely at one endpoint of its interval of convergence, then the power series is absolutely convergent at each endpoint.

22. Prove that if a power series converges at one endpoint of its interval of convergence and diverges at the other endpoint, then the power series is conditionally convergent at the endpoint at which it converges.

23. Prove that if the radius of convergence of the power series $\displaystyle\sum_{n=1}^{+\infty} u_n x^n$ is r, then the radius of convergence of the series $\displaystyle\sum_{n=1}^{+\infty} u_n x^{2n}$ is $\sqrt{r}$.

24. Prove that if $\displaystyle\lim_{n \to +\infty} \sqrt[n]{|u_n|} = L$ $(L \neq 0)$, then the radius of convergence of the power series $\displaystyle\sum_{n=1}^{+\infty} u_n x^n$ is $1/L$.

16.8 DIFFERENTIATION OF POWER SERIES

A power series $\displaystyle\sum_{n=0}^{+\infty} c_n x^n$ defines a function whose domain is the interval of convergence of the series.

• ILLUSTRATION 1: Consider the geometric series with $a = 1$ and $r = x$, which is $\displaystyle\sum_{n=0}^{+\infty} x^n$. By Theorem 16.3.6 this series converges to the sum $1/(1-x)$ if $|x| < 1$. Therefore, the power series $\displaystyle\sum_{n=0}^{+\infty} x^n$ defines the function f for which $f(x) = 1/(1-x)$ and $|x| < 1$. Hence, we can write

$$1 + x + x^2 + x^3 + \cdots + x^n + \cdots = \frac{1}{1-x} \qquad \text{if } |x| < 1 \qquad (1) \quad •$$

The series in (1) can be used to form other power series whose sums can be determined.

• ILLUSTRATION 2: If in (1) we replace x by $-x$, we have

$$1 - x + x^2 - x^3 + \cdots + (-1)^n x^n + \cdots = \frac{1}{1+x} \qquad \text{if } |x| < 1 \qquad (2)$$

Letting $x = x^2$ in (1), we get

$$1 + x^2 + x^4 + x^6 + \cdots + x^{2n} + \cdots = \frac{1}{1 - x^2} \qquad \text{if } |x| < 1 \qquad (3)$$

If x is replaced by $-x^2$ in (1) we obtain

$$1 - x^2 + x^4 - x^6 + \cdots + (-1)^n x^{2n} + \cdots = \frac{1}{1 + x^2} \quad \text{if } |x| < 1 \quad (4) \quad \bullet$$

In this section and the next we learn that other interesting series can be obtained from those like the above by differentiation and integration. We prove that if $R \neq 0$ is the radius of convergence of a power series which defines a function f, then f is differentiable on the open interval $(-R, R)$ and the derivative of f can be obtained by differentiating the power series term by term. Furthermore, we show that f is integrable on every closed subinterval of $(-R, R)$, and the integral of f is evaluated by integrating the power series term by term. We first need some preliminary theorems.

16.8.1 Theorem   If $\sum\limits_{n=0}^{+\infty} c_n x^n$ is a power series having a radius of convergence of $R > 0$, then the series $\sum\limits_{n=1}^{+\infty} n c_n x^{n-1}$ also has R as its radius of convergence.

This theorem states that the series, obtained by differentiating term by term each term of a given power series, will have the same radius of convergence as the given series.

PROOF: Let x be any number in the open interval $(-R, R)$. Then $|x| < R$. Choose a number x_1 so that $|x| < |x_1| < R$. Because $|x_1| < R$, $\sum\limits_{n=0}^{+\infty} c_n x_1^n$ is convergent. Hence, $\lim\limits_{n \to +\infty} c_n x_1^n = 0$. So if we take $\epsilon = 1$ in Definition 4.1.1, there exists a number $N > 0$ such that

$$|c_n x_1^n| < 1 \qquad \text{whenever } n > N$$

Let M be the largest of the numbers $|c_1 x_1|, |c_2 x_1^2|, |c_3 x_1^3|, \ldots, |c_N x_1^N|, 1$. Then

$$|c_n x_1^n| \leq M \qquad \text{for all positive integers } n \qquad (5)$$

Now

$$|n c_n x^{n-1}| = \left| n c_n \cdot \frac{x^{n-1}}{x_1^n} \cdot x_1^n \right| = n \frac{|c_n x_1^n|}{|x_1|} \left| \frac{x}{x_1} \right|^{n-1}$$

From (5) and the above equation, we get

$$|n c_n x^{n-1}| \leq n \frac{M}{|x_1|} \left| \frac{x}{x_1} \right|^{n-1} \qquad (6)$$

Applying the ratio test to the series

$$\frac{M}{|x_1|} \sum_{n=1}^{+\infty} n \left|\frac{x}{x_1}\right|^{n-1} \tag{7}$$

we have

$$\lim_{n \to +\infty} \left|\frac{u_{n+1}}{u_n}\right| = \lim_{n \to +\infty} \left|\frac{(n+1)|x|^n}{|x_1|^n} \cdot \frac{|x_1|^{n-1}}{n|x|^{n-1}}\right|$$

$$= \left|\frac{x}{x_1}\right| \lim_{n \to +\infty} \frac{n+1}{n}$$

$$= \left|\frac{x}{x_1}\right| < 1$$

Therefore, series (7) is absolutely convergent; so from (6) and the comparison test, the series $\sum_{n=1}^{+\infty} nc_n x^{n-1}$ is also absolutely convergent. Because x is any number in $(-R, R)$, it follows that if the radius of convergence of $\sum_{n=1}^{+\infty} nc_n x^{n-1}$ is R', then $R' \geq R$.

To complete the proof we must show that R' cannot be greater than R. Assume that $R' > R$ and let x_2 be a number such that $R < |x_2| < R'$. Because $|x_2| > R$, it follows that

$$\sum_{n=0}^{+\infty} c_n x_2{}^n \quad \text{is divergent} \tag{8}$$

Because $|x_2| < R'$, it follows that $\sum_{n=1}^{+\infty} nc_n x_2{}^{n-1}$ is absolutely convergent. Furthermore,

$$|x_2| \sum_{n=1}^{+\infty} |nc_n x_2{}^{n-1}| = \sum_{n=1}^{+\infty} |nc_n x_2{}^n|$$

and so from Theorem 16.3.8 we may conclude that

$$\sum_{n=1}^{+\infty} |nc_n x_2{}^n| \quad \text{is convergent} \tag{9}$$

If n is any positive integer

$$|c_n x_2{}^n| \leq n|c_n x_2{}^n| = |nc_n x_2{}^n| \tag{10}$$

From statement (9), inequality (10), and the comparison test it follows that $\sum_{n=1}^{+\infty} |c_n x_2{}^n|$ is convergent. Therefore, the series $\sum_{n=0}^{+\infty} c_n x_2{}^n$ is convergent, which contradicts statement (8). Hence, the assumption that $R' > R$ is false. Therefore, R' cannot be greater than R; and because we showed that $R' \geq R$, it follows that $R' = R$, which proves the theorem. ■

• ILLUSTRATION 3: We verify Theorem 16.8.1 for the power series

$$\sum_{n=0}^{+\infty} \frac{x^{n+1}}{(n+1)^2} = x + \frac{x^2}{4} + \frac{x^3}{9} + \cdots + \frac{x^{n+1}}{(n+1)^2} + \frac{x^{n+2}}{(n+2)^2} + \cdots$$

To find the radius of convergence, we apply the ratio test.

$$\lim_{n \to +\infty} \left| \frac{u_{n+1}}{u_n} \right| = \lim_{n \to +\infty} \left| \frac{(n+1)^2 x^{n+2}}{(n+2)^2 x^{n+1}} \right| = |x| \lim_{n \to +\infty} \left| \frac{n^2 + 2n + 1}{n^2 + 4n + 4} \right| = |x|$$

Hence, the power series is convergent when $|x| < 1$, and so its radius of convergence $R = 1$.

The power series obtained from the given series by differentiating term by term is

$$\sum_{n=0}^{+\infty} \frac{(n+1)x^n}{(n+1)^2} = \sum_{n=0}^{+\infty} \frac{x^n}{n+1} = 1 + \frac{x}{2} + \frac{x^2}{3} + \frac{x^3}{4} + \cdots + \frac{x^n}{n+1} + \frac{x^{n+1}}{n+2} + \cdots$$

Applying the ratio test for this power series, we have

$$\lim_{n \to +\infty} \left| \frac{u_{n+1}}{u_n} \right| = \lim_{n \to +\infty} \left| \frac{(n+1)x^{n+1}}{(n+2)x^n} \right| = |x| \lim_{n \to +\infty} \left| \frac{n+1}{n+2} \right| = |x|$$

This power series is convergent when $|x| < 1$; thus, its radius of convergence $R' = 1$. Because $R = R'$, Theorem 16.8.1 is verified. •

16.8.2 Theorem   If the radius of convergence of the power series $\sum_{n=0}^{+\infty} c_n x^n$ is $R > 0$, then R is also the radius of convergence of the series $\sum_{n=2}^{+\infty} n(n-1)c_n x^{n-2}$.

PROOF: If we apply Theorem 16.8.1 to the series $\sum_{n=1}^{+\infty} nc_n x^{n-1}$, we have the desired result. ∎

We are now in a position to prove the theorem regarding term-by-term differentiation of a power series.

16.8.3 Theorem   Let $\sum_{n=0}^{+\infty} c_n x^n$ be a power series whose radius of convergence is $R > 0$. Then if f is the function defined by

$$f(x) = \sum_{n=0}^{+\infty} c_n x^n \tag{11}$$

$f'(x)$ exists for every x in the open interval $(-R, R)$, and it is given by

$$f'(x) = \sum_{n=1}^{+\infty} nc_n x^{n-1}$$

PROOF: Let x and a be two distinct numbers in the open interval $(-R, R)$. Taylor's formula (formula (9) in Sec. 15.5), with $n = 1$, is

$$f(x) = f(a) + \frac{f'(a)}{1!}(x - a) + \frac{f''(\xi)}{2!}(x - a)^2$$

Using this formula with $f(x) = x^n$, we have for every positive integer n

$$x^n = a^n + na^{n-1}(x - a) + \tfrac{1}{2}n(n - 1)(\xi_n)^{n-2}(x - a)^2 \qquad (12)$$

where ξ_n is between a and x for every positive integer n. From (11) we have

$$f(x) - f(a) = \sum_{n=0}^{+\infty} c_n x^n - \sum_{n=0}^{+\infty} c_n a^n$$

$$= c_0 + \sum_{n=1}^{+\infty} c_n x^n - c_0 - \sum_{n=1}^{+\infty} c_n a^n$$

$$= \sum_{n=1}^{+\infty} c_n(x^n - a^n)$$

Dividing by $x - a$ (because $x \neq a$) and using (12), we have from the above equation

$$\frac{f(x) - f(a)}{x - a} = \frac{1}{x - a} \sum_{n=1}^{+\infty} c_n[na^{n-1}(x - a) + \tfrac{1}{2}n(n - 1)(\xi_n)^{n-2}(x - a)^2]$$

So

$$\frac{f(x) - f(a)}{x - a} = \sum_{n=1}^{+\infty} nc_n a^{n-1} + \tfrac{1}{2}(x - a)\sum_{n=2}^{+\infty} n(n - 1)c_n(\xi_n)^{n-2} \qquad (13)$$

Because a is in $(-R, R)$, it follows from Theorem 16.8.1 that $\sum_{n=1}^{+\infty} nc_n a^{n-1}$ is absolutely convergent.

Because both a and x are in $(-R, R)$, there is some number $K > 0$ such that $|a| < K < R$ and $|x| < K < R$. It follows from Theorem 16.8.2 that

$$\sum_{n=2}^{+\infty} n(n - 1)c_n K^{n-2}$$

is absolutely convergent. Then because

$$|n(n - 1)c_n(\xi_n)^{n-2}| < |n(n - 1)c_n K^{n-2}| \qquad (14)$$

for each ξ_n, we can conclude from the comparison test that

$$\sum_{n=2}^{+\infty} n(n - 1)c_n(\xi_n)^{n-2}$$

is absolutely convergent.

It follows from (13) that

$$\left| \frac{f(x) - f(a)}{x - a} - \sum_{n=1}^{+\infty} nc_n a^{n-1} \right| = \left| \tfrac{1}{2}(x - a) \sum_{n=2}^{+\infty} n(n-1)c_n(\xi_n)^{n-2} \right| \tag{15}$$

However, from Theorem 16.6.7 we know that if $\sum_{n=1}^{+\infty} u_n$ is absolutely convergent, then

$$\left| \sum_{n=1}^{+\infty} u_n \right| \le \sum_{n=1}^{+\infty} |u_n|$$

Applying this to the right side of (15), we obtain

$$\left| \frac{f(x) - f(a)}{x - a} - \sum_{n=1}^{+\infty} nc_n a^{n-1} \right| \le \tfrac{1}{2}|x - a| \sum_{n=2}^{+\infty} n(n-1)|c_n||\xi_n|^{n-2} \tag{16}$$

From (14) and (16) we get

$$\left| \frac{f(x) - f(a)}{x - a} - \sum_{n=1}^{+\infty} nc_n a^{n-1} \right| \le \tfrac{1}{2}|x - a| \sum_{n=2}^{+\infty} n(n-1)|c_n|K^{n-2} \tag{17}$$

where $0 < K < R$. Because the series on the right side of (17) is absolutely convergent, the limit of the right side, as x approaches a, is zero. Therefore, from (17) and Theorem 4.3.3 it follows that

$$\lim_{x \to a} \frac{f(x) - f(a)}{x - a} = \sum_{n=1}^{+\infty} nc_n a^{n-1}$$

or, equivalently,

$$f'(a) = \sum_{n=1}^{+\infty} nc_n a^{n-1}$$

and because a may be any number in the open interval $(-R, R)$, the theorem is proved.   ■

EXAMPLE 1:   Let f be the function defined by the power series of Illustration 3. (a) Find the domain of f; (b) write the power series which defines the function f' and find the domain of f'.

SOLUTION:

(a) $f(x) = \sum_{n=0}^{+\infty} \frac{x^{n+1}}{(n+1)^2}$

The domain of f is the interval of convergence of the power series. In Illustration 3 we showed that the radius of convergence of the power series is 1; that is, the series converges when $|x| < 1$. We now consider the power series when $|x| = 1$. When $x = 1$, the series is

$$1 + \frac{1}{4} + \frac{1}{9} + \cdots + \frac{1}{(n+1)^2} + \cdots$$

which is convergent because it is the p series with $p = 2$. When $x = -1$, we have the series $\sum_{n=0}^{+\infty} (-1)^{n+1}/(n+2)^2$, which is convergent because it is absolutely convergent. Hence, the domain of f is the interval $[-1, 1]$.

(b) From Theorem 16.8.3 it follows that f' is defined by

$$f'(x) = \sum_{n=0}^{+\infty} \frac{x^n}{n+1} \tag{18}$$

and that $f'(x)$ exists for every x in the open interval $(-1, 1)$. In Illustration 3 we showed that the radius of convergence of the power series in (18) is 1. We now consider the power series in (18) when $x = \pm 1$. When $x = 1$, the series is

$$1 + \frac{1}{2} + \frac{1}{3} + \frac{1}{4} + \cdots + \frac{1}{n+1} + \cdots$$

which is the harmonic series and hence is divergent. When $x = -1$, the series is

$$1 - \frac{1}{2} + \frac{1}{3} - \frac{1}{4} + \cdots + (-1)^n \frac{1}{n+1} + \cdots$$

which is a convergent alternating series. Therefore, the domain of f' is the interval $[-1, 1)$.

Example 1 illustrates the fact that if a function f is defined by a power series and this power series is differentiated term by term, the resulting power series, which defines f', has the same radius of convergence but not necessarily the same interval of convergence.

EXAMPLE 2:   Obtain a power-series representation of

$$\frac{1}{(1-x)^2}$$

SOLUTION: From (1) we have

$$\frac{1}{1-x} = 1 + x + x^2 + x^3 + \cdots + x^n + \cdots \qquad \text{if } |x| < 1$$

Using Theorem 16.8.3, differentiating on both sides of the above, we get

$$\frac{1}{(1-x)^2} = 1 + 2x + 3x^2 + \cdots + nx^{n-1} + \cdots \qquad \text{if } |x| < 1$$

EXAMPLE 3:   Show that

$$e^x = \sum_{n=0}^{+\infty} \frac{x^n}{n!}$$

$$= 1 + x + \frac{x^2}{2!} + \frac{x^3}{3!} + \cdots$$

for all real values of x.

SOLUTION: In Example 2 of Sec. 16.7 we showed that the power series $\sum_{n=0}^{+\infty} x^n/n!$ is absolutely convergent for all real values of x. Therefore, if f is the function defined by

$$f(x) = \sum_{n=0}^{+\infty} \frac{x^n}{n!} \tag{19}$$

the domain of f is the set of all real numbers; that is, the interval of convergence is $(-\infty, +\infty)$. It follows from Theorem 16.8.3 that for all real values of x

$$f'(x) = \sum_{n=1}^{+\infty} \frac{nx^{n-1}}{n!} \tag{20}$$

Because $n/n! = 1/(n-1)!$, (20) can be written as

$$f'(x) = \sum_{n=1}^{+\infty} \frac{x^{n-1}}{(n-1)!}$$

or, equivalently,

$$f'(x) = \sum_{n=0}^{+\infty} \frac{x^n}{n!} \tag{21}$$

Comparing (19) and (21), we see that $f'(x) = f(x)$ for all real values of x. Therefore, the function f satisfies the differential equation

$$\frac{dy}{dx} = y$$

for which the general solution is $y = Ce^x$. Hence, for some constant C, $f(x) = Ce^x$. From (19) we see that $f(0) = 1$. (Remember that we take $x^0 = 1$ even when $x = 0$ for convenience in writing the general term.) Therefore, $C = 1$, and so $f(x) = e^x$, and we have the desired result.

EXAMPLE 4:   Use the result of Example 3 to find a power-series representation of e^{-x}.

SOLUTION: If we replace x by $-x$ in the series for e^x, it follows that

$$e^{-x} = 1 - x + \frac{x^2}{2!} - \frac{x^3}{3!} + \cdots + (-1)^n \frac{x^n}{n!} + \cdots$$

for all real values of x.

EXAMPLE 5:   Use the series of Example 4 to find the value of e^{-1} correct to five decimal places.

SOLUTION: Taking $x = 1$ in the series for e^{-x}, we have

$$e^{-1} = 1 - 1 + \frac{1}{2!} - \frac{1}{3!} + \frac{1}{4!} - \frac{1}{5!} + \frac{1}{6!} - \frac{1}{7!} + \frac{1}{8!} - \frac{1}{9!} + \frac{1}{10!} - \cdots$$

$$= 1 - 1 + \frac{1}{2} - \frac{1}{6} + \frac{1}{24} - \frac{1}{120} + \frac{1}{720} - \frac{1}{5{,}040} + \frac{1}{40{,}320} - \frac{1}{362{,}880}$$

$$+ \frac{1}{3{,}628{,}800} - \cdots$$

$$\approx 1 - 1 + 0.5 - 0.166667 + 0.041667 - 0.008333 + 0.001389$$

$$- 0.000198 + 0.000025 - 0.000003 + 0.0000003 - \cdots$$

We have a convergent alternating series for which $|u_{n+1}| < |u_n|$. So if we use the first ten terms to approximate the sum, by Theorem 16.6.4 the error is less than the absolute value of the eleventh term. Adding the first ten terms, we obtain 0.367880. Rounding off to five decimal places gives

$$e^{-1} \approx 0.36788$$

In computation with infinite series two kinds of errors occur. One is the error given by the remainder after the first n terms. The other is the round-off error which occurs when each term of the series is approximated by a decimal with a finite number of places. In particular, in Example 5 we wanted the result accurate to five decimal places so we rounded off each term to six decimal places. After computing the sum, we rounded off this result to five decimal places. Of course, the error given by the remainder can be reduced by considering additional terms of the series, whereas the round-off error can be reduced by using more decimal places.

Exercises 16.8

In Exercises 1 through 8, a function f is defined by a power series. In each exercise do the following: (a) Find the radius of convergence of the given power series and the domain of f; (b) write the power series which defines the function f' and find its radius of convergence by using methods of Sec. 16.7 (thus verifying Theorem 16.8.1); (c) find the domain of f'.

1. $f(x) = \sum\limits_{n=1}^{+\infty} \dfrac{x^n}{n^2}$

2. $f(x) = \sum\limits_{n=1}^{+\infty} (-1)^{n-1} \dfrac{x^n}{n}$

3. $f(x) = \sum\limits_{n=1}^{+\infty} \dfrac{x^n}{\sqrt{n}}$

4. $f(x) = \sum\limits_{n=2}^{+\infty} \dfrac{(x-2)^n}{\sqrt{n-1}}$

5. $f(x) = \sum\limits_{n=1}^{+\infty} (-1)^{n-1} \dfrac{x^{2n-1}}{(2n-1)!}$

6. $f(x) = \sum\limits_{n=1}^{+\infty} \dfrac{x^{2n-2}}{(2n-2)!}$

7. $f(x) = \sum\limits_{n=1}^{+\infty} \dfrac{(x-1)^n}{n3^n}$

8. $f(x) = \sum\limits_{n=2}^{+\infty} (-1)^n \dfrac{(x-3)^n}{n(n-1)}$

9. Use the result of Example 2 to find a power-series representation of $1/(1-x)^3$.

10. Use the result of Example 3 to find a power-series representation of $e^{\sqrt{x}}$.

11. Obtain a power-series representation of $1/(1+x)^2$ if $|x| < 1$ by differentiating series (2) term by term.

12. Obtain a power-series representation of $x/(1+x^2)^2$ if $|x| < 1$ by differentiating series (4) term by term.

13. Use the result of Example 4 to find the value of $1/\sqrt{e}$ correct to five decimal places.

14. If $f(x) = \sum\limits_{n=0}^{+\infty} (-1)^n \dfrac{x^{2n}}{3^n}$, find $f'(\tfrac{1}{2})$ correct to four decimal places.

15. Use the results of Examples 3 and 4 to find a power-series representation of (a) $\sinh x$ and (b) $\cosh x$.

16. Show that each of the power series in parts (a) and (b) of Exercise 15 can be obtained from the other by term-by-term differentiation.

17. Use the result of Example 2 to find the sum of the series $\sum\limits_{n=1}^{+\infty} \dfrac{n}{2^n}$.

18. (a) Find a power-series representation for $(e^x - 1)/x$.

    (b) By differentiating term by term the power series in part (a), show that $\sum\limits_{n=1}^{+\infty} \dfrac{n}{(n+1)!} = 1$.

19. (a) Find a power-series representation for $x^2 e^{-x}$. (b) By differentiating term by term the power series in part (a), show that $\displaystyle\sum_{n=1}^{+\infty} (-2)^{n+1} \frac{n+2}{n!} = 4$.

20. Assume that the constant 0 has a power-series representation $\displaystyle\sum_{n=0}^{+\infty} c_n x^n$, where the radius of convergence $R > 0$. Prove that $c_n = 0$ for all n.

21. Suppose a function f has the power-series representation $\displaystyle\sum_{n=0}^{+\infty} c_n x^n$, where the radius of convergence $R > 0$. If $f'(x) = f(x)$ and $f(0) = 1$, find the power series by using only properties of power series and nothing about the exponential function.

22. (a) Using only properties of power series, find a power-series representation of the function f for which $f(x) > 0$ and $f'(x) = 2xf(x)$ for all x, and $f(0) = 1$. (b) Verify your result in part (a) by solving the differential equation $D_x y = 2xy$ having the boundary condition $y = 1$ when $x = 0$.

16.9 INTEGRATION OF POWER SERIES   The theorem regarding the term-by-term integration of a power series is a consequence of Theorem 16.8.3.

16.9.1 Theorem   Let $\displaystyle\sum_{n=0}^{+\infty} c_n x^n$ be a power series whose radius of convergence is $R > 0$. Then if f is the function defined by

$$f(x) = \sum_{n=0}^{+\infty} c_n x^n$$

f is integrable on every closed subinterval of $(-R, R)$, and we evaluate the integral of f by integrating the given power series term by term; that is, if x is in $(-R, R)$, then

$$\int_0^x f(t)\, dt = \sum_{n=0}^{+\infty} \frac{c_n}{n+1} x^{n+1}$$

Furthermore, R is the radius of convergence of the resulting series.

PROOF: Let g be the function defined by

$$g(x) = \sum_{n=0}^{+\infty} \frac{c_n}{n+1} x^{n+1}$$

Because the terms of the power-series representation of $f(x)$ are the derivatives of the terms of the power-series representation of $g(x)$, the two series have, by Theorem 16.8.1, the same radius of convergence. By Theorem 16.8.3 it follows that

$$g'(x) = f(x) \qquad \text{for every } x \text{ in } (-R, R)$$

By Theorem 16.8.2, it follows that $f'(x) = g''(x)$ for every x in $(-R, R)$. Because f is differentiable on $(-R, R)$, f is continuous there; consequently, f is continuous on every closed subinterval of $(-R, R)$. From Theorem

7.6.2 it follows that if x is in $(-R, R)$, then

$$\int_0^x f(t)\ dt = g(x) - g(0) = g(x)$$

or, equivalently,

$$\int_0^x f(t)\ dt = \sum_{n=0}^{+\infty} \frac{c_n}{n+1}\, x^{n+1}$$

■

Theorem 16.9.1 often is used to compute a definite integral which cannot be evaluated directly by finding an antiderivative of the integrand. Examples 1 and 2 illustrate the technique. The definite integral $\int_0^x e^{-t^2}\ dt$ appearing in these two examples represents the measure of the area of a region under the "normal probability curve."

EXAMPLE 1: Find a power-series representation of

$$\int_0^x e^{-t^2}\ dt$$

SOLUTION: In Example 4 of Sec. 16.8 we showed that

$$e^{-x} = \sum_{n=0}^{+\infty} \frac{(-1)^n x^n}{n!}$$

for all values of x. Replacing x by t^2, we get

$$e^{-t^2} = 1 - t^2 + \frac{t^4}{2!} - \frac{t^6}{3!} + \cdots + (-1)^n \frac{t^{2n}}{n!} + \cdots \qquad \text{for all values of } t$$

Applying Theorem 16.9.1, we integrate term by term and obtain

$$\int_0^x e^{-t^2}\ dt = \sum_{n=0}^{+\infty} \int_0^x (-1)^n \frac{t^{2n}}{n!}\ dt$$

$$= x - \frac{x^3}{3} + \frac{x^5}{2! \cdot 5} - \frac{x^7}{3! \cdot 7} + \cdots + (-1)^n \frac{x^{2n+1}}{n!(2n+1)} + \cdots$$

The power series represents the integral for all values of x.

EXAMPLE 2: Using the result of Example 1, compute accurate to three decimal places the value of

$$\int_0^{1/2} e^{-t^2}\ dt$$

SOLUTION: Replacing x by $\frac{1}{2}$ in the power series obtained in Example 1, we have

$$\int_0^{1/2} e^{-t^2}\ dt = \tfrac{1}{2} - \tfrac{1}{24} + \tfrac{1}{320} - \tfrac{1}{5376} + \cdots$$

$$\approx 0.5 - 0.0417 + 0.0031 - 0.0002 + \cdots$$

We have a convergent alternating series with $|u_{n+1}| < |u_n|$. Thus, if we use the first three terms to approximate the sum, by Theorem 16.6.4 the error is less than the absolute value of the fourth term. From the first three terms we get

$$\int_0^{1/2} e^{-t^2}\ dt \approx 0.461$$

EXAMPLE 3:   Obtain a power-series representation of $\ln(1 + x)$.

SOLUTION: Consider the function f defined by $f(t) = 1/(1 + t)$. A power-series representation of this function is given by series (2) in Sec. 16.8, which is

$$\frac{1}{1+t} = 1 - t + t^2 - t^3 + \cdots + (-1)^n t^n + \cdots \qquad \text{if } |t| < 1$$

Applying Theorem 16.9.1, we integrate term by term and obtain

$$\int_0^x \frac{dt}{1+t} = \sum_{n=0}^{+\infty} \int_0^x (-1)^n t^n \, dt \qquad \text{if } |x| < 1$$

and so

$$\ln(1 + x) = x - \frac{x^2}{2} + \frac{x^3}{3} - \frac{x^4}{4} + \cdots + (-1)^n \frac{x^{n+1}}{n+1} + \cdots \qquad \text{if } |x| < 1$$

or, equivalently,

$$\ln(1 + x) = \sum_{n=1}^{+\infty} (-1)^{n-1} \frac{x^n}{n} \qquad \text{if } |x| < 1 \tag{1}$$

Note that because $|x| < 1$, $|1 + x| = (1 + x)$. Thus, the absolute-value bars are not needed when writing $\ln(1 + x)$.

In Example 3, Theorem 16.9.1 allows us to conclude that the power series in (1) represents the function only for values of x in the open interval $(-1, 1)$. However, the power series is convergent at the right endpoint 1, as was shown in Example 1 of Sec. 16.6. When $x = -1$, the power series becomes the negative of the harmonic series and is divergent. Hence, the interval of convergence of the power series in (1) is $(-1, 1]$.

In the following illustration we show that the power series in (1) represents $\ln(1 + x)$ at $x = 1$ by proving that the sum of the series $\sum_{n=1}^{+\infty} (-1)^{n-1}/n$ is $\ln 2$.

● ILLUSTRATION 1: For the infinite series $\sum_{n=1}^{+\infty} (-1)^{n-1}/n$, the nth partial sum is

$$s_n = 1 - \frac{1}{2} + \frac{1}{3} - \frac{1}{4} + \cdots + (-1)^{n-1} \frac{1}{n} \tag{2}$$

It follows from Definition 16.3.2 that if we show $\lim_{n \to +\infty} s_n = \ln 2$, we will have proved that the sum of the series is $\ln 2$.

From algebra we have the following formula for the sum of a geometric progression:

$$a + ar + ar^2 + ar^3 + \cdots + ar^{n-1} = \frac{a - ar^n}{1 - r}$$

Using this formula with $a = 1$ and $r = -t$, we have

$$1 - t + t^2 - t^3 + \cdots + (-t)^{n-1} = \frac{1 - (-t)^n}{1 + t}$$

which we can write as

$$1 - t + t^2 - t^3 + \cdots + (-1)^{n-1}t^{n-1} = \frac{1}{1 + t} + (-1)^{n+1}\frac{t^n}{1 + t}$$

Integrating from 0 to 1, we get

$$\int_0^1 [1 - t + t^2 - t^3 + \cdots + (-1)^{n-1}t^{n-1}]\, dt = \int_0^1 \frac{dt}{1 + t} + (-1)^{n+1}\int_0^1 \frac{t^n}{1 + t}\, dt$$

which gives

$$1 - \frac{1}{2} + \frac{1}{3} - \frac{1}{4} + \cdots + (-1)^{n-1}\frac{1}{n} = \ln 2 + (-1)^{n+1}\int_0^1 \frac{t^n}{1 + t}\, dt \qquad (3)$$

Referring to Eq. (2), we see that the left side of Eq. (3) is s_n. Letting

$$R_n = (-1)^{n+1}\int_0^1 \frac{t^n}{1 + t}\, dt$$

Eq. (3) may be written as

$$s_n = \ln 2 + R_n \qquad (4)$$

Because $t^n/(1 + t) \leq t^n$ for all t in $[0, 1]$ it follows from Theorem 7.4.8 that

$$\int_0^1 \frac{t^n}{1 + t}\, dt \leq \int_0^1 t^n\, dt$$

Hence,

$$0 \leq |R_n| = \int_0^1 \frac{t^n}{1 + t}\, dt \leq \int_0^1 t^n\, dt = \frac{1}{n + 1}$$

Because $\lim\limits_{n \to +\infty} 1/(n + 1) = 0$, it follows from the above inequality and the squeeze theorem (4.3.3) that $\lim\limits_{n \to +\infty} R_n = 0$. So from Eq. (4) we get

$$\lim_{n \to +\infty} s_n = \ln 2 + \lim_{n \to +\infty} R_n$$

$$= \ln 2$$

Therefore,

$$\sum_{n=1}^{+\infty} (-1)^{n-1}\frac{1}{n} = 1 - \frac{1}{2} + \frac{1}{3} - \frac{1}{4} + \cdots = \ln 2 \qquad (5) \quad \bullet$$

The solution of Example 3 showed that the power series in (1) represents $\ln(x+1)$ if $|x| < 1$. Hence, with the result of Illustration 1 we can conclude that the power series in (1) represents $\ln(x+1)$ for all x in its interval of convergence $(-1, 1]$.

Although it is interesting that the sum of the series in (5) is $\ln 2$, this series converges too slowly to use it to calculate $\ln 2$. We now proceed to obtain a power series for computation of natural logarithms.

From (1) we have

$$\ln(1+x) = x - \frac{x^2}{2} + \frac{x^3}{3} - \cdots + (-1)^{n-1}\frac{x^n}{n} + \cdots \quad \text{for } x \text{ in } (-1, 1] \quad (6)$$

Replacing x by $-x$ in this series, we get

$$\ln(1-x) = -x - \frac{x^2}{2} - \frac{x^3}{3} - \frac{x^4}{4} - \cdots - \frac{x^n}{n} - \cdots \quad \text{for } x \text{ in } [-1, 1) \quad (7)$$

Subtracting term by term (7) from (6), we obtain

$$\ln\frac{1+x}{1-x} = 2\left(x + \frac{x^3}{3} + \frac{x^5}{5} + \cdots + \frac{x^{2n-1}}{2n-1} + \cdots\right) \quad \text{if } |x| < 1 \quad (8)$$

The series in (8) can be used to compute the value of the natural logarithm of any positive number.

● ILLUSTRATION 2: If y is any positive number, let

$$y = \frac{1+x}{1-x} \quad \text{and then} \quad x = \frac{y-1}{y+1} \quad \text{and } |x| < 1$$

For instance, if $y = 2$, then $x = \frac{1}{3}$. We have from (8)

$$\ln 2 = 2\left(\frac{1}{3} + \frac{1}{3^4} + \frac{1}{5 \cdot 3^5} + \frac{1}{7 \cdot 3^7} + \frac{1}{9 \cdot 3^9} + \frac{1}{11 \cdot 3^{11}} + \cdots\right)$$

$$= 2\left(\frac{1}{3} + \frac{1}{81} + \frac{1}{1{,}215} + \frac{1}{15{,}309} + \frac{1}{177{,}147} + \frac{1}{1{,}948{,}617} + \cdots\right)$$

$$\approx 2(0.333333 + 0.012346 + 0.000823 + 0.000065 + 0.000006$$

$$+ 0.000001 + \cdots)$$

Using the first six terms in parentheses, multiplying by 2, and rounding off to five decimal places, we get

$$\ln 2 \approx 0.69315 \qquad \qquad ●$$

EXAMPLE 4: Obtain a power-series representation of $\tan^{-1} x$.

SOLUTION: From series (4) in Sec. 16.8 we have

$$\frac{1}{1+x^2} = 1 - x^2 + x^4 - x^6 + \cdots + (-1)^n x^{2n} + \cdots \quad \text{if } |x| < 1$$

Applying Theorem 16.9.1 and integrating term by term, we get

$$\int_0^x \frac{1}{1+t^2}\, dt = x - \frac{x^3}{3} + \frac{x^5}{5} - \cdots + (-1)^n \frac{x^{2n+1}}{2n+1} + \cdots$$

Therefore,

$$\tan^{-1} x = \sum_{n=0}^{+\infty} (-1)^n \frac{x^{2n+1}}{2n+1} \qquad \text{if } |x| < 1 \tag{9}$$

Although Theorem 16.9.1 allows us to conclude that the power series in (9) represents $\tan^{-1} x$ only for values of x such that $|x| < 1$, it can be shown that the interval of convergence of the power series is $[-1, 1]$ and that the power series is a representation of $\tan^{-1} x$ for all x in its interval of convergence. (You are asked to do this in Exercise 16.) We therefore have

$$\tan^{-1} x = \sum_{n=0}^{+\infty} (-1)^n \frac{x^{2n+1}}{2n+1} = x - \frac{x^3}{3} + \frac{x^5}{5} - \cdots \qquad \text{if } |x| \le 1 \tag{10}$$

● ILLUSTRATION 3: Taking $x = 1$ in (10), we get

$$\frac{\pi}{4} = 1 - \frac{1}{3} + \frac{1}{5} - \frac{1}{7} + \cdots + (-1)^n \frac{1}{2n+1} + \cdots \qquad ●$$

The series in Illustration 3 is not suitable for computing π because it converges too slowly. The following example gives a better method.

EXAMPLE 5:   Prove that

$$\tfrac{1}{4}\pi = \tan^{-1}\tfrac{1}{2} + \tan^{-1}\tfrac{1}{3}$$

Use this formula and the power series for $\tan^{-1} x$ of Example 4 to compute the value of π accurate to four decimal places.

SOLUTION: Let $\alpha = \tan^{-1}\tfrac{1}{2}$ and $\beta = \tan^{-1}\tfrac{1}{3}$. Then

$$\tan(\alpha + \beta) = \frac{\tan \alpha + \tan \beta}{1 - \tan \alpha \tan \beta}$$

$$= \frac{\tfrac{1}{2} + \tfrac{1}{3}}{1 - \tfrac{1}{2} \cdot \tfrac{1}{3}}$$

$$= \frac{3 + 2}{6 - 1}$$

$$= 1$$

$$= \tan \tfrac{1}{4}\pi$$

Therefore,

$$\tfrac{1}{4}\pi = \alpha + \beta = \tan^{-1}\tfrac{1}{2} + \tan^{-1}\tfrac{1}{3} \tag{11}$$

From formula (10) with $x = \tfrac{1}{2}$ we get

$$\tan^{-1}\frac{1}{2} = \frac{1}{2} - \frac{1}{3}\left(\frac{1}{2}\right)^3 + \frac{1}{5}\left(\frac{1}{2}\right)^5 - \frac{1}{7}\left(\frac{1}{2}\right)^7 + \frac{1}{9}\left(\frac{1}{2}\right)^9 - \frac{1}{11}\left(\frac{1}{2}\right)^{11} + \frac{1}{13}\left(\frac{1}{2}\right)^{13}$$

$$-\frac{1}{15}\left(\frac{1}{2}\right)^{15}+\cdots$$

$$=\frac{1}{2}-\frac{1}{24}+\frac{1}{160}-\frac{1}{896}+\frac{1}{4,608}-\frac{1}{22,528}+\frac{1}{106,492}-\frac{1}{491,520}+\cdots$$

$$\approx 0.5-0.04167+0.00625-0.00112+0.00022-0.00004$$

$$+0.00001-0.000002+\cdots$$

Because the series is alternating and $|u_{n+1}|<|u_n|$, we know by Theorem 16.6.4 that if the first seven terms are used to approximate the sum of the series, the error is less than the absolute value of the eighth term. Therefore,

$$\tan^{-1}\tfrac{1}{2}\approx 0.46365 \tag{12}$$

Using formula (10) with $x=\tfrac{1}{3}$, we have

$$\tan^{-1}\frac{1}{3}=\frac{1}{3}-\frac{1}{3}\left(\frac{1}{3}\right)^3+\frac{1}{5}\left(\frac{1}{3}\right)^5-\frac{1}{7}\left(\frac{1}{3}\right)^7+\frac{1}{9}\left(\frac{1}{3}\right)^9-\frac{1}{11}\left(\frac{1}{3}\right)^{11}+\cdots$$

$$=\frac{1}{3}-\frac{1}{81}+\frac{1}{1,215}-\frac{1}{15,309}+\frac{1}{177,147}-\frac{1}{1,948,617}+\cdots$$

$$\approx 0.33333-0.01235+0.00082-0.00007+0.00001$$

$$-0.000001+\cdots$$

Using the first five terms to approximate the sum, we get

$$\tan^{-1}\tfrac{1}{3}\approx 0.32174 \tag{13}$$

Substituting from (12) and (13) into (11), we get

$$\tfrac{1}{4}\pi\approx 0.46365+0.32174=0.78539$$

Multiplying by 4 and rounding off to four decimal places gives $\pi\approx 3.1416$.

Exercises 16.9

In Exercises 1 through 7, compute the value of the given integral, accurate to four decimal places, by using series.

1. $\displaystyle\int_0^{1/2}\frac{dx}{1+x^3}$

2. $\displaystyle\int_0^{1/3}\frac{dx}{1+x^4}$

3. $\displaystyle\int_0^1 e^{-x^2}\,dx$

4. $\displaystyle\int_0^{1/2}f(x)\,dx,$ where $f(x)=\begin{cases}\dfrac{\ln(1+x)}{x} & \text{if }x\neq 0\\ 1 & \text{if }x=0\end{cases}$

5. $\displaystyle\int_0^{1/4}g(x)\,dx,$ where $g(x)=\begin{cases}\dfrac{\tan^{-1}x}{x} & \text{if }x\neq 0\\ 1 & \text{if }x=0\end{cases}$

6. $\displaystyle\int_0^1 h(x)\,dx,$ where $h(x)=\begin{cases}\dfrac{\sinh x}{x} & \text{if }x\neq 0\\ 1 & \text{if }x=0\end{cases}$

7. $\displaystyle\int_0^1 f(x)\,dx,$ where $f(x)=\begin{cases}\dfrac{e^x-1}{x} & \text{if }x\neq 0\\ 1 & \text{if }x=0\end{cases}$

8. Use the power series in Eq. (8) to compute ln 3 accurate to four decimal places.

9. Use the power series in Eq. (9) to compute $\tan^{-1} \frac{1}{4}$ accurate to four decimal places.

10. Integrate term by term from 0 to x a power-series representation for $(1 - t^2)^{-1}$ to obtain the power series in Eq. (8) for $\ln[(1 + x)/(1 - x)]$.

11. Find a power-series representation for $\tanh^{-1} x$ by integrating term by term from 0 to x a power-series representation for $(1 - t^2)^{-1}$.

12. Find a power series for xe^x by multiplying the series for e^x by x, and then integrate the resulting series term by term from 0 to 1 and show that $\displaystyle\sum_{n=1}^{+\infty} \frac{1}{n!(n + 2)} = \frac{1}{2}$.

13. By integrating term by term from 0 to x a power-series representation for $\ln(1 - t)$, show that

$$\sum_{n=2}^{+\infty} \frac{x^n}{(n - 1)n} = x + (1 - x) \ln(1 - x)$$

14. By integrating term by term from 0 to x a power-series representation for $t \tan^{-1} t$, show that

$$\sum_{n=1}^{+\infty} (-1)^{n+1} \frac{x^{2n+1}}{(2n - 1)(2n + 1)} = \frac{1}{2}[(x^2 + 1) \tan^{-1} x - x]$$

15. Find the power series in x of $f(x)$ if $f''(x) = -f(x)$, $f(0) = 0$, and $f'(0) = 1$. Also, find the radius of convergence of the resulting series.

16. Show that the interval of convergence of the power series in Eq. (9) is $[-1, 1]$ and that the power series is a representation of $\tan^{-1} x$ for all x in its interval of convergence.

16.10 TAYLOR SERIES

If f is the function defined by

$$f(x) = \sum_{n=0}^{+\infty} c_n x^n = c_0 + c_1 x + c_2 x^2 + c_3 x^3 + \cdots + c_n x^n + \cdots \qquad (1)$$

whose radius of convergence is $R > 0$, it follows from successive applications of Theorem 16.8.3 that f has derivatives of all orders on $(-R, R)$. We say that such a function is *infinitely differentiable* on $(-R, R)$. Successive differentiations of the function in (1) give

$$f'(x) = c_1 + 2c_2 x + 3c_3 x^2 + 4c_4 x^3 + \cdots + nc_n x^{n-1} + \cdots \qquad (2)$$

$$f''(x) = 2c_2 + 2 \cdot 3c_3 x + 3 \cdot 4c_4 x^2 + \cdots + (n - 1)nc_n x^{n-2} + \cdots \qquad (3)$$

$$f'''(x) = 2 \cdot 3c_3 + 2 \cdot 3 \cdot 4c_4 x + \cdots + (n - 2)(n - 1)nc_n x^{n-3} + \cdots \qquad (4)$$

$$f^{(iv)}(x) = 2 \cdot 3 \cdot 4c_4 + \cdots + (n - 3)(n - 2)(n - 1)nc_n x^{n-4} + \cdots \qquad (5)$$

etc. Letting $x = 0$ in (1), we get

$$f(0) = c_0$$

For $x = 0$ in (2) we see that

$$f'(0) = c_1$$

If in (3) we take $x = 0$, we have

$$f''(0) = 2c_2 \quad \text{and so} \quad c_2 = \frac{f''(0)}{2!}$$

From (4), taking $x = 0$, we get

$$f'''(0) = 2 \cdot 3c_3 \quad \text{and so} \quad c_3 = \frac{f'''(0)}{3!}$$

In a similar manner from (5), if $x = 0$, we obtain

$$f^{(iv)}(0) = 2 \cdot 3 \cdot 4c_4 \quad \text{and so} \quad c_4 = \frac{f^{(iv)}(0)}{4!}$$

In general, we have

$$c_n = \frac{f^{(n)}(0)}{n!} \qquad \text{for every positive integer } n \tag{6}$$

Formula (6) also holds when $n = 0$ if we take $f^{(0)}(0)$ to be $f(0)$ and $0! = 1$. So from (1) and (6) we can write the power series of f in x as

$$\sum_{n=0}^{+\infty} \frac{f^{(n)}(0)}{n!} x^n = f(0) + f'(0)x + \frac{f''(0)}{2!} x^2 + \cdots + \frac{f^{(n)}(0)}{n!} x^n + \cdots \tag{7}$$

In a more general sense, consider the function f as a power series in $(x - a)$; that is,

$$f(x) = \sum_{n=0}^{+\infty} c_n(x - a)^n$$

$$= c_0 + c_1(x - a) + c_2(x - a)^2 + \cdots + c_n(x - a)^n + \cdots \tag{8}$$

If the radius of convergence of this series is R, then f is infinitely differentiable on $(a - R, a + R)$. Successive differentiations of the function in (8) give

$$f'(x) = c_1 + 2c_2(x - a) + 3c_3(x - a)^2 + 4c_4(x - a)^3 + \cdots$$
$$+ nc_n(x - a)^{n-1} + \cdots$$

$$f''(x) = 2c_2 + 2 \cdot 3c_3(x - a) + 3 \cdot 4c_4(x - a)^2 + \cdots$$
$$+ (n - 1)nc_n(x - a)^{n-2} + \cdots$$

$$f'''(x) = 2 \cdot 3c_3 + 2 \cdot 3 \cdot 4c_4(x - a) + \cdots$$
$$+ (n - 2)(n - 1)nc_n(x - a)^{n-3} + \cdots$$

etc. Letting $x = a$ in the power-series representations of f and its derivatives, we get

$$c_0 = f(a) \qquad c_1 = f'(a) \qquad c_2 = \frac{f''(a)}{2!} \qquad c_3 = \frac{f'''(a)}{3!}$$

and in general

$$c_n = \frac{f^{(n)}(a)}{n!} \tag{9}$$

From (8) and (9) we can write the power series of f in $(x - a)$ as

$$\sum_{n=0}^{+\infty} \frac{f^{(n)}(a)}{n!} (x - a)^n = f(a) + f'(a)(x - a) + \frac{f''(a)}{2!}(x - a)^2$$
$$+ \cdots + \frac{f^{(n)}(a)}{n!}(x - a)^n + \cdots$$

(10)

The series in (10) is called the *Taylor series* of f at a. The special case of (10), when $a = 0$, is Eq. (7), which is called the *Maclaurin series*.

EXAMPLE 1: Find the Maclaurin series for e^x.

SOLUTION: If $f(x) = e^x$, $f^{(n)}(x) = e^x$ for all x; therefore, $f^{(n)}(0) = 1$ for all n. So from (7) we have the Maclaurin series for e^x:

$$1 + x + \frac{x^2}{2!} + \frac{x^3}{3!} + \cdots + \frac{x^n}{n!} + \cdots$$

(11)

Note that series (11) is the same as the series for e^x obtained in Example 3 of Sec. 16.8.

EXAMPLE 2: Find the Taylor series for $\sin x$ at a.

SOLUTION: If $f(x) = \sin x$, $f'(x) = \cos x$, $f''(x) = -\sin x$, $f'''(x) = -\cos x$, $f^{(iv)}(x) = \sin x$, and so forth. Thus, from formula (9) we have $c_0 = \sin a$, $c_1 = \cos a$, $c_2 = (-\sin a)/2!$, $c_3 = (-\cos a)/3!$, $c_4 = (\sin a)/4!$, and so on. The required Taylor series is obtained from (10), and it is

$$\sin a + \cos a(x - a) - \sin a \frac{(x - a)^2}{2!} - \cos a \frac{(x - a)^3}{3!}$$
$$+ \sin a \frac{(x - a)^4}{4!} + \cdots \quad (12)$$

We can deduce that a power-series representation of a function is unique. That is, if two functions have the same function values in some interval containing the number a, and if both functions have a power-series representation in $(x - a)$, then these series must be the same because the coefficients in the series are obtained from the values of the functions and their derivatives at a. Therefore, if a function has a power-series representation in $(x - a)$, this series must be its Taylor series at a. Hence, the Taylor series for a given function does not have to be obtained by using formula (10). Any method that gives a power series in $(x - a)$ representing the function will be the Taylor series of the function at a.

● ILLUSTRATION 1: To find the Taylor series for e^x at a, we can write $e^x = e^a e^{x-a}$ and then use series (11), where x is replaced by $(x - a)$. We then have

$$e^x = e^a \left[1 + (x - a) + \frac{(x - a)^2}{2!} + \frac{(x - a)^3}{3!} + \cdots + \frac{(x - a)^n}{n!} + \cdots \right] \quad ●$$

● ILLUSTRATION 2: We can use the series for $\ln(1 + x)$ found in Example 3 of Sec. 16.9 to find the Taylor series for $\ln x$ at a ($a > 0$) by writing

$$\ln x = \ln[a + (x - a)] = \ln a + \ln\left(1 + \frac{x - a}{a}\right)$$

Then because

$$\ln(1 + x) = \sum_{n=1}^{+\infty} (-1)^{n-1} \frac{x^n}{n} \qquad \text{if } -1 < x \leq 1$$

we have

$$\ln x = \ln a + \frac{x - a}{a} - \frac{(x - a)^2}{2a^2} + \frac{(x - a)^3}{3a^3} - \cdots$$

and the series represents $\ln x$ if $-1 < (x - a)/a \leq 1$ or, equivalently, $0 < x \leq 2a$. ●

A natural question that arises is: If a function has a Taylor series in $(x - a)$ having radius of convergence $R > 0$, does this series represent the function for all values of x in the interval $(a - R, a + R)$? For most elementary functions the answer is yes. However, there are functions for which the answer is no. The following example shows this.

EXAMPLE 3: Let f be the function defined by

$$f(x) = \begin{cases} e^{-1/x^2} & \text{if } x \neq 0 \\ 0 & \text{if } x = 0 \end{cases}$$

Find the Maclaurin series for f and show that it converges for all values of x but that it represents $f(x)$ only when $x = 0$.

SOLUTION: To find $f'(0)$ we use the definition of a derivative. We have

$$f'(0) = \lim_{x \to 0} \frac{e^{-1/x^2} - 0}{x - 0} = \lim_{x \to 0} \frac{\dfrac{1}{x}}{e^{1/x^2}}$$

Because $\lim_{x \to 0} (1/x) = +\infty$ and $\lim_{x \to 0} e^{1/x^2} = +\infty$, we use L'Hôpital's rule and get

$$f'(0) = \lim_{x \to 0} \frac{-\dfrac{1}{x^2}}{e^{1/x^2}\left(-\dfrac{2}{x^3}\right)} = \lim_{x \to 0} \frac{x}{2e^{1/x^2}} = 0$$

By a similar method, using the definition of a derivative and L'Hôpital's rule, we get 0 for every derivative. So $f^{(n)}(0) = 0$ for all n. Therefore, the Maclaurin series for the given function is $0 + 0 + 0 + \cdots + 0 + \cdots$. This series converges to 0 for all x; however, if $x \neq 0$, $f(x) = e^{-1/x^2} \neq 0$.

A theorem that gives a test for determining whether a function is represented by its Taylor series is the following.

16.10.1 Theorem

Let f be a function such that f and all of its derivatives exist in some interval $(a - r, a + r)$. Then the function is represented by its Taylor series

$$\sum_{n=0}^{+\infty} \frac{f^{(n)}(a)}{n!} (x - a)^n$$

for all x such that $|x - a| < r$ if and only if

$$\lim_{n \to +\infty} R_n(x) = \lim_{n \to +\infty} \frac{f^{(n+1)}(\xi_n)}{(n+1)!} (x-a)^{n+1} = 0$$

where each ξ_n is between x and a.

PROOF: In the interval $(a - r, a + r)$, the function f satisfies the hypothesis of Theorem 15.5.1 for which

$$f(x) = P_n(x) + R_n(x) \tag{13}$$

where $P_n(x)$ is the nth-degree Taylor polynomial of f at a and $R_n(x)$ is the remainder, given by

$$R_n(x) = \frac{f^{(n+1)}(\xi_n)}{(n+1)!} (x-a)^{n+1} \tag{14}$$

where each ξ_n is between x and a.

Now $P_n(x)$ is the nth partial sum of the Taylor series of f at a. So if we show that $\lim_{n \to +\infty} P_n(x)$ exists and equals $f(x)$ if and only if $\lim_{n \to +\infty} R_n(x) = 0$, the theorem will be proved. From Eq. (13) we have

$$P_n(x) = f(x) - R_n(x) \tag{15}$$

If $\lim_{n \to +\infty} R_n(x) = 0$, it follows from Eq. (15) that

$$\lim_{n \to +\infty} P_n(x) = f(x) - \lim_{n \to +\infty} R_n(x)$$
$$= f(x) - 0$$
$$= f(x)$$

Now under the hypothesis that $\lim_{n \to +\infty} P_n(x) = f(x)$ we wish to show that $\lim_{n \to +\infty} R_n(x) = 0$. From Eq. (13) we have

$$R_n(x) = f(x) - P_n(x)$$

and so

$$\lim_{n \to +\infty} R_n(x) = f(x) - \lim_{n \to +\infty} P_n(x)$$
$$= f(x) - f(x)$$
$$= 0$$

This proves the theorem.   ∎

Theorem 16.10.1 also holds for other forms of the remainder $R_n(x)$ besides the Lagrange form.

It is often difficult to apply Theorem 16.10.1 in practice because the values of ξ_n are arbitrary. However, sometimes an upper bound for $R_n(x)$ can be found, and we may be able to prove that the limit of the upper bound is zero as $n \to +\infty$. The following limit is helpful in some cases:

$$\lim_{n \to +\infty} \frac{x^n}{n!} = 0 \qquad \text{for all } x \tag{16}$$

This follows from Example 2 of Sec. 16.7, where we showed that the power series $\sum_{n=0}^{+\infty} x^n/n!$ is convergent for all values of x and hence the limit of its nth term must be zero. In a similar manner, because $\sum_{n=0}^{+\infty} (x-a)^n/n!$ is convergent for all values of x, we have

$$\lim_{n \to +\infty} \frac{(x-a)^n}{n!} = 0 \qquad \text{for all } x \tag{17}$$

EXAMPLE 4:   Use Theorem 16.10.1 to show that the Maclaurin series for e^x, found in Example 1, represents the function for all values of x.

SOLUTION: The Maclaurin series for e^x is series (11) and

$$R_n(x) = \frac{e^{\xi_n}}{(n+1)!} x^{n+1}$$

where each ξ_n is between 0 and x.

We must show that $\lim_{n \to +\infty} R_n = 0$ for all x. We distinguish three cases: $x > 0$, $x < 0$, and $x = 0$.

If $x > 0$, then $0 < \xi_n < x$; hence, $e^{\xi_n} < e^x$. So

$$0 < \frac{e^{\xi_n}}{(n+1)!} x^{n+1} < e^x \frac{x^{n+1}}{(n+1)!} \tag{18}$$

From (16) it follows that $\lim_{n \to +\infty} x^{n+1}/(n+1)! = 0$, and so

$$\lim_{n \to +\infty} e^x \frac{x^{n+1}}{(n+1)!} = 0$$

Therefore, from (18) and the squeeze theorem (4.3.3) we can conclude that $\lim_{n \to +\infty} R_n(x) = 0$.

If $x < 0$, then $x < \xi_n < 0$ and $0 < e^{\xi_n} < 1$. Therefore, if $x^{n+1} > 0$,

$$0 < \frac{e^{\xi_n}}{(n+1)!} x^{n+1} < \frac{x^{n+1}}{(n+1)!}$$

and if $x^{n+1} < 0$,

$$\frac{x^{n+1}}{(n+1)!} < \frac{e^{\xi_n}}{(n+1)!} x^{n+1} < 0$$

In either case, because $\lim_{n \to +\infty} x^{n+1}/(n+1)! = 0$, it follows that $\lim_{n \to +\infty} R_n = 0$.

Finally, if $x = 0$, the series has the sum of 1 which is e^0. Hence, we can conclude that the series (11) represents e^x for all values of x.

From the results of the above example we can write

$$e^x = \sum_{n=0}^{+\infty} \frac{x^n}{n!} = 1 + x + \frac{x^2}{2!} + \frac{x^3}{3!} + \cdots \qquad \text{for all } x \tag{19}$$

and this agrees with Example 3 of Sec. 16.8.

EXAMPLE 5: Show that the Taylor series for $\sin x$ at a, found in Example 2, represents the function for all values of x.

SOLUTION: We use Theorem 16.10.1; so we must show that

$$\lim_{n \to +\infty} R_n(x) = \lim_{n \to +\infty} \frac{f^{(n+1)}(\xi_n)}{(n+1)!} (x-a)^{n+1} = 0$$

Because $f(x) = \sin x$, $f^{(n+1)}(\xi_n)$ will be one of the following numbers: $\cos \xi_n$, $\sin \xi_n$, $-\cos \xi_n$, or $-\sin \xi_n$. In any case, $|f^{(n+1)}(\xi_n)| \le 1$. Hence,

$$0 < |R_n(x)| \le \frac{|x-a|^{n+1}}{(n+1)!} \tag{20}$$

From (17) we know that $\lim\limits_{n \to +\infty} |x-a|^{n+1}/(n+1)! = 0$. Thus, by the squeeze theorem (4.3.3) and (20) it follows that $\lim\limits_{n \to +\infty} R_n(x) = 0$.

EXAMPLE 6: Compute the value of $\sin 47°$ accurate to four decimal places.

SOLUTION: In Examples 2 and 5 we obtained the Taylor series for $\sin x$ at a which represents the function for all values of x. It is

$$\sin x = \sin a + \cos a(x-a) - \sin a \frac{(x-a)^2}{2!} - \cos a \frac{(x-a)^3}{3!} + \cdots$$

To make $(x-a)$ small we choose a value of a near the value of x for which we are computing the function value. We also need to know the sine and cosine of a. We therefore choose $a = \frac{1}{4}\pi$ and have

$$\sin x = \sin \tfrac{1}{4}\pi + \cos \tfrac{1}{4}\pi(x - \tfrac{1}{4}\pi) - \sin \tfrac{1}{4}\pi \frac{(x-\tfrac{1}{4}\pi)^2}{2!}$$
$$- \cos \tfrac{1}{4}\pi \frac{(x-\tfrac{1}{4}\pi)^3}{3!} + \cdots \tag{21}$$

Because $47°$ is equivalent to $\frac{47}{180}\pi$ radians $= (\frac{1}{4}\pi + \frac{1}{90}\pi)$ radians, from Eq. (21) we have

$$\sin \tfrac{47}{180}\pi = \tfrac{1}{2}\sqrt{2} + \tfrac{1}{2}\sqrt{2} \cdot \tfrac{1}{90}\pi - \tfrac{1}{2}\sqrt{2} \cdot \tfrac{1}{2}(\tfrac{1}{90}\pi)^2 - \tfrac{1}{2}\sqrt{2} \cdot \tfrac{1}{6}(\tfrac{1}{90}\pi)^3 + \cdots$$
$$\approx \tfrac{1}{2}\sqrt{2}(1 + 0.03490 - 0.00061 - 0.000002 + \cdots)$$

Taking $\sqrt{2} = 1.41421$ and using the first three terms of the series, we get

$$\sin \tfrac{47}{180}\pi \approx (0.70711)(1.03429) = 0.73136$$

Rounding off to four decimal places gives $\sin 47° \approx 0.7314$. The error introduced by using the first three terms is $R_2(\frac{47}{180}\pi)$, and from (20) we have

$$\left| R_2\left(\frac{47}{180}\pi\right) \right| \le \frac{(\frac{1}{90}\pi)^3}{3!} \approx 0.00001$$

Our result, then, is accurate to four decimal places.

The following Maclaurin series represent the function for all values of x:

$$\sin x = \sum_{n=0}^{+\infty} \frac{(-1)^n x^{2n+1}}{(2n+1)!} = x - \frac{x^3}{3!} + \frac{x^5}{5!} - \frac{x^7}{7!} + \cdots \qquad (22)$$

$$\cos x = \sum_{n=0}^{+\infty} \frac{(-1)^n x^{2n}}{(2n)!} = 1 - \frac{x^2}{2!} + \frac{x^4}{4!} - \frac{x^6}{6!} + \cdots \qquad (23)$$

$$\sinh x = \sum_{n=0}^{+\infty} \frac{x^{2n+1}}{(2n+1)!} = x + \frac{x^3}{3!} + \frac{x^5}{5!} + \frac{x^7}{7!} + \cdots \qquad (24)$$

$$\cosh x = \sum_{n=0}^{+\infty} \frac{x^{2n}}{(2n)!} = 1 + \frac{x^2}{2!} + \frac{x^4}{4!} + \frac{x^6}{6!} + \cdots \qquad (25)$$

Series (22) is a direct result of Examples 2 and 5 with $a = 0$. You are asked to verify series (23), (24), and (25) in Exercises 1, 2, and 3.

EXAMPLE 7: Evaluate

$$\int_{1/2}^{1} \frac{\sin x}{x}\, dx$$

accurate to six decimal places.

SOLUTION: We cannot find an antiderivative of the integrand in terms of elementary functions. However, using series (22) we have

$$\frac{\sin x}{x} = \frac{1}{x} \cdot \sin x$$

$$= \frac{1}{x}\left(x - \frac{x^3}{3!} + \frac{x^5}{5!} - \frac{x^7}{7!} + \frac{x^9}{9!} - \cdots \right)$$

$$= 1 - \frac{x^2}{3!} + \frac{x^4}{5!} - \frac{x^6}{7!} + \frac{x^8}{9!} - \cdots$$

which is true for all $x \ne 0$. Using term-by-term integration we get

$$\int_{1/2}^{1} \frac{\sin x}{x}\, dx = x - \frac{x^3}{3 \cdot 3!} + \frac{x^5}{5 \cdot 5!} - \frac{x^7}{7 \cdot 7!} + \frac{x^9}{9 \cdot 9!} - \cdots \Big]_{1/2}^{1}$$

$$\approx (1 - 0.0555555 + 0.0016667 - 0.0000283 + 0.0000003 - \cdots)$$

$$- (0.5 - 0.0069444 + 0.0000521 - 0.0000002 + \cdots)$$

In each set of parentheses we have a convergent alternating series with $|u_{n+1}| < |u_n|$. In the first set of parentheses we use the first four terms because the error obtained is less than 0.0000003. In the second set of parentheses we use the first three terms where the error obtained is less than 0.0000002. Doing the arithmetic and rounding off to six decimal places, we get

$$\int_{1/2}^{1} \frac{\sin x}{x} \, dx \approx 0.452975$$

Exercises 16.10

1. Prove that the series

$$\sum_{n=0}^{+\infty} \frac{(-1)^n x^{2n}}{(2n)!}$$

represents cos x for all values of x.

2. Prove that the series

$$\sum_{n=0}^{+\infty} \frac{x^{2n+1}}{(2n+1)!}$$

represents sinh x for all values of x.

3. Prove that the series

$$\sum_{n=0}^{+\infty} \frac{x^{2n}}{(2n)!}$$

represents cosh x for all values of x.

4. Obtain the Maclaurin series for the cosine function by differentiating the Maclaurin series for the sine function. Also obtain the Maclaurin series for the sine function by differentiating the one for the cosine function.

5. Obtain the Maclaurin series for the hyperbolic sine function by differentiating the Maclaurin series for the hyperbolic cosine function. Also differentiate the Maclaurin series for the hyperbolic sine function to obtain the one for the hyperbolic cosine function.

6. Find the Taylor series for e^x at 3 by using the Maclaurin series for e^x.

7. Use the Maclaurin series for $\ln(1 + x)$ to find the Taylor series for $\ln x$ at 2.

8. Given $\ln 2 = 0.6931$, use the series obtained in Exercise 7 to find $\ln 3$ accurate to four decimal places.

In Exercises 9 through 14, find a power-series representation for the given function at the number a and determine its radius of convergence.

9. $f(x) = \ln(1 + x); \; a = 1$

10. $f(x) = \dfrac{1}{x}; \; a = 1$

11. $f(x) = \sqrt{x}; \; a = 4$

12. $f(x) = 2^x; \; a = 0$

13. $f(x) = \cos x; \; a = \frac{1}{3}\pi$

14. $f(x) = \ln |x|; \; a = -1$

15. Find the Maclaurin series for $\sin^2 x$. (HINT: Use $\sin^2 x = \frac{1}{2}(1 - \cos 2x)$.)

16. Find the Maclaurin series for $\cos^2 x$. (HINT: Use $\cos^2 x = \frac{1}{2}(1 + \cos 2x)$.)

17. (a) Find the first three nonzero terms of the Maclaurin series for tan x. (b) Use the result of part (a) and term-by-term differentiation to find the first three nonzero terms of the Maclaurin series for $\sec^2 x$. (c) Use the result of part (a) and term-by-term integration to find the first three nonzero terms of the Maclaurin series for $\ln \cos x$.

In Exercises 18 through 23, use a power series to compute the value of the given quantity to the indicated accuracy.

18. $\sinh \frac{1}{2}$; five decimal places.

19. $\cos 58°$; four decimal places.

20. $\sqrt[5]{e}$; four decimal places.

21. $\sqrt[5]{30}$; five decimal places.

22. $\sqrt[3]{29}$; three decimal places.

23. $\ln(0.8)$; four decimal places.

24. Compute the value of e correct to seven decimal places, and prove that your answer has the required accuracy.

In Exercises 25 through 29, compute the value of the definite integral accurate to four decimal places.

25. $\displaystyle\int_{0}^{1/2} \sin x^2 \, dx$

26. $\displaystyle\int_{0}^{1} \cos \sqrt{x} \, dx$

27. $\displaystyle\int_{0}^{0.1} \ln(1 + \sin x) \, dx$

28. $\int_0^{1/3} f(x)\, dx$, where $f(x) = \begin{cases} \dfrac{\sin x}{x} & \text{if } x \neq 0 \\ 1 & \text{if } x = 0 \end{cases}$

29. $\int_0^1 g(x)\, dx$, where $g(x) = \begin{cases} \dfrac{1 - \cos x}{x} & \text{if } x \neq 0 \\ 0 & \text{if } x = 0 \end{cases}$

30. The function E defined by

$$E(x) = \frac{2}{\sqrt{\pi}} \int_0^x e^{-t^2}\, dt$$

is called the *error function*, and it is important in mathematical statistics. Find the Maclaurin series for the error function.

31. Determine a_n ($n = 0, 1, 2, 3, 4$) so that the polynomial

$$f(x) = 3x^4 - 17x^3 + 35x^2 - 32x + 17$$

is written in the form

$$f(x) = a_4(x - 1)^4 + a_3(x - 1)^3 + a_2(x - 1)^2 + a_1(x - 1) + a_0$$

16.11 THE BINOMIAL SERIES

In elementary algebra you learned that the binomial theorem expresses $(a + b)^m$ as a sum of powers of a and b, where m is a positive integer, as follows:

$$(a + b)^m = a^m + ma^{m-1}b + \frac{m(m - 1)}{2!} a^{m-2}b^2 + \cdots$$

$$+ \frac{m(m - 1) \cdot \ldots \cdot (m - k + 1)}{k!} a^{m-k}b^k + \cdots + b^m$$

We now take $a = 1$ and $b = x$, and apply the binomial theorem to the expression $(1 + x)^m$, where m is not a positive integer. We obtain the power series

$$1 + mx + \frac{m(m - 1)}{2!} x^2 + \frac{m(m - 1)(m - 2)}{3!} x^3 + \cdots$$

$$+ \frac{m(m - 1)(m - 2) \cdot \ldots \cdot (m - n + 1)}{n!} x^n + \cdots \tag{1}$$

Series (1) is the Maclaurin series for $(1 + x)^m$. It is called a *binomial series*. To find the radius of convergence of series (1), we apply the ratio test and get

$$\lim_{n \to +\infty} \left| \frac{u_{n+1}}{u_n} \right|$$

$$= \lim_{n \to +\infty} \left| \frac{\dfrac{m(m - 1) \cdot \ldots \cdot (m - n + 1)(m - n)}{(n + 1)!} x^{n+1}}{\dfrac{m(m - 1) \cdot \ldots \cdot (m - n + 1)}{n!} x^n} \right|$$

$$= \lim_{n \to +\infty} \left| \frac{m - n}{n + 1} \right| |x|$$

$$= \lim_{n \to +\infty} \left| \frac{\frac{m}{n} - 1}{1 + \frac{1}{n}} \right| |x|$$

$$= |x|$$

So the series is convergent if $|x| < 1$. We now prove that series (1) represents $(1 + x)^m$ for all real numbers m if x is in the open interval $(-1, 1)$. We do not do this by calculating $R_n(x)$ and showing that its limit is zero because this is quite difficult, as you will soon see if you attempt to do so. Instead, we use the following method. Let

$$f(x) = 1 + \sum_{n=1}^{+\infty} \frac{m(m-1) \cdot \ldots \cdot (m-n+1)}{n!} x^n \qquad |x| < 1 \qquad (2)$$

We wish to show that $f(x) = (1 + x)^m$, where $|x| < 1$. By Theorem 16.8.3 we have

$$f'(x) = \sum_{n=1}^{+\infty} \frac{m(m-1) \cdot \ldots \cdot (m-n+1)}{(n-1)!} x^{n-1} \qquad |x| < 1 \qquad (3)$$

Multiplying on both sides of Eq. (3) by x, we get from Theorem 16.3.8

$$xf'(x) = \sum_{n=1}^{+\infty} \frac{m(m-1) \cdot \ldots \cdot (m-n+1)}{(n-1)!} x^n \qquad (4)$$

Rewriting the right side of (3), we have

$$f'(x) = m + \sum_{n=2}^{+\infty} \frac{m(m-1) \cdot \ldots \cdot (m-n+1)}{(n-1)!} x^{n-1} \qquad (5)$$

Rewriting the summation in (5) by decreasing the lower limit by 1 and replacing n by $n + 1$, we get

$$f'(x) = m + \sum_{n=1}^{+\infty} (m-n) \frac{m(m-1) \cdot \ldots \cdot (m-n+1)}{n!} x^n \qquad (6)$$

If in (4) we multiply the numerator and the denominator by n, we get

$$xf'(x) = \sum_{n=1}^{+\infty} n \frac{m(m-1) \cdot \ldots \cdot (m-n+1)}{n!} x^n \qquad (7)$$

Because the series in (6) and (7) are absolutely convergent for $|x| < 1$, then by Theorem 16.3.9 we can add them term by term, and the resulting series will be absolutely convergent for $|x| < 1$. When we add we get

$$(1 + x)f'(x) = m \left[1 + \sum_{n=1}^{+\infty} \frac{m(m-1) \cdot \ldots \cdot (m-n+1)}{n!} x^n \right]$$

Because by (2) the expression in brackets is $f(x)$, we have

$$(1 + x)f'(x) = mf(x)$$

or, equivalently,

$$\frac{f'(x)}{f(x)} = \frac{m}{1+x}$$

The left side of the above equation is $D_x[\ln f(x)]$; so we can write

$$D_x[\ln f(x)] = \frac{m}{1+x}$$

However, we also know that

$$D_x[\ln(1+x)^m] = \frac{m}{1+x}$$

Because $\ln f(x)$ and $\ln(1+x)^m$ have the same derivative, they differ by a constant. Hence,

$$\ln f(x) = \ln(1+x)^m + C$$

We see from (2) that $f(0) = 1$. Therefore, $C = 0$ and we get

$$f(x) = (1+x)^m$$

We have proved the general binomial theorem, which we now state.

16.11.1 Theorem
Binomial Theorem

If m is any real number, then

$$(1+x)^m = 1 + \sum_{n=1}^{+\infty} \frac{m(m-1)(m-2) \cdot \ldots \cdot (m-n+1)}{n!} x^n \qquad (8)$$

for all values of x such that $|x| < 1$.

If m is a positive integer, the binomial series will terminate after a finite number of terms.

EXAMPLE 1: Express

$$\frac{1}{\sqrt{1+x}}$$

as a power series in x.

SOLUTION: From Theorem 16.11.1 we have, when $|x| < 1$,

$$(1+x)^{-1/2} = 1 - \frac{1}{2}x + \frac{(-\frac{1}{2})(-\frac{1}{2}-1)}{2!}x^2 + \frac{(-\frac{1}{2})(-\frac{1}{2}-1)(-\frac{1}{2}-2)}{3!}x^3$$

$$+ \cdots + \frac{(-\frac{1}{2})(-\frac{3}{2})(-\frac{5}{2}) \cdot \ldots \cdot (-\frac{1}{2}-n+1)}{n!}x^n + \cdots$$

$$= 1 - \frac{1}{2}x + \frac{1 \cdot 3}{2^2 \cdot 2!}x^2 - \frac{1 \cdot 3 \cdot 5}{2^3 \cdot 3!}x^3 + \cdots$$

$$+ (-1)^n \frac{1 \cdot 3 \cdot 5 \cdot \ldots \cdot (2n-1)}{2^n n!}x^n + \cdots$$

EXAMPLE 2: From the result of Example 1 obtain a binomial

SOLUTION: Replacing x by $-x^2$ in the series for $(1+x)^{-1/2}$, we get for $|x| < 1$

series for $(1 - x^2)^{-1/2}$ and use it to find a power series for $\sin^{-1} x$.

$$(1 - x^2)^{-1/2} = 1 + \frac{1}{2} x^2 + \frac{1 \cdot 3}{2^2 \cdot 2!} x^4 + \frac{1 \cdot 3 \cdot 5}{2^3 \cdot 3!} x^6 + \cdots$$

$$+ \frac{1 \cdot 3 \cdot 5 \cdot \ldots \cdot (2n - 1)}{2^n n!} x^{2n} + \cdots$$

Applying Theorem 16.9.1, we integrate term by term and obtain

$$\int_0^x \frac{dt}{\sqrt{1 - t^2}} = x + \frac{1}{2} \cdot \frac{x^3}{3} + \frac{1 \cdot 3}{2^2 \cdot 2!} \cdot \frac{x^5}{5} + \frac{1 \cdot 3 \cdot 5}{2^3 \cdot 3!} \cdot \frac{x^7}{7} + \cdots$$

$$+ \frac{1 \cdot 3 \cdot 5 \cdot \ldots \cdot (2n - 1)}{2^n n!} \cdot \frac{x^{2n+1}}{2n + 1} + \cdots$$

and so

$$\sin^{-1} x = x + \sum_{n=1}^{+\infty} \frac{1 \cdot 3 \cdot 5 \cdot \ldots \cdot (2n - 1)}{2^n n!} \cdot \frac{x^{2n+1}}{2n + 1} \quad \text{for } |x| < 1$$

EXAMPLE 3: Compute the value of $\sqrt[3]{25}$ accurate to three decimal places by using the binomial series for $(1 + x)^{1/3}$.

SOLUTION: From Eq. (8) we have

$$(1 + x)^{1/3} = 1 + \frac{1}{3} x + \left(\frac{1}{3}\right)\left(-\frac{2}{3}\right) \frac{x^2}{2!} + \left(\frac{1}{3}\right)\left(-\frac{2}{3}\right)\left(-\frac{5}{3}\right) \frac{x^3}{3!} + \cdots \quad (9)$$

$$\text{if } |x| < 1$$

We can write

$$\sqrt[3]{25} = \sqrt[3]{27} \sqrt[3]{\tfrac{25}{27}} = 3\sqrt[3]{1 - \tfrac{2}{27}} = 3(1 - \tfrac{2}{27})^{1/3} \quad (10)$$

Using Eq. (9) with $x = -\tfrac{2}{27}$, we get

$$\left(1 - \frac{2}{27}\right)^{1/3} = 1 + \frac{1}{3}\left(-\frac{2}{27}\right) - \frac{2}{3^2 \cdot 2!}\left(-\frac{2}{27}\right)^2 + \frac{2 \cdot 5}{3^3 \cdot 3!}\left(-\frac{2}{27}\right)^3 + \cdots$$

$$\approx 1 - 0.0247 - 0.0006 - 0.00003 - \cdots \quad (11)$$

If the first three terms of the above series are used, we see from Eq. (14) of Sec. 16.10 that the remainder is

$$R_2\left(-\frac{2}{27}\right) = \frac{f'''(\xi_2)}{3!}\left(-\frac{2}{27}\right)^3$$

$$= \left(\frac{1}{3}\right)\left(-\frac{2}{3}\right)\left(-\frac{5}{3}\right)\left(\frac{1}{3!}\right)(1 + \xi_2)^{(1/3)-3}\left(-\frac{2}{27}\right)^3$$

where $-\tfrac{2}{27} < \xi_2 < 0$. Therefore,

$$\left|R_2\left(-\frac{2}{27}\right)\right| = \left(\frac{2 \cdot 5}{3^3 \cdot 3!}\right) \frac{(1 + \xi_2)^{1/3}}{(1 + \xi_2)^3}\left(\frac{2}{27}\right)^3 \quad (12)$$

Because $-\tfrac{2}{27} < \xi_2 < 0$, it follows that

$$(1 + \xi_2)^{1/3} < 1^{1/3} = 1 \quad \text{and} \quad \frac{1}{(1 + \xi_2)^3} < \frac{1}{(\tfrac{25}{27})^3} \quad (13)$$

Furthermore,

$$\frac{2\cdot 5}{3^3\cdot 3!}=\frac{2\cdot 5}{3\cdot 3\cdot 3\cdot 1\cdot 2\cdot 3}=\frac{2}{3}\cdot\frac{5}{6}\cdot\frac{1}{9}<\frac{1}{9} \tag{14}$$

and so using inequalities (13) and (14) in (12) we see that

$$\left|R_2\left(-\frac{2}{27}\right)\right|<\frac{1}{9}\cdot\frac{1}{(\frac{25}{27})^3}\cdot\left(\frac{2}{27}\right)^3=\frac{8}{140,625}<0.00006$$

Using, then, the first three terms of series (11) gives

$$\left(1-\frac{2}{27}\right)^{1/3}\approx 0.9747$$

with an error less than 0.00006. From (10) we obtain

$$\sqrt[3]{25}\approx 3(0.9747)=2.9241$$

with an error less than $3(0.00006)=0.00018$. Rounding off to three decimal places gives $\sqrt[3]{25}\approx 2.924$.

Exercises 16.11

In Exercises 1 through 6, use a binomial series to find the Maclaurin series for the given function. Determine the radius of convergence of the resulting series.

1. $f(x)=\sqrt{1+x}$

2. $f(x)=(9+x^4)^{-1/2}$

3. $f(x)=(4+x^2)^{-1}$

4. $f(x)=\sqrt[3]{8+x}$

5. $f(x)=\dfrac{x^2}{\sqrt{1+x}}$

6. $f(x)=\dfrac{x}{\sqrt[3]{1+x^2}}$

7. Integrate term by term from 0 to x the binomial series for $(1+t^2)^{-1/2}$ to obtain the Maclaurin series for $\sinh^{-1}x$. Determine the radius of convergence.

8. Use a method similar to that of Exercise 7 to find the Maclaurin series for $\tanh^{-1}x$. Determine the radius of convergence.

In Exercises 9 through 12, compute the value of the given quantity accurate to three decimal places by using a binomial series.

9. $\sqrt{24}$

10. $\sqrt[3]{66}$

11. $\sqrt[4]{630}$

12. $\dfrac{1}{\sqrt[5]{31}}$

In Exercises 13 through 16, compute the value of the definite integral accurate to four decimal places.

13. $\displaystyle\int_0^{1/3}\frac{dx}{\sqrt[3]{x^2+1}}$

14. $\displaystyle\int_0^{1/2}\sqrt{1-x^3}\,dx$

15. $\displaystyle\int_0^{1/2}\frac{dx}{\sqrt{1-x^3}}$

16. $\displaystyle\int_0^{1/2}f(x)\,dx$, where $f(x)=\begin{cases}\dfrac{\sin^{-1}x}{x} & \text{if } x\neq 0\\ 1 & \text{if } x=0\end{cases}$

Review Exercises (Chapter 16)

In Exercises 1 through 6, write the first four numbers of the sequence and find the limit of the sequence, if it exists.

1. $\left\{\dfrac{3n}{n+2}\right\}$

2. $\left\{\dfrac{(-1)^{n-1}}{(n+1)^2}\right\}$

3. $\left\{\dfrac{n^2-1}{n^2+1}\right\}$

4. $\left\{\dfrac{n+3n^2}{4+2n^3}\right\}$

5. $\{2+(-1)^n\}$

6. $\left\{\dfrac{n^2}{n+2}-\dfrac{n^2}{n-2}\right\}$

In Exercises 7 through 13, determine if the series is convergent or divergent. If the series is convergent, find its sum.

7. $\displaystyle\sum_{n=1}^{+\infty} \left(\frac{3}{4}\right)^n$

8. $\displaystyle\sum_{n=1}^{+\infty} e^{-2n}$

9. $\displaystyle\sum_{n=1}^{+\infty} \frac{n-1}{n+1}$

10. $\displaystyle\sum_{n=0}^{+\infty} [(-1)^n + (-1)^{n+1}]$

11. $\displaystyle\sum_{n=0}^{+\infty} \sin^n \frac{1}{3}\pi$

12. $\displaystyle\sum_{n=0}^{+\infty} \cos^n \frac{1}{3}\pi$

13. $\displaystyle\sum_{n=1}^{+\infty} \frac{1}{(3n-1)(3n+2)}$ (HINT: To find the sum, first find the sequence of partial sums.)

In Exercises 14 through 25, determine if the series is convergent or divergent.

14. $\displaystyle\sum_{n=1}^{+\infty} \frac{1}{(2n+1)^3}$

15. $\displaystyle\sum_{n=1}^{+\infty} \frac{2}{n^2+6n}$

16. $\displaystyle\sum_{n=1}^{+\infty} \frac{3+\sin n}{n^2}$

17. $\displaystyle\sum_{n=1}^{+\infty} \cos\left(\frac{\pi}{2n^2-1}\right)$

18. $\displaystyle\sum_{n=1}^{+\infty} \frac{n}{\sqrt{3n+2}}$

19. $\displaystyle\sum_{n=1}^{+\infty} \frac{(n!)^2}{(2n)!}$

20. $\displaystyle\sum_{n=1}^{+\infty} \frac{(-1)^{n+1}}{1+\sqrt{n}}$

21. $\displaystyle\sum_{n=1}^{+\infty} (-1)^n \ln\frac{1}{n}$

22. $\displaystyle\sum_{n=1}^{+\infty} \frac{\ln n}{n^2}$

23. $\displaystyle\sum_{n=2}^{+\infty} \frac{1}{n(\ln n)^2}$

24. $\displaystyle\sum_{n=0}^{+\infty} \frac{n!}{10^n}$

25. $\displaystyle\sum_{n=1}^{+\infty} \frac{1}{1+2\ln n}$

In Exercises 26 through 33, determine if the given series is absolutely convergent, conditionally convergent, or divergent. Prove your answer.

26. $\displaystyle\sum_{n=0}^{+\infty} (-1)^n \frac{5^{2n+1}}{(2n+1)!}$

27. $\displaystyle\sum_{n=0}^{+\infty} (-1)^n \frac{n^2}{3^n}$

28. $\displaystyle\sum_{n=1}^{+\infty} (-1)^{n-1} \frac{6^n}{5^{n+1}}$

29. $\displaystyle\sum_{n=1}^{+\infty} (-1)^{n-1} \frac{1}{(n+1)^{3/4}}$

30. $\displaystyle\sum_{n=1}^{+\infty} (-1)^n \frac{\sqrt{2n-1}}{n}$

31. $\displaystyle\sum_{n=1}^{+\infty} (-1)^n \frac{n!}{10n}$

32. $\displaystyle\sum_{n=1}^{+\infty} c_n$, where $c_n = \begin{cases} -\dfrac{1}{n} & \text{if } \frac{1}{4}n \text{ is an integer} \\ \dfrac{1}{n^2} & \text{if } \frac{1}{4}n \text{ is not an integer} \end{cases}$

33. $\displaystyle\sum_{n=1}^{+\infty} c_n$, where $c_n = \begin{cases} -\dfrac{1}{n} & \text{if } n \text{ is a perfect square} \\ \dfrac{1}{n^2} & \text{if } n \text{ is not a perfect square} \end{cases}$

In Exercises 34 through 42, find the interval of convergence of the given power series.

34. $\displaystyle\sum_{n=0}^{+\infty} \frac{x^n}{2^n}$

35. $\displaystyle\sum_{n=1}^{+\infty} \frac{x^n}{\sqrt{n}}$

36. $\displaystyle\sum_{n=1}^{+\infty} \frac{(x-2)^n}{n}$

37. $\displaystyle\sum_{n=1}^{+\infty} \frac{x^n}{3^n(n^2+n)}$

38. $\displaystyle\sum_{n=1}^{+\infty} n(2x-1)^n$

39. $\displaystyle\sum_{n=0}^{+\infty} \frac{n!}{2^n}(x-3)^n$

40. $\displaystyle\sum_{n=1}^{+\infty} \frac{(-1)^{n-1}x^{2n-1}}{(2n-1)!}$

41. $\displaystyle\sum_{n=1}^{+\infty} \frac{n^2}{6^n}(x+1)^n$

42. $\displaystyle\sum_{n=1}^{+\infty} n^n x^n$

In Exercises 43 through 50, use a power series to compute the value of the given quantity accurate to four decimal places.

43. $\tan^{-1} \frac{1}{5}$

44. $\sin 0.3$

45. $\sqrt[3]{130}$

46. $\sin^{-1} 1$

47. $\cos 3°$

48. $\sqrt[4]{e}$

49. $\int_0^{1/4} \sqrt{x} \sin x \, dx$

50. $\int_0^1 \cos x^3 \, dx$

In Exercises 51 through 53, find the Maclaurin series for the given function and find its interval of convergence.

51. $f(x) = a^x (a > 0)$

52. $f(x) = \dfrac{1}{2 - x}$

53. $f(x) = \sin^3 x$

In Exercises 54 through 56, find the Taylor series for the given function at the given number.

54. $f(x) = e^{x-2}$; at 2

55. $f(x) = \sin 3x$; at $-\frac{1}{3}\pi$

56. $f(x) = \dfrac{1}{x}$; at 2

Exercises 57 through 61 pertain to the functions J_0 and J_1 defined by power series as follows:

$$J_0(x) = \sum_{n=0}^{+\infty} (-1)^n \frac{x^{2n}}{n!n!2^{2n}} \qquad J_1(x) = \sum_{n=0}^{+\infty} (-1)^n \frac{x^{2n+1}}{n!(n+1)!2^{2n+1}}$$

The functions J_0 and J_1 are called *Bessel functions of the first kind* of orders zero and one, respectively.

57. Show that both J_0 and J_1 converge for all real values of x.

58. Show that $J_0'(x) = -J_1(x)$.

59. Show that $D_x(xJ_1(x)) = xJ_0(x)$.

60. Show that $y = J_0(x)$ is a solution of the differential equation

$$x \frac{d^2y}{dx^2} + \frac{dy}{dx} + xy = 0$$

61. Show that $y = J_1(x)$ is a solution of the differential equation

$$x^2 \frac{d^2y}{dx^2} + x \frac{dy}{dx} + (x^2 - 1)y = 0$$

17

Vectors in the plane
and parametric equations

17.1 VECTORS IN THE PLANE

In the application of mathematics to physics and engineering, we are often concerned with quantities that possess both *magnitude* and *direction;* examples of these are *force, velocity, acceleration,* and *displacement.* Such quantities may be represented geometrically by a *directed line segment.* Physicists and engineers refer to a directed line segment as a *vector,* and the quantities that have both magnitude and direction are called *vector quantities.* The study of vectors is called *vector analysis.*

The approach to vector analysis can be on either a geometric or an analytic basis. If the geometric approach is taken, we first define a directed line segment as a line segment from a point P to a point Q and denote this directed line segment by $\overrightarrow{PQ}$. The point P is called the *initial point,* and the point Q is called the *terminal point.* Then two directed line segments $\overrightarrow{PQ}$ and $\overrightarrow{RS}$ are said to be equal if they have the same *length* and *direction,* and we write $\overrightarrow{PQ} = \overrightarrow{RS}$ (see Fig. 17.1.1). The directed line segment PQ is called the *vector* from P to Q. A vector is denoted by a single letter, set in boldface type, such as **A**. In some books, a letter in lightface type, with an arrow above it, is used to indicate a vector, for example, $\overrightarrow{A}$.

Continuing with the geometric approach to vector analysis, we note that if the directed line segment $\overrightarrow{PQ}$ is the vector **A**, and $\overrightarrow{PQ} = \overrightarrow{RS}$, the directed line segment $\overrightarrow{RS}$ is also the vector **A**. Then a vector is considered to remain unchanged if it is moved parallel to itself. With this interpretation of a vector, we can assume for convenience that every vector has its initial point at some fixed reference point. By taking this point as the origin of a rectangular cartesian-coordinate system, a vector can be defined analytically in terms of real numbers. Such a definition enables us to study vector analysis from a purely mathematical viewpoint.

In this book, we use the analytic approach; however, the geometric interpretation is used for illustrative purposes. We denote a vector in the plane by an ordered pair of real numbers and use the notation $\langle x, y \rangle$ instead of (x, y) to avoid confusing the notation for a vector with the notation for a point. We let V_2 be the set of all such ordered pairs. Following is the formal definition.

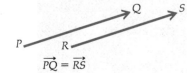

$\overrightarrow{PQ} = \overrightarrow{RS}$

Figure 17.1.1

17.1.1 Definition

A *vector in the plane* is an ordered pair of real numbers $\langle x, y \rangle$. The numbers x and y are called the *components* of the vector $\langle x, y \rangle$.

There is a one-to-one correspondence between the vectors $\langle x, y \rangle$ in the plane and the points (x, y) in the plane. Let the vector **A** be the ordered pair of real numbers $\langle a_1, a_2 \rangle$. If we let A denote the point (a_1, a_2), then the vector **A** may be represented geometrically by the directed line segment $\overrightarrow{OA}$. Such a directed line segment is called a *representation* of vector **A**. Any directed line segment which is equal to $\overrightarrow{OA}$ is also a representation of vector **A**. The particular representation of a vector which has its initial point at the origin is called the *position representation* of the vector.

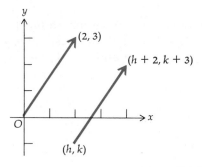

Figure 17.1.2

17.1.2 Definition

• ILLUSTRATION 1: The vector $\langle 2, 3 \rangle$ has as its position representation the directed line segment from the origin to the point $(2, 3)$. The representation of the vector $\langle 2, 3 \rangle$ whose initial point is (h, k) has as its terminal point $(h + 2, 3 + k)$; refer to Fig. 17.1.2. •

The vector $\langle 0, 0 \rangle$ is called the *zero vector*, and we denote it by **0**; that is,

$$\mathbf{0} = \langle 0, 0 \rangle$$

Any point is a representation of the zero vector.

The *magnitude* of a vector is the length of any of its representations, and the *direction* of a nonzero vector is the direction of any of its representations.

The magnitude of the vector **A** is denoted by $|\mathbf{A}|$.

17.1.3 Theorem   If **A** is the vector $\langle a_1, a_2 \rangle$, then $|\mathbf{A}| = \sqrt{a_1^2 + a_2^2}$

PROOF: Because by Definition 17.1.2, $|\mathbf{A}|$ is the length of any of the representations of **A**, then $|\mathbf{A}|$ will be the length of the position representation of **A**, which is the distance from the origin to the point (a_1, a_2). So from the formula for the distance between two points, we have

$$|\mathbf{A}| = \sqrt{(a_1 - 0)^2 + (a_2 - 0)^2} = \sqrt{a_1^2 + a_2^2} \qquad \blacksquare$$

It should be noted that $|\mathbf{A}|$ is a nonnegative number and not a vector. From Theorem 17.1.3 it follows that $|\mathbf{0}| = 0$.

• ILLUSTRATION 2: If $\mathbf{A} = \langle -3, 5 \rangle$, then

$$|\mathbf{A}| = \sqrt{(-3)^2 + 5^2} = \sqrt{34}$$

•

The direction of any nonzero vector is given by the radian measure θ of the angle from the positive x axis counterclockwise to the position representation of the vector: $0 \leq \theta < 2\pi$. So if $\mathbf{A} = \langle a_1, a_2 \rangle$, then $\tan \theta = a_2/a_1$ if $a_1 \neq 0$. If $a_1 = 0$ and $a_2 > 0$, then $\theta = \frac{1}{2}\pi$. If $a_1 = 0$ and $a_2 < 0$, then $\theta = \frac{3}{2}\pi$. Figures 17.1.3, 17.1.4, and 17.1.5 show the angle of radian measure θ for specific vectors $\langle a_1, a_2 \rangle$ whose position representations are drawn.

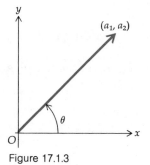

Figure 17.1.3

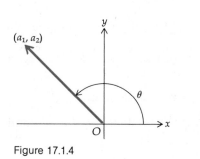

Figure 17.1.4

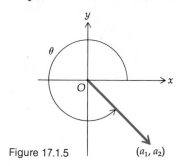

Figure 17.1.5

EXAMPLE 1: Find the radian measure of the angle giving the direction of each of the following vectors: (a) $\langle -1, 1 \rangle$; (b) $\langle 0, -5 \rangle$; (c) $\langle 1, -2 \rangle$.

SOLUTION: The position representation of each of the vectors in (a), (b), and (c) is shown in Figures 17.1.6, 17.1.7, and 17.1.8, respectively. (a) $\tan \theta = -1$; so $\theta = \frac{3}{4}\pi$; (b) $\tan \theta$ does not exist and $a_2 < 0$; $\theta = \frac{3}{2}\pi$; (c) $\tan \theta = -2$; $\theta = \tan^{-1}(-2) + 2\pi$.

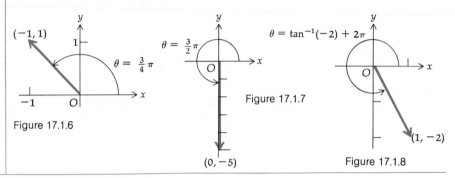

Figure 17.1.6

Figure 17.1.7

Figure 17.1.8

If the vector $\mathbf{A} = \langle a_1, a_2 \rangle$, then the representation of $\mathbf{A}$ whose initial point is (x, y) has as its endpoint $(x + a_1, y + a_2)$. In this way a vector may be thought of as a translation of the plane into itself. Figure 17.1.9 illustrates five representations of the vector $\mathbf{A} = \langle a_1, a_2 \rangle$. In each case, $\mathbf{A}$ translates the point (x_i, y_i) into the point $(x_i + a_1, y_i + a_2)$.

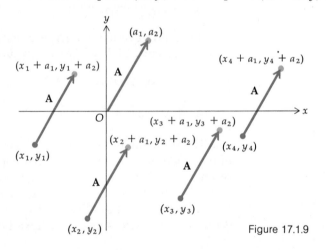

Figure 17.1.9

The following definition gives the method for adding two vectors.

17.1.4 Definition   The *sum* of two vectors $\mathbf{A} = \langle a_1, a_2 \rangle$ and $\mathbf{B} = \langle b_1, b_2 \rangle$ is the vector $\mathbf{A} + \mathbf{B}$, defined by

$$\mathbf{A} + \mathbf{B} = \langle a_1 + b_1, a_2 + b_2 \rangle$$

● ILLUSTRATION 3: If $\mathbf{A} = \langle 3, -1 \rangle$ and $\mathbf{B} = \langle -4, 5 \rangle$, then

$$\mathbf{A} + \mathbf{B} = \langle 3 + (-4), -1 + 5 \rangle = \langle -1, 4 \rangle$$

●

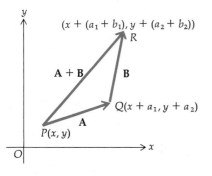

$(x + (a_1 + b_1), y + (a_2 + b_2))$

$A + B$ B

$Q(x + a_1, y + a_2)$

A

$P(x, y)$

Figure 17.1.10

The geometric interpretation of the sum of two vectors is shown in Fig. 17.1.10. Let $\mathbf{A} = \langle a_1, a_2 \rangle$ and $\mathbf{B} = \langle b_1, b_2 \rangle$ and let P be the point (x, y). Then $\mathbf{A}$ translates the point P into the point $(x + a_1, y + a_2) = Q$. The vector $\mathbf{B}$ translates the point Q into the point $((x + a_1) + b_1, (y + a_2) + b_2)$ or, equivalently, $(x + (a_1 + b_1), y + (a_2 + b_2)) = R$. Furthermore, $\mathbf{A} + \mathbf{B} = \langle a_1 + b_1, a_2 + b_2 \rangle$. Therefore, the vector $\mathbf{A} + \mathbf{B}$ translates the point P into the point $(x + (a_1 + b_1), y + (a_2 + b_2)) = R$. Thus, in Fig. 17.1.10 $\overrightarrow{PQ}$ is a representation of the vector $\mathbf{A}$, $\overrightarrow{QR}$ is a representation of the vector $\mathbf{B}$, and PR is a representation of the vector $\mathbf{A} + \mathbf{B}$. The representations of the vectors $\mathbf{A}$ and $\mathbf{B}$ are adjacent sides of a parallelogram, and the representation of the vector $\mathbf{A} + \mathbf{B}$ is a diagonal of the parallelogram. Thus, the rule for the addition of vectors is sometimes referred to as the *parallelogram law*.

17.1.5 Definition   If $\mathbf{A} = \langle a_1, a_2 \rangle$, then the vector $\langle -a_1, -a_2 \rangle$ is defined to be the *negative* of $\mathbf{A}$, denoted by $-\mathbf{A}$.

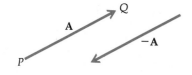

Q

A

$-\mathbf{A}$

P

Figure 17.1.11

If the directed line segment $\overrightarrow{PQ}$ is a representation of the vector $\mathbf{A}$, then the directed line segment $\overrightarrow{QP}$ is a representation of $-\mathbf{A}$. Any directed line segment which is parallel to $\overrightarrow{PQ}$, has the same length as $\overrightarrow{PQ}$, and has a direction opposite to that of $\overrightarrow{PQ}$ is also a representation of $-\mathbf{A}$ (see Fig. 17.1.11). We now define subtraction of two vectors.

17.1.6 Definition   The *difference* of the two vectors $\mathbf{A}$ and $\mathbf{B}$, denoted by $\mathbf{A} - \mathbf{B}$, is the vector obtained by adding $\mathbf{A}$ to the negative of $\mathbf{B}$; that is,

$$\mathbf{A} - \mathbf{B} = \mathbf{A} + (-\mathbf{B})$$

So if $\mathbf{A} = \langle a_1, a_2 \rangle$ and $\mathbf{B} = \langle b_1, b_2 \rangle$, then $-\mathbf{B} = \langle -b_1, -b_2 \rangle$, and so

$$\mathbf{A} - \mathbf{B} = \langle a_1 - b_1, a_2 - b_2 \rangle$$

● ILLUSTRATION 4: If $\mathbf{A} = \langle 4, -2 \rangle$ and $\mathbf{B} = \langle 6, -3 \rangle$, then

$$\mathbf{A} - \mathbf{B} = \langle 4, -2 \rangle - \langle 6, -3 \rangle$$
$$= \langle 4, -2 \rangle + \langle -6, 3 \rangle$$
$$= \langle -2, 1 \rangle \qquad ●$$

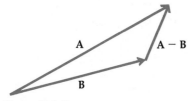

A $A - B$

B

Figure 17.1.12

To interpret the difference of two vectors geometrically, let the representations of the vectors $\mathbf{A}$ and $\mathbf{B}$ have the same initial point. Then the directed line segment from the endpoint of the representation of $\mathbf{B}$ to the endpoint of the representation of $\mathbf{A}$ is a representation of the vector $\mathbf{A} - \mathbf{B}$. This obeys the parallelogram law $\mathbf{B} + (\mathbf{A} - \mathbf{B}) = \mathbf{A}$ (see Fig. 17.1.12).

Another operation with vectors is *scalar multiplication*. A *scalar* is a real number. Following is the definition of the multiplication of a vector by a scalar.

17.1.7 Definition   If c is a scalar and $\mathbf{A}$ is the vector $\langle a_1, a_2 \rangle$, then the *product* of c and $\mathbf{A}$, denoted by $c\mathbf{A}$, is a vector and is given by

$$c\mathbf{A} = c\langle a_1, a_2 \rangle = \langle ca_1, ca_2 \rangle$$

● ILLUSTRATION 5: If $\mathbf{A} = \langle 4, -5 \rangle$, then

$$3\mathbf{A} = 3\langle 4, -5 \rangle = \langle 12, -15 \rangle$$ ●

EXAMPLE 2:   If $\mathbf{A}$ is any vector and c is any scalar, show that $0(\mathbf{A}) = \mathbf{0}$ and $c(\mathbf{0}) = \mathbf{0}$.

SOLUTION: From Definition 17.1.7 it follows that

$$0(\mathbf{A}) = 0\langle a_1, a_2 \rangle = \langle 0, 0 \rangle = \mathbf{0}$$

and

$$c(\mathbf{0}) = c\langle 0, 0 \rangle = \langle 0, 0 \rangle = \mathbf{0}$$

We compute the magnitude of the vector $c\mathbf{A}$ as follows.

$$\begin{aligned} c\mathbf{A} &= \sqrt{(ca_1)^2 + (ca_2)^2} \\ &= \sqrt{c^2(a_1{}^2 + a_2{}^2)} \\ &= \sqrt{c^2}\,\sqrt{a_1{}^2 + a_2{}^2} \\ &= |c|\,|\mathbf{A}| \end{aligned}$$

Therefore, the magnitude of $c\mathbf{A}$ is the absolute value of c times the magnitude of $\mathbf{A}$.

The geometric interpretation of the vector $c\mathbf{A}$ is given in Figs. 17.1.13 and 17.1.14. If $c > 0$, then $c\mathbf{A}$ is a vector whose representation has a length c times the magnitude of $\mathbf{A}$ and the same direction as $\mathbf{A}$; an example of this is shown in Fig. 17.1.13, where $c = 3$. If $c < 0$, then $c\mathbf{A}$ is a vector whose representation has a length which is $|c|$ times the magnitude of $\mathbf{A}$ and a direction opposite to that of $\mathbf{A}$. This is shown in Fig. 17.1.14, where $c = -\tfrac{1}{2}$.

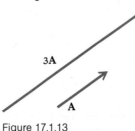

Figure 17.1.13

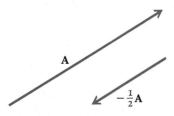

Figure 17.1.14

Exercises 17.1

In Exercises 1 through 6, draw the position representation of the given vector $\mathbf{A}$ and also the particular representation through the given point P; find the magnitude of $\mathbf{A}$.

1. $\mathbf{A} = \langle 3, 4 \rangle$; $P = (2, 1)$

2. $\mathbf{A} = \langle -2, 5 \rangle$; $P = (3, -4)$

3. $\mathbf{A} = \langle 0, -2 \rangle$; $P = (-3, 4)$

4. $\mathbf{A} = \langle 4, 0 \rangle$; $P = (2, 6)$

5. $\mathbf{A} = \langle 3, \sqrt{2} \rangle$; $P = (4, -\sqrt{2})$

6. $\mathbf{A} = \langle e, -\frac{1}{2} \rangle$; $P = (-2, -e)$

In Exercises 7 through 12, find the vector $\mathbf{A}$ having $\overrightarrow{PQ}$ as a representation. Draw $\overrightarrow{PQ}$ and the position representation of $\mathbf{A}$.

7. $P = (3, 7)$; $Q = (5, 4)$

8. $P = (5, 4)$; $Q = (3, 7)$

9. $P = (-3, 5)$; $Q = (-5, -2)$

10. $P = (0, \sqrt{3})$; $Q = (2, 3\sqrt{3})$

11. $P = (-5, -3)$; $Q = (0, 3)$

12. $P = (-\sqrt{2}, 0)$; $Q = (0, 0)$

In Exercises 13 through 16, find the point S so that $\overrightarrow{PQ}$ and $\overrightarrow{RS}$ are each representations of the same vector.

13. $P = (2, 5)$; $Q = (1, 6)$; $R = (-3, 2)$

14. $P = (-1, 4)$; $Q = (2, -3)$; $R = (-5, -2)$

15. $P = (0, 3)$; $Q = (5, -2)$; $R = (7, 0)$

16. $P = (-2, 0)$; $Q = (-3, -4)$; $R = (4, 2)$

In Exercises 17 through 22, find the sum of the given pairs of vectors and illustrate geometrically.

17. $\langle 2, 4 \rangle$; $\langle -3, 5 \rangle$

18. $\langle 0, 3 \rangle$; $\langle -2, 3 \rangle$

19. $\langle -3, 0 \rangle$; $\langle 4, -5 \rangle$

20. $\langle 2, 3 \rangle$; $\langle -\sqrt{2}, -1 \rangle$

21. $\langle 0, 0 \rangle$; $\langle -2, 2 \rangle$

22. $\langle 2, 5 \rangle$; $\langle 2, 5 \rangle$

In Exercises 23 through 28, subtract the second vector from the first and illustrate geometrically.

23. $\langle 4, 5 \rangle$; $\langle -3, 2 \rangle$

24. $\langle 0, 5 \rangle$; $\langle 2, 8 \rangle$

25. $\langle -3, -4 \rangle$; $\langle 6, 0 \rangle$

26. $\langle 1, e \rangle$; $\langle -3, 2e \rangle$

27. $\langle 0, \sqrt{3} \rangle$; $\langle -\sqrt{2}, 0 \rangle$

28. $\langle 3, 7 \rangle$; $\langle 3, 7 \rangle$

29. Given $\mathbf{A} = \langle 2, -5 \rangle$; $\mathbf{B} = \langle 3, 1 \rangle$; $\mathbf{C} = \langle -4, 2 \rangle$. (a) Find $\mathbf{A} + (\mathbf{B} + \mathbf{C})$ and illustrate geometrically. (b) Find $(\mathbf{A} + \mathbf{B}) + \mathbf{C}$ and illustrate geometrically.

In Exercises 30 through 35, let $\mathbf{A} = \langle 2, 4 \rangle$, $\mathbf{B} = \langle 4, -3 \rangle$ and $\mathbf{C} = \langle -3, 2 \rangle$.

30. Find $\mathbf{A} + \mathbf{B}$

31. Find $\mathbf{A} - \mathbf{B}$

32. Find $|\mathbf{C}|$

33. Find $|\mathbf{C} - \mathbf{B}|$

34. Find $2\mathbf{A} + 3\mathbf{B}$

35. Find $|7\mathbf{A} - \mathbf{B}|$

36. Given $\mathbf{A} = \langle 3, 2 \rangle$; $\mathbf{C} = \langle 8, 8 \rangle$; $\mathbf{A} + \mathbf{B} = \mathbf{C}$; find $|\mathbf{B}|$.

37. Let $\overrightarrow{PQ}$ be a representation of vector $\mathbf{A}$, $\overrightarrow{QR}$ be a representation of vector $\mathbf{B}$, and $\overrightarrow{RS}$ be a representation of vector $\mathbf{C}$. Prove that if $\overrightarrow{PQ}$, $\overrightarrow{QR}$, and $\overrightarrow{RS}$ are sides of a triangle, then $\mathbf{A} + \mathbf{B} + \mathbf{C} = 0$.

38. Prove analytically the triangle inequality for vectors $|\mathbf{A} + \mathbf{B}| \leq |\mathbf{A}| + |\mathbf{B}|$.

17.2 PROPERTIES OF VECTOR ADDITION AND SCALAR MULTIPLICATION

The following theorem gives laws satisfied by the operations of vector addition and scalar multiplication of any vectors in V_2.

17.2.1 Theorem

If $\mathbf{A}$, $\mathbf{B}$, and $\mathbf{C}$ are any vectors in V_2, and c and d are any scalars, then vector addition and scalar multiplication satisfy the following properties:

(i) $\mathbf{A} + \mathbf{B} = \mathbf{B} + \mathbf{A}$ (commutative law)

(ii) $\mathbf{A} + (\mathbf{B} + \mathbf{C}) = (\mathbf{A} + \mathbf{B}) + \mathbf{C}$ (associative law)

(iii) There is a vector $\mathbf{0}$ in V_2 for which
$\mathbf{A} + \mathbf{0} = \mathbf{A}$ (existence of additive identity)

(iv) There is a vector $-\mathbf{A}$ in V_2 such that
$\mathbf{A} + (-\mathbf{A}) = \mathbf{0}$ (existence of negative)

(v) $(cd)\mathbf{A} = c(d\mathbf{A})$ (associative law)
(vi) $c(\mathbf{A} + \mathbf{B}) = c\mathbf{A} + c\mathbf{B}$ (distributive law)
(vii) $(c + d)\mathbf{A} = c\mathbf{A} + d\mathbf{A}$ (distributive law)
(viii) $1(\mathbf{A}) = \mathbf{A}$ (existence of scalar multiplicative identity)

PROOF: We give the proofs of (i), (iv), and (vi) and leave the others as exercises (see Exercises 16 through 19). Let $\mathbf{A} = \langle a_1, a_2 \rangle$ and $\mathbf{B} = \langle b_1, b_2 \rangle$.

PROOF OF (i):   By the commutative law for real numbers, $a_1 + b_1 = b_1 + a_1$ and $a_2 + b_2 = b_2 + a_2$, and so we have

$$\mathbf{A} + \mathbf{B} = \langle a_1, a_2 \rangle + \langle b_1, b_2 \rangle$$
$$= \langle a_1 + b_1, a_2 + b_2 \rangle$$
$$= \langle b_1 + a_1, b_2 + a_2 \rangle$$
$$= \langle b_1, b_2 \rangle + \langle a_1, a_2 \rangle$$
$$= \mathbf{B} + \mathbf{A}$$

PROOF OF (iv): The vector $-\mathbf{A}$ is given by Definition 17.1.5 and we have

$$\mathbf{A} + (-\mathbf{A}) = \langle a_1, a_2 \rangle + \langle -a_1, -a_2 \rangle$$
$$= \langle a_1 + (-a_1), a_2 + (-a_2) \rangle$$
$$= \langle 0, 0 \rangle$$
$$= \mathbf{0}$$

PROOF OF (vi):
$$c(\mathbf{A} + \mathbf{B}) = c(\langle a_1, a_2 \rangle + \langle b_1, b_2 \rangle)$$
$$= c(\langle a_1 + b_1, a_2 + b_2 \rangle)$$
$$= \langle c(a_1 + b_1), c(a_2 + b_2) \rangle$$
$$= \langle ca_1 + cb_1, ca_2 + cb_2 \rangle$$
$$= \langle ca_1, ca_2 \rangle + \langle cb_1, cb_2 \rangle$$
$$= c\langle a_1, a_2 \rangle + c\langle b_1, b_2 \rangle$$
$$= c\mathbf{A} + c\mathbf{B}$$

EXAMPLE 1:   Verify (ii), (iii), (v), (vii), and (viii) of Theorem 17.2.1 if $\mathbf{A} = \langle 3, 4 \rangle$, $\mathbf{B} = \langle -2, 1 \rangle$, $\mathbf{C} = \langle 5, -3 \rangle$, $c = 2$, and $d = -6$.

SOLUTION:
$$\mathbf{A} + (\mathbf{B} + \mathbf{C}) = \langle 3, 4 \rangle + (\langle -2, 1 \rangle + \langle 5, -3 \rangle)$$
$$= \langle 3, 4 \rangle + \langle 3, -2 \rangle$$
$$= \langle 6, 2 \rangle$$
$$(\mathbf{A} + \mathbf{B}) + \mathbf{C} = (\langle 3, 4 \rangle + \langle -2, 1 \rangle) + \langle 5, -3 \rangle$$

$$= \langle 1, 5 \rangle + \langle 5, -3 \rangle$$

$$= \langle 6, 2 \rangle$$

Therefore, $\mathbf{A} + (\mathbf{B} + \mathbf{C}) = (\mathbf{A} + \mathbf{B}) + \mathbf{C}$, and so (ii) holds.

$$\mathbf{A} + \mathbf{0} = \langle 3, 4 \rangle + \langle 0, 0 \rangle = \langle 3, 4 \rangle = \mathbf{A}$$

Hence, (iii) holds.

$$(cd)\mathbf{A} = [(2)(-6)]\langle 3, 4 \rangle$$

$$= (-12)\langle 3, 4 \rangle$$

$$= \langle -36, -48 \rangle$$

$$c(d\mathbf{A}) = 2(-6\langle 3, 4 \rangle)$$

$$= 2\langle -18, -24 \rangle$$

$$= \langle -36, -48 \rangle$$

Thus, $(cd)\mathbf{A} = c(d\mathbf{A})$, and so (v) holds.

$$(c + d)\mathbf{A} = [2 + (-6)]\langle 3, 4 \rangle = (-4)\langle 3, 4 \rangle = \langle -12, -16 \rangle$$

$$c\mathbf{A} + d\mathbf{A} = 2\langle 3, 4 \rangle + (-6)\langle 3, 4 \rangle = \langle 6, 8 \rangle + \langle -18, -24 \rangle = \langle -12, -16 \rangle$$

Therefore, $(c + d)\mathbf{A} = c\mathbf{A} + d\mathbf{A}$, and (vii) holds.

$$1\mathbf{A} = 1\langle 3, 4 \rangle = \langle (1)(3), (1)(4) \rangle = \langle 3, 4 \rangle = \mathbf{A}$$

and so (viii) holds.

Theorem 17.2.1 is very important because every algebraic law for the operations of vector addition and scalar multiplication of vectors in V_2 can be derived from the eight properties stated in the theorem. These laws are similar to the laws of arithmetic of real numbers. Furthermore, in linear algebra, a "real vector space" is defined as a set of vectors together with a set of real numbers (scalars) and the two operations of vector addition and scalar multiplication which satisfy the eight properties given in Theorem 17.2.1. Following is the formal definition.

17.2.2 Definition A *real vector space V* is a set of elements, called *vectors*, together with a set of real numbers, called *scalars*, with two operations called *vector addition* and *scalar multiplication* such that for every pair of vectors $\mathbf{A}$ and $\mathbf{B}$ in V and for every scalar c, a vector $\mathbf{A} + \mathbf{B}$ and a vector $c\mathbf{A}$ are defined so that properties (i)–(viii) of Theorem 17.2.1 are satisfied.

From Definition 17.2.2 and Theorem 17.2.1 it follows that V_2 is a real vector space.

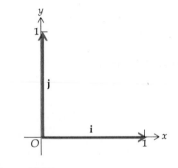

Figure 17.2.1

We now take an arbitrary vector in V_2 and write it in a special form.

$$\mathbf{A} = \langle a_1, a_2 \rangle = \langle a_1, 0 \rangle + \langle 0, a_2 \rangle = a_1 \langle 1, 0 \rangle + a_2 \langle 0, 1 \rangle$$

Because the magnitude of each of the two vectors $\langle 1, 0 \rangle$ and $\langle 0, 1 \rangle$ is one unit, they are called *unit vectors*. We introduce the following notations for these two unit vectors:

$$\mathbf{i} = \langle 1, 0 \rangle \quad \text{and} \quad \mathbf{j} = \langle 0, 1 \rangle$$

The position representation of each of these unit vectors is shown in Fig. 17.2.1. Because

$$\langle a_1, a_2 \rangle = a_1 \langle 1, 0 \rangle + a_2 \langle 0, 1 \rangle = a_1 \mathbf{i} + a_2 \mathbf{j}$$

it follows that any vector in V_2 can be written as a linear combination of the two vectors $\mathbf{i}$ and $\mathbf{j}$. Because of this the vectors $\mathbf{i}$ and $\mathbf{j}$ are said to form a *basis* for the vector space V_2. The number of elements in a basis of a vector space is called the *dimension* of the vector space. Hence, V_2 is a two-dimensional vector space.

● ILLUSTRATION 1: We express the vector $\langle 3, -4 \rangle$ in terms of $\mathbf{i}$ and $\mathbf{j}$.

$$\langle 3, -4 \rangle = 3 \langle 1, 0 \rangle + (-4) \langle 0, 1 \rangle = 3\mathbf{i} - 4\mathbf{j} \qquad ●$$

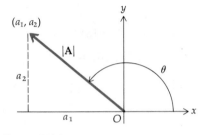

Figure 17.2.2

Let $\mathbf{A}$ be the vector $\langle a_1, a_2 \rangle$ and θ be the radian measure of the angle giving the direction of $\mathbf{A}$ (see Fig. 17.2.2 where (a_1, a_2) is in the second quadrant). $a_1 = |\mathbf{A}| \cos \theta$ and $a_2 = |\mathbf{A}| \sin \theta$. Because $\mathbf{A} = a_1 \mathbf{i} + a_2 \mathbf{j}$, we can write

$$\mathbf{A} = |\mathbf{A}| \cos \theta \mathbf{i} + |\mathbf{A}| \sin \theta \mathbf{j}$$

or, equivalently,

$$\mathbf{A} = |\mathbf{A}| (\cos \theta \mathbf{i} + \sin \theta \mathbf{j}) \qquad (1)$$

Equation (1) expresses the vector $\mathbf{A}$ in terms of its magnitude, the cosine and sine of the radian measure of the angle giving the direction of $\mathbf{A}$, and the unit vectors $\mathbf{i}$ and $\mathbf{j}$.

EXAMPLE 2:   Express the vector $\langle -5, -2 \rangle$ in the form of Eq. (1).

SOLUTION: Refer to Fig. 17.2.3, which shows the position representation of the vector $\langle -5, -2 \rangle$.

$$|\langle -5, -2 \rangle| = \sqrt{(-5)^2 + (-2)^2} = \sqrt{25 + 4} = \sqrt{29}$$

$$\sin \theta = -\frac{2}{\sqrt{29}} \quad \text{and} \quad \cos \theta = -\frac{5}{\sqrt{29}}$$

So from (1) we have

$$\langle -5, -2 \rangle = \sqrt{29} \left(-\frac{5}{\sqrt{29}} \mathbf{i} - \frac{2}{\sqrt{29}} \mathbf{j} \right)$$

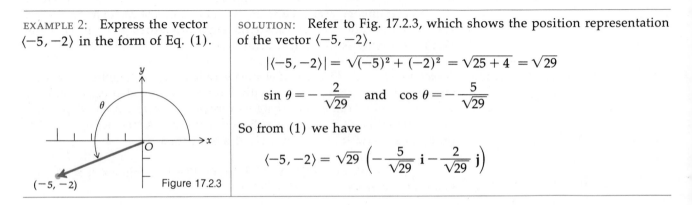

Figure 17.2.3

17.2.3 Theorem   If the nonzero vector $\mathbf{A} = a_1\mathbf{i} + a_2\mathbf{j}$, then the unit vector $\mathbf{U}$ having the same direction as $\mathbf{A}$ is given by

$$\mathbf{U} = \frac{a_1}{|\mathbf{A}|}\,\mathbf{i} + \frac{a_2}{|\mathbf{A}|}\,\mathbf{j} \qquad (2)$$

PROOF: From (2),

$$\mathbf{U} = \frac{1}{|\mathbf{A}|}\,(a_1\mathbf{i} + a_2\mathbf{j}) = \frac{1}{|\mathbf{A}|}\,(\mathbf{A})$$

Therefore, $\mathbf{U}$ is a positive scalar times the vector $\mathbf{A}$, and so the direction of $\mathbf{U}$ is the same as the direction of $\mathbf{A}$. Furthermore,

$$|\mathbf{U}| = \sqrt{\left(\frac{a_1}{|\mathbf{A}|}\right)^2 + \left(\frac{a_2}{|\mathbf{A}|}\right)^2}$$

$$= \frac{\sqrt{a_1{}^2 + a_2{}^2}}{|\mathbf{A}|}$$

$$= \frac{|\mathbf{A}|}{|\mathbf{A}|}$$

$$= 1$$

Therefore, $\mathbf{U}$ is the unit vector having the same direction as $\mathbf{A}$, and the theorem is proved.   ∎

EXAMPLE 3:   Given $\mathbf{A} = \langle 3, 1 \rangle$ and $\mathbf{B} = \langle -2, 4 \rangle$, find the unit vector having the same direction as $\mathbf{A} - \mathbf{B}$.

SOLUTION: $\mathbf{A} - \mathbf{B} = \langle 3, 1 \rangle - \langle -2, 4 \rangle = \langle 5, -3 \rangle$. So we may write

$$\mathbf{A} - \mathbf{B} = 5\mathbf{i} - 3\mathbf{j}$$

Then

$$|\mathbf{A} - \mathbf{B}| = \sqrt{5^2 + (-3)^2} = \sqrt{34}$$

By Theorem 17.2.3, the desired unit vector is given by

$$\mathbf{U} = \frac{5}{\sqrt{34}}\,\mathbf{i} - \frac{3}{\sqrt{34}}\,\mathbf{j}$$

Exercises 17.2

In Exercises 1 through 8, let $\mathbf{A} = 2\mathbf{i} + 3\mathbf{j}$ and $\mathbf{B} = 4\mathbf{i} - \mathbf{j}$.

1. Find $\mathbf{A} + \mathbf{B}$

2. Find $\mathbf{A} - \mathbf{B}$

3. Find $5\mathbf{A} - 6\mathbf{B}$

4. Find $|\mathbf{A}||\mathbf{B}|$

5. Find $|\mathbf{A} + \mathbf{B}|$

6. Find $|\mathbf{A}| + |\mathbf{B}|$

7. Find $|3\mathbf{A} - 2\mathbf{B}|$

8. Find $|3\mathbf{A}| - |2\mathbf{B}|$

9. Given $\mathbf{A} = 8\mathbf{i} + 5\mathbf{j}$ and $\mathbf{B} = 3\mathbf{i} - \mathbf{j}$; find a unit vector having the same direction as $\mathbf{A} + \mathbf{B}$.

10. Given $\mathbf{A} = -8\mathbf{i} + 7\mathbf{j}$; $\mathbf{B} = 6\mathbf{i} - 9\mathbf{j}$; $\mathbf{C} = -\mathbf{i} - \mathbf{j}$; find $|2\mathbf{A} - 3\mathbf{B} - \mathbf{C}|$.

11. Given $\mathbf{A} = -2\mathbf{i} + \mathbf{j}$; $\mathbf{B} = 3\mathbf{i} - 2\mathbf{j}$; $\mathbf{C} = 5\mathbf{i} - 4\mathbf{j}$; find scalars h and k such that $\mathbf{C} = h\mathbf{A} + k\mathbf{B}$.

In Exercises 12 through 15, (a) write the given vector in the form $r(\cos \theta\mathbf{i} + \sin \theta\mathbf{j})$, where r is the magnitude of the vector and θ is the radian measure of the angle giving the direction of the vector; and (b) find a unit vector having the same direction.

12. $3\mathbf{i} - 3\mathbf{j}$ 13. $-4\mathbf{i} + 4\sqrt{3}\mathbf{j}$ 14. $-16\mathbf{i}$ 15. $2\mathbf{j}$

16. Prove Theorem 17.2.1(ii).   17. Prove Theorem 17.2.1(v).

18. Prove Theorem 17.2.1(vii).   19. Prove Theorem 17.2.1(iii) and (viii).

20. Two vectors are said to be *independent* if and only if their position representations are not collinear. Furthermore, two vectors $\mathbf{A}$ and $\mathbf{B}$ are said to form a *basis* for the vector space V_2 if and only if any vector in V_2 can be written as a linear combination of $\mathbf{A}$ and $\mathbf{B}$. A theorem can be proved which states that two vectors form a basis for the vector space V_2 if they are independent. Show that this theorem holds for the two vectors $\langle 2, 5\rangle$ and $\langle 3, -1\rangle$ by doing the following: (a) Verify that the vectors are independent by showing that their position representations are not collinear; (b) verify that the vectors form a basis by showing that any vector $a_1\mathbf{i} + a_2\mathbf{j}$ can be written as $c(2\mathbf{i} + 5\mathbf{j}) + d(3\mathbf{i} - \mathbf{j})$, where c and d are scalars. (HINT: Find c and d in terms of a_1 and a_2.)

21. Refer to the first two sentences of Exercise 20. A theorem can be proved which states that two vectors form a basis for the vector space V_2 only if they are independent. Show that this theorem holds for the two vectors $\langle 3, -2\rangle$ and $\langle -6, 4\rangle$ by doing the following: (a) Verify that the vectors are dependent (not independent) by showing that their position representations are collinear; (b) verify that the vectors do not form a basis by taking a particular vector and showing that it cannot be written as $c(3\mathbf{i} + 2\mathbf{j}) + d(-6\mathbf{i} + 4\mathbf{j})$, where c and d are scalars.

17.3 DOT PRODUCT   In Sec. 17.1 we defined addition and subtraction of vectors and multiplication of a vector by a scalar. However, we did not consider the multiplication of two vectors. We now define a multiplication operation on two vectors which gives what is called the "dot product."

17.3.1 Definition   If $\mathbf{A} = \langle a_1, a_2\rangle$ and $\mathbf{B} = \langle b_1, b_2\rangle$ are two vectors in V_2, then the *dot product* of $\mathbf{A}$ and $\mathbf{B}$, denoted by $\mathbf{A} \cdot \mathbf{B}$, is given by

$$\mathbf{A} \cdot \mathbf{B} = \langle a_1, a_2\rangle \cdot \langle b_1, b_2\rangle = a_1b_1 + a_2b_2$$

The dot product of two vectors is a real number (or scalar) and not a vector. It is sometimes called the *scalar product* or *inner product*.

● ILLUSTRATION 1: If $\mathbf{A} = \langle 2, -3\rangle$ and $\mathbf{B} = \langle -\frac{1}{2}, 4\rangle$, then

$$\mathbf{A} \cdot \mathbf{B} = \langle 2, -3\rangle \cdot \langle -\tfrac{1}{2}, 4\rangle = (2)(-\tfrac{1}{2}) + (-3)(4) = -13$$ ●

The following dot products are useful and are easily verified (see Exercise 5).

$$\mathbf{i} \cdot \mathbf{i} = 1 \tag{1}$$

$$\mathbf{j} \cdot \mathbf{j} = 1 \tag{2}$$

$$\mathbf{i} \cdot \mathbf{j} = 0 \tag{3}$$

The following theorem states that dot multiplication is commutative and distributive with respect to vector addition.

17.3.2 Theorem   If **A**, **B**, and **C** are any vectors in V_2, then

(i) $\mathbf{A} \cdot \mathbf{B} = \mathbf{B} \cdot \mathbf{A}$ (commutative law)
(ii) $\mathbf{A} \cdot (\mathbf{B} + \mathbf{C}) = \mathbf{A} \cdot \mathbf{B} + \mathbf{A} \cdot \mathbf{C}$ (distributive law)

The proofs of (i) and (ii) are left as exercises (see Exercises 6 and 7).

Note that because $\mathbf{A} \cdot \mathbf{B}$ is a scalar, the expression $(\mathbf{A} \cdot \mathbf{B}) \cdot \mathbf{C}$ is meaningless. Hence, we do not consider associativity of dot multiplication.

Some other laws of dot multiplication are given in the following theorem.

17.3.3 Theorem   If **A** and **B** are any vectors in V_2 and c is any scalar, then

(i) $c(\mathbf{A} \cdot \mathbf{B}) = (c\mathbf{A}) \cdot \mathbf{B}$;
(ii) $\mathbf{0} \cdot \mathbf{A} = 0$;
(iii) $\mathbf{A} \cdot \mathbf{A} = |\mathbf{A}|^2$.

The proofs are left as exercises (see Exercises 8 through 10).

We now consider what is meant by the angle between two vectors, and this leads to another expression for the dot product of two vectors.

17.3.4 Definition   Let **A** and **B** be two nonzero vectors such that **A** is not a scalar multiple of **B**. If $\overrightarrow{OP}$ is the position representation of **A** and $\overrightarrow{OQ}$ is the position representation of **B**, then the *angle between the vectors* **A** and **B** is defined to be the angle of positive measure between $\overrightarrow{OP}$ and $\overrightarrow{OQ}$ interior to the triangle POQ. If $\mathbf{A} = c\mathbf{B}$, where c is a scalar, then if $c > 0$ the angle between the vectors has radian measure 0; if $c < 0$, the angle between the vectors has radian measure π.

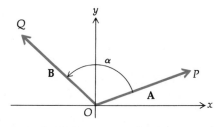

Figure 17.3.1

It follows from Definition 17.3.4 that if α is the radian measure of the angle between two vectors, then $0 \le \alpha \le \pi$. Figure 17.3.1 shows the angle between two vectors if **A** is not a scalar multiple of **B**.

The following theorem is perhaps the most important fact about the dot product of two vectors.

17.3.5 Theorem   If α is the radian measure of the angle between the two nonzero vectors **A** and **B**, then

$$\mathbf{A} \cdot \mathbf{B} = |\mathbf{A}||\mathbf{B}| \cos \alpha \qquad (4)$$

PROOF: Let $\mathbf{A} = a_1\mathbf{i} + a_2\mathbf{j}$ and $\mathbf{B} = b_1\mathbf{i} + b_2\mathbf{j}$. Let $\overrightarrow{OP}$ be the position representation of **A** and OQ be the position representation of **B**. Then the angle

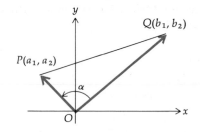

Figure 17.3.2

between the vectors **A** and **B** is the angle at the origin in triangle POQ (see Fig. 17.3.2); P is the point (a_1, a_2) and Q is the point (b_1, b_2). In triangle OPQ, $|\mathbf{A}|$ is the length of the side OP and $|\mathbf{B}|$ is the length of the side OQ. So from the law of cosines we obtain

$$\cos \alpha = \frac{|\mathbf{A}|^2 + |\mathbf{B}|^2 - |\overline{PQ}|^2}{2|\mathbf{A}||\mathbf{B}|}$$

$$= \frac{(a_1{}^2 + a_2{}^2) + (b_1{}^2 + b_2{}^2) - [(a_1 - b_1)^2 + (a_2 - b_2)^2]}{2|\mathbf{A}||\mathbf{B}|}$$

$$= \frac{2a_1 b_1 + 2a_2 b_2}{2|\mathbf{A}||\mathbf{B}|}$$

$$= \frac{a_1 b_1 + a_2 b_2}{|\mathbf{A}||\mathbf{B}|}$$

Hence,

$$\cos \alpha = \frac{\mathbf{A} \cdot \mathbf{B}}{|\mathbf{A}||\mathbf{B}|}$$

from which we obtain

$$\mathbf{A} \cdot \mathbf{B} = |\mathbf{A}||\mathbf{B}| \cos \alpha \qquad \blacksquare$$

Theorem 17.3.5 states that the dot product of two vectors is the product of the magnitudes of the vectors and the cosine of the radian measure of the angle between them.

● ILLUSTRATION 2: If $\mathbf{A} = 3\mathbf{i} - 2\mathbf{j}$, $\mathbf{B} = 2\mathbf{i} + \mathbf{j}$, and α is the radian measure of the angle between $\mathbf{A}$ and $\mathbf{B}$, then from Theorem 17.3.5, we have

$$\cos \alpha = \frac{\mathbf{A} \cdot \mathbf{B}}{|\mathbf{A}||\mathbf{B}|}$$

$$= \frac{(3)(2) + (-2)(1)}{\sqrt{9 + 4} \ \sqrt{4 + 1}}$$

$$= \frac{6 - 2}{\sqrt{13} \ \sqrt{5}}$$

$$= \frac{4}{\sqrt{65}} \qquad ●$$

We learned in Sec. 17.2 that if two nonzero vectors are scalar multiples of each other, then they have either the same or opposite directions. We have then the following definition.

17.3.6 Definition   Two vectors are said to be *parallel* if and only if one of the vectors is a scalar multiple of the other.

● ILLUSTRATION 3: The vectors $\langle 3, -4 \rangle$ and $\langle \frac{3}{4}, -1 \rangle$ are parallel because $\langle 3, -4 \rangle = 4 \langle \frac{3}{4}, -1 \rangle$. ●

If **A** is any vector, $\mathbf{0} = 0\mathbf{A}$; thus, from Definition 17.3.6 it follows that the zero vector is parallel to any vector.

It is left as an exercise for you to show that two nonzero vectors are parallel if and only if the radian measure of the angle between them is 0 or π (see Exercise 33).

If **A** and **B** are nonzero vectors, then from Eq. (4) it follows that

$$\cos \alpha = 0 \quad \text{if and only if} \quad \mathbf{A} \cdot \mathbf{B} = 0$$

Because $0 \le \alpha \le \pi$, it follows from this statement that

$$\alpha = \tfrac{1}{2}\pi \quad \text{if and only if} \quad \mathbf{A} \cdot \mathbf{B} = 0$$

We have, then, the following definition.

17.3.7 Definition   Two vectors **A** and **B** are said to be *orthogonal (perpendicular)* if and only if $\mathbf{A} \cdot \mathbf{B} = 0$.

● ILLUSTRATION 4: The vectors $\langle -4, 5 \rangle$ and $\langle 10, 8 \rangle$ are orthogonal because

$$\langle -4, 5 \rangle \cdot \langle 10, 8 \rangle = (-4)(10) + (5)(8)$$
$$= 0 \qquad \qquad ●$$

If **A** is any vector, $\mathbf{0} \cdot \mathbf{A} = 0$, and therefore it follows from Definition 17.3.7 that the zero vector is orthogonal to any vector.

EXAMPLE 1:   Given $\mathbf{A} = 3\mathbf{i} + 2\mathbf{j}$ and $\mathbf{B} = 2\mathbf{i} + k\mathbf{j}$, where k is a scalar, find (a) k so that **A** and **B** are orthogonal; (b) k so that **A** and **B** are parallel.

SOLUTION: (a) By Definition 17.3.7, **A** and **B** are orthogonal if and only if $\mathbf{A} \cdot \mathbf{B} = 0$; that is,

$$(3)(2) + 2(k) = 0$$

Hence,

$$k = -3$$

(b) From Definition 17.3.6, **A** and **B** are parallel if and only if there is some scalar c such that $\langle 3, 2 \rangle = c\langle 2, k \rangle$; that is,

$$3 = 2c \quad \text{and} \quad 2 = ck$$

Solving these two equations simultaneously, we obtain $k = \tfrac{4}{3}$.

A geometric interpretation of the dot product is obtained by considering the *projection* of a vector onto another vector. Let $\overrightarrow{OP}$ and $\overrightarrow{OQ}$ be representations of the vectors **A** and **B**, respectively. See Fig. 17.3.3. The projection of $\overrightarrow{OQ}$ in the direction of $\overrightarrow{OP}$ is the directed line segment $\overrightarrow{OR}$, where R is the foot of the perpendicular from Q to the line containing $\overrightarrow{OP}$. Then the vector for which $\overrightarrow{OR}$ is a representation is called the *vector projec-*

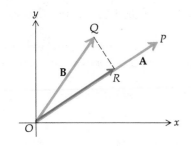

Figure 17.3.3

tion of the vector **B** onto the vector **A**. The *scalar projection* of **B** onto **A** is defined to be $|\mathbf{B}|$ cos α, where α is the radian measure of the angle between **A** and **B**. Note that $|\mathbf{B}|$ cos α may be either positive or negative depending on α. Because $\mathbf{A} \cdot \mathbf{B} = |\mathbf{A}||\mathbf{B}|$ cos α, it follows that

$$\mathbf{A} \cdot \mathbf{B} = |\mathbf{A}|(|\mathbf{B}| \cos \alpha) \tag{5}$$

Hence, the dot product of **A** and **B** is the magnitude of **A** multiplied by the scalar projection of **B** onto **A**. See Fig. 17.3.4a and b. Because dot multiplication is commutative, $\mathbf{A} \cdot \mathbf{B}$ is also the magnitude of **B** multiplied by the scalar projection of **A** onto **B**.

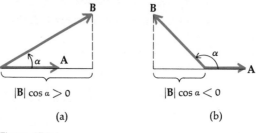

$|\mathbf{B}|$ cos $\alpha > 0$ $|\mathbf{B}|$ cos $\alpha < 0$

(a)   (b)

Figure 17.3.4

EXAMPLE 2: Given $\mathbf{A} = -5\mathbf{i} + \mathbf{j}$ and $\mathbf{B} = 4\mathbf{i} + 2\mathbf{j}$, find the vector projection of **B** onto **A**.

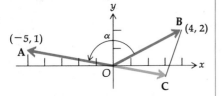

Figure 17.3.5

SOLUTION: Figure 17.3.5 shows the position representations of vectors **A** and **B** as well as that of **C**, which is the vector projection of **B** onto **A**. From (5) we get

$$|\mathbf{B}| \cos \alpha = \frac{\mathbf{A} \cdot \mathbf{B}}{|\mathbf{A}|} = \frac{(-5)(4) + (1)(2)}{\sqrt{26}} = \frac{-18}{\sqrt{26}}$$

Therefore, $|\mathbf{C}| = 18/\sqrt{26}$. Because cos $\alpha < 0, \frac{1}{2}\pi < \alpha < \pi$, and so the direction of **C** is opposite that of **A**. Hence, $\mathbf{C} = c\mathbf{A}$, and $c < 0$. Then we have

$$\mathbf{C} = -5c\mathbf{i} + c\mathbf{j}$$

Because $|\mathbf{C}| = 18/\sqrt{26}$, we get

$$\frac{18}{\sqrt{26}} = \sqrt{25c^2 + c^2}$$

and so $c = -\frac{9}{13}$, from which it follows that

$$\mathbf{C} = \frac{45}{13}\mathbf{i} - \frac{9}{13}\mathbf{j}$$

If $\mathbf{A} = a_1\mathbf{i} + a_2\mathbf{j}$, then

$$\mathbf{A} \cdot \mathbf{i} = a_1 \quad \text{and} \quad \mathbf{A} \cdot \mathbf{j} = a_2$$

Hence, the dot product of **A** and **i** gives the component of **A** in the direction of **i** and the dot product of **A** and **j** gives the component of **A** in the direction of **j**. To generalize this result, let **U** be any unit vector. Then from (5)

$$\mathbf{A} \cdot \mathbf{U} = |\mathbf{A}|(|\mathbf{U}| \cos \alpha) = |\mathbf{A}| \cos \alpha$$

and so $\mathbf{A} \cdot \mathbf{U}$ is the scalar projection of $\mathbf{A}$ onto $\mathbf{U}$, which is called the *component* of the vector $\mathbf{A}$ in the direction of $\mathbf{U}$. More generally, the *component* of a vector $\mathbf{A}$ in the direction of a vector $\mathbf{B}$ is the scalar projection of $\mathbf{A}$ onto a unit vector in the direction of $\mathbf{B}$.

In Sec. 8.5 we stated that if a constant force of F pounds moves an object a distance d feet along a straight line and the force is acting in the direction of motion, then if W is the number of foot-pounds in the work done by the force, $W = Fd$. Suppose, however, that the constant force is not directed along the line of motion. In this case the physicist defines the *work* done as the *product of the component of the force along the line of motion times the displacement*. If the object moves from the point A to the point B, we call the vector, having $\overrightarrow{AB}$ as a representation, the *displacement vector* and denote it by $\mathbf{V}(\overrightarrow{AB})$. So if the magnitude of a constant force vector $\mathbf{F}$ is expressed in pounds and the distance from A to B is expressed in feet, and α is the radian measure of the angle between the vectors $\mathbf{F}$ and $\mathbf{V}(\overrightarrow{AB})$, then if W is the number of foot-pounds in the work done by the force $\mathbf{F}$ in moving an object from A to B,

$$W = (|\mathbf{F}| \cos \alpha)|\mathbf{V}(\overrightarrow{AB})|$$
$$= |\mathbf{F}||\mathbf{V}(\overrightarrow{AB})| \cos \alpha$$
$$= \mathbf{F} \cdot \mathbf{V}(\overrightarrow{AB})$$

EXAMPLE 3:   Suppose that a force $\mathbf{F}$ has a magnitude of 6 lb and $\frac{1}{6}\pi$ is the radian measure of the angle giving its direction. Find the work done by $\mathbf{F}$ in moving an object along a straight line from the origin to the point $P(7, 1)$, where distance is measured in feet.

SOLUTION: Figure 17.3.6 shows the position representations of $\mathbf{F}$ and $\mathbf{V}(\overrightarrow{OP})$. If W ft-lb is the work done, then

$$W = \mathbf{F} \cdot \mathbf{V}(\overrightarrow{OP})$$

$\mathbf{F} = \langle 6 \cos \frac{1}{6}\pi, 6 \sin \frac{1}{6}\pi \rangle = \langle 3\sqrt{3}, 3 \rangle$, and $\mathbf{V}(\overrightarrow{OP}) = \langle 7, 1 \rangle$. So

$$W = \langle 3\sqrt{3}, 3 \rangle \cdot \langle 7, 1 \rangle = 21\sqrt{3} + 3 \approx 39.37$$

Therefore, the work done is 39.37 ft-lb.

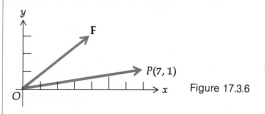

Figure 17.3.6

Vectors have geometric representations which are independent of the coordinate system used. Because of this, vector analysis can be used to prove certain theorems of plane geometry. This is illustrated in the following example.

EXAMPLE 4: Prove by vector analysis that the altitudes of a triangle meet in a point.

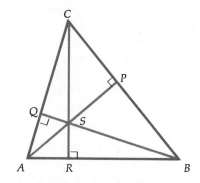

Figure 17.3.7

SOLUTION: Let ABC be a triangle having altitudes AP and BQ intersecting at point S. Draw a line through C and S intersecting AB at point R. We wish to prove that RC is perpendicular to AB (see Fig. 17.3.7).

Let $\vec{AB}$, $\vec{BC}$, $\vec{AC}$, $\vec{AS}$, $\vec{BS}$, $\vec{CS}$ be representations of vectors. Let $\mathbf{V}(\vec{AB})$ be the vector having directed line segment $\vec{AB}$ as a representation. In a similar manner, let $\mathbf{V}(\vec{BC})$, $\mathbf{V}(\vec{AC})$, $\mathbf{V}(\vec{AS})$, $\mathbf{V}(\vec{BS})$, and $\mathbf{V}(\vec{CS})$ be the vectors having the directed line segment in parentheses as a representation.

Because AP is an altitude of the triangle,

$$\mathbf{V}(\vec{AS}) \cdot \mathbf{V}(\vec{BC}) = 0 \tag{6}$$

Also, because BQ is an altitude of the triangle,

$$\mathbf{V}(\vec{BS}) \cdot \mathbf{V}(\vec{AC}) = 0 \tag{7}$$

To prove that RC is perpendicular to AB, we shall show that $\mathbf{V}(\vec{CS}) \cdot \mathbf{V}(\vec{AB}) = 0$

$$
\begin{aligned}
\mathbf{V}(\vec{CS}) \cdot \mathbf{V}(\vec{AB}) &= \mathbf{V}(\vec{CS}) \cdot [\mathbf{V}(\vec{AC}) + \mathbf{V}(\vec{CB})] \\
&= \mathbf{V}(\vec{CS}) \cdot \mathbf{V}(\vec{AC}) + \mathbf{V}(\vec{CS}) \cdot \mathbf{V}(\vec{CB}) \\
&= [\mathbf{V}(\vec{CB}) + \mathbf{V}(\vec{BS})] \cdot \mathbf{V}(\vec{AC}) \\
&\quad + [\mathbf{V}(\vec{CA}) + \mathbf{V}(\vec{AS})] \cdot \mathbf{V}(\vec{CB}) \\
&= \mathbf{V}(\vec{CB}) \cdot \mathbf{V}(\vec{AC}) + \mathbf{V}(\vec{BS}) \cdot \mathbf{V}(\vec{AC}) \\
&\quad + \mathbf{V}(\vec{CA}) \cdot \mathbf{V}(\vec{CB}) + \mathbf{V}(\vec{AS}) \cdot \mathbf{V}(\vec{CB})
\end{aligned}
$$

Replacing $\mathbf{V}(\vec{CA})$ by $-\mathbf{V}(\vec{AC})$ and using (6) and (7), we obtain

$$
\begin{aligned}
\mathbf{V}(\vec{CS}) \cdot \mathbf{V}(\vec{AB}) &= \mathbf{V}(\vec{CB}) \cdot \mathbf{V}(\vec{AC}) + 0 + [-\mathbf{V}(\vec{AC})] \cdot \mathbf{V}(\vec{CB}) + 0 \\
&= 0
\end{aligned}
$$

Therefore, altitudes AP, BQ, and RC meet in a point.

Exercises 17.3

In Exercises 1 through 4, find $\mathbf{A} \cdot \mathbf{B}$.

1. $\mathbf{A} = \langle -1, 2 \rangle$; $\mathbf{B} = \langle -4, 3 \rangle$

2. $\mathbf{A} = \langle \frac{1}{3}, -\frac{1}{2} \rangle$; $\mathbf{B} = \langle \frac{5}{2}, \frac{4}{3} \rangle$

3. $\mathbf{A} = 2\mathbf{i} - \mathbf{j}$; $\mathbf{B} = \mathbf{i} + 3\mathbf{j}$

4. $\mathbf{A} = -2\mathbf{i}$; $\mathbf{B} = -\mathbf{i} + \mathbf{j}$

5. Show that $\mathbf{i} \cdot \mathbf{i} = 1$; $\mathbf{j} \cdot \mathbf{j} = 1$; $\mathbf{i} \cdot \mathbf{j} = 0$.

6. Prove Theorem 17.3.2(i).

7. Prove Theorem 17.3.2(ii).

8. Prove Theorem 17.3.3(i).

9. Prove Theorem 17.3.3(ii).

10. Prove Theorem 17.3.3(iii).

In Exercises 11 through 14, if α is the radian measure of the angle between **A** and **B**, find $\cos \alpha$.

11. $\mathbf{A} = \langle 4, 3 \rangle$; $\mathbf{B} = \langle 1, -1 \rangle$

12. $\mathbf{A} = \langle -2, -3 \rangle$; $\mathbf{B} = \langle 3, 2 \rangle$

13. $\mathbf{A} = 5\mathbf{i} - 12\mathbf{j}$; $\mathbf{B} = 4\mathbf{i} + 3\mathbf{j}$

14. $\mathbf{A} = 2\mathbf{i} + 4\mathbf{j}$; $\mathbf{B} = -5\mathbf{j}$

15. Find k so that the radian measure of the angle between the vectors in Example 1 of this section is $\frac{1}{4}\pi$.

16. Given $\mathbf{A} = k\mathbf{i} - 2\mathbf{j}$ and $\mathbf{B} = k\mathbf{i} + 6\mathbf{j}$, where k is a scalar. Find k so that **A** and **B** are orthogonal.

17. Given $\mathbf{A} = 5\mathbf{i} - k\mathbf{j}$; $\mathbf{B} = k\mathbf{i} + 6\mathbf{j}$, where k is a scalar. Find (a) k so that **A** and **B** are orthogonal; (b) k so that **A** and **B** are parallel.

18. Find k so that the vectors given in Exercise 16 have opposite directions.

19. Given $\mathbf{A} = 5\mathbf{i} + 12\mathbf{j}$; $\mathbf{B} = \mathbf{i} + k\mathbf{j}$, where k is a scalar. Find k so that the radian measure of the angle between **A** and **B** is $\frac{1}{3}\pi$.

20. Find two unit vectors each having a representation whose initial point is $(2, 4)$ and which is tangent to the parabola $y = x^2$ there.

21. Find two unit vectors each having a representation whose initial point is $(2, 4)$ and which is normal to the parabola $y = x^2$ there.

22. If **A** is the vector $a_1\mathbf{i} + a_2\mathbf{j}$, find the unit vectors that are orthogonal to **A**.

23. If $\mathbf{A} = -8\mathbf{i} + 4\mathbf{j}$ and $\mathbf{B} = 7\mathbf{i} - 6\mathbf{j}$, find the vector projection of **A** onto **B**.

24. Find the vector projection of **B** onto **A** for the vectors of Exercise 23.

25. Find the component of the vector $\mathbf{A} = 5\mathbf{i} - 6\mathbf{j}$ in the direction of the vector $\mathbf{B} = 7\mathbf{i} + \mathbf{j}$.

26. For the vectors **A** and **B** of Exercise 25, find the component of the vector **B** in the direction of vector **A**.

27. A vector **F** represents a force which has a magnitude of 8 lb and $\frac{1}{3}\pi$ as the radian measure of the angle giving its direction. Find the work done by the force in moving an object (a) along the x axis from the origin to the point $(6, 0)$ and (b) along the y axis from the origin to the point $(0, 6)$. Distance is measured in feet.

28. Two forces represented by the vectors $\mathbf{F}_1$ and $\mathbf{F}_2$ act on a particle and cause it to move along a straight line from the point $(2, 5)$ to the point $(7, 3)$. If $\mathbf{F}_1 = 3\mathbf{i} - \mathbf{j}$ and $\mathbf{F}_2 = -4\mathbf{i} + 5\mathbf{j}$, the magnitudes of the forces are measured in pounds, and distance is measured in feet, find the work done by the two forces acting together.

29. If **A** and **B** are vectors, prove that
$$(\mathbf{A} + \mathbf{B}) \cdot (\mathbf{A} + \mathbf{B}) = \mathbf{A} \cdot \mathbf{A} + 2\mathbf{A} \cdot \mathbf{B} + \mathbf{B} \cdot \mathbf{B}$$

30. Prove by vector analysis that the medians of a triangle meet in a point.

31. Prove by vector analysis that the line segment joining the midpoints of two sides of a triangle is parallel to the third side and its length is one-half the length of the third side.

32. Prove by vector analysis that the line segment joining the midpoints of the nonparallel sides of a trapezoid is parallel to the parallel sides and its length is one-half the sum of the lengths of the parallel sides.

33. Prove that two nonzero vectors are parallel if and only if the radian measure of the angle between them is 0 or π.

17.4 VECTOR-VALUED FUNCTIONS AND PARAMETRIC EQUATIONS	We now consider a function whose domain is a set of real numbers and whose range is a set of vectors. Such a function is called a "vector-valued function." Following is the precise definition.
17.4.1 Definition	Let f and g be two real-valued functions of a real variable t. Then for every

number t in the domain common to f and $\mathring{g}$, there is a vector $\mathbf{R}$ defined by

$$\mathbf{R}(t) = f(t)\mathbf{i} + g(t)\mathbf{j} \tag{1}$$

and $\mathbf{R}$ is called a *vector-valued function*.

● ILLUSTRATION 1: Suppose

$$\mathbf{R}(t) = \sqrt{t-2}\,\mathbf{i} + (t-3)^{-1}\mathbf{j}$$

Let

$$f(t) = \sqrt{t-2} \text{ and } g(t) = (t-3)^{-1}$$

The domain of $\mathbf{R}$ is the set of values of t for which both $f(t)$ and $g(t)$ are defined. The function value $f(t)$ is defined for $t \geq 2$ and $g(t)$ is defined for all real numbers except 3. Therefore, the domain of $\mathbf{R}$ is $\{t | t \geq 2, t \neq 3\}$.   ●

If $\mathbf{R}$ is the vector-valued function defined by (1), as t assumes all values in the domain of $\mathbf{R}$, the endpoint of the position representation of the vector $\mathbf{R}(t)$ traces a curve C. For each such value of t, we obtain a point (x, y) on C for which

$$x = f(t) \quad \text{and} \quad y = g(t) \tag{2}$$

The curve C may be defined by Eq. (1) or Eqs. (2). Equation (1) is called a *vector equation* of C, and Eqs. (2) are called *parametric equations* of C. The variable t is a *parameter*. The curve C is also called a *graph*; that is, the set of all points (x, y) satisfying Eqs. (2) is the graph of the vector-valued function $\mathbf{R}$.

A vector equation of a curve, as well as parametric equations of a curve, gives the curve a direction at each point. That is, if we think of the curve as being traced by a particle, we can consider the positive direction along a curve as the direction in which the particle moves as the parameter t increases. In such a case as this, t may be taken to be the measure of the time, and the vector $\mathbf{R}(t)$ is called the *position vector*. Sometimes $\mathbf{R}(t)$ is referred to as the *radius vector*.

If the parameter t is eliminated from the pair of Eqs. (2), we obtain one equation in x and y, which is called a *cartesian equation* of C. It may happen that elimination of the parameter leads to a cartesian equation whose graph contains more points than the graph defined by either the vector equation or the parametric equations. This situation occurs in Example 4.

EXAMPLE 1:   Given the vector equation

$$\mathbf{R}(t) = 2 \cos t\,\mathbf{i} + 2 \sin t\,\mathbf{j}$$

(a) draw a sketch of the graph of

SOLUTION: The domain of $\mathbf{R}$ is the set of all real numbers. We could tabulate values of x and y for particular values of t. However, if we find the magnitude of the position vector, we have for every t

$$|\mathbf{R}(t)| = \sqrt{4 \cos^2 t + 4 \sin^2 t} = 2\sqrt{\cos^2 t + \sin^2 t} = 2$$

this equation, and (b) find a cartesian equation of the graph.

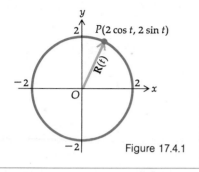

Figure 17.4.1

Therefore, the endpoint of the position representation of each vector $\mathbf{R}(t)$ is two units from the origin. By letting t take on all numbers in the closed interval $[0, 2\pi]$, we obtain a circle having its center at the origin and radius 2. This is the entire graph because any value of t will give a point on this circle. A sketch of the circle is shown in Fig. 17.4.1. Parametric equations of the graph are

$$x = 2 \cos t \quad \text{and} \quad y = 2 \sin t$$

A cartesian equation of the graph can be found by eliminating t from the two parametric equations, which when squaring on both sides of each equation and adding gives

$$x^2 + y^2 = 4$$

As previously stated, upon eliminating t from parametric equations (2) we obtain a cartesian equation. The cartesian equation either implicitly or explicitly defines y as one or more functions of x. That is, if $x = f(t)$ and $y = g(t)$, then $y = h(x)$. If h is a differentiable function of x and f is a differentiable function of t, it follows from the chain rule that

$$D_t y = (D_x y)(D_t x)$$

or

$$g'(t) = (h'(x))(f'(t))$$

or, by using differential notation,

$$\frac{dy}{dt} = \frac{dy}{dx} \frac{dx}{dt}$$

If $dx/dt \neq 0$, we can divide on both sides of the above equation by dx/dt and obtain

$$\frac{dy}{dx} = \frac{\dfrac{dy}{dt}}{\dfrac{dx}{dt}} \tag{3}$$

Equation (3) enables us to find the derivative of y with respect to x directly from the parametric equations.

EXAMPLE 2: Given $x = 3t^2$ and $y = 4t^3$, find dy/dx and d^2y/dx^2 without eliminating t.

SOLUTION: Applying (3), we have

$$\frac{dy}{dx} = \frac{\dfrac{dy}{dt}}{\dfrac{dx}{dt}} = \frac{12t^2}{6t} = 2t$$

$$\frac{d^2y}{dx^2} = \frac{d(y')}{dx} = \frac{\dfrac{d(y')}{dt}}{\dfrac{dx}{dt}}$$

Because $y' = 2t$, $d(y')/dt = 2$; thus, we have from the above equation

$$\frac{d^2y}{dx^2} = \frac{2}{6t} = \frac{1}{3t}$$

EXAMPLE 3:   (a) Draw a sketch of the graph of the curve defined by the parametric equations of Example 2, and (b) find a cartesian equation of the graph in (a).

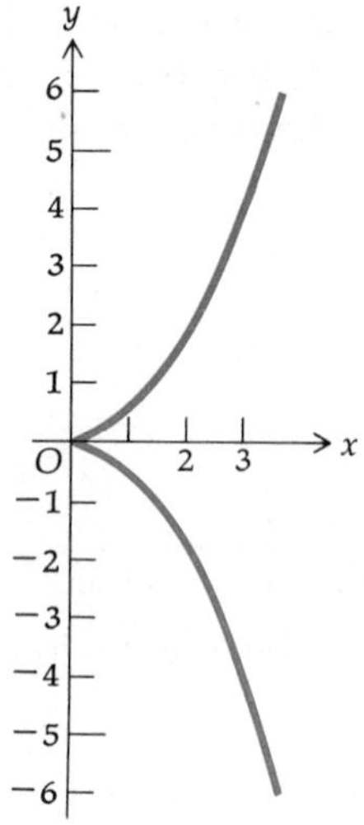

Figure 17.4.2

SOLUTION: Because $x = 3t^2$, we conclude that x is never negative. Table 17.4.1 gives values of x and y for particular values of t. Because $D_x y = 2t$, we see that when $t = 0$, $D_x y = 0$; hence, the tangent line is horizontal at the point $(0, 0)$. A sketch of the graph is shown in Fig. 17.4.2. From the two parametric equations $x = 3t^2$ and $y = 4t^3$, we get $x^3 = 27t^6$ and $y^2 = 16t^6$. Therefore,

$$\frac{x^3}{27} = \frac{y^2}{16}$$

or, equivalently,

$$16x^3 = 27y^2 \tag{4}$$

which is the cartesian equation desired.

Table 17.4.1

t	x	y
0	0	0
$\frac{1}{2}$	$\frac{3}{4}$	$\frac{1}{2}$
1	3	4
2	12	32
$-\frac{1}{2}$	$\frac{3}{4}$	$-\frac{1}{2}$
-1	3	-4
-2	12	-32

● ILLUSTRATION 2: If in Eq. (4) we differentiate implicitly, we have

$$48x^2 = 54y \frac{dy}{dx}$$

and solving for dy/dx, we get

$$\frac{dy}{dx} = \frac{8x^2}{9y}$$

Substituting for x and y in terms of t from the given parametric equations, we obtain

$$\frac{dy}{dx} = \frac{8(3t^2)^2}{9(4t^3)} = 2t$$

which agrees with the value of dy/dx found in Example 2.   ●

EXAMPLE 4: Draw a sketch of the graph of the curve defined by the parametric equations

$$x = \cosh t \quad \text{and} \quad y = \sinh t \quad (5)$$

Also find a cartesian equation of the graph.

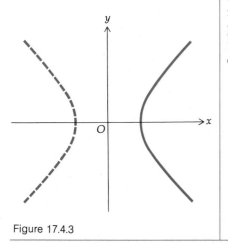

Figure 17.4.3

SOLUTION: Squaring on both sides of the given equations and subtracting, we have

$$x^2 - y^2 = \cosh^2 t - \sinh^2 t$$

From the identity $\cosh^2 t - \sinh^2 t = 1$, this equation becomes

$$x^2 - y^2 = 1 \qquad (6)$$

Equation (6) is an equation of an equilateral hyperbola. Note that for t any real number, $\cosh t$ is never less than 1. Thus, the curve defined by parametric equations (5) consists of only the points on the right branch of the hyperbola. A sketch of this curve is shown in Fig. 17.4.3. A cartesian equation is $x^2 - y^2 = 1$, where $x \geq 1$.

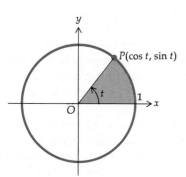

Figure 17.4.4

The results of Example 4 can be used to show how the function values of the hyperbolic sine and hyperbolic cosine functions have the same relationship to the equilateral hyperbola as the trigonometric sine and cosine functions have to the circle. The equations

$$x = \cos t \quad \text{and} \quad y = \sin t \qquad (7)$$

are a set of parametric equations of the unit circle because if t is eliminated from them by squaring on both sides of each and adding, we obtain

$$x^2 + y^2 = \cos^2 t + \sin^2 t = 1$$

The parameter t in Eqs. (7) can be interpreted as the number of radians in the measure of the angle between the x axis and a line from the origin to $P(\cos t, \sin t)$ on the unit circle. See Fig. 17.4.4 Because the area of a circular sector of radius r units and a central angle of radian measure t is

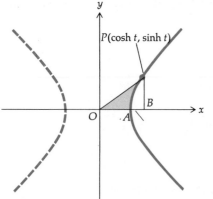

Figure 17.4.5

given by $\frac{1}{2}r^2t$ square units, the area of the circular sector in Fig. 17.4.4 is $\frac{1}{2}t$ square units because $r = 1$.

In Example 4 we showed that parametric equations (5) are a set of parametric equations of the right branch of the equilateral hyperbola $x^2 - y^2 = 1$. This hyperbola is called the *unit hyperbola*. Let $P(\cosh t, \sinh t)$ be a point on this curve, and let us calculate the area of the sector AOP shown in Fig. 17.4.5. The sector AOP is the region bounded by the x axis, the line OP, and the arc AP of the unit hyperbola. If A_1 square units is the area of sector AOP, A_2 square units is the area of triangle OBP, and A_3 square units is the area of region ABP, we have

$$A_1 = A_2 - A_3 \tag{8}$$

Using the formula for determining the area of a triangle, we get

$$A_2 = \tfrac{1}{2}\cosh t \sinh t \tag{9}$$

We find A_3 by integration:

$$A_3 = \int_0^t \sinh u \; d(\cosh u)$$

$$= \int_0^t \sinh^2 u \; du$$

$$= \tfrac{1}{2}\int_0^t (\cosh 2u - 1) \; du$$

$$= \tfrac{1}{4}\sinh 2u - \tfrac{1}{2}u \Big]_0^t$$

and so

$$A_3 = \tfrac{1}{2}\cosh t \sinh t - \tfrac{1}{2}t \tag{10}$$

Substituting from (9) and (10) into (8), we have

$$A_1 = \tfrac{1}{2}\cosh t \sinh t - (\tfrac{1}{2}\cosh t \sinh t - \tfrac{1}{2}t)$$

$$= \tfrac{1}{2}t$$

So we see that the number of square units in the area of circular sector AOP of Fig. 17.4.4 and the number of square units in the area of sector AOP of Fig. 17.4.5 is, in each case, one-half the value of the parameter associated with the point P. For the unit circle, the parameter t is the radian measure of the angle AOP. The parameter t for the unit hyperbola is not interpreted as the measure of an angle; however, sometimes the term *hyperbolic radian* is used in connection with t.

In Sec. 15.1, where Cauchy's mean-value theorem (15.1.3) was stated and proved, we indicated that a geometric interpretation would be given in this section because parametric equations are needed. Recall that the theorem states that if f and g are two functions such that (i) f and g are continuous on $[a, b]$, (ii) f and g are differentiable on (a, b), and (iii) for all x in (a, b) $g'(x) \neq 0$, then there exists a number z in the open interval (a, b) such that

$$\frac{f(b) - f(a)}{g(b) - g(a)} = \frac{f'(z)}{g'(z)}$$

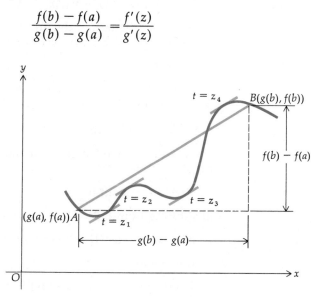

Figure 17.4.6

Figure 17.4.6 shows a curve having the parametric equations $x = g(t)$ and $y = f(t)$, where $a \leq t \leq b$. The slope of the curve in the figure at a particular point is given by

$$\frac{dy}{dx} = \frac{f'(t)}{g'(t)}$$

and the slope of the line segment through the points $A(g(a), f(a))$ and $B(g(b), f(b))$ is given by

$$\frac{f(b) - f(a)}{g(b) - g(a)}$$

Cauchy's mean-value theorem states that the slopes are equal for at least one value of t between a and b. For the curve shown in Fig. 17.4.6, there are four values of t satisfying the conclusion of the theorem: $t = z_1$, $t = z_2$, $t = z_3$, and $t = z_4$.

We now show how parametric equations can be used to define a curve which is described by a physical motion. The curve we consider is a *cycloid*, which is the curve traced by a point on the circumference of a circle as the circle rolls along a straight line. Suppose the circle has radius a. Let the fixed straight line on which the circle rolls be the x axis, and let the origin be one of the points at which the given point P comes in contact with the x axis. See Fig. 17.4.7, which shows the circle after it has rolled through an angle of t radians.

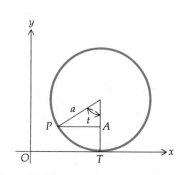

Figure 17.4.7

We see from Fig. 17.4.7 that

$$\mathbf{V}(\overrightarrow{OT}) + \mathbf{V}(\overrightarrow{TA}) + \mathbf{V}(\overrightarrow{AP}) = \mathbf{V}(\overrightarrow{OP}) \tag{11}$$

$|\mathbf{V}(\overrightarrow{OT})| =$ length of the arc $PT = at$. Because the direction of $\mathbf{V}(\overrightarrow{OT})$ is along the positive x axis, we conclude that

$$\mathbf{V}(\overrightarrow{OT}) = at\mathbf{i} \tag{12}$$

Also, $|\mathbf{V}(\overrightarrow{TA})| = a - a \cos t$. And because the direction of $\mathbf{V}(\overrightarrow{TA})$ is the same as the direction of $\mathbf{j}$, we have

$$\mathbf{V}(\overrightarrow{TA}) = a(1 - \cos t)\mathbf{j} \tag{13}$$

$|\mathbf{V}(\overrightarrow{AP})| = a \sin t$, and the direction of $\mathbf{V}(\overrightarrow{AP})$ is the same as the direction of $-\mathbf{i}$; thus,

$$\mathbf{V}(\overrightarrow{AP}) = -a \sin t\mathbf{i} \tag{14}$$

Substituting from (12), (13), and (14) into (11), we obtain

$$at\mathbf{i} + a(1 - \cos t)\mathbf{j} - a \sin t\mathbf{i} = \mathbf{V}(\overrightarrow{OP})$$

or, equivalently,

$$\mathbf{V}(\overrightarrow{OP}) = a(t - \sin t)\mathbf{i} + a(1 - \cos t)\mathbf{j} \tag{15}$$

Equation (15) is a vector equation of the cycloid. So parametric equations of the cycloid are

$$x = a(t - \sin t) \quad \text{and} \quad y = a(1 - \cos t) \tag{16}$$

where t is any real number. A sketch of a portion of the cycloid is shown in Fig. 17.4.8.

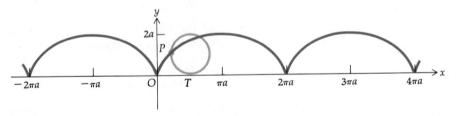

Figure 17.4.8

Exercises 17.4

In Exercises 1 through 6, find the domain of the vector-valued function **R**.

1. $\mathbf{R}(t) = (1/t)\mathbf{i} + \sqrt{4 - t}\,\mathbf{j}$

2. $\mathbf{R}(t) = (t^2 + 3)\mathbf{i} + (t - 1)\mathbf{j}$

3. $\mathbf{R}(t) = (\sin^{-1} t)\mathbf{i} + (\cos^{-1} t)\mathbf{j}$

4. $\mathbf{R}(t) = \ln(t + 1)\mathbf{i} + (\tan^{-1} t)\mathbf{j}$

5. $\mathbf{R}(t) = \sqrt{t^2 - 9}\,\mathbf{i} + \sqrt{t^2 + 2t - 8}\,\mathbf{j}$

6. $\mathbf{R}(t) = \sqrt{t - 4}\,\mathbf{i} + \sqrt{4 - t}\,\mathbf{j}$

In Exercises 7 through 12, find dy/dx and d^2y/dx^2 without eliminating the parameter.

7. $x = 3t, \ y = 2t^2$

8. $x = 1 - t^2, \ y = 1 + t$

9. $x = t^2 e^t, \ y = t \ln t$

10. $x = e^{2t}, \ y = 1 + \cos t$

11. $x = a \cos t, \ y = b \sin t$

12. $x = a \cosh t, \ y = b \sinh t$

In Exercises 13 through 16, draw a sketch of the graph of the given vector equation and find a cartesian equation of the graph.

13. $\mathbf{R}(t) = t^2\mathbf{i} + (t+1)\mathbf{j}$ 14. $\mathbf{R}(t) = \dfrac{4}{t^2}\mathbf{i} + \dfrac{4}{t}\mathbf{j}$ 15. $\mathbf{R}(t) = 3\cosh t\mathbf{i} + 5\sinh t\mathbf{j}$

16. $\mathbf{R}(t) = \cos t\mathbf{i} + \cos t\mathbf{j}$; t in $[0, \frac{1}{2}\pi]$

In Exercises 17 and 18, find equations of the horizontal tangent lines by finding the values of t for which $dy/dt = 0$, and find equations of the vertical tangent lines by finding the values of t for which $dx/dt = 0$. Then draw a sketch of the graph of the given pair of parameteric equations.

17. $x = 4t^2 - 4t$, $y = 1 - 4t^2$ 18. $x = \dfrac{3at}{1+t^3}$, $y = \dfrac{3at^2}{1+t^3}$

19. Find an equation of the tangent line to the curve, $y = 5\cos\theta$, $x = 2\sin\theta$, at the point where $\theta = \frac{1}{3}\pi$.

20. A projectile moves so that the coordinates of its position at any time t are given by the equations $x = 60t$ and $y = 80t - 16t^2$. Draw a sketch of the path of the projectile.

21. Find dy/dx, d^2y/dx^2, and d^3y/dx^3 at the point on the cycloid having Eqs. (16) for which y has its largest value when x is in the closed interval $[0, 2\pi a]$.

22. Show that the slope of the tangent line at $t = t_1$ to the cycloid having Eqs. (16) is $\cot\frac{1}{2}t_1$. Deduce then that the tangent line is vertical when $t = 2n\pi$, where n is any integer.

23. A hypocycloid is the curve traced by a point P on a circle of radius b which is rolling inside a fixed circle of radius a, $a > b$. If the origin is at the center of the fixed circle, $A(a, 0)$ is one of the points at which the point P comes in contact with the fixed circle, B is the moving point of tangency of the two circles, and the parameter t is the number of radians in the angle AOB, prove that parametric equations of the hypocycloid are

$$x = (a - b)\cos t + b\cos\dfrac{a - b}{b}t$$

and

$$y = (a - b)\sin t - b\sin\dfrac{a - b}{b}t$$

24. If $a = 4b$ in Exercise 23, we have a *hypocycloid of four cusps*. Show that parametric equations of this curve are $x = a\cos^3 t$ and $y = a\sin^3 t$.

25. Use the parametric equations of Exercise 24 to find a cartesian equation of the hypocycloid of four cusps, and draw a sketch of the graph of the resulting equation.

26. Parametric equations for the *tractrix* are

$$x = t - a\tanh\dfrac{t}{a} \qquad y = a\operatorname{sech}\dfrac{t}{a}$$

Draw a sketch of the curve for $a = 4$.

27. Prove that the parameter t in the parametric equations of a tractrix (see Exercise 26) is the x intercept of the tangent line.

28. Show that the tractrix of Exercise 26 is a curve such that the length of the segment of every tangent line from the point of tangency to the point of intersection with the x axis is constant and equal to a.

29. Find the area of the region bounded by the x axis and one arch of the cycloid, having Eqs. (16).

30. Find the centroid of the region of Exercise 29.

17.5 CALCULUS OF VECTOR-VALUED FUNCTIONS

We now discuss limits, continuity, and derivatives of vector-valued functions.

17.5.1 Definition

Let $\mathbf{R}$ be a vector-valued function whose function values are given by

$$\mathbf{R}(t) = f(t)\mathbf{i} + g(t)\mathbf{j}$$

Then the *limit of* $\mathbf{R}(t)$ *as t approaches* t_1 is defined by

$$\lim_{t \to t_1} \mathbf{R}(t) = \left[\lim_{t \to t_1} f(t)\right]\mathbf{i} + \left[\lim_{t \to t_1} g(t)\right]\mathbf{j}$$

if $\lim_{t \to t_1} f(t)$ and $\lim_{t \to t_1} g(t)$ both exist.

● ILLUSTRATION 1: If $\mathbf{R}(t) = \cos t\mathbf{i} + 2e^t\mathbf{j}$, then

$$\lim_{t \to 0} \mathbf{R}(t) = (\lim_{t \to 0} \cos t)\mathbf{i} + (\lim_{t \to 0} 2e^t)\mathbf{j} = \mathbf{i} + 2\mathbf{j}$$

●

17.5.2 Definition

The vector-valued function $\mathbf{R}$ is *continuous* at t_1 if and only if the following three conditions are satisfied:

    (i) $\mathbf{R}(t_1)$ exists;

    (ii) $\lim_{t \to t_1} \mathbf{R}(t)$ exists;

    (iii) $\lim_{t \to t_1} \mathbf{R}(t) = \mathbf{R}(t_1)$.

From Definitions 17.5.1 and 17.5.2, it follows that the vector-valued function $\mathbf{R}$, defined by $\mathbf{R}(t) = f(t)\mathbf{i} + g(t)\mathbf{j}$, is continuous at t_1 if and only if f and g are continuous there.

In the following definition the expression

$$\frac{\mathbf{R}(t + \Delta t) - \mathbf{R}(t)}{\Delta t}$$

is used. This is the division of a vector by a scalar which has not yet been defined. By this expression we mean

$$\frac{1}{\Delta t}[\mathbf{R}(t + \Delta t) - \mathbf{R}(t)]$$

17.5.3 Definition

If $\mathbf{R}$ is a vector-valued function, then the *derivative* of $\mathbf{R}$ is another vector-valued function, denoted by $\mathbf{R}'$ and defined by

$$\mathbf{R}'(t) = \lim_{\Delta t \to 0} \frac{\mathbf{R}(t + \Delta t) - \mathbf{R}(t)}{\Delta t}$$

if this limit exists.

The notation $D_t\mathbf{R}(t)$ is sometimes used in place of $\mathbf{R}'(t)$.

The following theorem follows from Definition 17.5.3 and the definition of the derivative of a real-valued function.

17.5.4 Theorem If **R** is a vector-valued function defined by

$$\mathbf{R}(t) = f(t)\mathbf{i} + g(t)\mathbf{j} \tag{1}$$

then

$$\mathbf{R}'(t) = f'(t)\mathbf{i} + g'(t)\mathbf{j}$$

if $f'(t)$ and $g'(t)$ exist.

PROOF: From Definition 17.5.3

$$\mathbf{R}'(t) = \lim_{\Delta t \to 0} \frac{\mathbf{R}(t + \Delta t) - \mathbf{R}(t)}{\Delta t}$$

$$= \lim_{\Delta t \to 0} \frac{[f(t + \Delta t)\mathbf{i} + g(t + \Delta t)\mathbf{j}] - [f(t)\mathbf{i} + g(t)\mathbf{j}]}{\Delta t}$$

$$= \lim_{\Delta t \to 0} \frac{[f(t + \Delta t) - f(t)]}{\Delta t}\mathbf{i} + \lim_{\Delta t \to 0} \frac{[g(t + \Delta t) - g(t)]}{\Delta t}\mathbf{j}$$

$$= f'(t)\mathbf{i} + g'(t)\mathbf{j} \qquad\blacksquare$$

The direction of $\mathbf{R}'(t)$ is given by θ $(0 \le \theta < 2\pi)$, where

$$\tan \theta = \frac{g'(t)}{f'(t)} = \frac{\dfrac{dy}{dt}}{\dfrac{dx}{dt}} = \frac{dy}{dx}$$

From the above equation, we see that the direction of $\mathbf{R}'(t)$ is along the tangent line to the curve having vector equation (1) at the point $(f(t), g(t))$.

A geometric interpretation of Definition 17.5.3 is obtained by considering representations of the vectors $\mathbf{R}(t), \mathbf{R}(t + \Delta t)$, and $\mathbf{R}'(t)$. Refer to Fig. 17.5.1. The curve C is traced by the endpoint of the position representation of $\mathbf{R}(t)$ as t assumes all values in the domain of **R**. Let $\overrightarrow{OP}$ be the position representation of $\mathbf{R}(t)$ and OQ be the position representation of $\mathbf{R}(t + \Delta T)$. Then $\mathbf{R}(t + \Delta t) - \mathbf{R}(t)$ is a vector for which $\overrightarrow{PQ}$ is a representation. If the vector $\mathbf{R}(t + \Delta t) - \mathbf{R}(t)$ is multiplied by the scalar $1/\Delta t$, we obtain a vector having the same direction and whose magnitude is $1/|\Delta t|$ times the magnitude of $\mathbf{R}(t + \Delta t) - \mathbf{R}(t)$. As Δt approaches zero, the vector $[\mathbf{R}(t + \Delta t) - \mathbf{R}(t)]/\Delta t$ approaches a vector having one of its representations tangent to the curve C at the point P.

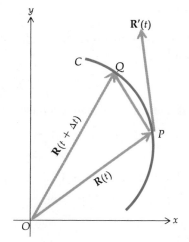

Figure 17.5.1

● ILLUSTRATION 2: If $\mathbf{R}(t) = (2 + \sin t)\mathbf{i} + \cos t\mathbf{j}$, then

$$\mathbf{R}'(t) = \cos t\mathbf{i} - \sin t\mathbf{j} \qquad \bullet$$

Higher-order derivatives of vector-valued functions are defined as for higher-order derivatives of real-valued functions. So if $\mathbf{R}$ is a vector-valued function defined by $\mathbf{R}(t) = f(t)\mathbf{i} + g(t)\mathbf{j}$, the second derivative of $\mathbf{R}$, denoted by $\mathbf{R}''(t)$, is given by

$$\mathbf{R}''(t) = D_t[\mathbf{R}'(t)]$$

We also have the notation $D_t^2\mathbf{R}(t)$ in place of $\mathbf{R}''(t)$. By applying Theorem 17.5.4 to $\mathbf{R}'(t)$, we obtain

$$\mathbf{R}''(t) = f''(t)\mathbf{i} + g''(t)\mathbf{j}$$

if $f''(t)$ and $g''(t)$ exist.

● ILLUSTRATION 3: If $\mathbf{R}(t) = (\ln t)\mathbf{i} + \left(\dfrac{1}{t}\right)\mathbf{j}$, then

$$\mathbf{R}'(t) = \frac{1}{t}\mathbf{i} - \frac{1}{t^2}\mathbf{j}$$

and

$$\mathbf{R}''(t) = -\frac{1}{t^2}\mathbf{i} + \frac{2}{t^3}\mathbf{j} \qquad \bullet$$

17.5.5 Definition   A vector-valued function $\mathbf{R}$ is said to be *differentiable* on an interval if $\mathbf{R}'(t)$ exists for all values of t in the interval.

The following theorems give differentiation formulas for vector-valued functions. The proofs are based on Theorem 17.5.4 and theorems on differentiation of real-valued functions.

17.5.6 Theorem   If $\mathbf{R}$ and $\mathbf{Q}$ are differentiable vector-valued functions on an interval, then $\mathbf{R} + \mathbf{Q}$ is differentiable on the interval, and

$$D_t[\mathbf{R}(t) + \mathbf{Q}(t)] = D_t\mathbf{R}(t) + D_t\mathbf{Q}(t)$$

The proof of this theorem is left as an exercise (see Exercise 16).

EXAMPLE 1:   If

$$\mathbf{R}(t) = t^2\mathbf{i} + (t - 1)\mathbf{j}$$

and

$$\mathbf{Q}(t) = \sin t\mathbf{i} + \cos t\mathbf{j}$$

verify Theorem 17.5.6.

SOLUTION:

$$D_t[\mathbf{R}(t) + \mathbf{Q}(t)] = D_t([t^2\mathbf{i} + (t - 1)\mathbf{j}] + [\sin t\mathbf{i} + \cos t\mathbf{j}])$$
$$= D_t[(t^2 + \sin t)\mathbf{i} + (t - 1 + \cos t)\mathbf{j}]$$
$$= (2t + \cos t)\mathbf{i} + (1 - \sin t)\mathbf{j}$$
$$D_t\mathbf{R}(t) + D_t\mathbf{Q}(t) = D_t[t^2\mathbf{i} + (t - 1)\mathbf{j}] + D_t(\sin t\mathbf{i} + \cos t\mathbf{j})$$

$$= (2t\mathbf{i} + \mathbf{j}) + (\cos t\mathbf{i} - \sin t\mathbf{j})$$

$$= (2t + \cos t)\mathbf{i} + (1 - \sin t)\mathbf{j}$$

Hence, $D_t[\mathbf{R}(t) + \mathbf{Q}(t)] = D_t\mathbf{R}(t) + D_t\mathbf{Q}(t)$.

17.5.7 Theorem   If $\mathbf{R}$ and $\mathbf{Q}$ are differentiable vector-valued functions on an interval, then $\mathbf{R} \cdot \mathbf{Q}$ is differentiable on the interval, and

$$D_t[\mathbf{R}(t) \cdot \mathbf{Q}(t)] = [D_t\mathbf{R}(t)] \cdot \mathbf{Q}(t) + \mathbf{R}(t) \cdot [D_t\mathbf{Q}(t)]$$

PROOF: Let $\mathbf{R}(t) = f_1(t)\mathbf{i} + g_1(t)\mathbf{j}$ and $\mathbf{Q}(t) = f_2(t)\mathbf{i} + g_2(t)\mathbf{j}$. Then by Theorem 17.5.4

$$D_t\mathbf{R}(t) = f_1'(t)\mathbf{i} + g_1'(t)\mathbf{j} \quad \text{and} \quad D_t\mathbf{Q}(t) = f_2'(t)\mathbf{i} + g_2'(t)\mathbf{j}$$

$$\mathbf{R}(t) \cdot \mathbf{Q}(t) = [f_1(t)][f_2(t)] + [g_1(t)][g_2(t)]$$

So

$$D_t[\mathbf{R}(t) \cdot \mathbf{Q}(t)]$$

$$= [f_1'(t)][f_2(t)] + [f_1(t)][f_2'(t)] + [g_1'(t)][g_2(t)] + [g_1(t)][g_2'(t)]$$

$$= \{[f_1'(t)][f_2(t)] + [g_1'(t)][g_2(t)]\} + \{[f_1(t)][f_2'(t)] + [g_1(t)][g_2'(t)]\}$$

$$= [D_t\mathbf{R}(t)] \cdot \mathbf{Q}(t) + \mathbf{R}(t) \cdot [D_t\mathbf{Q}(t)] \qquad \blacksquare$$

EXAMPLE 2:   Verify Theorem 17.5.7 for the vectors given in Example 1.

SOLUTION: $\mathbf{R}(t) \cdot \mathbf{Q}(t) = t^2 \sin t + (t - 1) \cos t$.

Therefore,

$$D_t[\mathbf{R}(t) \cdot \mathbf{Q}(t)] = 2t \sin t + t^2 \cos t + \cos t + (t - 1)(-\sin t)$$

$$D_t[\mathbf{R}(t) \cdot \mathbf{Q}(t)] = (t + 1) \sin t + (t^2 + 1) \cos t \qquad (2)$$

Because

$$D_t\mathbf{R}(t) = D_t[t^2\mathbf{i} + (t - 1)\mathbf{j}] = 2t\mathbf{i} + \mathbf{j}$$

$$[D_t\mathbf{R}(t)] \cdot \mathbf{Q}(t) = (2t\mathbf{i} + \mathbf{j}) \cdot (\sin t\mathbf{i} + \cos t\mathbf{j})$$

$$= 2t \sin t + \cos t$$

Because

$$D_t\mathbf{Q}(t) = D_t[\sin t\mathbf{i} + \cos t\mathbf{j}] = \cos t\mathbf{i} - \sin t\mathbf{j}$$

$$\mathbf{R}(t) \cdot [D_t\mathbf{Q}(t)] = [t^2\mathbf{i} + (t - 1)\mathbf{j}] \cdot (\cos t\mathbf{i} - \sin t\mathbf{j})$$

$$= t^2 \cos t - (t - 1) \sin t$$

Therefore,

$$[D_t\mathbf{R}(t)] \cdot \mathbf{Q}(t) + \mathbf{R}(t) \cdot [D_t\mathbf{Q}(t)] = (2t \sin t + \cos t)$$

$$+ [t^2 \cos t - (t - 1) \sin t]$$

Thus,

$$[D_t\mathbf{R}(t)] \cdot \mathbf{Q}(t) + \mathbf{R}(t) \cdot [D_t\mathbf{Q}(t)] = (t+1)\sin t + (t^2+1)\cos t \qquad (3)$$

Comparing Eqs. (2) and (3), we see that Theorem 17.5.7 holds.

17.5.8 Theorem If $\mathbf{R}$ is a differentiable vector-valued function on an interval and f is a differentiable real-valued function on the interval, then

$$D_t\{[f(t)][\mathbf{R}(t)]\} = [D_tf(t)]\mathbf{R}(t) + f(t)\,D_t\mathbf{R}(t)$$

The proof is left as an exercise (see Exercise 17).

The following theorem is the chain rule for vector-valued functions. The proof which is left as an exercise (see Exercise 18) is based on Theorems 2.6.6 and 3.6.1, which involve the analogous conclusions for real-valued functions.

17.5.9 Theorem Suppose that $\mathbf{F}$ is a vector-valued function, h is a real-valued function such that $\phi = h(t)$, and $\mathbf{G}(t) = \mathbf{F}(h(t))$. If h is continuous at t and $\mathbf{F}$ is continuous at $h(t)$, then $\mathbf{G}$ is continuous at t. Furthermore, if $D_t\phi$ and $D_\phi\mathbf{G}(t)$ exist, then $D_t\mathbf{G}(t)$ exists and is given by

$$D_t\mathbf{G}(t) = [D_\phi\mathbf{G}(t)]D_t\phi$$

We now define an indefinite integral (or antiderivative) of a vector-valued function.

17.5.10 Definition If $\mathbf{Q}$ is the vector-valued function given by

$$\mathbf{Q}(t) = f(t)\mathbf{i} + g(t)\mathbf{j}$$

then the *indefinite integral of* $\mathbf{Q}(t)$ is defined by

$$\int \mathbf{Q}(t)\,dt = \mathbf{i}\int f(t)\,dt + \mathbf{j}\int g(t)\,dt \qquad (4)$$

This definition is consistent with the definition of an indefinite integral of a real-valued function because if we take the derivative on both sides of (4) with respect to t, we have

$$D_t\int \mathbf{Q}(t)\,dt = \mathbf{i}D_t\int f(t)\,dt + \mathbf{j}D_t\int g(t)\,dt$$

which gives us

$$D_t\int \mathbf{Q}(t)\,dt = \mathbf{i}f(t) + \mathbf{j}g(t)$$

For each of the indefinite integrals on the right side of (4) there occurs an arbitrary scalar constant. When each of these scalars is multiplied by either $\mathbf{i}$ or $\mathbf{j}$, there occurs an arbitrary constant vector in the sum. So we have

$$\int Q(t) \ dt = R(t) + C$$

where $D_t R(t) = Q(t)$ and C is an arbitrary constant vector.

EXAMPLE 3: Find the most general vector-valued function whose derivative is

$$Q(t) = \sin ti - 3 \cos tj$$

SOLUTION: If $D_t R(t) = Q(t)$, then $R(t) = \int Q(t) \ dt$, or

$$R(t) = i \int \sin t \ dt - 3j \int \cos t \ dt$$

$$= i(-\cos t + C_1) - 3j(\sin t + C_2)$$

$$= -\cos ti - 3 \sin tj + (C_1 i - 3C_2 j)$$

$$= -\cos ti - 3 \sin tj + C$$

EXAMPLE 4: Find the vector $R(t)$ for which

$$D_t R(t) = e^{-t} i + e^t j$$

and for which $R(0) = i + j$.

SOLUTION: $R(t) = i \int e^{-t} \ dt + j \int e^t \ dt$

So

$$R(t) = i(-e^{-t} + C_1) + j(e^t + C_2)$$

Because $R(0) = i + j$, we have

$$i + j = i(-1 + C_1) + j(1 + C_2)$$

So

$$C_1 - 1 = 1 \quad \text{and} \quad C_2 + 1 = 1$$

Therefore,

$$C_1 = 2 \quad \text{and} \quad C_2 = 0$$

So

$$R(t) = (-e^{-t} + 2)i + e^t j$$

The following theorem will be useful later.

17.5.11 Theorem   If R is a differentiable vector-valued function on an interval and $|R(t)|$ is constant for all t in the interval, then the vectors $R(t)$ and $D_t R(t)$ are orthogonal.

PROOF: Let $|R(t)| = k$. Then by Theorem 17.3.3(iii),

$$R(t) \cdot R(t) = k^2$$

Differentiating on both sides with respect to t and using Theorem 17.5.7

we obtain

$$[D_t\mathbf{R}(t)] \cdot \mathbf{R}(t) + \mathbf{R}(t) \cdot [D_t\mathbf{R}(t)] = 0$$

Hence,

$$2\mathbf{R}(t) \cdot D_t\mathbf{R}(t) = 0$$

Because the dot product of $\mathbf{R}(t)$ and $D_t\mathbf{R}(t)$ is zero, it follows from Definition 17.3.7 that $\mathbf{R}(t)$ and $D_t\mathbf{R}(t)$ are orthogonal. ∎

The geometric interpretation of Theorem 17.5.11 is evident. If the vector $\mathbf{R}(t)$ has constant magnitude, then the position representation $\overrightarrow{OP}$ of $\mathbf{R}(t)$ has its terminal point P on the circle with its center at the origin and radius k. So the graph of $\mathbf{R}$ is this circle. Because $D_t\mathbf{R}(t)$ and $\mathbf{R}(t)$ are orthogonal, $\overrightarrow{OP}$ is perpendicular to a representation of $D_t\mathbf{R}(t)$. Figure 17.5.2 shows a sketch of a quarter circle, the position representation $\overrightarrow{OP}$ of $\mathbf{R}(t)$, and the representation $\overrightarrow{PB}$ of $D_t\mathbf{R}(t)$.

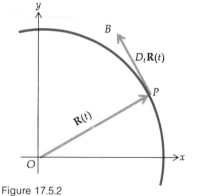

Figure 17.5.2

Exercises 17.5

In Exercises 1 through 4, find the indicated limit, if it exists.

1. $\mathbf{R}(t) = (t-2)\mathbf{i} + \dfrac{t^2-4}{t-2}\mathbf{j}$; $\lim_{t\to2}\mathbf{R}(t)$

2. $\mathbf{R}(t) = e^{t+1}\mathbf{i} + |t+1|\mathbf{j}$; $\lim_{t\to-1}\mathbf{R}(t)$

3. $\mathbf{R}(t) = 2\sin t\mathbf{i} + \cos t\mathbf{j}$; $\lim_{t\to\pi/2}\mathbf{R}(t)$

4. $\mathbf{R}(t) = \dfrac{t^2-2t-3}{t-3}\mathbf{i} + \dfrac{t^2-5t+6}{t-3}\mathbf{j}$; $\lim_{t\to3}\mathbf{R}(t)$

In Exercises 5 through 10, find $\mathbf{R}'(t)$ and $\mathbf{R}''(t)$.

5. $\mathbf{R}(t) = (t^2-3)\mathbf{i} + (2t+1)\mathbf{j}$

6. $\mathbf{R}(t) = \dfrac{t-1}{t+1}\mathbf{i} + \dfrac{t-2}{t}\mathbf{j}$

7. $\mathbf{R}(t) = e^{2t}\mathbf{i} + \ln t\mathbf{j}$

8. $\mathbf{R}(t) = \cos 2t\mathbf{i} + \tan t\mathbf{j}$

9. $\mathbf{R}(t) = \tan^{-1}t\mathbf{i} + 2^t\mathbf{j}$

10. $\mathbf{R}(t) = \sqrt{2t+1}\mathbf{i} + (t-1)^2\mathbf{j}$

In Exercises 11 and 12, find $D_t|\mathbf{R}(t)|$.

11. $\mathbf{R}(t) = (t-1)\mathbf{i} + (2-t)\mathbf{j}$

12. $\mathbf{R}(t) = (e^t+1)\mathbf{i} + (e^t-1)\mathbf{j}$

In Exercises 13 through 15, find $\mathbf{R}'(t) \cdot \mathbf{R}''(t)$.

13. $\mathbf{R}(t) = (2t^2-1)\mathbf{i} + (t^2+3)\mathbf{j}$

14. $\mathbf{R}(t) = -\cos 2t\mathbf{i} + \sin 2t\mathbf{j}$

15. $\mathbf{R}(t) = e^{2t}\mathbf{i} + e^{-2t}\mathbf{j}$

16. Prove Theorem 17.5.6.

17. Prove Theorem 17.5.8.

18. Prove Theorem 17.5.9.

In Exercises 19 through 22, find the most general vector whose derivative has the given function value.

19. $\tan t\mathbf{i} - \dfrac{1}{t}\mathbf{j}$

20. $\dfrac{1}{4+t^2}\mathbf{i} - \dfrac{4}{1-t^2}\mathbf{j}$

21. $\ln t\mathbf{i} + t^2\mathbf{j}$

22. $3^t\mathbf{i} - 2^t\mathbf{j}$

23. If $\mathbf{R}'(t) = \sin^2 t\mathbf{i} + 2\cos^2 t\mathbf{j}$, and $\mathbf{R}(\pi) = \mathbf{0}$, find $\mathbf{R}(t)$.

24. If $\mathbf{R}'(t) = e^t\sin t\mathbf{i} + e^t\cos t\mathbf{j}$, and $\mathbf{R}(0) = \mathbf{i} - \mathbf{j}$, find $\mathbf{R}(t)$.

25. Given the vector equation $\mathbf{R}(t) = \cos t\mathbf{i} + \sin t\mathbf{j}$. Find a cartesian equation of the curve which is traced by the endpoint of the position representation of $\mathbf{R}'(t)$. Find $\mathbf{R}(t) \cdot \mathbf{R}'(t)$. Interpret the result geometrically.

26. Given $\mathbf{R}(t) = 2t\mathbf{i} + (t^2 - 1)\mathbf{j}$ and $\mathbf{Q}(t) = 3t\mathbf{i}$. If $\alpha(t)$ is the radian measure of the angle between $\mathbf{R}(t)$ and $\mathbf{Q}(t)$, find $D_t\alpha(t)$.

27. Suppose $\mathbf{R}$ and $\mathbf{R}'$ are vector-valued functions defined on an interval and $\mathbf{R}'$ is differentiable on the interval. Prove

$$D_t[\mathbf{R}'(t) \cdot \mathbf{R}(t)] = |\mathbf{R}'(t)|^2 + \mathbf{R}(t) \cdot \mathbf{R}''(t)$$

28. If $|\mathbf{R}(t)| = h(t)$, prove that $\mathbf{R}(t) \cdot \mathbf{R}'(t) = [h(t)][h'(t)]$.

29. If the vector-valued function $\mathbf{R}$ and the real-valued function f are both differentiable on an interval and $f(t) \neq 0$ on the interval, prove that $\mathbf{R}/f$ is also differentiable on the interval and

$$D_t\left[\frac{\mathbf{R}(t)}{f(t)}\right] = \frac{f(t)\mathbf{R}'(t) - f'(t)\mathbf{R}(t)}{[f(t)]^2}$$

30. Prove that if $\mathbf{A}$ and $\mathbf{B}$ are constant vectors and f and g are integrable functions, then

$$\int [\mathbf{A}f(t) + \mathbf{B}g(t)] \, dt = \mathbf{A} \int f(t) \, dt + \mathbf{B} \int g(t) \, dt$$

(HINT: Express $\mathbf{A}$ and $\mathbf{B}$ in terms of $\mathbf{i}$ and $\mathbf{j}$.)

17.6 LENGTH OF ARC

In Sec. 8.10 we obtained a formula for finding the length of arc of a curve having an equation of the form $y = f(x)$. This is a special kind of curve because the graph of a function f cannot be intersected by a vertical line in more than one point.

We now develop a method for finding the length of arc of some other kinds of curves. Let C be the curve having parametric equations

$$x = f(t) \quad \text{and} \quad y = g(t) \tag{1}$$

and suppose that f and g are continuous on the closed interval $[a, b]$. We wish to assign a number L to represent the number of units in the length of arc of C from $t = a$ to $t = b$. We proceed as in Sec. 8.10.

Let Δ be a partition of the closed interval $[a, b]$ formed by dividing the interval into n subintervals by choosing $n - 1$ numbers between a and b. Let $t_0 = a$ and $t_n = b$, and let $t_1, t_2, \ldots, t_{n-1}$ be intermediate numbers:

$$t_0 < t_1 < \cdots < t_{n-1} < t_n$$

The ith subinterval is $[t_{i-1}, t_i]$ and the number of units in its length, denoted by $\Delta_i t$, is $t_i - t_{i-1}$, where $i = 1, 2, \ldots, n$. Let $\|\Delta\|$ be the norm of the partition; so each $\Delta_i t \leq \|\Delta\|$.

Associated with each number t_i is a point $P_i(f(t_i), g(t_i))$ on C. From each point P_{i-1} draw a line segment to the next point P_i (see Fig. 17.6.1). The number of units in the length of the line segment from P_{i-1} to P_i is denoted by $|\overline{P_{i-1}P_i}|$. From the distance formula we have

$$|\overline{P_{i-1}P_i}| = \sqrt{[f(t_i) - f(t_{i-1})]^2 + [g(t_i) - g(t_{i-1})]^2} \tag{2}$$

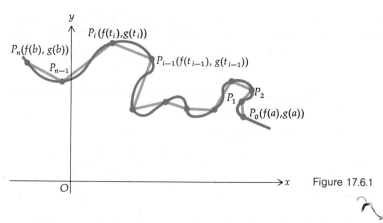

Figure 17.6.1

The sum of the numbers of units of lengths of the n line segments is

$$\sum_{i=1}^{n} |\overline{P_{i-1}P_i}| \tag{3}$$

Our intuitive notion of the length of the arc from $t = a$ to $t = b$ leads us to define the number of units of the length of arc as the limit of the sum in (3) as $\|\Delta\|$ approaches zero.

17.6.1 Definition   Let the curve C have parametric equations $x = f(t)$ and $y = g(t)$. Then if there exists a number L having the property that for any $\epsilon > 0$ there is a $\delta > 0$ such that

$$\left| \sum_{i=1}^{n} |\overline{P_{i-1}P_i}| - L \right| < \epsilon$$

for every partition Δ of the interval $[a, b]$ for which $\|\Delta\| < \delta$, we write

$$L = \lim_{\|\Delta\| \to 0} \sum_{i=1}^{n} |\overline{P_{i-1}P_i}| \tag{4}$$

and L units is called the *length of arc* of the curve C from the point $(f(a), g(a))$ to the point $(f(b), g(b))$.

The arc of the curve is rectifiable if the limit in (4) exists.

If f' and g' are continuous on $[a, b]$, we can find a formula for evaluating the limit in (4). We proceed as follows.

Because f' and g' are continuous on $[a, b]$, they are continuous on each subinterval of the partition Δ. So the hypothesis of the mean-value theorem (Theorem 4.7.2) is satisfied by f and g on each $[t_{i-1}, t_i]$; therefore, there are numbers z_i and w_i in the open interval (t_{i-1}, t_i) such that

$$f(t_i) - f(t_{i-1}) = f'(z_i) \, \Delta_i t \tag{5}$$

and

$$g(t_i) - g(t_{i-1}) = g'(w_i) \, \Delta_i t \tag{6}$$

Substituting from (5) and (6) into (2), we obtain

$$|\overline{P_{i-1}P_i}| = \sqrt{[f'(z_i)\,\Delta_i t]^2 + [g'(w_i)\,\Delta_i t]^2}$$

or, equivalently,

$$|\overline{P_{i-1}P_i}| = \sqrt{[f'(z_i)]^2 + [g'(w_i)]^2}\,\Delta_i t \tag{7}$$

where z_i and w_i are in the open interval (t_{i-1}, t_i). Then from (4) and (7), if the limit exists,

$$L = \lim_{||\Delta|| \to 0} \sum_{i=1}^{n} \sqrt{[f'(z_i)]^2 + [g'(w_i)]^2}\,\Delta_i t \tag{8}$$

The sum in (8) is not a Riemann sum because z_i and w_i are not necessarily the same numbers. So we cannot apply the definition of a definite integral to evaluate the limit in (8). However, there is a theorem which we can apply to evaluate this limit. We state the theorem, but a proof is not given because it is beyond the scope of this book. You can find a proof in an advanced calculus text.

17.6.2 Theorem   If the functions F and G are continuous on the closed interval $[a, b]$, then the function $\sqrt{F^2 + G^2}$ is also continuous on $[a, b]$, and if Δ is a partition of the interval $[a, b]$ $(\Delta: a = t_0 < t_1 < \cdots < t_{i-1} < t_i < \cdots < t_n = b)$, and z_i and w_i are any numbers in (t_{i-1}, t_i), then

$$\lim_{||\Delta|| \to 0} \sum_{i=1}^{n} \sqrt{[F(z_i)]^2 + [G(w_i)]^2}\,\Delta_i t = \int_a^b \sqrt{[F(t)]^2 + [G(t)]^2}\,dt \tag{9}$$

Applying (9) to (8), where F is f' and G is g', we have

$$L = \int_a^b \sqrt{[f'(t)]^2 + [g'(t)]^2}\,dt$$

We state this result as a theorem.

17.6.3 Theorem   Let the curve C have parametric equations $x = f(t)$ and $y = g(t)$, and suppose that f' and g' are continuous on the closed interval $[a, b]$. Then the length of arc L units of the curve C from the point $(f(a), g(a))$ to the point $(f(b), g(b))$ is determined by

$$L = \int_a^b \sqrt{[f'(t)]^2 + [g'(t)]^2}\,dt \tag{10}$$

EXAMPLE 1:   Find the length of the arc of the curve having parametric equations $x = t^3$ and $y = 2t^2$ in each of the following cases: (a) from $t = 0$ to $t = 1$; (b) from $t = -2$ to $t = 0$.

SOLUTION: A sketch of the curve is shown in Fig. 17.6.2. (a) Letting $x = f(t)$, $f'(t) = D_t x = 3t^2$; and letting $y = g(t)$, $g'(t) = D_t y = 4t$. So from Theorem 17.6.3, if L units is the length of the arc of the curve from $t = 0$ to $t = 1$,

$$L = \int_0^1 \sqrt{9t^4 + 16t^2}\,dt$$

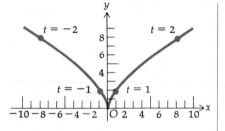

Figure 17.6.2

$$= \int_0^1 t\sqrt{9t^2 + 16}\ dt$$

$$= \tfrac{1}{18} \cdot \tfrac{2}{3}(9t^2 + 16)^{3/2}\Big]_0^1$$

$$= \tfrac{1}{27}\left[(25)^{3/2} - (16)^{3/2}\right]$$

$$= \tfrac{1}{27}(125 - 64)$$

$$= \tfrac{61}{27}$$

(b) If L units is the length of the arc of the curve from $t = -2$ to $t = 0$, we have from Theorem 17.6.3

$$L = \int_{-2}^0 \sqrt{9t^4 + 16t^2}\ dt = \int_{-2}^0 \sqrt{t^2}\ \sqrt{9t^2 + 16}\ dt$$

Because $-2 \le t \le 0$, $\sqrt{t^2} = -t$. So we have

$$L = \int_{-2}^0 -t\sqrt{9t^2 + 16}\ dt$$

$$= -\tfrac{1}{27}(9t^2 + 16)^{3/2}\Big]_{-2}^0$$

$$= -\tfrac{1}{27}\left[(16)^{3/2} - (50)^{3/2}\right]$$

$$= \tfrac{1}{27}(250\sqrt{2} - 64)$$

$$\approx 10.7$$

The curve C has parametric equations (1). Let s units be the length of arc of C from the point $(f(t_0),\ g(t_0))$ to the point $(f(t),\ g(t))$, and let s increase as t increases. Then s is a function of t and is given by

$$s = \int_{t_0}^t \sqrt{[f'(u)]^2 + [g'(u)]^2}\ du \qquad (11)$$

From Theorem 7.6.1, we have

$$\frac{ds}{dt} = \sqrt{[f'(t)]^2 + [g'(t)]^2} \qquad (12)$$

A vector equation of C is

$$\mathbf{R}(t) = f(t)\mathbf{i} + g(t)\mathbf{j} \qquad (13)$$

Because

$$\mathbf{R}'(t) = f'(t)\mathbf{i} + g'(t)\mathbf{j}$$

we have

$$|\mathbf{R}'(t)| = \sqrt{[f'(t)]^2 + [g'(t)]^2} \qquad (14)$$

Substituting from (14) into (12), we obtain

$$|\mathbf{R}'(t)| = \frac{ds}{dt} \tag{15}$$

From (15) we conclude that if s units is the length of arc of curve C having vector equation (13) measured from some fixed point to the point $(f(t), g(t))$ where s increases as t increases, then the derivative of s with respect to t is the magnitude of the derivative of the position vector at the point $(f(t), g(t))$.

If we substitute from (14) into (10), we obtain $L = \int_a^b |\mathbf{R}'(t)| \, dt$. So Theorem 17.6.3 can be stated in terms of vectors in the following way.

17.6.4 Theorem   Let the curve C have the vector equation $\mathbf{R}(t) = f(t)\mathbf{i} + g(t)\mathbf{j}$, and suppose that f' and g' are continuous on the closed interval $[a, b]$. Then the length of arc of C, traced by the terminal point of the position representation of $\mathbf{R}(t)$ as t increases from a to b, is determined by

$$L = \int_a^b |\mathbf{R}'(t)| \, dt \tag{16}$$

EXAMPLE 2:   Find the length of the arc traced by the terminal point of the position representation of $\mathbf{R}(t)$ as t increases from 1 to 4 if

$$\mathbf{R}(t) = e^t \sin t \, \mathbf{i} + e^t \cos t \, \mathbf{j}$$

SOLUTION: $\mathbf{R}'(t) = (e^t \sin t + e^t \cos t)\mathbf{i} + (e^t \cos t - e^t \sin t)\mathbf{j}$.
Therefore,

$$|\mathbf{R}'(t)| = e^t \sqrt{\sin^2 t + 2 \sin t \cos t + \cos^2 t + \cos^2 t - 2 \sin t \cos t + \sin^2 t}$$

$$= e^t \sqrt{2}$$

From (16) we have

$$L = \int_1^4 \sqrt{2} e^t \, dt = \sqrt{2} e^t \bigg]_1^4 = \sqrt{2}(e^4 - e)$$

An alternate form of formula (10) for the length of an arc of a curve C, having parametric equations $x = f(t)$ and $y = g(t)$, is obtained by replacing $f'(t)$ by dx/dt and $g'(t)$ by dy/dt. We have

$$L = \int_a^b \sqrt{\left(\frac{dx}{dt}\right)^2 + \left(\frac{dy}{dt}\right)^2} \, dt \tag{17}$$

Now suppose that we wish to find the length of arc of a curve C whose polar equation is $r = F(\theta)$. If (x, y) is the cartesian representation of a point P on C and (r, θ) is a polar representation of P, then

$$x = r \cos \theta \quad \text{and} \quad y = r \sin \theta \tag{18}$$

Replacing r by $F(\theta)$ in Eqs. (18), we have

$$x = F(\theta) \cos \theta \quad \text{and} \quad y = F(\theta) \sin \theta \tag{19}$$

Equations (19) can be considered as parametric equations of C where θ is the parameter instead of t. Therefore, if F' is continuous on the closed interval $[\alpha, \beta]$, the formula for the length of arc of the curve C whose polar equation is $r = F(\theta)$ is obtained from (17) by taking $t = \theta$. So we have

$$L = \int \sqrt{\left(\frac{dx}{d\theta}\right)^2 + \left(\frac{dy}{d\theta}\right)^2}\ d\theta \tag{20}$$

From (18) we have

$$\frac{dx}{d\theta} = \cos\theta\,\frac{dr}{d\theta} - r\sin\theta \quad \text{and} \quad \frac{dy}{d\theta} = \sin\theta\,\frac{dr}{d\theta} + r\cos\theta$$

Therefore,

$$\sqrt{\left(\frac{dx}{d\theta}\right)^2 + \left(\frac{dy}{d\theta}\right)^2} = \sqrt{\left(\cos\theta\,\frac{dr}{d\theta} - r\sin\theta\right)^2 + \left(\sin\theta\,\frac{dr}{d\theta} + r\cos\theta\right)^2}$$

$$= \sqrt{\cos^2\theta\left(\frac{dr}{d\theta}\right)^2 - 2r\sin\theta\cos\theta\,\frac{dr}{d\theta} + r^2\sin^2\theta + \sin^2\theta\left(\frac{dr}{d\theta}\right)^2 + 2r\sin\theta\cos\theta\,\frac{dr}{d\theta} + r^2\cos^2\theta}$$

$$= \sqrt{(\cos^2\theta + \sin^2\theta)\left(\frac{dr}{d\theta}\right)^2 + (\sin^2\theta + \cos^2\theta)r^2}$$

$$= \sqrt{\left(\frac{dr}{d\theta}\right)^2 + r^2}$$

Substituting this into (20), we obtain

$$L = \int_\alpha^\beta \sqrt{\left(\frac{dr}{d\theta}\right)^2 + r^2}\ d\theta \tag{21}$$

EXAMPLE 3:   Find the length of the cardioid $r = 2(1 + \cos\theta)$.

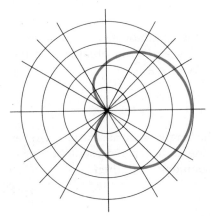

Figure 17.6.3

SOLUTION: A sketch of the curve is shown in Fig. 17.6.3. To obtain the length of the entire curve, we can let θ take on values from 0 to 2π or we can make use of the symmetry of the curve and find half the length by letting θ take on values from 0 to π.

Because $r = 2(1 + \cos\theta)$, $dr/d\theta = -2\sin\theta$. Substituting into (21), integrating from 0 to π, and multiplying by 2, we have

$$L = 2\int_0^\pi \sqrt{(-2\sin\theta)^2 + 4(1 + \cos\theta)^2}\ d\theta$$

$$= 4\int_0^\pi \sqrt{\sin^2\theta + 1 + 2\cos\theta + \cos^2\theta}\ d\theta$$

$$= 4\sqrt{2}\int_0^\pi \sqrt{1 + \cos\theta}\ d\theta$$

To evaluate this integral, we use the identity $\cos^2\tfrac{1}{2}\theta = \tfrac{1}{2}(1 + \cos\theta)$, which gives $\sqrt{1 + \cos\theta} = \sqrt{2}\,|\cos\tfrac{1}{2}\theta|$. Because $0 \le \theta \le \pi$, $0 \le \tfrac{1}{2}\theta \le \tfrac{1}{2}\pi$; thus, $\cos\tfrac{1}{2}\theta \ge 0$. Therefore, $\sqrt{1 + \cos\theta} = \sqrt{2}\cos\tfrac{1}{2}\theta$. So we have

$$L = 4\sqrt{2}\int_0^\pi \sqrt{2}\cos\tfrac{1}{2}\theta\ d\theta = 16\sin\tfrac{1}{2}\theta\Big]_0^\pi = 16$$

Exercises 17.6

Find the length of arc in each of the following exercises. When a appears, $a > 0$.

1. $x = \frac{1}{2}t^2 + t$, $y = \frac{1}{2}t^2 - t$; from $t = 0$ to $t = 1$.

2. $x = t^3$, $y = 3t^2$; from $t = -2$ to $t = 0$.

3. $\mathbf{R}(t) = 2t^2\mathbf{i} + 2t^3\mathbf{j}$; from $t = 1$ to $t = 2$.

4. $\mathbf{R}(t) = a(\cos t + t \sin t)\mathbf{i} + a(\sin t - t \cos t)\mathbf{j}$; from $t = 0$ to $t = \frac{1}{3}\pi$.

5. The entire hypocycloid of four cusps: $x = a \cos^3 t$, $y = a \sin^3 t$.

6. $x = e^{-t} \cos t$, $y = e^{-t} \sin t$; from $t = 0$ to $t = \pi$.

7. The tractrix $x = t - a \tanh \dfrac{t}{a}$, $y = a \operatorname{sech} \dfrac{t}{a}$ from $t = -a$ to $t = 2a$.

8. One arch of the cycloid: $x = a(t - \sin t)$, $y = a(1 - \cos t)$.

9. The circumference of the circle: $\mathbf{R}(t) = a \cos t\mathbf{i} + a \sin t\mathbf{j}$.

10. The circumference of the circle: $r = a \sin \theta$.

11. The circumference of the circle: $r = a$.

12. The entire curve: $r = 1 - \sin \theta$.

13. The entire curve: $r = 3 \cos^2 \frac{1}{2}\theta$.

14. $r = a\theta$; from $\theta = 0$ to $\theta = 2\pi$.

15. $r = a \sin^3 \frac{1}{3}\theta$; from $\theta = 0$ to $\theta = \theta_1$.

16. $r = a\theta^2$; from $\theta = 0$ to $\theta = \pi$.

17.7 PLANE MOTION   The previous discussion of the motion of a particle was confined to straight-line motion. In this connection, we defined the velocity and acceleration of a particle moving along a straight line. We now consider the motion of a particle along a curve in the plane.

Suppose that C is the plane curve having parametric equations $x = f(t)$, $y = g(t)$, where t units denotes time. Then

$$\mathbf{R}(t) = f(t)\mathbf{i} + g(t)\mathbf{j}$$

is a vector equation of C. As t varies, the endpoint $P(f(t), g(t))$ of $\overrightarrow{OP}$ moves along the curve C. The position at time t units of a particle moving along C is the point $P(f(t), g(t))$. The *velocity vector* of the particle at time t units is defined to be $\mathbf{R}'(t)$. We denote the velocity vector by the symbol $\mathbf{V}(t)$ instead of $\mathbf{R}'(t)$.

17.7.1 Definition   Let C be the curve having parametric equations $x = f(t)$ and $y = g(t)$. If a particle is moving along C so that its position at any time t units is the point (x, y), then the *instantaneous velocity* of the particle at time t units is determined by the velocity vector

$$\mathbf{V}(t) = f'(t)\mathbf{i} + g'(t)\mathbf{j}$$

if $f'(t)$ and $g'(t)$ exist.

In Sec. 17.5 we saw that the direction of $\mathbf{R}'(t)$ at the point $P(f(t), g(t))$ is along the tangent line to the curve C at P. Therefore, the velocity vector $\mathbf{V}(t)$ has this direction at P.

The magnitude of the velocity vector is a measure of the *speed* of the particle at time t and is given by

$$|\mathbf{V}(t)| = \sqrt{[f'(t)]^2 + [g'(t)]^2} \tag{1}$$

Note that the velocity is a vector and the speed is a scalar. As shown in Sec. 17.6, the expression on the right side of (1) is ds/dt. So the speed is the rate of change of s with respect to t, and we write

$$|\mathbf{V}(t)| = \frac{ds}{dt} \tag{2}$$

The *acceleration vector* of the particle at time t units is defined to be the derivative of the velocity vector or, equivalently, the second derivative of the position vector. The acceleration vector is denoted by $\mathbf{A}(t)$.

17.7.2 Definition The *instantaneous acceleration* at time t units of a particle moving along a curve C, having parametric equations $x = f(t)$ and $y = g(t)$, is determined by the acceleration vector

$$\mathbf{A}(t) = \mathbf{V}'(t) = \mathbf{R}''(t)$$

where $\mathbf{R}(t) = f(t)\mathbf{i} + g(t)\mathbf{j}$ and $\mathbf{R}''(t)$ exists.

Figure 17.7.1 shows the representations of the velocity vector and the acceleration vector whose initial point is the point P on C.

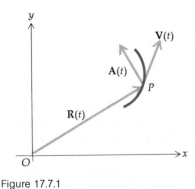

Figure 17.7.1

EXAMPLE 1: A particle is moving along the curve having parametric equations $x = 4 \cos \frac{1}{2}t$ and $y = 4 \sin \frac{1}{2}t$. If t is the number of seconds in the time and x and y represent number of feet, find the speed and magnitude of the particle's acceleration vector at time t sec. Draw a sketch of the particle's path, and also draw the representations of the velocity and acceleration vectors having initial point where $t = \frac{1}{3}\pi$.

SOLUTION: A vector equation of C is

$$\mathbf{R}(t) = 4 \cos \tfrac{1}{2}t\mathbf{i} + 4 \sin \tfrac{1}{2}t\mathbf{j}$$
$$\mathbf{V}(t) = \mathbf{R}'(t) = -2 \sin \tfrac{1}{2}t\mathbf{i} + 2 \cos \tfrac{1}{2}t\mathbf{j}$$
$$\mathbf{A}(t) = \mathbf{V}'(t) = -\cos \tfrac{1}{2}t\mathbf{i} - \sin \tfrac{1}{2}t\mathbf{j}$$
$$|\mathbf{V}(t)| = \sqrt{(-2 \sin \tfrac{1}{2}t)^2 + (2 \cos \tfrac{1}{2}t)^2}$$
$$= \sqrt{4 \sin^2 \tfrac{1}{2}t + 4 \cos^2 \tfrac{1}{2}t}$$
$$= 2$$
$$|\mathbf{A}(t)| = \sqrt{(-\cos \tfrac{1}{2}t)^2 + (-\sin \tfrac{1}{2}t)^2} = 1$$

Therefore, the speed of the particle is constant and is 2 ft/sec. The magnitude of the acceleration vector is also constant and is 1 ft/sec².

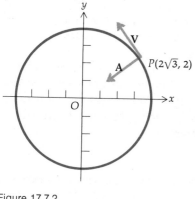

Figure 17.7.2

Eliminating t between the parametric equations of C, we obtain the cartesian equation $x^2 + y^2 = 16$, which is a circle with its center at 0 and radius 4.

When $t = \frac{1}{3}\pi$, the direction of $\mathbf{V}(t)$ is given by $\frac{1}{2}\pi < \theta < \pi$ and

$$\tan \theta = -\frac{\cos \frac{1}{6}\pi}{\sin \frac{1}{6}\pi} = -\cot \frac{1}{6}\pi = -\sqrt{3}$$

and the direction of $\mathbf{A}(t)$ is given by $\pi < \theta < \frac{3}{2}\pi$ and

$$\tan \theta = \frac{\sin \frac{1}{6}\pi}{\cos \frac{1}{6}\pi} = \tan \frac{1}{6}\pi = \frac{1}{\sqrt{3}}$$

Figure 17.7.2 shows the representations of the velocity and acceleration vectors having initial point where $t = \frac{1}{3}\pi$.

EXAMPLE 2: The position of a moving particle at time t units is given by the vector equation

$$\mathbf{R}(t) = e^{-2t}\mathbf{i} + 3e^t\mathbf{j}$$

Find $\mathbf{V}(t)$, $\mathbf{A}(t)$, $|\mathbf{V}(t)|$, $|\mathbf{A}(t)|$.

Draw a sketch of the path of the particle and the representations of the velocity and acceleration vectors having initial point where $t = \frac{1}{2}$.

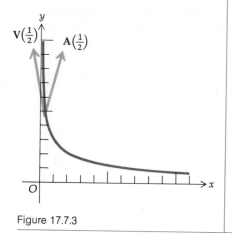

Figure 17.7.3

SOLUTION:

$$\mathbf{V}(t) = \mathbf{R}'(t) = -2e^{-2t}\mathbf{i} + 3e^t\mathbf{j}$$

$$\mathbf{A}(t) = \mathbf{V}'(t) = 4e^{-2t}\mathbf{i} + 3e^t\mathbf{j}$$

$$|\mathbf{V}(t)| = \sqrt{4e^{-4t} + 9e^{2t}}$$

$$|\mathbf{A}(t)| = \sqrt{16e^{-4t} + 9e^{2t}}$$

$$|\mathbf{V}(\tfrac{1}{2})| = \sqrt{4e^{-2} + 9e} \approx 5.01$$

$$|\mathbf{A}(\tfrac{1}{2})| = \sqrt{16e^{-2} + 9e} \approx 5.15$$

Parametric equations of the path of the particle are $x = e^{-2t}$ and $y = 3e^t$. Eliminating t between these two equations, we obtain

$$xy^2 = 9$$

Because $x > 0$ and $y > 0$, the path of the particle is the portion of the curve $xy^2 = 9$ in the first quadrant. Figure 17.7.3 shows the path of the particle and the velocity and acceleration vectors when $t = \frac{1}{2}$. The slope of $\mathbf{V}(\frac{1}{2})$ is $-\frac{3}{2}e^{3/2} \approx -6.7$, and the slope of $\mathbf{A}(\frac{1}{2})$ is $\frac{3}{4}e^{3/2} \approx 3.4$.

We now derive the equations of motion of a projectile by assuming that the projectile is moving in a vertical plane. We also assume that the only force acting on the projectile is its weight, which has a downward direction and a magnitude of mg lb, where m slugs is its mass and g ft/sec²

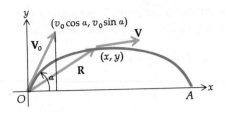

Figure 17.7.4

is the constant of acceleration caused by gravity. We are neglecting the force attributed to air resistance (which for heavy bodies traveling at small speeds has no noticeable effect). The positive direction is taken as vertically upward and horizontally to the right.

Suppose, then, that a projectile is shot from a gun having an angle of elevation of radian measure α. Let the number of feet per second in the initial speed, or *muzzle speed*, be denoted by v_0. We set up the coordinate axes so that the gun is located at the origin. Refer to Fig. 17.7.4. The initial velocity vector, $\mathbf{V}_0$, of the projectile is given by

$$\mathbf{V}_0 = v_0 \cos \alpha \mathbf{i} + v_0 \sin \alpha \mathbf{j} \tag{3}$$

Let $t =$ the number of seconds in the time that has elapsed since the gun was fired;

$x =$ the number of feet in the horizontal distance of the projectile from the starting point at t sec;

$y =$ the number of feet in the vertical distance of the projectile from the starting point at t sec;

$\mathbf{R}(t) =$ the position vector of the projectile at t sec;

$\mathbf{V}(t) =$ the velocity vector of the projectile at t sec;

$\mathbf{A}(t) =$ the acceleration vector of the projectile at t sec.

x is a function of t; so we write $x(t)$. Similarly, y is a function of t; so we write $y(t)$. Then

$$\mathbf{R}(t) = x(t)\mathbf{i} + y(t)\mathbf{j} \tag{4}$$

$$\mathbf{V}(t) = \mathbf{R}'(t) \tag{5}$$

$$\mathbf{A}(t) = \mathbf{V}'(t) \tag{6}$$

Because the only force acting on the projectile has a magnitude of mg lb and is in the downward direction, then if $\mathbf{F}$ denotes this force we have

$$\mathbf{F} = -mg\mathbf{j} \tag{7}$$

Newton's second law of motion states that the net force which is acting on a body is its "mass times acceleration." So

$$\mathbf{F} = m\mathbf{A} \tag{8}$$

From (7) and (8) we obtain

$$m\mathbf{A} = -mg\mathbf{j}$$

Dividing by m, we have

$$\mathbf{A} = -g\mathbf{j} \tag{9}$$

Because $\mathbf{A}(t) = \mathbf{V}'(t)$, we have from (9)

$$\mathbf{V}'(t) = -g\mathbf{j} \tag{10}$$

Integrating on both sides of Eq. (10) with respect to t, we obtain

$$\mathbf{V}(t) = -gt\mathbf{j} + \mathbf{C}_1 \tag{11}$$

where C_1 is a vector constant of integration.

When $t = 0$, $V = V_0$. So $C_1 = V_0$. Therefore, from (11) we have

$$V(t) = -gt\mathbf{j} + V_0$$

or, because $V(t) = R'(t)$, we have

$$R'(t) = -gt\mathbf{j} + V_0 \tag{12}$$

Integrating on both sides of the vector equation (12) with respect to t, we obtain

$$R(t) = -\tfrac{1}{2}gt^2\mathbf{j} + V_0 t + C_2$$

where C_2 is a vector constant of integration.

When $t = 0$, $R = 0$ because the projectile is at the origin at the start. So $C_2 = 0$. Therefore,

$$R(t) = -\tfrac{1}{2}gt^2\mathbf{j} + V_0 t \tag{13}$$

Substituting the value of V_0 from Eq. (3) into (13), we obtain

$$R(t) = -\tfrac{1}{2}gt^2\mathbf{j} + (v_0 \cos \alpha \mathbf{i} + v_0 \sin \alpha \mathbf{j})t$$

or, equivalently,

$$R(t) = tv_0 \cos \alpha \mathbf{i} + (tv_0 \sin \alpha - \tfrac{1}{2}gt^2)\mathbf{j} \tag{14}$$

Equation (14) gives the position vector of the projectile at time t sec. From this equation, we can discuss the motion of the projectile. We are usually concerned with the following questions:

1. What is the range of the projectile? The range is the distance $|\overline{OA}|$ along the x axis (see Fig. 17.7.4).
2. What is the total time of flight, that is, the time it takes the projectile to go from O to A?
3. What is the maximum height of the projectile?
4. What is a cartesian equation of the curve traveled by the projectile?
5. What is the velocity vector of the projectile at impact?

These questions are answered in the following example.

EXAMPLE 3: A projectile is shot from a gun at an angle of elevation of radian measure $\tfrac{1}{6}\pi$. Its muzzle speed is 480 ft/sec. Find (a) the position vector of the projectile at any time; (b) the time of flight; (c) the range; (d) the maximum height; (e) the velocity vector of the projectile at impact; (f) the position vector and the

SOLUTION: $v_0 = 480$ and $\alpha = \tfrac{1}{6}\pi$. So

$$V_0 = 480 \cos \tfrac{1}{6}\pi \mathbf{i} + 480 \sin \tfrac{1}{6}\pi \mathbf{j}$$

$$= 240\sqrt{3}\mathbf{i} + 240\mathbf{j}$$

(a) The position vector at t sec is given by Eq. (14), which in this case is

$$R(t) = 240\sqrt{3}t\mathbf{i} + (240t - \tfrac{1}{2}gt^2)\mathbf{j} \tag{15}$$

velocity vector at 2 sec; (g) the speed at 2 sec; (h) a cartesian equation of the curve traveled by the projectile.

So if (x, y) is the position of the projectile at t sec, $x = 240 \sqrt{3}t$ and $y = 240t - \frac{1}{2}gt^2$.

(b) To find the time of flight, we find t when $y = 0$. From part (a), we get $y = 0$ and have

$$240t - \tfrac{1}{2}gt^2 = 0$$

$$t(240 - \tfrac{1}{2}gt) = 0$$

$$t = 0 \quad \text{and} \quad t = \frac{480}{g}$$

The value $t = 0$ is when the projectile is fired because then $y = 0$. If we take $g = 32$, the time of flight is determined by $t = 480/g = 480/32 = 15$. So the time of flight is 15 sec.

(c) To find the range, we must find x when $t = 15$. From part (a), $x = 240 \sqrt{3}t$. So when $t = 15$, $x = 3600 \sqrt{3}$. Therefore, the range is 6235 ft (approximately).

(d) The maximum height is attained when $D_t y = 0$, that is, when the vertical component of the velocity vector is 0. Because

$$y = 240t - \tfrac{1}{2}gt^2$$

$$D_t y = 240 - gt$$

So $D_t y = 0$ when $t = 240/g$. If we take $g = 32$, the maximum height is attained when $t = 7\frac{1}{2}$, which is half the total time of flight. When $t = 7\frac{1}{2}$, $y = 900$. So the maximum height attained is 900 ft.

(e) Because the time of flight is 15 sec, the velocity vector at impact is $\mathbf{V}(15)$. Finding $\mathbf{V}(t)$ by using (15), we have

$$\mathbf{V}(t) = D_t \mathbf{R}(t) = 240 \sqrt{3}\mathbf{i} + (240 - gt)\mathbf{j}$$

Taking $g = 32$, we get

$$\mathbf{V}(15) = 240 \sqrt{3}\mathbf{i} - 240\mathbf{j}$$

(f) Taking $t = 2$ in Eq. (15), we obtain

$$\mathbf{R}(2) = 480 \sqrt{3}\mathbf{i} + 416\mathbf{j}$$

Because $\mathbf{V}(t) = \mathbf{R}'(t)$, we have

$$\mathbf{V}(t) = 240 \sqrt{3}\mathbf{i} + (240 - gt)\mathbf{j}$$

So

$$\mathbf{V}(2) = 240 \sqrt{3}\mathbf{i} + 176\mathbf{j}$$

(g) The speed when $t = 2$ is determined by

$$|\mathbf{V}(2)| = \sqrt{(240 \sqrt{3})^2 + (176)^2}$$

$$= 32 \sqrt{199}$$

So at 2 sec the speed is approximately 451.4 ft/sec.

(h) To find a cartesian equation, we eliminate t between the parametric equations

$$x = 240\sqrt{3}\,t$$

$$y = 240t - \tfrac{1}{2}gt^2$$

Solving the first equation for t and substituting into the second equation, we obtain

$$y = \frac{1}{\sqrt{3}}\,x - \frac{1}{10{,}800}\,x^2$$

which is an equation of a parabola.

Exercises 17.7

In Exercises 1 through 6, a particle is moving along the curve having the given parametric equations, where t sec is the time. Find: (a) the velocity vector $\mathbf{V}(t)$; (b) the acceleration vector $\mathbf{A}(t)$; (c) the speed at $t = t_1$; (d) the magnitude of the acceleration vector at $t = t_1$. Draw a sketch of the path of the particle and the representations of the velocity vector and the acceleration vector at $t = t_1$.

1. $x = t^2 + 4$, $y = t - 2$; $t_1 = 3$

2. $x = 2 \cos t$, $y = 3 \sin t$; $t_1 = \tfrac{1}{3}\pi$

3. $x = t$, $y = \ln \sec t$; $t_1 = \tfrac{1}{4}\pi$

4. $x = 2/t$, $y = -\tfrac{1}{4}t$; $t_1 = 4$

5. $x = \sin t$, $y = \tan t$; $t_1 = \tfrac{1}{6}\pi$

6. $x = e^{2t}$, $y = e^{3t}$; $t_1 = 0$

In Exercises 7 through 12, the position of a moving particle at t sec is determined from a vector equation. Find: (a) $\mathbf{V}(t_1)$; (b) $\mathbf{A}(t_1)$; (c) $|\mathbf{V}(t_1)|$; (d) $|\mathbf{A}(t_1)|$. Draw a sketch of a portion of the path of the particle containing the position of the particle at $t = t_1$, and draw the representations of $\mathbf{V}(t_1)$ and $\mathbf{A}(t_1)$ having initial point where $t = t_1$.

7. $\mathbf{R}(t) = (2t - 1)\mathbf{i} + (t^2 + 1)\mathbf{j}$; $t_1 = 3$

8. $\mathbf{R}(t) = (t^2 + 3t)\mathbf{i} + (1 - 3t^2)\mathbf{j}$; $t_1 = \tfrac{1}{2}$

9. $\mathbf{R}(t) = \cos 2t\mathbf{i} - 3 \sin t\mathbf{j}$; $t_1 = \pi$

10. $\mathbf{R}(t) = e^{-t}\mathbf{i} + e^{2t}\mathbf{j}$; $t_1 = \ln 2$

11. $\mathbf{R}(t) = 2(1 - \cos t)\mathbf{i} + 2(1 - \sin t)\mathbf{j}$; $t_1 = \tfrac{5}{6}\pi$

12. $\mathbf{R}(t) = \ln(t + 2)\mathbf{i} + \tfrac{1}{3}t^2\mathbf{j}$; $t_1 = 1$

13. Find the position vector $\mathbf{R}(t)$ if the velocity vector

$$\mathbf{V}(t) = \frac{1}{(t - 1)^2}\,\mathbf{i} - (t + 1)\mathbf{j} \quad \text{and} \quad \mathbf{R}(0) = 3\mathbf{i} + 2\mathbf{j}$$

14. Find the position vector $\mathbf{R}(t)$ if the acceleration vector

$$\mathbf{A}(t) = 2 \cos 2t\mathbf{i} + 2 \sin 2t\mathbf{j} \quad \text{and} \quad \mathbf{V}(0) = \mathbf{i} + \mathbf{j}, \text{ and } \mathbf{R}(0) = \tfrac{1}{2}\mathbf{i} - \tfrac{1}{2}\mathbf{j}$$

15. A projectile is shot from a gun at an angle of elevation of 45° with a muzzle speed of 2500 ft/sec. Find (a) the range of the projectile, (b) the maximum height reached, and (c) the velocity at impact.

16. A projectile is shot from a gun at an angle of elevation of 60°. The muzzle speed is 160 ft/sec. Find (a) the position vector of the projectile at t sec; (b) the time of flight; (c) the range; (d) the maximum height reached; (e) the velocity at impact; (f) the speed at 4 sec.

17. A projectile is shot from the top of a building 96 ft high from a gun at an angle of 30° with the horizontal. If the muzzle speed is 1600 ft/sec, find the time of flight and the distance from the base of the building to the point where the projectile lands.

18. A child throws a ball horizontally from the top of a cliff 256 ft high with an initial speed of 50 ft/sec. Find the time of flight of the ball and the distance from the base of the cliff to the point where the ball lands.

19. A child throws a ball with an initial speed of 60 ft/sec at an angle of elevation of 60° toward a tall building which is 25 ft from the child. If the child's hand is 5 ft from the ground, show that the ball hits the building, and find the direction of the ball when it hits the building.

20. The muzzle speed of a gun is 160 ft/sec. At what angle of elevation should the gun be fired so that a projectile will hit an object on the same level as the gun and a distance of 400 ft from it?

21. What is the muzzle speed of a gun if a projectile fired from it has a range of 2000 ft and reaches a maximum height of 1000 ft?

17.8 THE UNIT TANGENT AND UNIT NORMAL VECTORS AND ARC LENGTH AS A PARAMETER

We previously noted that a unit vector is a vector having a magnitude of 1, examples of which are the two unit vectors $\mathbf{i}$ and $\mathbf{j}$. With each point on a curve in the plane we now associate two other unit vectors, the "unit tangent vector" and the "unit normal vector."

17.8.1 Definition

If $\mathbf{R}(t)$ is the position vector of curve C at a point P on C, then the *unit tangent vector* of C at P, denoted by $\mathbf{T}(t)$, is the unit vector in the direction of $D_t\mathbf{R}(t)$ if $D_t\mathbf{R}(t) \neq 0$.

The unit vector in the direction of $D_t\mathbf{R}(t)$ is given by $D_t\mathbf{R}(t)/|D_t\mathbf{R}(t)|$; so we may write

$$\mathbf{T}(t) = \frac{D_t\mathbf{R}(t)}{|D_t\mathbf{R}(t)|} \qquad (1)$$

Because $\mathbf{T}(t)$ is a unit vector, it follows from Theorem 17.5.11 that $D_t\mathbf{T}(t)$ must be orthogonal to $\mathbf{T}(t)$. $D_t\mathbf{T}(t)$ is not necessarily a unit vector. However, the vector $D_t\mathbf{T}(t)/|D_t\mathbf{T}(t)|$ is of unit magnitude and has the same direction as $D_t\mathbf{T}(t)$. Therefore, $D_t\mathbf{T}(t)/|D_t\mathbf{T}(t)|$ is a unit vector which is orthogonal to $\mathbf{T}(t)$, and it is called the "unit normal vector."

17.8.2 Definition

If $\mathbf{T}(t)$ is the unit tangent vector of curve C at a point P on C, then the *unit normal vector*, denoted by $\mathbf{N}(t)$, is the unit vector in the direction of $D_t\mathbf{T}(t)$.

From Definition 17.8.2 and the previous discussion, we conclude that

$$\mathbf{N}(t) = \frac{D_t\mathbf{T}(t)}{|D_t\mathbf{T}(t)|} \qquad (2)$$

EXAMPLE 1: Given the curve having parametric equations $x = t^3 - 3t$ and $y = 3t^2$, find $\mathbf{T}(t)$ and $\mathbf{N}(t)$. Draw a sketch of a portion of the curve at $t = 2$ and

SOLUTION: A vector equation of the curve is

$$\mathbf{R}(t) = (t^3 - 3t)\mathbf{i} + 3t^2\mathbf{j}$$

So

$$D_t\mathbf{R}(t) = (3t^2 - 3)\mathbf{i} + 6t\mathbf{j}$$

draw the representations of **T**(2) and **N**(2) having their initial point at $t = 2$.

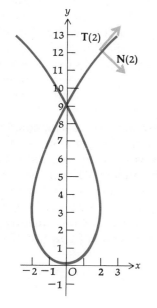

Figure 17.8.1

Then

$$|D_t\mathbf{R}(t)| = \sqrt{(3t^2 - 3)^2 + 36t^2} = \sqrt{9(t^4 + 2t^2 + 1)} = 3(t^2 + 1)$$

Applying (1), we get

$$\mathbf{T}(t) = \frac{t^2 - 1}{t^2 + 1}\mathbf{i} + \frac{2t}{t^2 + 1}\mathbf{j}$$

Differentiating $\mathbf{T}(t)$ with respect to t, we obtain

$$D_t\mathbf{T}(t) = \frac{4t}{(t^2 + 1)^2}\mathbf{i} + \frac{2 - 2t^2}{(t^2 + 1)^2}\mathbf{j}$$

Therefore,

$$|D_t\mathbf{T}(t)| = \sqrt{\frac{16t^2}{(t^2 + 1)^4} + \frac{4 - 8t^2 + 4t^4}{(t^2 + 1)^4}}$$

$$= \sqrt{\frac{4 + 8t^2 + 4t^4}{(t^2 + 1)^4}}$$

$$= \sqrt{\frac{4(t^2 + 1)^2}{(t^2 + 1)^4}}$$

$$= \frac{2}{t^2 + 1}$$

Applying (2), we have

$$\mathbf{N}(t) = \frac{2t}{t^2 + 1}\mathbf{i} + \frac{1 - t^2}{t^2 + 1}\mathbf{j}$$

Finding $\mathbf{R}(t)$, $\mathbf{T}(t)$, and $\mathbf{N}(t)$, when $t = 2$, we obtain

$$\mathbf{R}(2) = 2\mathbf{i} + 12\mathbf{j} \qquad \mathbf{T}(2) = \tfrac{3}{5}\mathbf{i} + \tfrac{4}{5}\mathbf{j} \qquad \mathbf{N}(2) = \tfrac{4}{5}\mathbf{i} - \tfrac{3}{5}\mathbf{j}$$

The required sketch is shown in Fig. 17.8.1.

From Eq. (1) we obtain

$$D_t\mathbf{R}(t) = |D_t\mathbf{R}(t)|\mathbf{T}(t) \tag{3}$$

The right side of (3) is the product of a scalar and a vector. To differentiate this product, we apply Theorem 17.5.8, and we have

$$D_t^2\mathbf{R}(t) = [D_t|D_t\mathbf{R}(t)|]\mathbf{T}(t) + |D_t\mathbf{R}(t)|[D_t\mathbf{T}(t)] \tag{4}$$

From (2) we obtain

$$D_t\mathbf{T}(t) = |D_t\mathbf{T}(t)|\mathbf{N}(t) \tag{5}$$

Substituting from (5) into (4), we get

$$D_t^2\mathbf{R}(t) = [D_t|D_t\mathbf{R}(t)|]\mathbf{T}(t) + |D_t\mathbf{R}(t)||D_t\mathbf{T}(t)|\mathbf{N}(t) \tag{6}$$

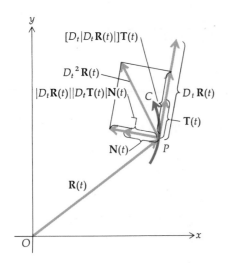

Figure 17.8.2

Equation (3) expresses the vector $D_t\mathbf{R}(t)$ as a scalar times the unit tangent vector, and Eq. (6) expresses the vector $D_t^2\mathbf{R}(t)$ as a scalar times the unit tangent vector plus a scalar times the unit normal vector. The coefficient of $\mathbf{T}(t)$ on the right side of (6) is the component of the vector $D_t^2\mathbf{R}(t)$ in the direction of the unit tangent vector. The coefficient of $\mathbf{N}(t)$ on the right side of (6) is the component of $D_t^2\mathbf{R}(t)$ in the direction of the unit normal vector. Figure 17.8.2 shows a portion of a curve C with the position representation of $\mathbf{R}(t)$ and the representations of $\mathbf{T}(t)$, $\mathbf{N}(t)$, $D_t\mathbf{R}(t)$, $D_t^2\mathbf{R}(t)$, $[D_t|D_t\mathbf{R}(t)|]\mathbf{T}(t)$, and $|D_t\mathbf{R}(t)||D_t\mathbf{T}(t)|\mathbf{N}(t)$, all of whose initial points are at the point P on C. Note that the representation of the unit normal vector $\mathbf{N}$ is on the concave side of the curve. This is proved in general in Sec. 17.9.

Sometimes instead of a parameter t, we wish to use as a parameter the number of units of arc length s from an arbitrarily chosen point $P_0(x_0, y_0)$ on curve C to the point $P(x, y)$ on C. Let s increase as t increases so that s is positive if the length of arc is measured in the direction of increasing t and s is negative if the length of arc is measured in the opposite direction. Therefore, s units is a directed distance. Also, $D_t s > 0$. To each value of s there corresponds a unique point P on the curve C. Consequently, the coordinates of P are functions of s, and s is a function of t. In Sec. 17.6 we showed that

$$|D_t\mathbf{R}(t)| = D_t s \tag{7}$$

Substituting from (7) into (1), we get

$$\mathbf{T}(t) = \frac{D_t\mathbf{R}(t)}{D_t s}$$

So

$$D_t\mathbf{R}(t) = D_t s\mathbf{T}(t)$$

If the parameter is s instead of t, we have from the above equation, by taking $t = s$ and noting that $D_t s = 1$,

$$D_s\mathbf{R}(s) = \mathbf{T}(s)$$

This result is stated as a theorem.

17.8.3 Theorem If the vector equation of a curve C is $\mathbf{R}(s) = f(s)\mathbf{i} + g(s)\mathbf{j}$, where s units is the length of arc measured from a particular point P_0 on C to the point P, then the unit tangent vector of C at P is given by

$$\mathbf{T}(s) = D_s\mathbf{R}(s)$$

Now suppose that the parametric equations of a curve C involve a parameter t, and we wish to find parametric equations of C, with s, the number of units of arc length measured from some fixed point, as the parameter. Often the operations involved are quite complicated. However, the method used is illustrated in the following example.

EXAMPLE 2:   Suppose that parametric equations of the curve C are $x = t^3$ and $y = t^2$, where $t \geq 0$. Find parametric equations of C having s as a parameter, where s is the number of units of arc length measured from the point where $t = 0$.

SOLUTION: If P_0 is the point where $t = 0$, P_0 is the origin. The vector equation of C is

$$\mathbf{R}(t) = t^3\mathbf{i} + t^2\mathbf{j}$$

Because $D_t s = |D_t \mathbf{R}(t)|$, we differentiate the above vector and obtain

$$D_t \mathbf{R}(t) = 3t^2\mathbf{i} + 2t\mathbf{j}$$

So

$$|D_t \mathbf{R}(t)| = \sqrt{9t^4 + 4t^2} = \sqrt{t^2}\ \sqrt{9t^2 + 4}$$

Because $t \geq 0$, $\sqrt{t^2} = t$. Thus, we have

$$|D_t \mathbf{R}(t)| = t\sqrt{9t^2 + 4}$$

Therefore,

$$D_t s = t\sqrt{9t^2 + 4}$$

and so

$$s = \int_0^t u\sqrt{9u^2 + 4}\ du$$

$$= \tfrac{1}{18} \int_0^t 18u\sqrt{9u^2 + 4}\ du$$

$$= \tfrac{1}{27}(9u^2 + 4)^{3/2} \Big]_0^t$$

We obtain

$$s = \tfrac{1}{27}(9t^2 + 4)^{3/2} - \tfrac{8}{27} \tag{8}$$

Solving Eq. (8) for t in terms of s, we have

$$(9t^2 + 4)^{3/2} = 27s + 8$$

$$9t^2 + 4 = (27s + 8)^{2/3}$$

Because $t \geq 0$, we get

$$t = \tfrac{1}{3}\sqrt{(27s + 8)^{2/3} - 4}$$

Substituting this value of t into the given parametric equations for C, we obtain

$$x = \tfrac{1}{27}[(27s + 8)^{2/3} - 4]^{3/2} \quad \text{and} \quad y = \tfrac{1}{9}[(27s + 8)^{2/3} - 4] \tag{9}$$

Now because $D_s \mathbf{R}(s) = \mathbf{T}(s)$, it follows that if $\mathbf{R}(s) = x(s)\mathbf{i} + y(s)\mathbf{j}$, then $\mathbf{T}(s) = (D_s x)\mathbf{i} + (D_s y)\mathbf{j}$. And because $\mathbf{T}(s)$ is a unit vector, we have

$$(D_s x)^2 + (D_s y)^2 = 1 \tag{10}$$

Equation (10) can be used to check Eqs. (9). This check is left as an exercise (see Exercise 11).

Exercises 17.8

In Exercises 1 through 8, for the given curve, find $\mathbf{T}(t)$ and $\mathbf{N}(t)$, and at $t = t_1$ draw a sketch of a portion of the curve and draw the representations of $\mathbf{T}(t_1)$ and $\mathbf{N}(t_1)$ having initial point at $t = t_1$.

1. $x = \frac{1}{3}t^3 - t$, $y = t^2$; $t_1 = 2$

2. $x = \frac{1}{2}t^2$, $y = \frac{1}{3}t^3$; $t_1 = 1$

3. $\mathbf{R}(t) = e^t\mathbf{i} + e^{-t}\mathbf{j}$; $t_1 = 0$

4. $\mathbf{R}(t) = 3 \cos t\mathbf{i} + 3 \sin t\mathbf{j}$; $t_1 = \frac{1}{2}\pi$

5. $x = \cos kt$, $y = \sin kt$, $k > 0$; $t_1 = \pi/k$

6. $x = t - \sin t$, $y = 1 - \cos t$; $t_1 = \pi$

7. $\mathbf{R}(t) = \ln \cos t\mathbf{i} + \ln \sin t\mathbf{j}$, $0 < t < \frac{1}{2}\pi$; $t_1 = \frac{1}{4}\pi$

8. $\mathbf{R}(t) = t \cos t\mathbf{i} + t \sin t\mathbf{j}$; $t_1 = 0$

9. If the vector equation of curve C is $\mathbf{R}(t) = 3t^2\mathbf{i} + (t^3 - 3t)\mathbf{j}$, find the cosine of the measure of the angle between the vectors $\mathbf{R}(2)$ and $\mathbf{T}(2)$.

10. If the vector equation of curve C is $\mathbf{R}(t) = (4 - 3t^2)\mathbf{i} + (t^3 - 3t)\mathbf{j}$, find the radian measure of the angle between the vectors $\mathbf{N}(1)$ and $D_t^2\mathbf{R}(1)$.

11. Check Eqs. (9) of the solution of Example 2 by using Eq. (10).

In Exercises 12 through 15, find parametric equations of the curve having arc length s as a parameter, where s is measured from the point where $t = 0$. Check your result by using Eq. (10).

12. $x = a \cos t$, $y = a \sin t$

13. $x = 2 + \cos t$, $y = 3 + \sin t$

14. $x = 2(\cos t + t \sin t)$, $y = 2(\sin t - t \cos t)$

15. One cusp of the hypocycloid of four cusps: $\mathbf{R}(t) = a \cos^3 t\mathbf{i} + a \sin^3 t\mathbf{j}$, $0 \le t \le \frac{1}{2}\pi$.

16. Given the cycloid $x = 2(t - \sin t)$, $y = 2(1 - \cos t)$, express the arc length s as a function of t, where s is measured from the point where $t = 0$.

17. Prove that parametric equations of the catenary $y = a \cosh (x/a)$ where the parameter s is the number of units in the length of the arc from the point $(0, a)$ to the point (x, y) and $s \ge 0$ when $x \ge 0$ and $s < 0$ when $x < 0$, are

$$x = a \sinh^{-1}\frac{s}{a} \quad \text{and} \quad y = \sqrt{a^2 + s^2}$$

17.9 CURVATURE   Let ϕ be the radian measure of the angle giving the direction of the unit tangent vector associated with a curve C. Therefore, ϕ is the radian measure of the angle from the direction of the positive x axis counterclockwise to the direction of the unit tangent vector $\mathbf{T}(t)$. See Fig. 17.9.1.

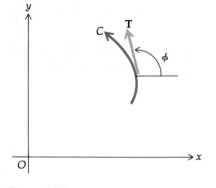

Figure 17.9.1

Because $|\mathbf{T}(t)| = 1$, it follows from Eq. (1) in Sec. 17.2 that

$$\mathbf{T}(t) = \cos \phi \mathbf{i} + \sin \phi \mathbf{j} \tag{1}$$

Differentiating with respect to ϕ, we obtain

$$D_\phi \mathbf{T}(t) = -\sin \phi \mathbf{i} + \cos \phi \mathbf{j} \tag{2}$$

Because $|D_\phi \mathbf{T}(t)| = \sqrt{(-\sin \phi)^2 + (\cos \phi)^2} = 1$, $D_\phi \mathbf{T}(t)$ is a unit vector. Because $\mathbf{T}(t)$ has constant magnitude it follows from Theorem 17.5.11 that $D_\phi \mathbf{T}(t)$ is orthogonal to $\mathbf{T}(t)$.

Replacing $-\sin \phi$ by $\cos(\tfrac{1}{2}\pi + \phi)$ and $\cos \phi$ by $\sin(\tfrac{1}{2}\pi + \phi)$, we write (2) as

$$D_\phi \mathbf{T}(t) = \cos(\tfrac{1}{2}\pi + \phi)\mathbf{i} + \sin(\tfrac{1}{2}\pi + \phi)\mathbf{j} \tag{3}$$

From (3) and the previous discussion, the vector $D_\phi \mathbf{T}(t)$ is a unit vector orthogonal to $\mathbf{T}(t)$ in the direction $\tfrac{1}{2}\pi$ counterclockwise from the direction of $\mathbf{T}(t)$. The unit normal vector $\mathbf{N}(t)$ is also orthogonal to $\mathbf{T}(t)$. By the chain rule (Theorem 17.5.9), we have

$$D_t \mathbf{T}(t) = [D_\phi \mathbf{T}(t)]D_t \phi \tag{4}$$

Because the direction of $\mathbf{N}(t)$ is the same as the direction of $D_t \mathbf{T}(t)$, we see from (4) that the direction of $\mathbf{N}(t)$ is the same as the direction of $D_\phi \mathbf{T}(t)$ if $D_t \phi > 0$ (i.e., if $\mathbf{T}(t)$ turns counterclockwise as t increases), and the direction of $\mathbf{N}(t)$ is opposite that of $D_\phi \mathbf{T}(t)$ if $D_t \phi < 0$ (i.e., if $\mathbf{T}(t)$ turns clockwise as t increases). Because both $D_\phi \mathbf{T}(t)$ and $\mathbf{N}(t)$ are unit vectors, we conclude that

$$D_\phi \mathbf{T}(t) = \begin{cases} \mathbf{N}(t) & \text{if } D_t \phi > 0 \\ -\mathbf{N}(t) & \text{if } D_t \phi < 0 \end{cases} \tag{5}$$

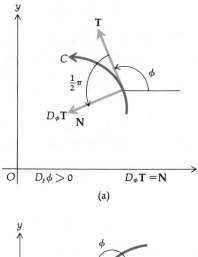

● ILLUSTRATION 1: In Fig. 17.9.2a, b, c, and d various cases are shown; in a and b, $D_t \phi > 0$, and in c and d, $D_t \phi < 0$. The positive direction along the curve C is indicated by the tip of the arrow on C. In each figure are shown the angle of radian measure ϕ and representations of the vectors $\mathbf{T}(t)$,

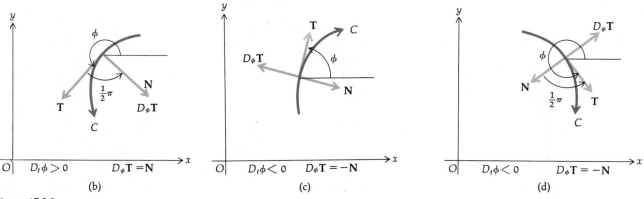

Figure 17.9.2

$D_\phi\mathbf{T}(t)$, and $\mathbf{N}(t)$. *The representation of the unit normal vector* $\mathbf{N}(t)$ *is always on the concave side of the curve.* ●

Consider now $D_s\mathbf{T}(t)$, where s units is the arc length measured from an arbitrarily chosen point on C to point P and s increases as t increases. By the chain rule

$$D_s\mathbf{T}(t) = D_\phi\mathbf{T}(t)D_s\phi$$

Hence,

$$|D_s\mathbf{T}(t)| = |D_\phi\mathbf{T}(t)D_s\phi| = |D_\phi\mathbf{T}(t)||D_s\phi|$$

But because $D_\phi\mathbf{T}(t)$ is a unit vector, $|D_\phi\mathbf{T}(t)| = 1$; thus, we have

$$|D_s\mathbf{T}(t)| = |D_s\phi| \tag{6}$$

The number $|D_s\phi|$ is the absolute value of the rate of change of the measure of the angle giving the direction of the unit tangent vector $\mathbf{T}(t)$ at a point on a curve with respect to the measure of arc length along the curve. This number is called the *curvature* of the curve at the point. Before giving the formal definition of curvature, let us see that taking it as this number is consistent with what we intuitively think of as the curvature. For example, at point P on C, ϕ is the radian measure of the angle giving the direction of the vector $\mathbf{T}(t)$, and s units is the arc length from a point P_0 on C to P. Let Q be a point on C for which the radian measure of the angle giving the direction of $\mathbf{T}(t + \Delta t)$ at Q is $\phi + \Delta\phi$ and $s + \Delta s$ units is the arc length from P_0 to Q. Then the arc length from P to Q is Δs units, and the ratio $\Delta\phi/\Delta s$ seems like a good measure of what we would intuitively think of as the *average curvature* along arc PQ.

● ILLUSTRATION 2: See Fig. 17.9.3a, b, c, and d: In a, $\Delta\phi > 0$ and $\Delta s > 0$; in b, $\Delta\phi > 0$ and $\Delta s < 0$; in c, $\Delta\phi < 0$ and $\Delta s > 0$; and in d, $\Delta\phi < 0$ and $\Delta s < 0$. ●

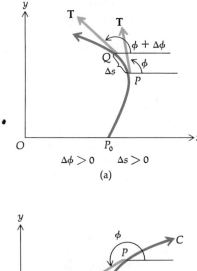

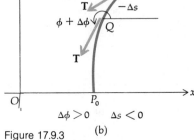

(a)

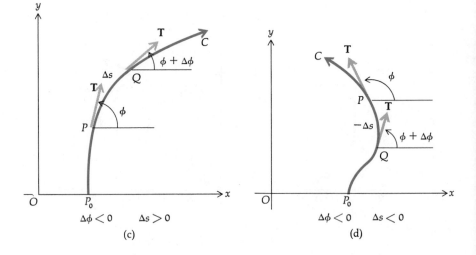

Figure 17.9.3

(b)

(c)

(d)

17.9.1 Definition   If $\mathbf{T}(t)$ is the unit tangent vector to a curve C at a point P, s is the arc length measured from an arbitrarily chosen point on C to P, and s increases as t increases, then the *curvature vector* of C at P, denoted by $\mathbf{K}(t)$, is given by

$$\mathbf{K}(t) = D_s\mathbf{T}(t) \tag{7}$$

The *curvature* of C at P, denoted by $K(t)$, is the magnitude of the curvature vector.

To find the curvature vector and the curvature for a particular curve it is convenient to have a formula expressing the curvature vector in terms of derivatives with respect to t. By the chain rule

$$D_t\mathbf{T}(t) = [D_s\mathbf{T}(t)]D_ts$$

Replacing D_ts by $|D_t\mathbf{R}(t)|$ and dividing by this, we obtain $D_s\mathbf{T}(t) = D_t\mathbf{T}(t)/|D_t\mathbf{R}(t)|$. So from (7) we have for the curvature vector

$$\mathbf{K}(t) = \frac{D_t\mathbf{T}(t)}{|D_t\mathbf{R}(t)|} \tag{8}$$

Because $K(t) = |\mathbf{K}(t)|$, the curvature is given by

$$K(t) = \left| \frac{D_t\mathbf{T}(t)}{|D_t\mathbf{R}(t)|} \right| \tag{9}$$

EXAMPLE 1:   Given the circle

$$x = a \cos t, y = a \sin t \quad a > 0$$

find the curvature vector and the curvature at any t.

SOLUTION: The vector equation of the circle is

$$\mathbf{R}(t) = a \cos t\mathbf{i} + a \sin t\mathbf{j}$$

So

$$D_t\mathbf{R}(t) = -a \sin t\mathbf{i} + a \cos t\mathbf{j}$$

$$|D_t\mathbf{R}(t)| = \sqrt{(-a \sin t)^2 + (a \cos t)^2} = a$$

So

$$\mathbf{T}(t) = \frac{D_t\mathbf{R}(t)}{|D_t\mathbf{R}(t)|} = -\sin t\mathbf{i} + \cos t\mathbf{j}$$

$$D_t\mathbf{T}(t) = -\cos t\mathbf{i} - \sin t\mathbf{j}$$

$$\frac{D_t\mathbf{T}(t)}{|D_t\mathbf{R}(t)|} = -\frac{\cos t}{a}\mathbf{i} - \frac{\sin t}{a}\mathbf{j}$$

So the curvature vector

$$\mathbf{K}(t) = -\frac{1}{a} \cos t\mathbf{i} - \frac{1}{a} \sin t\mathbf{j}$$

and the curvature

$$K(t) = |\mathbf{K}(t)| = \frac{1}{a}$$

The result of Example 1 states that the curvature of a circle is constant and is the reciprocal of the radius.

Suppose that we are given a curve C and at a particular point P the curvature exists and is $K(t)$, where $K(t) \neq 0$. Consider the circle which is tangent to curve C at P and has curvature $K(t)$ at P. From Example 1, we know that the radius of this circle is $1/K(t)$ and that its center is on a line perpendicular to the tangent line in the direction of $\mathbf{N}(t)$. This circle is called the *circle of curvature*, and its radius is the *radius of curvature* of C at P. The circle of curvature is sometimes referred to as the *osculating circle*.

17.9.2 Definition   If $K(t)$ is the curvature of a curve C at point P and $K(t) \neq 0$, then the *radius of curvature* of C at P, denoted by $\rho(t)$, is defined by

$$\rho(t) = \frac{1}{K(t)}$$

EXAMPLE 2:   Given that a vector equation of a curve C is

$$\mathbf{R}(t) = 2t\mathbf{i} + (t^2 - 1)\mathbf{j}$$

find the curvature and the radius of curvature at $t = 1$. Draw a sketch of a portion of the curve, the unit tangent vector, and the circle of curvature at $t = 1$.

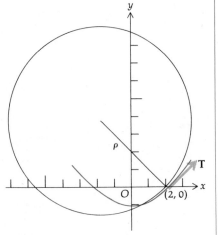

Figure 17.9.4

SOLUTION:

$$\mathbf{R}(t) = 2t\mathbf{i} + (t^2 - 1)\mathbf{j}$$

$$D_t\mathbf{R}(t) = 2\mathbf{i} + 2t\mathbf{j}$$

$$|D_t\mathbf{R}(t)| = 2\sqrt{1 + t^2}$$

$$\mathbf{T}(t) = \frac{D_t\mathbf{R}(t)}{|D_t\mathbf{R}(t)|} = \frac{1}{\sqrt{1 + t^2}}\mathbf{i} + \frac{t}{\sqrt{1 + t^2}}\mathbf{j}$$

$$D_t\mathbf{T}(t) = -\frac{t}{(1 + t^2)^{3/2}}\mathbf{i} + \frac{1}{(1 + t^2)^{3/2}}\mathbf{j}$$

$$\frac{D_t\mathbf{T}(t)}{|D_t\mathbf{R}(t)|} = -\frac{t}{2(1 + t^2)^2}\mathbf{i} + \frac{t}{2(1 + t^2)^2}\mathbf{j}$$

$$K(t) = \left|\frac{D_t\mathbf{T}(t)}{|D_t\mathbf{R}(t)|}\right| = \sqrt{\frac{t^2}{4(1 + t^2)^4} + \frac{1}{4(1 + t^2)^4}}$$

$$K(t) = \frac{1}{2(1 + t^2)^{3/2}}$$

So

$$K(1) = \frac{1}{4\sqrt{2}} \qquad \rho(1) = 4\sqrt{2}$$

and

$$\mathbf{T}(1) = \frac{1}{\sqrt{2}}\mathbf{i} + \frac{1}{\sqrt{2}}\mathbf{j}$$

Figure 17.9.4 shows the sketch that is required. The accompanying

Table 17.9.1 gives the corresponding values of x and y for $t = -2, -1, 0, 1,$ and 2.

Table 17.9.1

t	x	y
-2	-4	3
-1	-2	0
0	0	-1
1	2	0
2	4	3

We now find a formula for computing the curvature directly from parametric equations of the curve, $x = f(t)$ and $y = g(t)$. From Eq. (6) $|D_s\mathbf{T}(t)| = |D_s\phi|$, and so

$$K(t) = |D_s\phi|$$

Assuming that s and t increase together, we have

$$D_s\phi = \frac{d\phi}{ds} = \frac{\dfrac{d\phi}{dt}}{\dfrac{ds}{dt}} = \frac{\dfrac{d\phi}{dt}}{\sqrt{[f'(t)]^2 + [g'(t)]^2}}$$

So

$$D_s\phi = \frac{\dfrac{d\phi}{dt}}{\sqrt{\left(\dfrac{dx}{dt}\right)^2 + \left(\dfrac{dy}{dt}\right)^2}} \tag{10}$$

To find $d\phi/dt$, we observe that because ϕ is the radian measure of the angle giving the direction of the unit tangent vector,

$$\tan \phi = \frac{dy}{dx} = \frac{\dfrac{dy}{dt}}{\dfrac{dx}{dt}} \tag{11}$$

Differentiating implicitly with respect to t the left and right members of (11), we obtain

$$\sec^2 \phi \, \frac{d\phi}{dt} = \frac{\left(\dfrac{dx}{dt}\right)\left(\dfrac{d^2y}{dt^2}\right) - \left(\dfrac{dy}{dt}\right)\left(\dfrac{d^2x}{dt^2}\right)}{\left(\dfrac{dx}{dt}\right)^2}$$

So

$$\frac{d\phi}{dt} = \frac{\left(\dfrac{dx}{dt}\right)\left(\dfrac{d^2y}{dt^2}\right) - \left(\dfrac{dy}{dt}\right)\left(\dfrac{d^2x}{dt^2}\right)}{\sec^2\phi\left(\dfrac{dx}{dt}\right)^2} \tag{12}$$

But

$$\sec^2\phi = 1 + \tan^2\phi = 1 + \frac{\left(\dfrac{dy}{dt}\right)^2}{\left(\dfrac{dx}{dt}\right)^2}$$

Substituting this expression for $\sec^2\phi$ in (12), we get

$$\frac{d\phi}{dt} = \frac{\left(\dfrac{dx}{dt}\right)\left(\dfrac{d^2y}{dt^2}\right) - \left(\dfrac{dy}{dt}\right)\left(\dfrac{d^2x}{dt^2}\right)}{\left(\dfrac{dx}{dt}\right)^2 + \left(\dfrac{dy}{dt}\right)^2} \tag{13}$$

Substituting from (13) into (10), and because $K(t) = |D_s\phi|$, we have

$$K(t) = \frac{\left|\left(\dfrac{dx}{dt}\right)\left(\dfrac{d^2y}{dt^2}\right) - \left(\dfrac{dy}{dt}\right)\left(\dfrac{d^2x}{dt^2}\right)\right|}{\left[\left(\dfrac{dx}{dt}\right)^2 + \left(\dfrac{dy}{dt}\right)^2\right]^{3/2}} \tag{14}$$

EXAMPLE 3:   Find the curvature of the curve in Example 2 by using formula (14).

SOLUTION: Parametric equations of C are $x = 2t$ and $y = t^2 - 1$. Hence,

$$\frac{dx}{dt} = 2 \qquad \frac{d^2x}{dt^2} = 0 \qquad \frac{dy}{dt} = 2t \qquad \frac{d^2y}{dt^2} = 2$$

From (14) we have, then,

$$K(t) = \frac{|2(2) - 2t(0)|}{[(2)^2 + (2t)^2]^{3/2}} = \frac{4}{(4 + 4t^2)^{3/2}} = \frac{1}{2(1 + t^2)^{3/2}}$$

Suppose that we are given a cartesian equation of a curve, either in the form $y = F(x)$ or $x = G(y)$. Special cases of formula (14) can be used to find the curvature of a curve in such situations.

If $y = F(x)$ is an equation of a curve C, a set of parametric equations of C is $x = t$ and $y = F(t)$. Then $dx/dt = 1$, $d^2x/dt^2 = 0$, $dy/dt = dy/dx$, and $d^2y/dt^2 = d^2y/dx^2$. Substituting into (14), we obtain

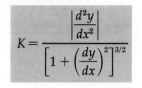

$$K = \frac{\left|\dfrac{d^2y}{dx^2}\right|}{\left[1 + \left(\dfrac{dy}{dx}\right)^2\right]^{3/2}} \tag{15}$$

Similarly, if an equation of a curve C is $x = G(y)$, we obtain

$$K = \frac{\left|\dfrac{d^2x}{dy^2}\right|}{\left[1 + \left(\dfrac{dx}{dy}\right)^2\right]^{3/2}}$$ (16)

EXAMPLE 4:   If the curve C has an equation $xy = 1$, find the radius of curvature of C at the point $(1, 1)$ and draw a sketch of the curve and the circle of curvature at $(1, 1)$.

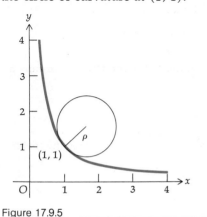

Figure 17.9.5

SOLUTION: Solving for y, we obtain $y = 1/x$. So $dy/dx = -1/x^2$ and $d^2y/dx^2 = 2/x^3$. Applying formula (15), we have

$$K = \frac{\left|\dfrac{2}{x^3}\right|}{\left[1 + \left(\dfrac{1}{x^4}\right)\right]^{3/2}} = \frac{2x^6}{|x^3|(x^4+1)^{3/2}} = \frac{2x^4}{|x|(x^4+1)^{3/2}}$$

Because $\rho = 1/K$, we have

$$\rho = \frac{|x|(x^4+1)^{3/2}}{2x^4}$$

So at $(1, 1)$, $\rho = \sqrt{2}$. The required sketch is shown in Fig. 17.9.5.

Exercises 17.9

In Exercises 1 through 4, find the curvature K and the radius of curvature ρ at the point where $t = t_1$. Use formula (9) to find K. Draw a sketch showing a portion of the curve, the unit tangent vector, and the circle of curvature at $t = t_1$.

1. $\mathbf{R}(t) = 2t\mathbf{i} + (t^2 - 1)\mathbf{j}$; $t_1 = 1$

2. $\mathbf{R}(t) = (t^2 - 2t)\mathbf{i} + (t^3 - t)\mathbf{j}$; $t_1 = 1$

3. $\mathbf{R}(t) = 2e^t\mathbf{i} + 2e^{-t}\mathbf{j}$; $t_1 = 0$

4. $\mathbf{R}(t) = \sin t\mathbf{i} + \sin 2t\mathbf{j}$; $t_1 = \tfrac{1}{2}\pi$

In Exercises 5 and 6, find the curvature K by using formula (14). Then find K and ρ at the point where $t = t_1$ and draw a sketch showing a portion of the curve, the unit tangent vector, and the circle of curvature at $t = t_1$.

5. $x = \dfrac{1}{1+t}$, $y = \dfrac{1}{1-t}$; $t_1 = 0$

6. $x = e^t + e^{-t}$, $y = e^t - e^{-t}$; $t_1 = 0$

In Exercises 7 through 12, find the curvature K and the radius of curvature ρ at the given point. Draw a sketch showing a portion of the curve, a piece of the tangent line, and the circle of curvature at the given point.

7. $y = 2\sqrt{x}$; $(0, 0)$

8. $y^2 = x^3$; $(\tfrac{1}{4}, \tfrac{1}{8})$

9. $y = e^x$; $(0, 1)$

10. $4x^2 + 9y^2 = 36$; $(0, 2)$

11. $x = \sin y$; $(\tfrac{1}{2}, \tfrac{1}{6}\pi)$

12. $x = \tan y$; $(1, \tfrac{1}{4}\pi)$

In Exercises 13 through 18, find the radius of curvature at any point on the given curve.

13. $y = \sin^{-1} x$

14. $y = \ln \sec x$

15. $x^{1/2} + y^{1/2} = a^{1/2}$

16. $\mathbf{R}(t) = e^t \sin t\,\mathbf{i} + e^t \cos t\,\mathbf{j}$

17. The cycloid $x = a(t - \sin t),\ y = a(1 - \cos t)$

18. The tractrix $x = t - a \tanh \dfrac{t}{a},\ y = a \operatorname{sech} \dfrac{t}{a}$

19. Show that the curvature of the catenary $y = a \cosh (x/a)$ at any point (x, y) on the curve is a/y^2. Draw the circle of curvature at $(0, a)$. Show that the curvature K is an absolute maximum at the point $(0, a)$ without referring to $K'(x)$.

In Exercises 20 through 23, find a point on the given curve at which the curvature is an absolute maximum.

20. $y = e^x$

21. $y = 6x - x^2$

22. $y = \sin x$

23. $\mathbf{R}(t) = (2t - 3)\mathbf{i} + (t^2 - 1)\mathbf{j}$

24. If a polar equation of a curve is $r = F(\theta)$, prove that the curvature K is given by the formula

$$K = \frac{|r^2 + 2(dr/d\theta)^2 - r(d^2r/d\theta^2)|}{[r^2 + (dr/d\theta)^2]^{3/2}}$$

In Exercises 25 through 28, find the curvature K and the radius of curvature ρ at the indicated point. Use the formula of Exercise 24 to find K.

25. $r = 4 \cos 2\theta;\ \theta = \frac{1}{12}\pi$

26. $r = 1 - \sin \theta;\ \theta = 0$

27. $r = a \sec^2 \frac{1}{2}\theta;\ \theta = \frac{2}{3}\pi$

28. $r = a\theta;\ \theta = 1$

29. The center of the circle of curvature of a curve C at a point P is called the *center of curvature* at P. Prove that the coordinates of the center of curvature of a curve at $P(x, y)$ are given by

$$x_c = x - \frac{(dy/dx)[1 + (dy/dx)^2]}{d^2y/dx^2} \qquad y_c = y + \frac{(dy/dx)^2 + 1}{d^2y/dx^2}$$

In Exercises 30 through 32, find the curvature K, the radius of curvature ρ, and the center of curvature at the given point. Draw a sketch of the curve and the circle of curvature.

30. $y = \cos x;\ (\frac{1}{3}\pi, \frac{1}{2})$

31. $y = x^4 - x^2;\ (0, 0)$

32. $y = \ln x;\ (1, 0)$

In Exercises 33 through 36, find the coordinates of the center of curvature at any point.

33. $y^2 = 4px$

34. $y^3 = a^2 x$

35. $\mathbf{R}(t) = a \cos t\,\mathbf{i} + b \sin t\,\mathbf{j}$

36. $\mathbf{R}(t) = a \cos^3 t\,\mathbf{i} + a \sin^3 t\,\mathbf{j}$

17.10 TANGENTIAL AND NORMAL COMPONENTS OF ACCELERATION

If a particle is moving along a curve C having the vector equation

$$\mathbf{R}(t) = f(t)\mathbf{i} + g(t)\mathbf{j} \tag{1}$$

from Definition 17.7.1, the velocity vector at P is given by

$$\mathbf{V}(t) = D_t\mathbf{R}(t) \tag{2}$$

From Sec. 17.8, if $\mathbf{T}(t)$ is the unit tangent vector at P, s is the length of arc of C from a fixed point P_0 to P, and s increases as t increases, we have

$$D_t\mathbf{R}(t) = D_t s[\mathbf{T}(t)] \tag{3}$$

Substituting from (3) into (2), we have

$$\mathbf{V}(t) = D_t s[\mathbf{T}(t)] \tag{4}$$

Equation (4) expresses the velocity vector at a point as a scalar times the unit tangent vector at the point. We now proceed to express the acceleration vector at a point in terms of the unit tangent and unit normal vectors at the point. From Definition 17.7.2 the acceleration vector at P is given by

$$\mathbf{A}(t) = D_t^2 \mathbf{R}(t) \tag{5}$$

From Eq. (6) in Sec. 17.8 we have

$$D_t^2 \mathbf{R}(t) = [D_t|D_t\mathbf{R}(t)|]\mathbf{T}(t) + |D_t\mathbf{R}(t)||D_t\mathbf{T}(t)|\mathbf{N}(t) \tag{6}$$

Because

$$D_t s = |D_t\mathbf{R}(t)| \tag{7}$$

if we differentiate with respect to t, we obtain

$$D_t^2 s = D_t|D_t\mathbf{R}(t)| \tag{8}$$

Furthermore,

$$|D_t\mathbf{R}(t)||D_t\mathbf{T}(t)| = |D_t\mathbf{R}(t)|^2 \left|\frac{D_t\mathbf{T}(t)}{|D_t\mathbf{R}(t)|}\right| \tag{9}$$

Applying (7) above and Eq. (9) of Sec. 17.9 to the right side of (9), we have

$$|D_t\mathbf{R}(t)||D_t\mathbf{T}(t)| = (D_t s)^2 K(t) \tag{10}$$

Substituting from (5), (8), and (10) into (6), we obtain

$$\mathbf{A}(t) = (D_t^2 s)\mathbf{T}(t) + (D_t s)^2 K(t)\mathbf{N}(t) \tag{11}$$

Equation (11) expresses the acceleration vector as the sum of a scalar times the unit tangent vector and a scalar times the unit normal vector. The coefficient of $\mathbf{T}(t)$ is called the *tangential component* of the acceleration vector and is denoted by $A_T(t)$, whereas the coefficient of $\mathbf{N}(t)$ is called the *normal component* of the acceleration vector and is denoted by $A_N(t)$. So

$$A_T(t) = D_t^2 s \tag{12}$$

and

$$A_N(t) = (D_t s)^2 K(t) \tag{13}$$

or, equivalently,

$$A_N(t) = \frac{(D_t s)^2}{\rho(t)} \tag{14}$$

Because the number of units in the speed of the particle at time t units is $|\mathbf{V}(t)| = D_t s$, $A_T(t)$ is the derivative of the measure of the speed of the particle and $A_N(t)$ is the square of the measure of the speed divided by the radius of curvature.

From Newton's second law of motion

$$\mathbf{F} = m\mathbf{A}$$

where $\mathbf{F}$ is the force vector applied to the moving object, m is the measure of the mass of the object, and $\mathbf{A}$ is the acceleration vector of the object. In curvilinear motion, the normal component of $\mathbf{F}$ is the force normal to the curve necessary to keep the object on the curve. For example, if an automobile is going around a curve at a high speed, then the normal force must have a large magnitude to keep the car on the road. Also, if the curve is sharp, the radius of curvature is a small number, and so the magnitude of the normal force must be a large number.

Equation (4) indicates that the tangential component of the velocity vector is $D_t s$ and that the normal component of the velocity vector is zero.

Substituting from (12) and (13) into (11), we have

$$\mathbf{A}(t) = A_T(t)\mathbf{T}(t) + A_N(t)\mathbf{N}(t) \tag{15}$$

from which it follows that

$$|\mathbf{A}(t)| = \sqrt{[A_T(t)]^2 + [A_N(t)]^2}$$

Solving for $A_N(t)$, noting from (13) that $A_N(t)$ is nonnegative, we have

$$A_N(t) = \sqrt{|\mathbf{A}(t)|^2 - [A_T(t)]^2} \tag{16}$$

EXAMPLE 1:   A particle is moving along the curve having the vector equation

$$\mathbf{R}(t) = (t^2 - 1)\mathbf{i} + (\tfrac{1}{3}t^3 - t)\mathbf{j}$$

Find each of the following vectors: $\mathbf{V}(t), \mathbf{A}(t), \mathbf{T}(t)$, and $\mathbf{N}(t)$. Also, find the following scalars: $|\mathbf{V}(t)|$, $A_T(t), A_N(t)$, and $K(t)$. Find the particular values when $t = 2$. Draw a sketch showing a portion of the curve at the point where $t = 2$, and representations of $\mathbf{V}(2), \mathbf{A}(2)$, $A_T(2)\mathbf{T}(2)$, and $A_N(2)\mathbf{N}(2)$, having their initial point at $t = 2$.

SOLUTION:

$$\mathbf{V}(t) = D_t\mathbf{R}(t) = 2t\mathbf{i} + (t^2 - 1)\mathbf{j}$$

$$\mathbf{A}(t) = D_t\mathbf{V}(t) = 2\mathbf{i} + 2t\mathbf{j}$$

$$|\mathbf{V}(t)| = \sqrt{4t^2 + t^4 - 2t^2 + 1} = \sqrt{t^4 + 2t^2 + 1} = t^2 + 1$$

$$|\mathbf{A}(t)| = \sqrt{4 + 4t^2} = 2\sqrt{1 + t^2}$$

$$D_t s = |\mathbf{V}(t)| = t^2 + 1$$

$$A_T(t) = D_t^2 s = 2t$$

From (16)

$$A_N(t) = \sqrt{|\mathbf{A}(t)|^2 - [A_T(t)]^2} = \sqrt{4 + 4t^2 - 4t^2} = 2$$

$$\mathbf{T}(t) = \frac{\mathbf{V}(t)}{|\mathbf{V}(t)|} = \frac{2t}{t^2 + 1}\mathbf{i} + \frac{t^2 - 1}{t^2 + 1}\mathbf{j}$$

To find $\mathbf{N}(t)$, we use the following formula which comes from (11):

$$\mathbf{N}(t) = \frac{1}{(D_t s)^2 K(t)}[\mathbf{A}(t) - (D_t^2 s)\mathbf{T}(t)] \tag{17}$$

$$\mathbf{A}(t) - (D_t{}^2 s)\mathbf{T}(t) = 2\mathbf{i} + 2t\mathbf{j} - 2t\left(\frac{2t}{t^2+1}\mathbf{i} + \frac{t^2-1}{t^2+1}\mathbf{j}\right)$$

$$\mathbf{A}(t) - (D_t{}^2 s)\mathbf{T}(t) = \frac{2}{t^2+1}\left[(1-t^2)\mathbf{i} + 2t\mathbf{j}\right] \tag{18}$$

From (17) we see that $\mathbf{N}(t)$ is a scalar times the vector in (18). Because $\mathbf{N}(t)$ is a unit vector, $\mathbf{N}(t)$ can be obtained by dividing the vector in (18) by its magnitude. Thus, we have

$$\mathbf{N}(t) = \frac{(1-t^2)\mathbf{i} + 2t\mathbf{j}}{\sqrt{(1-t^2)^2 + (2t)^2}} = \frac{1-t^2}{1+t^2}\mathbf{i} + \frac{2t}{1+t^2}\mathbf{j}$$

$K(t)$ is found from (13), and we have

$$K(t) = \frac{A_N(t)}{(D_t s)^2} = \frac{2}{(t^2+1)^2}$$

When $t=2$, we obtain $\mathbf{V}(2) = 4\mathbf{i} + 3\mathbf{j}$, $\mathbf{A}(2) = 2\mathbf{i} + 4\mathbf{j}$, $|\mathbf{V}(2)| = 5$, $A_T(2) = 4$, $A_N(2) = 2$, $\mathbf{T}(2) = \frac{4}{5}\mathbf{i} + \frac{3}{5}\mathbf{j}$, $\mathbf{N}(2) = -\frac{3}{5}\mathbf{i} + \frac{4}{5}\mathbf{j}$, $K(2) = \frac{2}{25}$. The required sketch is shown in Fig. 17.10.1.

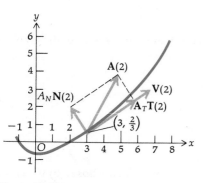

Figure 17.10.1

Exercises 17.10

In Exercises 1 through 6, a particle is moving along the curve having the given vector equation. In each problem, find the vectors $\mathbf{V}(t)$, $\mathbf{A}(t)$, $\mathbf{T}(t)$, and $\mathbf{N}(t)$, and the following scalars for an arbitrary value of t: $|\mathbf{V}(t)|$, A_T, A_N, $K(t)$. Also find the particular values when $t = t_1$. At $t = t_1$, draw a sketch of a portion of the curve and representations of the vectors $\mathbf{V}(t_1)$, $\mathbf{A}(t_1)$, $A_T\mathbf{T}(t_1)$, and $A_N\mathbf{N}(t_1)$.

1. $\mathbf{R}(t) = (2t+3)\mathbf{i} + (t^2-1)\mathbf{j}$; $t_1 = 2$
2. $\mathbf{R}(t) = (t-1)\mathbf{i} + t^2\mathbf{j}$; $t_1 = 1$
3. $\mathbf{R}(t) = 5\cos 3t\mathbf{i} + 5\sin 3t\mathbf{j}$; $t_1 = \frac{1}{3}\pi$
4. $\mathbf{R}(t) = \cos t^2\mathbf{i} + \sin t^2\mathbf{j}$; $t_1 = \frac{1}{2}\sqrt{\pi}$
5. $\mathbf{R}(t) = e^t\mathbf{i} + e^{-t}\mathbf{j}$; $t_1 = 0$
6. $\mathbf{R}(t) = 3t^2\mathbf{i} + 2t^3\mathbf{j}$; $t_1 = 1$

7. A particle is moving along the parabola $y^2 = 8x$ and its speed is constant. Find each of the following when the particle is at $(2, 4)$: the position vector, the velocity vector, the acceleration vector, the unit tangent vector, the unit normal vector, A_T, and A_N.

8. A particle is moving along the top branch of the hyperbola $y^2 - x^2 = 9$, such that $D_t x$ is a positive constant. Find each of the following when the particle is at $(4, 5)$: the position vector, the velocity vector, the acceleration vector, the unit tangent vector, the unit normal vector, A_T, and A_N.

Review Exercises (Chapter 17)

In Exercises 1 through 12, let $\mathbf{A} = 4\mathbf{i} - 6\mathbf{j}$, $\mathbf{B} = \mathbf{i} + 7\mathbf{j}$, and $\mathbf{C} = 9\mathbf{i} - 5\mathbf{j}$.

1. Find $3\mathbf{B} - 7\mathbf{A}$
2. Find $4\mathbf{A} + \mathbf{B} - 6\mathbf{C}$
3. Find $5\mathbf{B} - 3\mathbf{C}$
4. Find $|5\mathbf{B}| - |3\mathbf{C}|$
5. Find $(\mathbf{A} - \mathbf{B}) \cdot \mathbf{C}$
6. Find $(\mathbf{A} \cdot \mathbf{B})\mathbf{C}$

7. Find a unit vector having the same direction as $2\mathbf{A} + \mathbf{B}$.

8. Find the unit vectors that are orthogonal to $\mathbf{B}$.

9. Find scalars h and k such that $\mathbf{A} = h\mathbf{B} + k\mathbf{C}$.

10. Find the vector projection of $\mathbf{C}$ onto $\mathbf{A}$.

11. Find the component of $\mathbf{A}$ in the direction of $\mathbf{B}$.

12. Find $\cos \alpha$ if α is the radian measure of the angle between $\mathbf{A}$ and $\mathbf{C}$.

In Exercises 13 and 14, for the vector-valued function, find (a) the domain of $\mathbf{R}$; (b) $\lim\limits_{t \to 1} \mathbf{R}(t)$; (c) $D_t\mathbf{R}(t)$.

13. $\mathbf{R}(t) = \dfrac{1}{t+1}\mathbf{i} + \dfrac{\sqrt{t}-1}{t-1}\mathbf{j}$

14. $\mathbf{R}(t) = |t-1|\mathbf{i} + \ln t\,\mathbf{j}$

In Exercises 15 and 16, find equations of the horizontal and vertical tangent lines, and then draw a sketch of the graph of the given pair of parametric equations.

15. $x = 12 - t^2$, $y = 12t - t^3$

16. $x = \dfrac{2at^2}{1+t^2}$, $y = \dfrac{2at^3}{1+t^2}$, $a > 0$ (the cissoid of Diocles)

17. Find the length of the arc of the curve $\mathbf{R}(t) = (2-t)\mathbf{i} + t^2\mathbf{j}$ from $t = 0$ to $t = 3$.

18. Find the length of the arc of the curve $r = 3 \sec \theta$ from $\theta = 0$ to $\theta = \frac{1}{4}\pi$.

19. (a) Show that the curve defined by the parametric equations, $x = a \sin t$ and $y = b \cos t$, is an ellipse. (b) If s is the measure of the length of arc of the ellipse of part (a), show that

$$s = 4 \int_0^{\pi/2} a\sqrt{1 - k^2 \sin^2 t}\; dt$$

where $k^2 = (a^2 - b^2)/a^2 < 1$. This integral is called an *elliptic integral* and cannot be evaluated exactly in terms of elementary functions. There are tables available that give the value of the integral in terms of k.

20. Draw a sketch of the graph of the vector equation $\mathbf{R}(t) = e^t\mathbf{i} + e^{-t}\mathbf{j}$ and find a cartesian equation of the graph.

21. Show that the curvature of the curve $y = \ln x$ at any point (x, y) is $x/(x^2 + 1)^{3/2}$. Also show that the absolute maximum curvature is $2/3\sqrt{3}$ which occurs at the point $(\frac{1}{2}\sqrt{2}, -\frac{1}{2} \ln 2)$.

22. Find the curvature at any point of the branch of the hyperbola defined by $x = a \cosh t$, $y = b \sinh t$. Also show that the curvature is an absolute maximum at the vertex.

23. Find the radius of curvature at any point on the curve $x = a(\cos t + t \sin t)$, $y = a(\sin t - t \cos t)$.

24. Find the curvature, the radius of curvature, and the center of curvature of the curve $y = e^{-x}$ at the point $(0, 1)$.

25. For the hypocycloid of four cusps, $x = a \cos^3 t$ and $y = a \sin^3 t$, find dy/dx and d^2y/dx^2 without eliminating the parameter.

26. A particle is moving along a curve having the vector equation $\mathbf{R}(t) = 3t\mathbf{i} + (4t - t^2)\mathbf{j}$. Find a cartesian equation of the path of the particle. Also find the velocity vector and the acceleration vector at $t = 1$.

27. Find the tangential and normal components of the acceleration vector for the particle of Exercise 26.

28. If a particle is moving along a curve, under what conditions will the acceleration vector and the unit tangent vector have the same or opposite directions?

In Exercises 29 and 30, for the given curve find $\mathbf{T}(t)$ and $\mathbf{N}(t)$, and at $t = t_1$ draw a sketch of a portion of the curve and draw the representations of $\mathbf{T}(t_1)$ and $\mathbf{N}(t_1)$ having initial point at $t = t_1$.

29. $\mathbf{R}(t) = (e^t + e^{-t})\mathbf{i} + 2t\mathbf{j}$; $t_1 = 2$

30. $\mathbf{R}(t) = 3(\cos t + t \sin t)\mathbf{i} + 3(\sin t - t \cos t)\mathbf{j}$, $t > 0$; $t_1 = \frac{1}{2}\pi$

31. Given the curve having parametric equations $x = 4t$, $y = \frac{1}{3}(2t+1)^{3/2}$, $t \geq 0$, find parametric equations having the measure of arc length s as a parameter, where arc length is measured from the point where $t = 0$. Check your result by using Eq. (10) of Sec. 17.8

32. Find the radian measure of the angle of elevation at which a gun should be fired in order to obtain the maximum range for a given muzzle speed.

33. Find a formula for obtaining the maximum height reached by a projectile fired from a gun having a given muzzle speed of v_0 ft/sec and an angle of elevation of radian measure α.

34. Find the position vector $\mathbf{R}(t)$ if the acceleration vector

$$\mathbf{A}(t) = t^2 \mathbf{i} - \frac{1}{t^2}\mathbf{j}$$

and $\mathbf{V}(1) = \mathbf{j}$, and $\mathbf{R}(1) = -\frac{1}{4}\mathbf{i} + \frac{1}{2}\mathbf{j}$.

35. Prove by vector analysis that the diagonals of a parallelogram bisect each other.

36. Given triangle ABC, points D, E, and F are on sides AB, BC, and AC, respectively, and $\mathbf{V}(\overrightarrow{AD}) = \frac{1}{3}\mathbf{V}(\overrightarrow{AB})$; $\mathbf{V}(\overrightarrow{BE}) = \frac{1}{3}\mathbf{V}(\overrightarrow{BC})$; $\mathbf{V}(\overrightarrow{CF}) = \frac{1}{3}\mathbf{V}(\overrightarrow{CA})$. Prove $\mathbf{V}(\overrightarrow{AE}) + \mathbf{V}(\overrightarrow{BF}) + \mathbf{V}(\overrightarrow{CD}) = \mathbf{0}$.

In Exercises 37 and 38, find the velocity and acceleration vectors, the speed, and the tangential and normal components of acceleration.

37. $\mathbf{R}(t) = \cosh 2t\mathbf{i} + \sinh 2t\mathbf{j}$

38. $\mathbf{R}(t) = (2 \tan^{-1} t - t)\mathbf{i} + \ln(1 + t^2)\mathbf{j}$

39. An *epicycloid* is the curve traced by a point P on the circumference of a circle of radius b which is rolling externally on a fixed circle of radius a. If the origin is at the center of the fixed circle, $A(a, 0)$ is one of the points at which the given point P comes in contact with the fixed circle, B is the moving point of tangency of the two circles, and the parameter t is the radian measure of the angle AOB, prove that parametric equations of the epicycloid are

$$x = (a + b) \cos t - b \cos \frac{a+b}{b} t$$

and

$$y = (a + b) \sin t - b \sin \frac{a+b}{b} t$$

18

Vectors in three-dimensional space and solid analytic geometry

18.1 R^3, THE THREE-DIMENSIONAL NUMBER SPACE

In Chapter 1 we discussed the number line R^1 (the one-dimensional number space) and the number plane R^2 (the two-dimensional number space). We identified the real numbers in R^1 with points on a horizontal axis and the real number pairs in R^2 with points in a geometric plane. In an analogous fashion, we now introduce the set of all ordered triples of real numbers.

18.1.1 Definition

The set of all ordered triples of real numbers is called the *three-dimensional number space* and is denoted by R^3. Each ordered triple (x, y, z) is called a *point* in the three-dimensional number space.

To represent R^3 in a geometric three-dimensional space we consider the directed distances of a point from three mutually perpendicular planes. The planes are formed by first considering three mutually perpendicular lines which intersect at a point that we call the *origin* and denote by the letter O. These lines, called the coordinate axes, are designated as the x axis, the y axis, and the z axis. Usually the x axis and the y axis are taken in a horizontal plane, and the z axis is vertical. A positive direction is selected on each axis. If the positive directions are chosen as in Fig. 18.1.1, the coordinate system is called a *right-handed system*. This terminology follows from the fact that if the right hand is placed so the thumb is pointed in the positive direction of the x axis and the index finger is pointed in the positive direction of the y axis, then the middle finger is pointed in the positive direction of the z axis. If the middle finger is pointed in the negative direction of the z axis, then the coordinate system is called *left handed*. A left-handed system is shown in Fig. 18.1.2. In general, we use a right-handed system. The three axes determine three coordinate planes: the xy plane containing the x and y axes, the xz plane containing the x and z axes, and the yz plane containing the y and z axes.

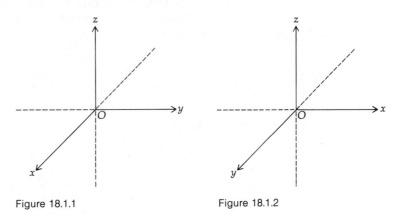

Figure 18.1.1   Figure 18.1.2

An ordered triple of real numbers (x, y, z) is associated with each point P in a geometric three-dimensional space. The directed distance of P

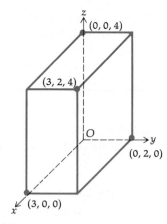

Figure 18.1.3

from the yz plane is called the x coordinate, the directed distance of P from the xz plane is called the y coordinate, and the z coordinate is the directed distance of P from the xy plane. These three coordinates are called the *rectangular cartesian coordinates* of the point, and there is a one-to-one correspondence (called a *rectangular cartesian coordinate system*) between all such ordered triples of real numbers and the points in a geometric three-dimensional space. Hence, we identify R^3 with the geometric three-dimensional space, and we call an ordered triple (x, y, z) a point. The point $(3, 2, 4)$ is shown in Fig. 18.1.3, and the point $(4, -2, -5)$ is shown in Fig. 18.1.4. The three coordinate planes divide the space into eight parts, called *octants*. The first octant is the one in which all three coordinates are positive.

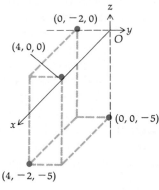

Figure 18.1.4

A line is parallel to a plane if and only if the distance from any point on the line to the plane is the same.

● ILLUSTRATION 1: A line parallel to the yz plane, one parallel to the xz plane, and one parallel to the xy plane are shown in Fig. 18.1.5a, b, and c, respectively.   ●

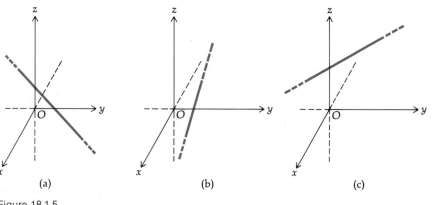

Figure 18.1.5

We consider all lines lying in a given plane as being parallel to the plane, in which case the distance from any point on the line to the plane is zero. The following theorem follows immediately.

18.1.2 Theorem   (i) A line is parallel to the yz plane if and only if all points on the line have equal x coordinates.
(ii) A line is parallel to the xz plane if and only if all points on the line have equal y coordinates.
(iii) A line is parallel to the xy plane if and only if all points on the line have equal z coordinates.

In three-dimensional space, if a line is parallel to each of two intersecting planes, it is parallel to the line of intersection of the two planes. Also, if a given line is parallel to a second line, then the given line is parallel to any plane containing the second line. Theorem 18.1.3 follows from these two facts from solid geometry and from Theorem 18.1.2.

18.1.3 Theorem   (i) A line is parallel to the x axis if and only if all points on the line have equal y coordinates and equal z coordinates.
(ii) A line is parallel to the y axis if and only if all points on the line have equal x coordinates and equal z coordinates.
(iii) A line is parallel to the z axis if and only if all points on the line have equal x coordinates and equal y coordinates.

● ILLUSTRATION 2: A line parallel to the x axis, a line parallel to the y axis, and a line parallel to the z axis are shown in Fig. 18.1.6a, b, and c, respectively.   ●

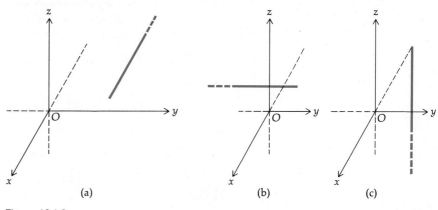

(a)   (b)   (c)

Figure 18.1.6

The formulas for finding the directed distance from one point to another on a line parallel to a coordinate axis follow from the definition of directed distance given in Sec. 1.4 and are stated in the following theorem.

18.1.4 Theorem

(i) If $A(x_1, y, z)$ and $B(x_2, y, z)$ are two points on a line parallel to the x axis, then the directed distance from A to B, denoted by $\overline{AB}$, is given by

$$\overline{AB} = x_2 - x_1$$

(ii) If $C(x, y_1, z)$ and $D(x, y_2, z)$ are two points on a line parallel to the y axis, then the directed distance from C to D, denoted by $\overline{CD}$, is given by

$$\overline{CD} = y_2 - y_1$$

(iii) If $E(x, y, z_1)$ and $F(x, y, z_2)$ are two points on a line parallel to the z axis, then the directed distance from E to F, denoted by $\overline{EF}$, is given by

$$\overline{EF} = z_2 - z_1$$

• ILLUSTRATION 3: The directed distance $\overline{PQ}$ from the point $P(2, -5, -4)$ to the point $Q(2, -3, -4)$ is given by Theorem 18.1.4(ii). We have

$$\overline{PQ} = (-3) - (-5) = 2$$ •

The following theorem gives a formula for finding the undirected distance between any two points in three-dimensional space.

18.1.5 Theorem

The undirected distance between the two points $P_1(x_1, y_1, z_1)$ and $P_2(x_2, y_2, z_2)$ is given by

$$|\overline{P_1 P_2}| = \sqrt{(x_2 - x_1)^2 + (y_2 - y_1)^2 + (z_2 - z_1)^2}$$

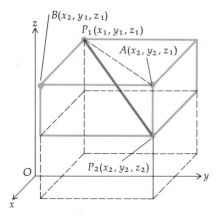

PROOF: Construct a rectangular parallelepiped having P_1 and P_2 as opposite vertices and faces parallel to the coordinate planes (see Fig. 18.1.7). By the Pythagorean theorem we have

$$|\overline{P_1 P_2}|^2 = |\overline{P_1 A}|^2 + |\overline{AP_2}|^2 \tag{1}$$

Because

$$|\overline{P_1 A}|^2 = |\overline{P_1 B}|^2 + |\overline{BA}|^2 \tag{2}$$

we obtain, by substituting from (2) into (1),

$$|\overline{P_1 P_2}|^2 = |\overline{P_1 B}|^2 + |\overline{BA}|^2 + |\overline{AP_2}|^2 \tag{3}$$

Applying Theorem 18.1.4(i), (ii), and (iii) to the right side of (3), we obtain

$$|\overline{P_1 P_2}|^2 = (x_2 - x_1)^2 + (y_2 - y_1)^2 + (z_2 - z_1)^2$$

So

$$|\overline{P_1 P_2}| = \sqrt{(x_2 - x_1)^2 + (y_2 - y_1)^2 + (z_2 - z_1)^2}$$

and the theorem is proved. ∎

Figure 18.1.7

EXAMPLE 1: Find the undirected distance between the points $P(-3, 4, -1)$ and $Q(2, 5, -4)$.	SOLUTION: From Theorem 18.1.5, we have $$\lvert \overline{PQ} \rvert = \sqrt{(2+3)^2 + (5-4)^2 + (-4+1)^2} = \sqrt{25+1+9} = \sqrt{35}$$

Note that the formula for the distance between two points in R^3 is merely an extension of the corresponding formula for the distance between two points in R^2 given in Theorem 1.4.1. It is also noteworthy that the undirected distance between two points x_2 and x_1 in R^1 is given by

$$\lvert x_2 - x_1 \rvert = \sqrt{(x_2 - x_1)^2}$$

The formulas for the coordinates of the midpoint of a line segment are derived by forming congruent triangles and proceeding in a manner analogous to the two-dimensional case. These formulas are given in Theorem 18.1.6, and the proof is left as an exercise (see Exercise 15).

18.1.6 Theorem The coordinates of the midpoint of the line segment having endpoints $P_1(x_1, y_1, z_1)$ and $P_2(x_2, y_2, z_2)$ are given by

$$\bar{x} = \frac{x_1 + x_2}{2} \qquad \bar{y} = \frac{y_1 + y_2}{2} \qquad \bar{z} = \frac{z_1 + z_2}{2}$$

18.1.7 Definition The *graph of an equation* in R^3 is the set of all points (x, y, z) whose coordinates are numbers satisfying the equation.

The graph of an equation in R^3 is called a *surface*. One particular surface is the sphere, which is now defined.

18.1.8 Definition A *sphere* is the set of all points in three-dimensional space equidistant from a fixed point. The fixed point is called the *center* of the sphere and the measure of the constant distance is called the *radius* of the sphere.

18.1.9 Theorem An equation of the sphere of radius r and center at (h, k, l) is

$$(x - h)^2 + (y - k)^2 + (z - l)^2 = r^2 \tag{4}$$

PROOF: Let the point (h, k, l) be denoted by C (see Fig. 18.1.8). The point $P(x, y, z)$ is a point on the sphere if and only if

$$\lvert \overline{CP} \rvert = r$$

or, equivalently,

$$\sqrt{(x - h)^2 + (y - k)^2 + (z - l)^2} = r$$

Squaring on both sides of the above equation, we obtain the desired result. ∎

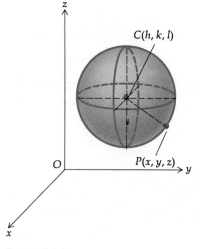

$C(h, k, l)$

O

$P(x, y, z)$

Figure 18.1.8

If the center of the sphere is at the origin, then $h = k = l = 0$, and so an equation of this sphere is

$$x^2 + y^2 + z^2 = r^2$$

If we expand the terms of Eq. (4) and regroup the terms, we have

$$x^2 + y^2 + z^2 - 2hx - 2ky - 2lz + (h^2 + k^2 + l^2 - r^2) = 0$$

This equation is of the form

$$x^2 + y^2 + z^2 + Gx + Hy + Iz + J = 0 \qquad (5)$$

where G, H, I, and J are constants. Equation (5) is called the *general form* of an equation of a sphere, whereas Eq. (4) is called the *center-radius* form. Because every sphere has a center and a radius, its equation can be put in the center-radius form and hence the general form.

It can be shown that any equation of the form (5) can be put in the form

$$(x - h)^2 + (y - k)^2 + (z - l)^2 = K \qquad (6)$$

where

$$h = -\tfrac{1}{2}G \qquad k = -\tfrac{1}{2}H \qquad l = -\tfrac{1}{2}I \qquad K = \tfrac{1}{4}(G^2 + H^2 + I^2 - 4J)$$

It is left as an exercise to show this (see Exercise 16).

If $K > 0$, then Eq. (6) is of the form of Eq. (4), and so the graph of the equation is a sphere having its center at (h, k, l) and radius $\sqrt{K}$. If $K = 0$, the graph of the equation is the point (h, k, l). This is called a *point-sphere*. If $K < 0$, the graph is the empty set because the sum of the squares of three real numbers is nonnegative. We state this result as a theorem.

18.1.10 Theorem   The graph of any second-degree equation in x, y, and z, of the form

$$x^2 + y^2 + z^2 + Gx + Hy + Iz + J = 0$$

is either a sphere, a point-sphere, or the empty set.

EXAMPLE 2:   Draw a sketch of the graph of the equation

$$x^2 + y^2 + z^2 - 6x - 4y + 2z = 2$$

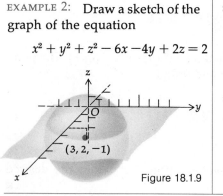

$(3, 2, -1)$

Figure 18.1.9

SOLUTION: Regrouping terms and completing the squares, we have

$$x^2 - 6x + 9 + y^2 - 4y + 4 + z^2 + 2z + 1 = 2 + 9 + 4 + 1$$

$$(x - 3)^2 + (y - 2)^2 + (z + 1)^2 = 16$$

So the graph is a sphere having its center at $(3, 2, -1)$ and radius 4. A sketch of the graph is shown in Fig. 18.1.9.

EXAMPLE 3: Find an equation of the sphere having the points $A(-5, 6, -2)$ and $B(9, -4, 0)$ as endpoints of a diameter.

SOLUTION: The center of the sphere will be the midpoint of the line segment AB. Let this point be $C(\bar{x}, \bar{y}, \bar{z})$. By Theorem 18.1.6, we get

$$\bar{x} = \frac{9-5}{2} = 2 \qquad \bar{y} = \frac{-4+6}{2} = 1 \qquad \bar{z} = \frac{0-2}{2} = -1$$

So C is the point $(2, 1, -1)$. The radius of the sphere is given by

$$r = |\overline{CB}| = \sqrt{(9-2)^2 + (-4-1)^2 + (0+1)^2} = \sqrt{75}$$

Therefore, from Theorem 18.1.9, an equation of the sphere is

$$(x-2)^2 + (y-1)^2 + (z+1)^2 = 75$$

or, equivalently,

$$x^2 + y^2 + z^2 - 4x - 2y + 2z - 69 = 0$$

Exercises 18.1

In Exercises 1 through 4, the given points A and B are opposite vertices of a rectangular parallelepiped, having its faces parallel to the coordinate planes. In each problem (a) draw a sketch of the figure, (b) find the coordinates of the other six vertices, (c) find the length of the diagonal AB.

1. $A(0, 0, 0)$; $B(7, 2, 3)$

2. $A(1, 1, 1)$; $B(3, 4, 2)$

3. $A(-1, 1, 2)$; $B(2, 3, 5)$

4. $A(2, -1, -3)$; $B(4, 0, -1)$

5. The vertex opposite one corner of a room is 18 ft east, 15 ft south, and 12 ft up from the first corner. (a) Draw a sketch of the figure, (b) determine the length of the diagonal joining two opposite vertices, (c) find the coordinates of all eight vertices of the room.

In Exercises 6 through 9, find (a) the undirected distance between the points A and B, and (b) the midpoint of the line segment joining A and B.

6. $A(3, 4, 2)$; $B(1, 6, 3)$

7. $A(2, -4, 1)$; $B(\frac{1}{2}, 2, 3)$

8. $A(4, -3, 2)$; $B(-2, 3, -5)$

9. $A(-2, -\frac{1}{2}, 5)$; $B(5, 1, -4)$

10. Prove that the three points $(1, -1, 3)$, $(2, 1, 7)$, and $(4, 2, 6)$ are the vertices of a right triangle, and find its area.

11. A line is drawn through the point $(6, 4, 2)$ perpendicular to the yz plane. Find the coordinates of the points on this line at a distance of 10 units from the point $(0, 4, 0)$.

12. Solve Exercise 11 if the line is drawn perpendicular to the xy plane.

13. Prove that the three points $(-3, 2, 4)$, $(6, 1, 2)$, and $(-12, 3, 6)$ are collinear by using the distance formula.

14. Find the vertices of the triangle whose sides have midpoints at $(3, 2, 3)$, $(-1, 1, 5)$, and $(0, 3, 4)$.

15. Prove Theorem 18.1.6.

16. Show that any equation of the form $x^2 + y^2 + z^2 + Gx + Hy + Iz + J = 0$ can be put in the form $(x-h)^2 + (y-k)^2 + (z-l)^2 = K$.

In Exercises 17 through 21, determine the graph of the given equation.

17. $x^2 + y^2 + z^2 - 8x + 4y + 2z - 4 = 0$

18. $x^2 + y^2 + z^2 - 8y + 6z - 25 = 0$

19. $x^2 + y^2 + z^2 - 6z + 9 = 0$

20. $x^2 + y^2 + z^2 - x - y - 3z + 2 = 0$ 21. $x^2 + y^2 + z^2 - 6x + 2y - 4z + 19 = 0$

In Exercises 22 through 24, find an equation of the sphere satisfying the given conditions.

22. A diameter is the line segment having endpoints at $(6, 2, -5)$ and $(-4, 0, 7)$.

23. It is concentric with the sphere having equation $x^2 + y^2 + z^2 - 2y + 8z - 9 = 0$.

24. It contains the points $(0, 0, 4)$, $(2, 1, 3)$, and $(0, 2, 6)$ and has its center in the yz plane.

25. Prove analytically that the four diagonals joining opposite vertices of a rectangular parallelepiped bisect each other.

26. If P, Q, R, and S are four points in three-dimensional space and A, B, C, and D are the midpoints of PQ, QR, RS, and SP, respectively, prove analytically that $ABCD$ is a parallelogram.

18.2 VECTORS IN THREE-DIMENSIONAL SPACE

The presentation of topics in solid analytic geometry is simplified by the use of vectors in three-dimensional space. The definitions and theorems given in Secs. 17.1 and 17.2 for vectors in the plane are easily extended.

18.2.1 Definition   A *vector in three-dimensional space* is an ordered triple of real numbers $\langle x, y, z \rangle$. The numbers x, y, and z are called the *components* of the vector $\langle x, y, z \rangle$.

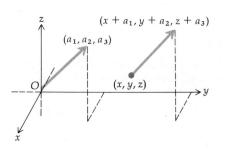

Figure 18.2.1

We let V_3 be the set of all ordered triples $\langle x, y, z \rangle$ for which x, y, and z are real numbers. In this chapter, a vector is always in V_3 unless otherwise stated.

Just as for vectors in V_2, a vector in V_3 can be represented by a directed line segment. If $\mathbf{A} = \langle a_1, a_2, a_3 \rangle$, then the directed line segment having its initial point at the origin and its terminal point at the point (a_1, a_2, a_3) is called the *position representation of* $\mathbf{A}$. A directed line segment having its initial point at (x, y, z) and its terminal point at $(x + a_1, y + a_2, z + a_3)$ is also a representation of the vector $\mathbf{A}$. See Fig. 18.2.1.

The *zero vector* is the vector $\langle 0, 0, 0 \rangle$ and is denoted by $\mathbf{0}$. Any point is a representation of the zero vector.

The *magnitude* of a vector is the length of any of its representations. If the vector $\mathbf{A} = \langle a_1, a_2, a_3 \rangle$, the magnitude of $\mathbf{A}$ is denoted by $|\mathbf{A}|$, and it follows that

$$|\mathbf{A}| = \sqrt{a_1^2 + a_2^2 + a_3^2}$$

The *direction* of a nonzero vector in V_3 is given by three angles, called the *direction angles* of the vector.

18.2.2 Definition   The *direction angles* of a nonzero vector are the three angles that have the smallest nonnegative radian measures α, β, and γ measured from the positive x, y, and z axes, respectively, to the position representation of the vector.

The radian measure of each direction angle of a vector is greater than

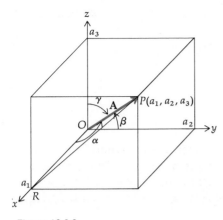

Figure 18.2.2

or equal to 0 and less than or equal to π. The direction angles having radian measures α, β, and γ of the vector $\mathbf{A} = \langle a_1, a_2, a_3 \rangle$ are shown in Fig. 18.2.2. In this figure the components of $\mathbf{A}$ are all positive numbers, and the direction angles of this vector all have positive radian measure less than $\frac{1}{2}\pi$. From the figure we see that triangle POR is a right triangle and

$$\cos \alpha = \frac{|\overrightarrow{OR}|}{|\overrightarrow{OP}|} = \frac{a_1}{|\mathbf{A}|}$$

It can be shown that the same formula holds if $\frac{1}{2}\pi \leq \alpha \leq \pi$. Similar formulas can be found for $\cos \beta$ and $\cos \gamma$, and we have

$$\cos \alpha = \frac{a_1}{|\mathbf{A}|} \qquad \cos \beta = \frac{a_2}{|\mathbf{A}|} \qquad \cos \gamma = \frac{a_3}{|\mathbf{A}|} \qquad (1)$$

The three numbers $\cos \alpha$, $\cos \beta$, and $\cos \gamma$ are called the *direction cosines* of vector $\mathbf{A}$. The zero vector has no direction angles and hence no direction cosines.

● ILLUSTRATION 1: We find the magnitude and direction cosines of the vector $\mathbf{A} = \langle 3, 2, -6 \rangle$.

$$|\mathbf{A}| = \sqrt{(3)^2 + (2)^2 + (-6)^2} = \sqrt{9 + 4 + 36} = \sqrt{49} = 7$$

From Eqs. (1) we get

$$\cos \alpha = \tfrac{3}{7} \qquad \cos \beta = \tfrac{2}{7} \qquad \cos \gamma = -\tfrac{6}{7} \qquad ●$$

If we are given the magnitude of a vector and its direction cosines, the vector is uniquely determined because from (1) it follows that

$$a_1 = |\mathbf{A}| \cos \alpha \qquad a_2 = |\mathbf{A}| \cos \beta \qquad a_3 = |\mathbf{A}| \cos \gamma \qquad (2)$$

The three direction cosines of a vector are not independent of each other, as we see by the following theorem.

18.2.3 Theorem If $\cos \alpha$, $\cos \beta$, and $\cos \gamma$ are the direction cosines of a vector, then

$$\cos^2 \alpha + \cos^2 \beta + \cos^2 \gamma = 1$$

PROOF: If $\mathbf{A} = \langle a_1, a_2, a_3 \rangle$, then the direction cosines of $\mathbf{A}$ are given by (1) and we have

$$\cos^2 \alpha + \cos^2 \beta + \cos^2 \gamma = \frac{a_1{}^2}{|\mathbf{A}|^2} + \frac{a_2{}^2}{|\mathbf{A}|^2} + \frac{a_3{}^2}{|\mathbf{A}|^2}$$

$$= \frac{a_1{}^2 + a_2{}^2 + a_3{}^2}{|\mathbf{A}|^2}$$

$$= \frac{|\mathbf{A}|^2}{|\mathbf{A}|^2}$$

$$= 1 \qquad ■$$

● ILLUSTRATION 2: We verify Theorem 18.2.3 for the vector of Illustration 1. We have

$$\sqrt{\cos^2 \alpha + \cos^2 \beta + \cos^2 \gamma} = \sqrt{(\tfrac{3}{7})^2 + (\tfrac{2}{7})^2 + (-\tfrac{6}{7})^2}$$

$$= \sqrt{\tfrac{9}{49} + \tfrac{4}{49} + \tfrac{36}{49}}$$

$$= \sqrt{\tfrac{49}{49}}$$

$$= 1$$

●

The vector $\mathbf{A} = \langle a_1, a_2, a_3 \rangle$ is a unit vector if $|\mathbf{A}| = 1$, and from Eqs. (1) we see that the components of a unit vector are its direction cosines.

The operations of addition, subtraction, and scalar multiplication of vectors in V_3 are given definitions analogous to the corresponding definitions for vectors in V_2.

18.2.4 Definition   If $\mathbf{A} = \langle a_1, a_2, a_3 \rangle$ and $\mathbf{B} = \langle b_1, b_2, b_3 \rangle$, then the sum of these vectors is given by

$$\mathbf{A} + \mathbf{B} = \langle a_1 + b_1, a_2 + b_2, a_3 + b_3 \rangle$$

EXAMPLE 1:   Given $\mathbf{A} = \langle 5, -2, 6 \rangle$ and $\mathbf{B} = \langle 8, -5, -4 \rangle$, find $\mathbf{A} + \mathbf{B}$.

SOLUTION: $\mathbf{A} + \mathbf{B} = \langle 5 + 8, (-2) + (-5), 6 + (-4) \rangle = \langle 13, -7, 2 \rangle$.

The geometric interpretation of the sum of two vectors in V_3 is similar to that for vectors in V_2. See Fig. 18.2.3. If P is the point (x, y, z), $\mathbf{A} = \langle a_1, a_2, a_3 \rangle$ and $\overrightarrow{PQ}$ is a representation of $\mathbf{A}$, then Q is the point $(x + a_1, y + a_2, z + a_3)$. Let $\mathbf{B} = \langle b_1, b_2, b_3 \rangle$ and let $\overrightarrow{QR}$ be a representation of $\mathbf{B}$. Then R is the point $(x + (a_1 + b_1), y + (a_2 + b_2), z + (a_3 + b_3))$. Therefore, $\overrightarrow{PR}$ is a representation of the vector $\mathbf{A} + \mathbf{B}$, and the parallelogram law holds.

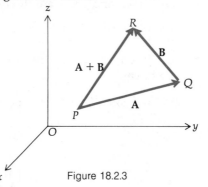

Figure 18.2.3

18.2.5 Definition   If $\mathbf{A} = \langle a_1, a_2, a_3 \rangle$, then the vector $\langle -a_1, -a_2, -a_3 \rangle$ is defined to be the *negative* of $\mathbf{A}$, denoted by $-\mathbf{A}$.

18.2.6 Definition   The *difference* of the two vectors **A** and **B**, denoted by **A** − **B**, is defined by

$$\mathbf{A} - \mathbf{B} = \mathbf{A} + (-\mathbf{B})$$

From Definitions 18.2.5 and 18.2.6 it follows that if $\mathbf{A} = \langle a_1, a_2, a_3 \rangle$ and $\mathbf{B} = \langle b_1, b_2, b_3 \rangle$, then $-\mathbf{B} = \langle -b_1, -b_2, -b_3 \rangle$ and

$$\mathbf{A} - \mathbf{B} = \langle a_1 - b_1, a_2 - b_2, a_3 - b_3 \rangle$$

EXAMPLE 2: For the vectors **A** and **B** of Example 1, find **A** − **B**.

SOLUTION:
$$\mathbf{A} - \mathbf{B} = \langle 5, -2, 6 \rangle - \langle 8, -5, -4 \rangle$$
$$= \langle 5, -2, 6 \rangle + \langle -8, 5, 4 \rangle$$
$$= \langle -3, 3, 10 \rangle$$

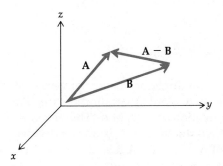

Figure 18.2.4

The difference of two vectors in V_3 is also interpreted geometrically as it is in V_2. See Fig. 18.2.4. A representation of the vector **A** − **B** is obtained by choosing representations of **A** and **B** having the same initial point. Then a representation of the vector **A** − **B** is the directed line segment from the terminal point of the representation of **B** to the terminal point of the representation of **A**.

● ILLUSTRATION 3: Given the points $P(1, 3, 5)$ and $Q(2, -1, 4)$, Fig. 18.2.5 shows $\overrightarrow{PQ}$ as well as $\overrightarrow{OP}$ and $\overrightarrow{OQ}$. We see from the figure that $\mathbf{V}(\overrightarrow{PQ}) = \mathbf{V}(\overrightarrow{OQ}) - \mathbf{V}(\overrightarrow{OP})$. Hence,

$$\mathbf{V}(\overrightarrow{PQ}) = \langle 2, -1, 4 \rangle - \langle 1, 3, 5 \rangle = \langle 1, -4, -1 \rangle \qquad ●$$

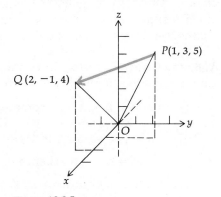

Figure 18.2.5

18.2.7 Definition   If c is a scalar and **A** is the vector $\langle a_1, a_2, a_3 \rangle$, then the product of c and **A**, denoted by $c\mathbf{A}$, is a vector and is given by

$$c\mathbf{A} = c\langle a_1, a_2, a_3 \rangle = \langle ca_1, ca_2, ca_3 \rangle$$

EXAMPLE 3: Given $\mathbf{A} =$ $\langle -4, 7, -2 \rangle$, find $3\mathbf{A}$ and $-5\mathbf{A}$.

SOLUTION:

$$3\mathbf{A} = 3\langle -4, 7, -2 \rangle = \langle -12, 21, -6 \rangle$$

and

$$-5\mathbf{A} = (-5)\langle -4, 7, -2 \rangle = \langle 20, -35, 10 \rangle$$

Suppose that $\mathbf{A} = \langle a_1, a_2, a_3 \rangle$ is a nonzero vector having direction cosines $\cos \alpha$, $\cos \beta$, and $\cos \gamma$, and c is any nonzero scalar. Then $c\mathbf{A} = \langle ca_1, ca_2, ca_3 \rangle$; and if $\cos \alpha_1$, $\cos \beta_1$, and $\cos \gamma_1$ are the direction cosines of $c\mathbf{A}$, we have from Eqs. (1)

$$\cos \alpha_1 = \frac{ca_1}{|c\mathbf{A}|} \qquad \cos \beta_1 = \frac{ca_2}{|c\mathbf{A}|} \qquad \cos \gamma_1 = \frac{ca_3}{|c\mathbf{A}|}$$

or, equivalently,

$$\cos \alpha_1 = \frac{c}{|c|} \frac{a_1}{|\mathbf{A}|} \qquad \cos \beta_1 = \frac{c}{|c|} \frac{a_2}{|\mathbf{A}|} \qquad \cos \gamma_1 = \frac{c}{|c|} \frac{a_3}{|\mathbf{A}|}$$

from which we get

$$\cos \alpha_1 = \frac{c}{|c|} \cos \alpha \qquad \cos \beta_1 = \frac{c}{|c|} \cos \beta \qquad \cos \gamma_1 = \frac{c}{|c|} \cos \gamma \qquad (3)$$

So if $c > 0$, it follows from Eqs. (3) that the direction cosines of vector $c\mathbf{A}$ are the same as the direction cosines of $\mathbf{A}$. And if $c < 0$, the direction cosines of $c\mathbf{A}$ are the negatives of the direction cosines of $\mathbf{A}$. Therefore, we conclude that if c is a nonzero scalar, then the vector $c\mathbf{A}$ is a vector whose magnitude is $|c|$ times the magnitude of $\mathbf{A}$. If $c > 0$, $c\mathbf{A}$ has the same direction as $\mathbf{A}$, whereas if $c < 0$, the direction of $c\mathbf{A}$ is opposite that of $\mathbf{A}$.

The operations of vector addition and scalar multiplication of any vectors in V_3 satisfy properties identical with those given in Theorem 17.2.1. These are given in the following theorem, and the proofs are left as exercises (see Exercises 1 through 6).

18.2.8 Theorem   If $\mathbf{A}$, $\mathbf{B}$, and $\mathbf{C}$ are any vectors in V_3 and c and d are any scalars, then vector addition and scalar multiplication satisfy the following properties:

(i) $\mathbf{A} + \mathbf{B} = \mathbf{B} + \mathbf{A}$ (commutative law)

(ii) $\mathbf{A} + (\mathbf{B} + \mathbf{C}) = (\mathbf{A} + \mathbf{B}) + \mathbf{C}$ (associative law)

(iii) There is a vector $\mathbf{0}$ in V_3 for which

$$\mathbf{A} + \mathbf{0} = \mathbf{A} \qquad \text{(existence of additive identity)}$$

(iv) There is a vector $-\mathbf{A}$ in V_3 such that

$$\mathbf{A} + (-\mathbf{A}) = \mathbf{0} \qquad \text{(existence of negative)}$$

(v) $(cd)\mathbf{A} = c(d\mathbf{A})$ (associative law)

(vi) $c(\mathbf{A} + \mathbf{B}) = c\mathbf{A} + c\mathbf{B}$ (distributive law)

(vii) $(c + d)\mathbf{A} = c\mathbf{A} + d\mathbf{A}$ (distributive law)

(viii) $1(\mathbf{A}) = \mathbf{A}$ (existence of scalar multiplicative identity)

From Definition 17.2.2 and Theorem 18.2.8 it follows that V_3 is a real vector space. The three unit vectors

$$\mathbf{i} = \langle 1, 0, 0 \rangle \qquad \mathbf{j} = \langle 0, 1, 0 \rangle \qquad \mathbf{k} = \langle 0, 0, 1 \rangle$$

form a basis for the vector space V_3 because any vector $\langle a_1, a_2, a_3 \rangle$ can be written in terms of them as follows:

$$\langle a_1, a_2, a_3 \rangle = a_1 \langle 1, 0, 0 \rangle + a_2 \langle 0, 1, 0 \rangle + a_3 \langle 0, 0, 1 \rangle$$

Hence, if $\mathbf{A} = \langle a_1, a_2, a_3 \rangle$, we also can write

$$\mathbf{A} = a_1 \mathbf{i} + a_2 \mathbf{j} + a_3 \mathbf{k} \tag{4}$$

Because there are three elements in a basis, V_3 is a three-dimensional vector space.

Substituting from Eqs. (2) into Eq. (4), we have

$$\mathbf{A} = |\mathbf{A}| \cos \alpha \mathbf{i} + |\mathbf{A}| \cos \beta \mathbf{j} + |\mathbf{A}| \cos \gamma \mathbf{k}$$

or, equivalently,

$$\mathbf{A} = |\mathbf{A}| (\cos \alpha \mathbf{i} + \cos \beta \mathbf{j} + \cos \gamma \mathbf{k}) \tag{5}$$

Equation (5) enables us to express any nonzero vector in terms of its magnitude and direction cosines.

EXAMPLE 4: Express the vector of Illustration 1 in terms of its magnitude and direction cosines.

SOLUTION: In Illustration 1, $\mathbf{A} = \langle 3, 2, -6 \rangle$, $|\mathbf{A}| = 7$, $\cos \alpha = \frac{3}{7}$, $\cos \beta = \frac{2}{7}$, and $\cos \gamma = -\frac{6}{7}$. Hence, from Eq. (5) we have

$$\mathbf{A} = 7(\tfrac{3}{7}\mathbf{i} + \tfrac{2}{7}\mathbf{j} - \tfrac{6}{7}\mathbf{k})$$

18.2.9 Theorem   If the nonzero vector $\mathbf{A} = a_1 \mathbf{i} + a_2 \mathbf{j} + a_3 \mathbf{k}$, then the unit vector $\mathbf{U}$ having the same direction as $\mathbf{A}$ is given by

$$\mathbf{U} = \frac{a_1}{|\mathbf{A}|}\mathbf{i} + \frac{a_2}{|\mathbf{A}|}\mathbf{j} + \frac{a_3}{|\mathbf{A}|}\mathbf{k}$$

The proof of Theorem 18.2.9 is analogous to the proof of Theorem 17.2.3 for a vector in V_2 and is left as an exercise (see Exercise 30).

EXAMPLE 5: Given the points $R(2, -1, 3)$ and $S(3, 4, 6)$, find the unit vector having the same direction as $\mathbf{V}(\overrightarrow{RS})$.

SOLUTION:

$$\mathbf{V}(\overrightarrow{RS}) = \langle 3, 4, 6 \rangle - \langle 2, -1, 3 \rangle = \langle 1, 5, 3 \rangle$$

$$= \mathbf{i} + 5\mathbf{j} + 3\mathbf{k}$$

So

$$|\mathbf{V}(\overrightarrow{RS})| = \sqrt{1^2 + 5^2 + 3^2} = \sqrt{35}$$

Therefore, by Theorem 18.2.9 the desired unit vector is

$$\mathbf{U} = \frac{1}{\sqrt{35}} \mathbf{i} + \frac{5}{\sqrt{35}} \mathbf{j} + \frac{3}{\sqrt{35}} \mathbf{k}$$

Exercises 18.2

1. Prove Theorem 18.2.8(i).

2. Prove Theorem 18.2.8(ii).

3. Prove Theorem 18.2.8(iii), (iv), and (viii).

4. Prove Theorem 18.2.8(v).

5. Prove Theorem 18.2.8(vi).

6. Prove Theorem 18.2.8(vii).

In Exercises 7 through 18, let $\mathbf{A} = \langle 1, 2, 3 \rangle$, $\mathbf{B} = \langle 4, -3, -1 \rangle$, $\mathbf{C} = \langle -5, -3, 5 \rangle$, $\mathbf{D} = \langle -2, 1, 6 \rangle$.

7. Find $\mathbf{A} + 5\mathbf{B}$

8. Find $2\mathbf{A} - \mathbf{C}$

9. Find $7\mathbf{C} - 5\mathbf{D}$

10. Find $4\mathbf{B} + 6\mathbf{C} - 2\mathbf{D}$

11. Find $|7\mathbf{C}| - |5\mathbf{D}|$

12. Find $|4\mathbf{B}| + |6\mathbf{C}| - |2\mathbf{D}|$

13. Find $\mathbf{C} + 3\mathbf{D} - 8\mathbf{A}$

14. Find $3\mathbf{A} - 2\mathbf{B} + \mathbf{C} - 12\mathbf{D}$

15. Find $|\mathbf{A}||\mathbf{B}|(\mathbf{C} - \mathbf{D})$

16. Find $|\mathbf{A}|\mathbf{C} - |\mathbf{B}|\mathbf{D}$

17. Find scalars a and b such that $a(\mathbf{A} + \mathbf{B}) + b(\mathbf{C} + \mathbf{D}) = \mathbf{0}$.

18. Find scalars a, b, and c such that $a\mathbf{A} + b\mathbf{B} + c\mathbf{C} = \mathbf{D}$.

In Exercises 19 through 22, find the direction cosines of the vector $\mathbf{V}(\overrightarrow{P_1 P_2})$ and check the answers by verifying that the sum of their squares is 1.

19. $P_1(3, -1, -4)$; $P_2(7, 2, 4)$

20. $P_1(1, 3, 5)$; $P_2(2, -1, 4)$

21. $P_1(4, -3, -1)$; $P_2(-2, -4, -8)$

22. $P_1(-2, 6, 5)$; $P_2(2, 4, 1)$

23. Using the points P_1 and P_2 of Exercise 19, find the point Q such that $\mathbf{V}(\overrightarrow{P_1 P_2}) = 3\mathbf{V}(\overrightarrow{P_1 Q})$.

24. Using the points P_1 and P_2 of Exercise 20, find the point R such that $\mathbf{V}(\overrightarrow{P_1 R}) = -2\mathbf{V}(\overrightarrow{P_2 R})$.

In Exercises 25 through 28, express the given vector in terms of its magnitude and direction cosines.

25. $-6\mathbf{i} + 2\mathbf{j} + 3\mathbf{k}$

26. $2\mathbf{i} - 2\mathbf{j} + \mathbf{k}$

27. $-2\mathbf{i} + \mathbf{j} - 3\mathbf{k}$

28. $3\mathbf{i} + 4\mathbf{j} - 5\mathbf{k}$

29. If the radian measure of each direction angle of a vector is the same, what is it?

30. Prove Theorem 18.2.9.

In Exercises 31 and 32, find the unit vector having the same direction as $\mathbf{V}(\overrightarrow{P_1 P_2})$.

31. $P_1(4, -1, -6)$; $P_2(5, 7, -2)$

32. $P_1(-8, -5, 2)$; $P_2(-3, -9, 4)$

33. Three vectors in V_3 are said to be *independent* if and only if their position representations do not lie in a plane, and three vectors $\mathbf{E}_1$, $\mathbf{E}_2$, and $\mathbf{E}_3$ are said to form a *basis* for the vector space V_3 if and only if any vector in V_3 can be written as a linear combination of $\mathbf{E}_1$, $\mathbf{E}_2$, and $\mathbf{E}_3$. A theorem can be proved which states that three vectors form a basis for the vector space V_3 if they are independent. Show that this theorem holds for the three vectors $\langle 1, 0, 0 \rangle$, $\langle 1, 1, 0 \rangle$, and $\langle 1, 1, 1 \rangle$ by doing the following: (a) Verify that the vectors are independent by showing that their position representations are not coplanar; (b) verify that the vectors form a basis by showing that any vector $\mathbf{A}$ can be written

$$A = r\langle 1, 0, 0 \rangle + s\langle 1, 1, 0 \rangle + t\langle 1, 1, 1 \rangle \tag{6}$$

where r, s, and t are scalars. (c) If $A = \langle 6, -2, 5 \rangle$, find the particular values of r, s, and t so that Eq. (6) holds.

34. Refer to the first sentence of Exercise 33. A theorem can be proved which states that three vectors form a basis for the vector space V_3 only if they are independent. Show that this theorem holds for the three vectors $F_1 = \langle 1, 0, 1 \rangle$, $F_2 = \langle 1, 1, 1 \rangle$, and $F_3 = \langle 2, 1, 2 \rangle$ by doing the following: (a) Verify that F_1, F_2, and F_3 are not independent by showing that their position representations are coplanar; (b) verify that the vectors do not form a basis by showing that every vector in V_3 cannot be written as a linear combination of F_1, F_2, and F_3.

18.3 THE DOT PRODUCT IN V_3

The definition of the dot product of two vectors in V_3 is an extension of the definition for vectors in V_2.

18.3.1 Definition

If $A = \langle a_1, a_2, a_3 \rangle$ and $B = \langle b_1, b_2, b_3 \rangle$, then the *dot product* of A and B, denoted by $A \cdot B$, is given by

$$A \cdot B = \langle a_1, a_2, a_3 \rangle \cdot \langle b_1, b_2, b_3 \rangle = a_1 b_1 + a_2 b_2 + a_3 b_3$$

● ILLUSTRATION 1: If $A = \langle 4, 2, -6 \rangle$ and $B = \langle -5, 3, -2 \rangle$, then

$$\begin{aligned}
A \cdot B &= \langle 4, 2, -6 \rangle \cdot \langle -5, 3, -2 \rangle \\
&= 4(-5) + 2(3) + (-6)(-2) \\
&= -20 + 6 + 12 \\
&= -2
\end{aligned}$$

●

For the unit vectors i, j, and k, we have

$$i \cdot i = j \cdot j = k \cdot k = 1$$

and

$$i \cdot j = i \cdot k = j \cdot k = 0$$

Laws of dot multiplication that are given in Theorem 18.3.2 are the same as those in Theorems 17.3.2 and 17.3.3 for vectors in V_2. The proofs are left as exercises (see Exercises 1 through 4).

18.3.2 Theorem

If A, B, and C are any vectors in V_3 and c is a scalar, then

(i) $A \cdot B = B \cdot A$ (commutative law)
(ii) $A \cdot (B + C) = A \cdot B + A \cdot C$ (distributive law)
(iii) $c(A \cdot B) = (cA) \cdot B$
(iv) $0 \cdot A = 0$
(v) $A \cdot A = |A|^2$

Before giving a geometric representation of the dot product for vectors in V_3, we do as we did with vectors in V_2. We define the angle between two vectors and then express the dot product in terms of the cosine of the radian measure of this angle.

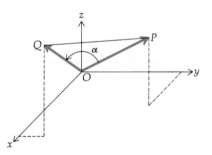

Figure 18.3.1

18.3.3 Definition   Let **A** and **B** be two nonzero vectors in V_3 such that **A** is not a scalar multiple of **B**. If $\overrightarrow{OP}$ is the position representation of **A** and $\overrightarrow{OQ}$ is the position representation of **B**, then the angle between the vectors **A** and **B** is defined to be the angle of positive measure between $\overrightarrow{OP}$ and $\overrightarrow{OQ}$ interior to the triangle POQ. If $\mathbf{A} = c\mathbf{B}$, where c is a scalar, then if $c > 0$, the angle between the vectors has radian measure 0, and if $c < 0$, the angle between the vectors has radian measure π.

Figure 18.3.1 shows the angle of radian measure θ between the two vectors if **A** is not a scalar multiple of **B**.

18.3.4 Theorem   If θ is the radian measure of the angle between the two nonzero vectors **A** and **B** in V_3, then

$$\mathbf{A} \cdot \mathbf{B} = |\mathbf{A}||\mathbf{B}| \cos \theta \qquad (1)$$

The proof of Theorem 18.3.4 is analogous to the proof of Theorem 17.3.5 for vectors in V_2 and is left as an exercise (see Exercise 15).

If **U** is a unit vector in the direction of **A**, we have from (1)

$$\mathbf{U} \cdot \mathbf{B} = |\mathbf{U}||\mathbf{B}| \cos \theta = |\mathbf{B}| \cos \theta$$

As with vectors in V_2, $|\mathbf{B}| \cos \theta$ is the *scalar projection* of **B** onto **A** and the *component* of **B** in the direction of **A**. It follows from Theorem 18.3.4 that the dot product of two vectors **A** and **B** is the product of the magnitude, $|\mathbf{A}|$, of one vector by the scalar projection, $|\mathbf{B}| \cos \theta$, of the second vector onto the first.

EXAMPLE 1:   Given the vectors $\mathbf{A} = 6\mathbf{i} - 3\mathbf{j} + 2\mathbf{k}$ and $\mathbf{B} = 2\mathbf{i} + \mathbf{j} - 3\mathbf{k}$, find (a) the component of **B** in the direction of **A**, (b) the vector projection of **B** onto **A**; and (c) $\cos \theta$ if θ is the radian measure of the angle between **A** and **B**.

SOLUTION: $|\mathbf{A}| = \sqrt{6^2 + (-3)^2 + 2^2} = \sqrt{36 + 9 + 4} = 7$. Hence, a unit vector in the direction of **A** is

$$\mathbf{U} = \tfrac{6}{7}\mathbf{i} - \tfrac{3}{7}\mathbf{j} + \tfrac{2}{7}\mathbf{k}$$

Because $\mathbf{U} \cdot \mathbf{B} = |\mathbf{B}| \cos \theta$, the component of **B** in the direction of **A** is

$$\mathbf{U} \cdot \mathbf{B} = (\tfrac{6}{7}\mathbf{i} - \tfrac{3}{7}\mathbf{j} + \tfrac{2}{7}\mathbf{k}) \cdot (2\mathbf{i} + \mathbf{j} - 3\mathbf{k})$$

$$= \tfrac{12}{7} - \tfrac{3}{7} - \tfrac{6}{7}$$

$$= \tfrac{3}{7}$$

The vector projection of **B** onto **A** is therefore

$$\tfrac{3}{7}\mathbf{U} = \tfrac{18}{49}\mathbf{i} - \tfrac{9}{49}\mathbf{j} + \tfrac{6}{49}\mathbf{k}$$

From Eq. (1)

$$\cos \theta = \frac{\mathbf{A} \cdot \mathbf{B}}{|\mathbf{A}||\mathbf{B}|} = \frac{\mathbf{U} \cdot \mathbf{B}}{|\mathbf{B}|}$$

Because $\mathbf{U} \cdot \mathbf{B} = \frac{3}{7}$ and $|\mathbf{B}| = \sqrt{2^2 + 1^2 + (-3)^2} = \sqrt{14}$

$$\cos \theta = \frac{3}{7\sqrt{14}} = \frac{3\sqrt{14}}{98}$$

EXAMPLE 2: Find the distance from the point $P(4, 1, 6)$ to the line through the points $A(8, 3, 2)$ and $B(2, -3, 5)$.

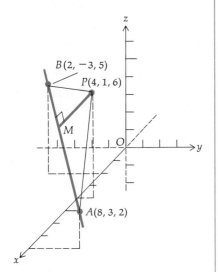

Figure 18.3.2

SOLUTION: Figure 18.3.2 shows the point P and a sketch of the line through A and B. The point M is the foot of the perpendicular line from P to the line through A and B. Let d units be the distance $|\overline{PM}|$. To find d we find $|\overline{AM}|$ and $|\overline{AP}|$ and use the Pythagorean theorem. $|\overline{AP}|$ is the magnitude of the vector $\mathbf{V}(\overrightarrow{AP})$.

$$\mathbf{V}(\overrightarrow{AP}) = \mathbf{V}(\overrightarrow{OP}) - \mathbf{V}(\overrightarrow{OA})$$
$$= \langle 4, 1, 6 \rangle - \langle 8, 3, 2 \rangle$$
$$= \langle -4, -2, 4 \rangle$$

Hence,

$$|\overline{AP}| = \sqrt{(-4)^2 + (-2)^2 + 4^2} = \sqrt{36} = 6$$

To find $|\overline{AM}|$ we find the scalar projection of $\mathbf{V}(\overrightarrow{AP})$ onto $\mathbf{V}(\overrightarrow{AB})$.

$$\mathbf{V}(\overrightarrow{AB}) = \mathbf{V}(\overrightarrow{OB}) - \mathbf{V}(\overrightarrow{OA})$$
$$= \langle 2, -3, 5 \rangle - \langle 8, 3, 2 \rangle$$
$$= \langle -6, -6, 3 \rangle$$

The scalar projection of $\mathbf{V}(\overrightarrow{AP})$ onto $\mathbf{V}(\overrightarrow{AB})$ is then

$$\frac{\mathbf{V}(\overrightarrow{AP}) \cdot \mathbf{V}(\overrightarrow{AB})}{|\mathbf{V}(\overrightarrow{AB})|} = \frac{\langle -4, -2, 4 \rangle \cdot \langle -6, -6, 3 \rangle}{\sqrt{36 + 36 + 9}}$$

$$= \frac{24 + 12 + 12}{\sqrt{81}}$$

$$= \tfrac{48}{9}$$

Thus, $|\overline{AM}| = \tfrac{48}{9}$, and so

$$d = \sqrt{|\overline{AP}|^2 - |\overline{AM}|^2}$$
$$= \sqrt{36 - (\tfrac{48}{9})^2}$$
$$= 6\sqrt{1 - \tfrac{64}{81}}$$
$$= \tfrac{2}{3}\sqrt{17}$$

The definition of parallel vectors in V_3 is analogous to Definition 17.3.6 for vectors in V_2, and we state it formally.

18.3.5 Definition   Two vectors in V_3 are said to be *parallel* if and only if one of the vectors is a scalar multiple of the other.

The following theorem follows from Definition 18.3.5 and Theorem 18.3.4. Its proof is left as an exercise (see Exercise 16).

18.3.6 Theorem   Two nonzero vectors in V_3 are parallel if and only if the radian measure of the angle between them is 0 or π.

The following definition of orthogonal vectors in V_3 corresponds to Definition 17.3.7 for vectors in V_2.

18.3.7 Definition   If **A** and **B** are two vectors in V_3, **A** and **B** are said to be *orthogonal* if and only if $\mathbf{A} \cdot \mathbf{B} = 0$.

EXAMPLE 3:   Prove by using vectors that the points $A(4,9,1)$, $B(-2,6,3)$, and $C(6,3,-2)$ are the vertices of a right triangle.

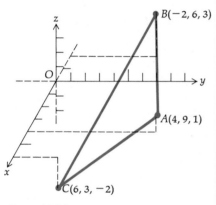

Figure 18.3.3

SOLUTION: Triangle CAB is shown in Fig. 18.3.3. From the figure it looks as if the angle at A is the one that may be a right angle. We shall find $\mathbf{V}(\overrightarrow{AB})$ and $\mathbf{V}(\overrightarrow{AC})$, and if the dot product of these two vectors is zero, the angle is a right angle.

$$\mathbf{V}(\overrightarrow{AB}) = \mathbf{V}(\overrightarrow{OB}) - \mathbf{V}(\overrightarrow{OA})$$
$$= \langle -2, 6, 3 \rangle - \langle 4, 9, 1 \rangle$$
$$= \langle -6, -3, 2 \rangle$$
$$\mathbf{V}(\overrightarrow{AC}) = \mathbf{V}(\overrightarrow{OC}) - \mathbf{V}(\overrightarrow{OA})$$
$$= \langle 6, 3, -2 \rangle - \langle 4, 9, 1 \rangle$$
$$= \langle 2, -6, -3 \rangle$$
$$\mathbf{V}(\overrightarrow{AB}) \cdot \mathbf{V}(\overrightarrow{AC}) = \langle -6, -3, 2 \rangle \cdot \langle 2, -6, -3 \rangle = -12 + 18 - 6 = 0$$

Therefore, $\mathbf{V}(\overrightarrow{AB})$ and $\mathbf{V}(\overrightarrow{AC})$ are orthogonal, and so the angle at A in triangle CAB is a right angle.

Exercises 18.3

1. Prove Theorem 18.3.2(i).

2. Prove Theorem 18.3.2(ii).

3. Prove Theorem 18.3.2(iii).

4. Prove Theorem 18.3.2(iv) and (v).

In Exercises 5 through 14, let $\mathbf{A} = \langle -4, -2, 4 \rangle$, $\mathbf{B} = \langle 2, 7, -1 \rangle$, $\mathbf{C} = \langle 6, -3, 0 \rangle$, and $\mathbf{D} = \langle 5, 4, -3 \rangle$.

5. Find $\mathbf{A} \cdot (\mathbf{B} + \mathbf{C})$

6. Find $\mathbf{A} \cdot \mathbf{B} + \mathbf{A} \cdot \mathbf{C}$

7. Find $(\mathbf{A} \cdot \mathbf{B})(\mathbf{C} \cdot \mathbf{D})$

8. Find $\mathbf{A} \cdot \mathbf{D} - \mathbf{B} \cdot \mathbf{C}$

9. Find $(\mathbf{B} \cdot \mathbf{D})\mathbf{A} - (\mathbf{D} \cdot \mathbf{A})\mathbf{B}$

10. Find $(2\mathbf{A} + 3\mathbf{B}) \cdot (4\mathbf{C} - \mathbf{D})$

11. Find the cosine of the measure of the angle between **A** and **B**.

12. Find the cosine of the measure of the angle between **C** and **D**.

13. Find (a) the component of **C** in the direction of **A** and (b) the vector projection of **C** onto **A**.

14. Find (a) the component of **B** in the direction of **D** and (b) the vector projection of **B** onto **D**.

15. Prove Theorem 18.3.4.   16. Prove Theorem 18.3.6.

17. Prove by using vectors that the points $(2, 2, 2)$, $(2, 0, 1)$, $(4, 1, -1)$, and $(4, 3, 0)$ are the vertices of a rectangle.

18. Prove by using vectors that the points $(2, 2, 2)$, $(0, 1, 2)$, $(-1, 3, 3)$, and $(3, 0, 1)$ are the vertices of a parallelogram.

19. Find the distance from the point $(2, -1, -4)$ to the line through the points $(3, -2, 2)$ and $(-9, -6, 6)$.

20. Find the distance from the point $(3, 2, 1)$ to the line through the points $(1, 2, 9)$ and $(-3, -6, -3)$.

21. Find the area of the triangle having vertices at $(-2, 3, 1)$, $(1, 2, 3)$, and $(3, -1, 2)$.

22. If a force has the vector representation $\mathbf{F} = 5\mathbf{i} - 3\mathbf{k}$, find the work done by the force in moving an object from the point $P_1(4, 1, 3)$ along a straight line to the point $P_2(-5, 6, 2)$. The magnitude of the force is measured in pounds and distance is measured in feet. (HINT: Review Sec. 17.3.)

23. A force is represented by the vector $\mathbf{F}$, has a magnitude of 10 lb, and direction cosines of $\mathbf{F}$ are $\cos \alpha = \frac{1}{6}\sqrt{6}$ and $\cos \beta = \frac{1}{3}\sqrt{6}$. If the force moves an object from the origin along a straight line to the point $(7, -4, 2)$, find the work done. Distance is measured in feet. (See hint for Exercise 22.)

24. If **A** and **B** are nonzero vectors, prove that the vector $\mathbf{A} - c\mathbf{B}$ is orthogonal to **B** if $c = \mathbf{A} \cdot \mathbf{B}/|\mathbf{B}|^2$.

25. If $\mathbf{A} = 12\mathbf{i} + 9\mathbf{j} - 5\mathbf{k}$ and $\mathbf{B} = 4\mathbf{i} + 3\mathbf{j} - 5\mathbf{k}$, use the result of Exercise 24 to find the value of the scalar c so that the vector $\mathbf{B} - c\mathbf{A}$ is orthogonal to **A**.

26. For the vectors of Exercise 25, use the result of Exercise 24 to find the value of the scalar d so that the vector $\mathbf{A} - d\mathbf{B}$ is orthogonal to **B**.

27. Prove that if **A** and **B** are any vectors, then the vectors $|\mathbf{B}|\mathbf{A} + |\mathbf{A}|\mathbf{B}$ and $|\mathbf{B}|\mathbf{A} - |\mathbf{A}|\mathbf{B}$ are orthogonal.

28. Prove that if **A** and **B** are any nonzero vectors and $\mathbf{C} = |\mathbf{B}|\mathbf{A} + |\mathbf{A}|\mathbf{B}$, then the angle between **A** and **C** has the same measure as the angle between **B** and **C**.

18.4 PLANES

The graph of an equation in two variables, x and y, is a curve in the xy plane. The simplest kind of curve in two-dimensional space is a straight line, and the general equation of a straight line is of the form $Ax + By + C = 0$, which is an equation of the first degree. In three-dimensional space, the graph of an equation in three variables, x, y, and z, is a surface. The simplest kind of surface is a *plane*, and we shall see that an equation of a plane is an equation of the first degree in three variables.

18.4.1 Definition

If **N** is a given nonzero vector and P_0 is a given point, then the set of all points P for which $\mathbf{V}(\overrightarrow{P_0P})$ and **N** are orthogonal is defined to be a *plane* through P_0 having **N** as a *normal vector*.

Figure 18.4.1 shows a portion of a plane through the point $P_0(x_0, y_0, z_0)$ and the representation of the normal vector **N** having its initial point at P_0.

In plane analytic geometry we can obtain an equation of a line if we are given a point on the line and its direction (slope). In an analogous manner, in solid analytic geometry an equation of a plane can be determined by knowing a point in the plane and the direction of a normal vector.

18.4.2 Theorem   If $P_0(x_0, y_0, z_0)$ is a point in a plane and a normal vector to the plane is $\mathbf{N} = \langle a, b, c \rangle$, then an equation of the plane is

$$a(x - x_0) + b(y - y_0) + c(z - z_0) = 0 \qquad (1)$$

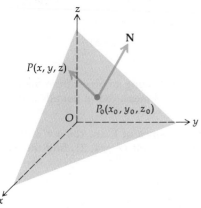

Figure 18.4.1

PROOF: Refer to Fig. 18.4.1. Let $P(x, y, z)$ be any point in the plane. $\mathbf{V}(\overrightarrow{P_0P})$ is the vector having $\overrightarrow{P_0P}$ as a representation, and so

$$\mathbf{V}(\overrightarrow{P_0P}) = \langle x - x_0, y - y_0, z - z_0 \rangle \qquad (2)$$

From Definitions 18.4.1 and 18.3.7, it follows that

$$\mathbf{V}(\overrightarrow{P_0P}) \cdot \mathbf{N} = 0$$

Because $\mathbf{N} = \langle a, b, c \rangle$, from (2) and the above equation we obtain

$$a(x - x_0) + b(y - y_0) + c(z - z_0) = 0 \qquad (3)$$

which is the desired equation.   ∎

EXAMPLE 1:   Find an equation of the plane containing the point $(2, 1, 3)$ and having $3\mathbf{i} - 4\mathbf{j} + \mathbf{k}$ as a normal vector.

SOLUTION: Using (1) with the point $(x_0, y_0, z_0) = (2, 1, 3)$ and the vector $\langle a, b, c \rangle = \langle 3, -4, 1 \rangle$, we have as an equation of the required plane

$$3(x - 2) - 4(y - 1) + (z - 3) = 0$$

or, equivalently,

$$3x - 4y + z - 5 = 0$$

18.4.3 Theorem   If a, b, and c are not all zero, the graph of an equation of the form

$$ax + by + cz + d = 0 \qquad (4)$$

is a plane and $\langle a, b, c \rangle$ is a normal vector to the plane.

PROOF: Suppose that $b \neq 0$. Then the point $(0, -d/b, 0)$ is on the graph of the equation because its coordinates satisfy the equation. The given equation can be written as

$$a(x - 0) + b \left(y + \frac{d}{b} \right) + c(z - 0) = 0$$

which from Theorem 18.4.2 is an equation of a plane through the point $(0, -d/b, 0)$ and for which $\langle a, b, c \rangle$ is a normal vector. This proves the theorem if $b \neq 0$. A similar argument holds if $b = 0$ and either $a \neq 0$ or $c \neq 0$.   ∎

Equations (1) and (4) are called *cartesian equations* of a plane. Equa-

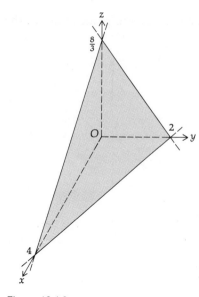

Figure 18.4.2

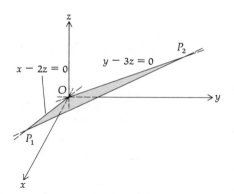

Figure 18.4.3

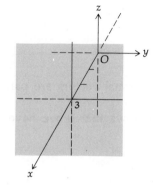

Figure 18.4.4

tion (1) is analogous to the point-slope form of an equation of a line in two dimensions. Equation (4) is the general first-degree equation in three variables and it is called a *linear equation.*

A plane is determined by three noncollinear points, by a line and a point not on the line, by two intersecting lines, or by two parallel lines. To draw a sketch of a plane from its equation, it is convenient to find the points at which the plane intersects each of the coordinate axes. The x coordinate of the point at which the plane intersects the x axis is called the *x intercept* of the plane; the y coordinate of the point at which the plane intersects the y axis is called the *y intercept* of the plane; and the *z intercept* of the plane is the z coordinate of the point at which the plane intersects the z axis.

● ILLUSTRATION 1: We wish to draw a sketch of the plane having the equation

$$2x + 4y + 3z = 8$$

By substituting zero for y and z, we obtain $x = 4$; so the x intercept of the plane is 4. In a similar manner we obtain the y intercept and the z intercept, which are 2 and $\frac{8}{3}$, respectively. Plotting the points corresponding to these intercepts and connecting them with lines, we have the sketch of the plane shown in Fig. 18.4.2. Note that only a portion of the plane is shown in the figure.   ●

● ILLUSTRATION 2: To draw a sketch of the plane having the equation

$$3x + 2y - 6z = 0$$

we first notice that because the equation is satisfied when x, y, and z are all zero, the plane intersects each of the axes at the origin. If we set $x = 0$ in the given equation, we obtain $y - 3z = 0$, which is a line in the yz plane; this is the line of intersection of the yz plane with the given plane. Similarly, the line of intersection of the xz plane with the given plane is obtained by setting $y = 0$, and we get $x - 2z = 0$. Drawing a sketch of each of these two lines and drawing a line segment from a point on one of the lines to a point on the other line, we obtain Fig. 18.4.3.   ●

In Illustration 2 the line in the yz plane and the line in the xz plane used to draw the sketch of the plane are called the *traces* of the given plane in the yz plane and the xz plane, respectively. The equation $x = 0$ is an equation of the yz plane because the point (x, y, z) is in the yz plane if and only if $x = 0$. Similarly, the equations $y = 0$ and $z = 0$ are equations of the xz plane and the xy plane, respectively.

A plane parallel to the yz plane has an equation of the form $x = k$, where k is a constant. Figure 18.4.4 shows a sketch of the plane having the equation $x = 3$. A plane parallel to the xz plane has an equation of the form $y = k$, and a plane parallel to the xy plane has an equation of the form

$z = k$. Figures 18.4.5 and 18.4.6 show sketches of the planes having the equations $y = -5$ and $z = 6$, respectively.

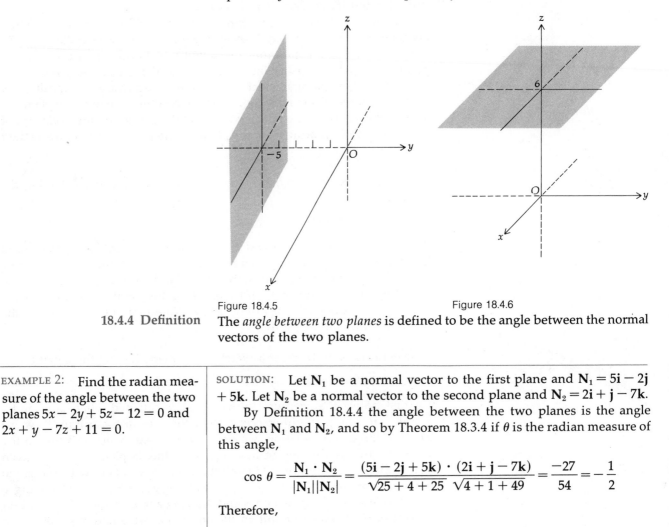

Figure 18.4.5   Figure 18.4.6

18.4.4 Definition   The *angle between two planes* is defined to be the angle between the normal vectors of the two planes.

EXAMPLE 2:   Find the radian measure of the angle between the two planes $5x - 2y + 5z - 12 = 0$ and $2x + y - 7z + 11 = 0$.

SOLUTION: Let $\mathbf{N}_1$ be a normal vector to the first plane and $\mathbf{N}_1 = 5\mathbf{i} - 2\mathbf{j} + 5\mathbf{k}$. Let $\mathbf{N}_2$ be a normal vector to the second plane and $\mathbf{N}_2 = 2\mathbf{i} + \mathbf{j} - 7\mathbf{k}$.

By Definition 18.4.4 the angle between the two planes is the angle between $\mathbf{N}_1$ and $\mathbf{N}_2$, and so by Theorem 18.3.4 if θ is the radian measure of this angle,

$$\cos \theta = \frac{\mathbf{N}_1 \cdot \mathbf{N}_2}{|\mathbf{N}_1||\mathbf{N}_2|} = \frac{(5\mathbf{i} - 2\mathbf{j} + 5\mathbf{k}) \cdot (2\mathbf{i} + \mathbf{j} - 7\mathbf{k})}{\sqrt{25 + 4 + 25} \; \sqrt{4 + 1 + 49}} = \frac{-27}{54} = -\frac{1}{2}$$

Therefore,

$$\theta = \tfrac{2}{3}\pi$$

18.4.5 Definition   Two planes are *parallel* if and only if their normal vectors are parallel.

From Definitions 18.4.5 and 18.3.5, it follows that if we have two planes with equations

$$a_1x + b_1y + c_1z + d_1 = 0 \tag{5}$$

and

$$a_2x + b_2y + c_2z + d_2 = 0 \tag{6}$$

and normal vectors $N_1 = \langle a_1, b_1, c_1 \rangle$ and $N_2 = \langle a_2, b_2, c_2 \rangle$, respectively, then the two planes are parallel if and only if

$$N_1 = kN_2 \qquad \text{where } k \text{ is a constant}$$

Figure 18.4.7 shows sketches of two parallel planes and representations of some of their normal vectors.

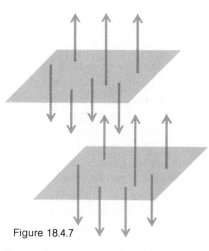

Figure 18.4.7

18.4.6 Definition Two planes are *perpendicular* if and only if their normal vectors are orthogonal.

From Definitions 18.4.6 and 18.3.7 it follows that two planes having normal vectors N_1 and N_2 are perpendicular if and only if

$$N_1 \cdot N_2 = 0 \qquad (7)$$

EXAMPLE 3: Find an equation of the plane perpendicular to each of the planes $x - y + z = 0$ and $2x + y - 4z - 5 = 0$ and containing the point $(4, 0, -2)$.

SOLUTION: Let M be the required plane and $\langle a, b, c \rangle$ be a normal vector of M. Let M_1 be the plane having equation $x - y + z = 0$. By Theorem 18.4.3 a normal vector of M_1 is $\langle 1, -1, 1 \rangle$. Because M and M_1 are perpendicular, it follows from Eq. (7) that

$$\langle a, b, c \rangle \cdot \langle 1, -1, 1 \rangle = 0$$

or, equivalently,

$$b = 2a$$

$$a - b + c = 0 \qquad (8)$$

Let M_2 be the plane having the equation $2x + y - 4z - 5 = 0$. A normal vector of M_2 is $\langle 2, 1, -4 \rangle$. Because M and M_2 are perpendicular, we have

$$\langle a, b, c \rangle \cdot \langle 2, 1, -4 \rangle = 0$$

or, equivalently,

$$c = a$$

$$2a + b - 4c = 0 \qquad (9)$$

Solving Eqs. (8) and (9) simultaneously for b and c in terms of a, we get $b = 2a$ and $c = a$. Therefore, a normal vector of M is $\langle a, 2a, a \rangle$. Because $(4, 0, -2)$ is a point in M, it follows from Theorem 18.4.2 that an equation of M is

$$a(x - 4) + 2a(y - 0) + a(z + 2) = 0$$

or, equivalently,

$$x + 2y + z - 2 = 0$$

Consider now the plane having the equation $ax + by + d = 0$ and the xy plane whose equation is $z = 0$. Normal vectors to these planes are $\langle a, b, 0 \rangle$ and $\langle 0, 0, 1 \rangle$, respectively. Because $\langle a, b, 0 \rangle \cdot \langle 0, 0, 1 \rangle = 0$, the two planes are perpendicular. This means that a plane having an equation with no z term is perpendicular to the xy plane. Figure 18.4.8 illustrates this. In a similar manner, we can conclude that a plane having an equation with no x term is perpendicular to the yz plane (see Fig. 18.4.9), and a plane having an equation with no y term is perpendicular to the xz plane (see Fig. 18.4.10).

An important application of the use of vectors is in finding the undirected distance from a plane to a point. The following example illustrates this.

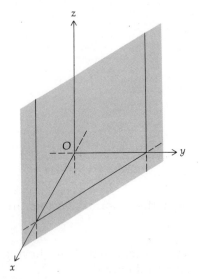

Figure 18.4.8

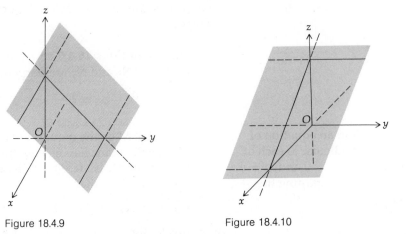

Figure 18.4.9

Figure 18.4.10

EXAMPLE 4: Find the distance from the plane $2x - y + 2z + 10 = 0$ to the point $(1, 4, 6)$.

SOLUTION: Let P be the point $(1, 4, 6)$ and choose any point Q in the plane. For simplicity, choose the point Q as the point where the plane intersects the x axis, that is, the point $(-5, 0, 0)$. The vector having $\overrightarrow{QP}$ as a representation is given by

$$\mathbf{V}(\overrightarrow{QP}) = 6\mathbf{i} + 4\mathbf{j} + 6\mathbf{k}$$

A normal vector to the given plane is

$$\mathbf{N} = 2\mathbf{i} - \mathbf{j} + 2\mathbf{k}$$

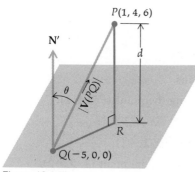

$P(1, 4, 6)$

N'

$|V(\overrightarrow{PQ})|$

θ

d

R

$Q(-5, 0, 0)$

Figure 18.4.11

The negative of $\mathbf{N}$ is also a normal vector to the given plane and

$$-\mathbf{N} = -2\mathbf{i} + \mathbf{j} - 2\mathbf{k}$$

We are not certain which of the two vectors, $\mathbf{N}$ or $-\mathbf{N}$, makes the smaller angle with vector $\mathbf{V}(\overrightarrow{QP})$. Let $\mathbf{N}'$ be the one of the two vectors $\mathbf{N}$ or $-\mathbf{N}$ which makes an angle of radian measure $\theta < \frac{1}{2}\pi$ with $\mathbf{V}(\overrightarrow{QP})$. In Fig. 18.4.11 we show a portion of the given plane containing the point $Q(-5, 0, 0)$, the representation of the vector $\mathbf{N}'$ having its initial point at Q, the point $P(1, 4, 6)$, the directed line segment $\overrightarrow{QP}$, and the point R, which is the foot of the perpendicular from P to the plane. For simplicity, we did not include the coordinate axes in this figure. The distance $|\overrightarrow{RP}|$ is the required distance, which we call d. We see from Fig. 18.4.11 that

$$d = |\mathbf{V}(\overrightarrow{QP})| \cos \theta \tag{10}$$

Because θ is the radian measure of the angle between $\mathbf{N}'$ and $\mathbf{V}(\overrightarrow{QP})$, we have

$$\cos \theta = \frac{\mathbf{N}' \cdot \mathbf{V}(\overrightarrow{QP})}{|\mathbf{N}'||\mathbf{V}(\overrightarrow{QP})|} \tag{11}$$

Substituting from (11) into (10) and replacing $|\mathbf{N}'|$ by $|\mathbf{N}|$, we obtain

$$d = \frac{|\mathbf{V}(\overrightarrow{QP})|(\mathbf{N}' \cdot \mathbf{V}(\overrightarrow{QP}))}{|\mathbf{N}||\mathbf{V}(\overrightarrow{QP})|} = \frac{\mathbf{N}' \cdot \mathbf{V}(\overrightarrow{QP})}{|\mathbf{N}|}$$

Because d is an undirected distance, it is nonnegative; hence, we can replace the numerator in the above expression by the absolute value of the dot product of $\mathbf{N}$ and $\mathbf{V}(\overrightarrow{QP})$. Therefore,

$$d = \frac{|\mathbf{N} \cdot \mathbf{V}(\overrightarrow{QP})|}{|\mathbf{N}|} = \frac{|(2\mathbf{i} - \mathbf{j} + 2\mathbf{k}) \cdot (6\mathbf{i} + 4\mathbf{j} + 6\mathbf{k})|}{\sqrt{4 + 1 + 4}} = \frac{20}{3}$$

Exercises 18.4

In Exercises 1 through 4, find an equation of the plane containing the given point P and having the given vector $\mathbf{N}$ as a normal vector.

1. $P(3, 1, 2)$; $\mathbf{N} = \langle 1, 2, -3 \rangle$

2. $P(-1, 8, 3)$; $\mathbf{N} = \langle -7, -1, 1 \rangle$

3. $P(2, 1, -1)$; $\mathbf{N} = -\mathbf{i} + 3\mathbf{j} + 4\mathbf{k}$

4. $P(1, 0, 0)$; $\mathbf{N} = \mathbf{i} + \mathbf{k}$

In Exercises 5 and 6, find an equation of the plane containing the given three points.

5. $(3, 4, 1)$, $(1, 7, 1)$, $(-1, -2, 5)$

6. $(0, 0, 2)$, $(2, 4, 1)$, $(-2, 3, 3)$

In Exercises 7 through 12, draw a sketch of the given plane and find two unit vectors which are normal to the plane.

7. $2x - y + 2z - 6 = 0$

8. $4x - 4y - 2z - 9 = 0$

9. $4x + 3y - 12z = 0$

10. $y + 2z - 4 = 0$

11. $3x + 2z - 6 = 0$

12. $z = 5$

In Exercises 13 through 17, find an equation of the plane satisfying the given conditions.

13. Perpendicular to the line through the points $(2, 2, -4)$ and $(7, -1, 3)$ and containing the point $(-5, 1, 2)$.

14. Parallel to the plane $4x - 2y + z - 1 = 0$ and containing the point $(2, 6, -1)$.

15. Perpendicular to the plane $x + 3y - z - 7 = 0$ and containing the points $(2, 0, 5)$ and $(0, 2, -1)$.

16. Perpendicular to each of the planes $x - y + z = 0$ and $2x + y - 4z - 5 = 0$ and containing the point $(4, 0, -2)$.

17. Perpendicular to the yz plane, containing the point $(2, 1, 1)$, and making an angle of radian measure $\cos^{-1}(\frac{2}{3})$ with the plane $2x - y + 2z - 3 = 0$.

18. Find the cosine of the measure of the angle between the planes $2x - y - 2z - 5 = 0$ and $6x - 2y + 3z + 8 = 0$.

19. Find the cosine of the measure of the angle between the planes $3x + 4y = 0$ and $4x - 7y + 4z - 6 = 0$.

20. Find the distance from the plane $2x + 2y - z - 6 = 0$ to the point $(2, 2, -4)$.

21. Find the distance from the plane $5x + 11y + 2z - 30 = 0$ to the point $(-2, 6, 3)$.

22. Find the perpendicular distance between the parallel planes

$$4x - 8y - z + 9 = 0 \quad \text{and} \quad 4x - 8y - z - 6 = 0$$

23. Find the perpendicular distance between the parallel planes

$$4y - 3z - 6 = 0 \quad \text{and} \quad 8y - 6z - 27 = 0$$

24. Prove that the undirected distance from the plane $ax + by + cz + d = 0$ to the point (x_0, y_0, z_0) is given by

$$\frac{|ax_0 + by_0 + cz_0 + d|}{\sqrt{a^2 + b^2 + c^2}}$$

25. Prove that the perpendicular distance between the two parallel planes $ax + by + cz + d_1 = 0$ and $ax + by + cz + d_2 = 0$ is given by

$$\frac{|d_1 - d_2|}{\sqrt{a^2 + b^2 + c^2}}$$

26. If a, b, and c are nonzero and are the x intercept, y intercept, and z intercept, respectively, of a plane, prove that an equation of the plane is

$$\frac{x}{a} + \frac{y}{b} + \frac{z}{c} = 1$$

This is called the *intercept form* of an equation of a plane.

18.5 LINES IN R^3 Let L be a line in R^3 such that it contains a given point $P_0(x_0, y_0, z_0)$ and is parallel to the representations of a given vector $\mathbf{R} = \langle a, b, c \rangle$. Figure 18.5.1 shows a sketch of line L and the position representation of vector $\mathbf{R}$. Line L is the set of points $P(x, y, z)$ such that $\mathbf{V}(\overrightarrow{P_0 P})$ is parallel to the vector $\mathbf{R}$. So

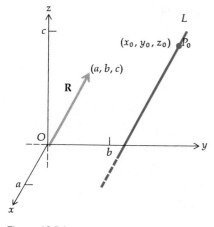

Figure 18.5.1

P is on the line L if and only if there is a nonzero scalar t such that

$$\mathbf{V}(\overrightarrow{P_0P}) = t\mathbf{R} \qquad (1)$$

Because $\mathbf{V}(\overrightarrow{P_0P}) = \langle x - x_0, y - y_0, z - z_0 \rangle$ we obtain from (1)

$$\langle x - x_0, y - y_0, z - z_0 \rangle = t\langle a, b, c \rangle$$

from which it follows that

$$x - x_0 = ta \qquad y - y_0 = tb \qquad z - z_0 = tc$$

or, equivalently,

$$x = x_0 + ta \qquad y = y_0 + tb \qquad z = z_0 + tc \qquad (2)$$

Letting the parameter t be any real number (i.e., t takes on all values in the interval $(-\infty, +\infty)$), the point P may be any point on the line L. Therefore, Eqs. (2) represent the line L, and we call these equations *parametric equations* of the line.

• ILLUSTRATION 1: From Eqs. (2), parametric equations of the line that is parallel to the representations of the vector $\mathbf{R} = \langle 11, 8, 10 \rangle$ and that contains the point $(8, 12, 6)$ are

$$x = 8 + 11t \qquad y = 12 + 8t \qquad z = 6 + 10t$$

Figure 18.5.2 shows a sketch of the line and the position representation of $\mathbf{R}$.
•

If none of the numbers a, b, or c is zero, we can eliminate t from Eqs. (2) and obtain

$$\frac{x - x_0}{a} = \frac{y - y_0}{b} = \frac{z - z_0}{c} \qquad (3)$$

These equations are called *symmetric equations* of the line.

The vector $\mathbf{R} = \langle a, b, c \rangle$ determines the direction of the line, and the numbers a, b, and c are called *direction numbers* of the line. Any vector parallel to $\mathbf{R}$ has either the same or the opposite direction as $\mathbf{R}$; hence, such a vector can be used in place of $\mathbf{R}$ in the above discussion. Because the components of any vector parallel to $\mathbf{R}$ are proportional to the components of $\mathbf{R}$, we can conclude that any set of three numbers proportional to a, b, and c also can serve as a set of direction numbers of the line. So a line has an unlimited number of sets of direction numbers. We write a set of direction numbers of a line in brackets as $[a, b, c]$.

• ILLUSTRATION 2: If $[2, 3, -4]$ represents a set of direction numbers of a line, other sets of direction numbers of the same line can be represented as $[4, 6, -8]$, $[1, \frac{3}{2}, -2]$, and $[2/\sqrt{29}, 3/\sqrt{29}, -4/\sqrt{29}]$.
•

• ILLUSTRATION 3: A set of direction numbers of the line of Illustration 1

Figure 18.5.2

is $[11, 8, 10]$, and the line contains the point $(8, 12, 6)$. Thus, from (3) we have as symmetric equations of this line

$$\frac{x-8}{11} = \frac{y-12}{8} = \frac{z-6}{10}$$

⬤

EXAMPLE 1: Find two sets of symmetric equations of the line through the two points $(-3, 2, 4)$ and $(6, 1, 2)$.

SOLUTION: Let P_1 be the point $(-3, 2, 4)$ and P_2 be the point $(6, 1, 2)$. Then the required line is parallel to the representations of the vector $\mathbf{V}(\overrightarrow{P_1P_2})$, and so the components of this vector constitute a set of direction numbers of the line. $\mathbf{V}(\overrightarrow{P_1P_2}) = \langle 9, -1, -2 \rangle$. Taking P_0 as the point $(-3, 2, 4)$, we have from (3) the equations

$$\frac{x+3}{9} = \frac{y-2}{-1} = \frac{z-4}{-2}$$

Another set of symmetric equations of this line is obtained by taking P_0 as the point $(6, 1, 2)$, and we have

$$\frac{x-6}{9} = \frac{y-1}{-1} = \frac{z-2}{-2}$$

Equations (3) are equivalent to the system of three equations

$$b(x - x_0) = a(y - y_0) \quad c(x - x_0) = a(z - z_0) \quad c(y - y_0) = b(z - z_0) \quad (4)$$

Actually, the three equations in (4) are not independent because any one of them can be derived from the other two. Each of the equations in (4) is an equation of a plane containing the line L represented by Eqs. (3). Any two of these planes have as their intersection the line L; hence, any two of the Eqs. (4) define the line. However, there is an unlimited number of planes which contain a given line and because any two of them will determine the line, we conclude that there is an unlimited number of pairs of equations which represent a line.

If one of the numbers a, b, or c is zero, we do not use symmetric equations (3). However, suppose for example that $b = 0$ and neither a nor c is zero. Then we can write as equations of the line

$$\frac{x - x_0}{a} = \frac{z - z_0}{c} \quad \text{and} \quad y = y_0 \quad (5)$$

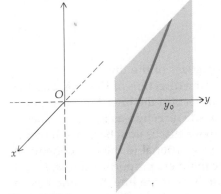

Figure 18.5.3

A line having symmetric equations (5) lies in the plane $y = y_0$ and hence is parallel to the xz plane. Figure 18.5.3 shows such a line.

EXAMPLE 2: Given the two planes

$$x + 3y - z - 9 = 0$$

SOLUTION: If we solve the two given equations for x and y in terms of z, we obtain

$$x = -z + 2 \quad y = \tfrac{2}{3}z + \tfrac{7}{3}$$

and

$$2x - 3y + 4z + 3 = 0$$

For the line of intersection of these two planes, find (a) a set of symmetric equations and (b) a set of parametric equations.

from which we get

$$\frac{x-2}{-1} = \frac{y - \frac{7}{3}}{\frac{2}{3}} = \frac{z-0}{1}$$

or, equivalently,

$$\frac{x-2}{-3} = \frac{y - \frac{7}{3}}{2} = \frac{z-0}{3}$$

which is a set of symmetric equations of the line. A set of parametric equations can be obtained by setting each of the above ratios equal to t, and we have

$$x = 2 - 3t \qquad y = \tfrac{7}{3} + 2t \qquad z = 3t$$

EXAMPLE 3: Find the direction cosines of a vector whose representations are parallel to the line of Example 2.

SOLUTION: From the symmetric equations of the line in Example 2, we see that a set of direction numbers of the line is $[-3, 2, 3]$. Therefore, the vector $\langle -3, 2, 3 \rangle$ is a vector whose representations are parallel to the line. The direction cosines of this vector are as follows: $\cos \alpha = -3/\sqrt{22}$, $\cos \beta = 2/\sqrt{22}$, $\cos \gamma = 3/\sqrt{22}$.

EXAMPLE 4: Find equations of the line through the point $(1, -1, 1)$, perpendicular to the line

$$3x = 2y = z$$

and parallel to the plane

$$x + y - z = 0$$

SOLUTION: Let $[a, b, c]$ be a set of direction numbers of the required line. The equations $3x = 2y = z$ can be written as

$$\frac{x-0}{\frac{1}{3}} = \frac{y-0}{\frac{1}{2}} = \frac{z-0}{1}$$

which are symmetric equations of a line. A set of direction numbers of this line is $[\frac{1}{3}, \frac{1}{2}, 1]$. Because the required line is perpendicular to this line, it follows that the vectors $\langle a, b, c \rangle$ and $\langle \frac{1}{3}, \frac{1}{2}, 1 \rangle$ are orthogonal. So

$$\langle a, b, c \rangle \cdot \langle \tfrac{1}{3}, \tfrac{1}{2}, 1 \rangle = 0$$

or, equivalently,

$$\tfrac{1}{3}a + \tfrac{1}{2}b + c = 0 \tag{6}$$

A normal vector to the plane $x + y - z = 0$ is $\langle 1, 1, -1 \rangle$. Because the required line is parallel to this plane, it is perpendicular to representations of the normal vector. Hence, the vectors $\langle a, b, c \rangle$ and $\langle 1, 1, -1 \rangle$ are orthogonal, and so

$$\langle a, b, c \rangle \cdot \langle 1, 1, -1 \rangle = 0$$

or, equivalently,

$$a + b - c = 0 \tag{7}$$

Solving Eqs. (6) and (7) simultaneously for a and b in terms of c we get $a = 9c$ and $b = -8c$. The required line then has the set of direction numbers $[9c, -8c, c]$ and contains the point $(1, -1, 1)$. Therefore, symmetric equations of the line are

$$\frac{x-1}{9c} = \frac{y+1}{-8c} = \frac{z-1}{c}$$

or, equivalently,

$$\frac{x-1}{9} = \frac{y+1}{-8} = \frac{z-1}{1}$$

EXAMPLE 5: If l_1 is the line through $A(1, 2, 7)$ and $B(-2, 3, -4)$ and l_2 is the line through $C(2, -1, 4)$ and $D(5, 7, -3)$, prove that l_1 and l_2 are skew lines (i.e., they do not lie in one plane).

SOLUTION: To show that two lines do not lie in one plane we demonstrate that they do not intersect and are not parallel. Parametric equations of a line are

$$x = x_0 + ta \qquad y = y_0 + tb \qquad z = z_0 + tc$$

where $[a, b, c]$ is a set of direction numbers of the line and (x_0, y_0, z_0) is any point on the line. Because $\mathbf{V}(\overrightarrow{AB}) = \langle -3, 1, -11 \rangle$, a set of direction numbers of l_1 is $[-3, 1, -11]$. Taking A as the point P_0, we have as parametric equations of l_1

$$x = 1 - 3t \qquad y = 2 + t \qquad z = 7 - 11t \tag{8}$$

Because $\mathbf{V}(\overrightarrow{CD}) = \langle 3, 8, -7 \rangle$, and l_2 contains the point C, we have as parametric equations of l_2

$$x = 2 + 3s \qquad y = -1 + 8s \qquad z = 4 - 7s \tag{9}$$

Because the sets of direction numbers are not proportional, l_1 and l_2 are not parallel. For the lines to intersect, there have to be a value of t and a value of s which give the same point (x_1, y_1, z_1) in both sets of Eqs. (8) and (9). Therefore, we equate the right sides of the respective equations and obtain

$$1 - 3t = 2 + 3s$$

$$2 + t = -1 + 8s$$

$$7 - 11t = 4 - 7s$$

Solving the first two equations simultaneously, we obtain $s = \frac{8}{27}$ and $t = -\frac{17}{27}$. This set of values does not satisfy the third equation; hence, the two lines do not intersect. Thus, l_1 and l_2 are skew lines.

Exercises 18.5

In Exercises 1 through 6, find parametric and symmetric equations for the line satisfying the given conditions.

1. Through the two points $(1, 2, 1)$ and $(5, -1, 1)$.

2. Through the point $(5, 3, 2)$ with direction numbers $[4, 1, -1]$.

3. Through the point $(4, -5, 20)$ and perpendicular to the plane $x + 3y - 6z - 8 = 0$.

4. Through the origin and perpendicular to the lines having direction numbers $[4, 2, 1]$ and $[-3, -2, 1]$.

5. Through the origin and perpendicular to the line $\frac{1}{4}(x - 10) = \frac{1}{3}y = \frac{1}{2}z$ at their intersection.

6. Through the point $(2, 0, -4)$ and parallel to each of the planes $2x + y - z = 0$ and $x + 3y + 5z = 0$.

7. Show that the lines

$$\frac{x + 1}{2} = \frac{y + 4}{-5} = \frac{z - 2}{3} \quad \text{and} \quad \frac{x - 3}{-2} = \frac{y + 14}{5} = \frac{z - 8}{-3}$$

are coincident.

8. Prove that the line $x + 1 = -\frac{1}{2}(y - 6) = z$ lies in the plane $3x + y - z = 3$.

The planes through a line which are perpendicular to the coordinate planes are called the *projecting planes* of the line. In Exercises 9 through 12, find equations of the projecting planes of the given line and draw a sketch of the line.

9. $3x - 2y + 5z - 30 = 0$
$\quad 2x + 3y - 10z - 6 = 0$

10. $x + y - 3z + 1 = 0$
$\quad 2x - y - 3z + 14 = 0$

11. $x - 2y - 3z + 6 = 0$
$\quad x + y + z - 1 = 0$

12. $2x - y + z - 7 = 0$
$\quad 4x - y + 3z - 13 = 0$

13. Find the cosine of the measure of the smallest angle between the two lines $x = 2y + 4, z = -y + 4$, and $x = y + 7$, $2z = y + 2$.

14. Find an equation of the plane containing the point $(6, 2, 4)$ and the line $\frac{1}{5}(x - 1) = \frac{1}{6}(y + 2) = \frac{1}{7}(z - 3)$.

In Exercises 15 and 16, find an equation of the plane containing the given intersecting lines.

15. $\dfrac{x - 2}{4} = \dfrac{y + 3}{-1} = \dfrac{z + 2}{3} \quad \text{and} \quad \begin{cases} 3x + 2y + z + 2 = 0 \\ x - y + 2z - 1 = 0 \end{cases}$

16. $\dfrac{x}{2} = \dfrac{y - 2}{3} = \dfrac{z - 1}{1} \quad \text{and} \quad \dfrac{x}{1} = \dfrac{y - 2}{-1} = \dfrac{z - 1}{1}$

17. Show that the lines

$$\begin{cases} 3x - y - z = 0 \\ 8x - 2y - 3z + 1 = 0 \end{cases} \quad \text{and} \quad \begin{cases} x - 3y + z + 3 = 0 \\ 3x - y - z + 5 = 0 \end{cases}$$

are parallel and find an equation of the plane determined by these lines.

18. Find equations of the line through the point $(1, -1, 1)$, perpendicular to the line $3x = 2y = z$, and parallel to the plane $x + y - z = 0$.

19. Find equations of the line through the point $(3, 6, 4)$, intersecting the z axis, and parallel to the plane $x - 3y + 5z - 6 = 0$.

20. Find equations of the line through the origin, perpendicular to the line $x = y - 5, z = 2y - 3$, and intersecting the line $y = 2x + 1, z = x + 2$.

21. Find the perpendicular distance from the point $(-1, 3, -1)$ to the line $x - 2z = 7, y = 1$.

22. Find the perpendicular distance from the origin to the line

$$x = -2 + \tfrac{6}{7}t \qquad y = 7 - \tfrac{2}{7}t \qquad z = 4 + \tfrac{3}{7}t$$

23. Prove that the lines

$$\frac{x - 1}{5} = \frac{y - 2}{-2} = \frac{z + 1}{-3} \quad \text{and} \quad \frac{x - 2}{1} = \frac{y + 1}{-3} = \frac{z + 3}{2}$$

are skew lines.

24. Find equations of the line through the point $(3, -4, -5)$ which intersects each of the skew lines of Exercise 23.

18.6 CROSS PRODUCT

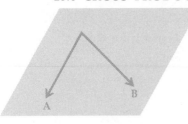

Figure 18.6.1

Let **A** and **B** be two nonparallel vectors. Representations of these two vectors having the same initial point determine a plane as shown in Fig. 18.6.1. We show that a vector whose representations are perpendicular to this plane is given by the vector operation called the "cross product" of the two vectors **A** and **B**. The cross product is a vector operation for vectors in V_3 that we did not have for vectors in V_2. We first define this operation and then consider its algebraic and geometric properties.

18.6.1 Definition If $\mathbf{A} = \langle a_1, a_2, a_3 \rangle$ and $\mathbf{B} = \langle b_1, b_2, b_3 \rangle$, then the *cross product* of **A** and **B**, denoted by $\mathbf{A} \times \mathbf{B}$, is given by

$$\mathbf{A} \times \mathbf{B} = \langle a_2 b_3 - a_3 b_2, \, a_3 b_1 - a_1 b_3, \, a_1 b_2 - a_2 b_1 \rangle \tag{1}$$

Because the cross product of two vectors is a vector, the cross product also is called the *vector product*. The operation of obtaining the cross product is called *vector multiplication*.

• ILLUSTRATION 1: If $\mathbf{A} = \langle 2, 1, -3 \rangle$ and $\mathbf{B} = \langle 3, -1, 4 \rangle$, then from Definition 18.6.1 we have

$$\mathbf{A} \times \mathbf{B} = \langle 2, 1, -3 \rangle \times \langle 3, -1, 4 \rangle$$
$$= \langle (1)(4) - (-3)(-1), \, (-3)(3) - (2)(4), \, (2)(-1) - (1)(3) \rangle$$
$$= \langle 4 - 3, -9 - 8, -2 - 3 \rangle$$
$$= \langle 1, -17, -5 \rangle$$
$$= \mathbf{i} - 17\mathbf{j} - 5\mathbf{k} \qquad \bullet$$

There is a mnenomic device for remembering formula (1) that makes use of determinant notation. A second-order determinant is defined by the equation

$$\begin{vmatrix} a & b \\ c & d \end{vmatrix} = ad - bc$$

where a, b, and c are real numbers. For example,

$$\begin{vmatrix} 3 & 6 \\ -2 & 5 \end{vmatrix} = 3(5) - (6)(-2) = 27$$

Therefore, formula (1) can be written as

$$\mathbf{A} \times \mathbf{B} = \begin{vmatrix} a_2 & a_3 \\ b_2 & b_3 \end{vmatrix} \mathbf{i} - \begin{vmatrix} a_1 & a_3 \\ b_1 & b_3 \end{vmatrix} \mathbf{j} + \begin{vmatrix} a_1 & a_2 \\ b_1 & b_2 \end{vmatrix} \mathbf{k}$$

The right side of the above expression can be written symbolically as

$$\begin{vmatrix} \mathbf{i} & \mathbf{j} & \mathbf{k} \\ a_1 & a_2 & a_3 \\ b_1 & b_2 & b_3 \end{vmatrix}$$

which is the notation for a third-order determinant. However, observe that the first row contains vectors and not real numbers as is customary with determinant notation.

● ILLUSTRATION 2: We use the mnemonic device employing determinant notation to find the cross product of the vectors of Illustration 1.

$$\mathbf{A} \times \mathbf{B} = \begin{vmatrix} \mathbf{i} & \mathbf{j} & \mathbf{k} \\ 2 & 1 & -3 \\ 3 & -1 & 4 \end{vmatrix}$$

$$= \begin{vmatrix} 1 & -3 \\ -1 & 4 \end{vmatrix} \mathbf{i} - \begin{vmatrix} 2 & -3 \\ 3 & 4 \end{vmatrix} \mathbf{j} + \begin{vmatrix} 2 & 1 \\ 3 & -1 \end{vmatrix} \mathbf{k}$$

$$= [(1)(4) - (-3)(-1)]\mathbf{i} - [(2)(4) - (-3)(3)]\mathbf{j}$$
$$+ [(2)(-1) - (1)(3)]\mathbf{k}$$

$$= \mathbf{i} - 17\mathbf{j} - 5\mathbf{k} \qquad \qquad ●$$

18.6.2 Theorem   If $\mathbf{A}$ is any vector in V_3, then

      (i) $\mathbf{A} \times \mathbf{A} = \mathbf{0}$
     (ii) $\mathbf{0} \times \mathbf{A} = \mathbf{0}$
    (iii) $\mathbf{A} \times \mathbf{0} = \mathbf{0}$

PROOF OF (i): If $\mathbf{A} = \langle a_1, a_2, a_3 \rangle$, then by Definition 18.6.1 we have

$$\mathbf{A} \times \mathbf{A} = \langle a_2 a_3 - a_3 a_2, a_3 a_1 - a_1 a_3, a_1 a_2 - a_2 a_1 \rangle$$

$$= \langle 0, 0, 0 \rangle$$

$$= \mathbf{0}$$

The proofs of (ii) and (iii) are left as exercises (see Exercise 13).   ■

By applying Definition 18.6.1 to pairs of unit vectors $\mathbf{i}, \mathbf{j}$, and $\mathbf{k}$, we obtain the following:

$$\mathbf{i} \times \mathbf{i} = \mathbf{j} \times \mathbf{j} = \mathbf{k} \times \mathbf{k} = \mathbf{0}$$

$$\mathbf{i} \times \mathbf{j} = \mathbf{k} \qquad \mathbf{j} \times \mathbf{k} = \mathbf{i} \qquad \mathbf{k} \times \mathbf{i} = \mathbf{j}$$

$$\mathbf{j} \times \mathbf{i} = -\mathbf{k} \qquad \mathbf{k} \times \mathbf{j} = -\mathbf{i} \qquad \mathbf{i} \times \mathbf{k} = -\mathbf{j}$$

As an aid in remembering the above cross products, we first notice that the cross product of any one of the unit vectors $\mathbf{i}, \mathbf{j}$, or $\mathbf{k}$ with itself is the zero vector. The other six cross products can be obtained from Fig. 18.6.2 by applying the following rule: The cross product of two consecutive vectors, in the clockwise direction, is the next vector; and the cross product of two consecutive vectors, in the counterclockwise direction, is the negative of the next vector.

It can be easily seen that cross multiplication of two vectors is not

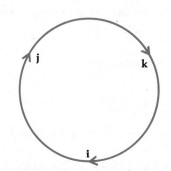

Figure 18.6.2

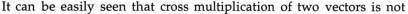

commutative because in particular $\mathbf{i} \times \mathbf{j} \neq \mathbf{j} \times \mathbf{i}$. However, $\mathbf{i} \times \mathbf{j} = \mathbf{k}$ and $\mathbf{j} \times \mathbf{i} = -\mathbf{k}$; and so $\mathbf{i} \times \mathbf{j} = -(\mathbf{j} \times \mathbf{i})$. It is true in general that $\mathbf{A} \times \mathbf{B} = -(\mathbf{B} \times \mathbf{A})$, which we state and prove as a theorem.

18.6.3 Theorem   If $\mathbf{A}$ and $\mathbf{B}$ are any vectors in V_3,

$$\mathbf{A} \times \mathbf{B} = -(\mathbf{B} \times \mathbf{A})$$

PROOF: If $\mathbf{A} = \langle a_1, a_2, a_3 \rangle$ and $\mathbf{B} = \langle b_1, b_2, b_3 \rangle$, then by Definition 18.6.1 we have

$$\mathbf{A} \times \mathbf{B} = \langle a_2 b_3 - a_3 b_2, \ a_3 b_1 - a_1 b_3, \ a_1 b_2 - a_2 b_1 \rangle$$
$$= -1 \langle a_3 b_2 - a_2 b_3, \ a_1 b_3 - a_3 b_1, \ a_2 b_1 - a_1 b_2 \rangle$$
$$= -(\mathbf{B} \times \mathbf{A}) \qquad \blacksquare$$

Cross multiplication of vectors is not associative. This is shown by the following example:

$$\mathbf{i} \times (\mathbf{i} \times \mathbf{j}) = \mathbf{i} \times \mathbf{k} = -\mathbf{j}$$
$$(\mathbf{i} \times \mathbf{i}) \times \mathbf{j} = \mathbf{0} \times \mathbf{j} = \mathbf{0}$$

So

$$\mathbf{i} \times (\mathbf{i} \times \mathbf{j}) \neq (\mathbf{i} \times \mathbf{i}) \times \mathbf{j}$$

Cross multiplication of vectors is distributive with respect to vector addition, as given by the following theorem.

18.6.4 Theorem   If $\mathbf{A}$, $\mathbf{B}$, and $\mathbf{C}$ are any vectors in V_3, then

$$\mathbf{A} \times (\mathbf{B} + \mathbf{C}) = \mathbf{A} \times \mathbf{B} + \mathbf{A} \times \mathbf{C} \qquad (2)$$

Theorem 18.6.4 can be proved by letting $\mathbf{A} = \langle a_1, a_2, a_3 \rangle$, $\mathbf{B} = \langle b_1, b_2, b_3 \rangle$, and $\mathbf{C} = \langle c_1, c_2, c_3 \rangle$, and then showing that the components of the vector on the left side of (2) are the same as the components of the vector on the right side of (2). The details are left as an exercise (see Exercise 14).

18.6.5 Theorem   If $\mathbf{A}$ and $\mathbf{B}$ are any two vectors in V_3 and c is a scalar, then

(i) $(c\mathbf{A}) \times \mathbf{B} = \mathbf{A} \times (c\mathbf{B})$;
(ii) $(c\mathbf{A}) \times \mathbf{B} = c(\mathbf{A} \times \mathbf{B})$.

The proof of Theorem 18.6.5 is left as exercises (see Exercises 15 and 16).

Repeated applications of Theorems 18.6.4 and 18.6.5 enable us to compute the cross product of two vectors by using laws of algebra, provided we do not change the order of the vectors in cross multiplication, which is prohibited by Theorem 18.6.3. The following illustration demonstrates this.

● ILLUSTRATION 3: We find the cross product of the vectors in Illustration 1 by applying Theorems 18.6.4 and 18.6.5.

$$\mathbf{A} \times \mathbf{B} = (2\mathbf{i} + \mathbf{j} - 3\mathbf{k}) \times (3\mathbf{i} - \mathbf{j} + 4\mathbf{k})$$

$$= 6(\mathbf{i} \times \mathbf{i}) - 2(\mathbf{i} \times \mathbf{j}) + 8(\mathbf{i} \times \mathbf{k}) + 3(\mathbf{j} \times \mathbf{i}) - 1(\mathbf{j} \times \mathbf{j})$$

$$+ 4(\mathbf{j} \times \mathbf{k}) - 9(\mathbf{k} \times \mathbf{i}) + 3(\mathbf{k} \times \mathbf{j}) - 12(\mathbf{k} \times \mathbf{k})$$

$$= 6(\mathbf{0}) - 2(\mathbf{k}) + 8(-\mathbf{j}) + 3(-\mathbf{k}) - 1(\mathbf{0})$$

$$+ 4(\mathbf{i}) - 9(\mathbf{j}) + 3(-\mathbf{i}) - 12(\mathbf{0})$$

$$= -2\mathbf{k} - 8\mathbf{j} - 3\mathbf{k} + 4\mathbf{i} - 9\mathbf{j} - 3\mathbf{i}$$

$$= \mathbf{i} - 17\mathbf{j} - 5\mathbf{k} \qquad \qquad ●$$

The method used in Illustration 3 gives a way of finding the cross product without having to remember formula (1) or to use determinant notation. Actually all the steps shown in the solution need not be included because the various cross products of the unit vectors can be obtained immediately by using Fig. 18.6.2 and the corresponding rule.

● ILLUSTRATION 4: We prove that if $\mathbf{A}$ and $\mathbf{B}$ are any two vectors in V_3, then

$$|\mathbf{A} \times \mathbf{B}|^2 = |\mathbf{A}|^2|\mathbf{B}|^2 - (\mathbf{A} \cdot \mathbf{B})^2$$

Let $\mathbf{A} = \langle a_1, a_2, a_3 \rangle$ and $\mathbf{B} = \langle b_1, b_2, b_3 \rangle$. Then

$$|\mathbf{A} \times \mathbf{B}|^2 = (a_2b_3 - a_3b_2)^2 + (a_3b_1 - a_1b_3)^2 + (a_1b_2 - a_2b_1)^2$$

$$= a_2{}^2b_3{}^2 - 2a_2a_3b_2b_3 + a_3{}^2b_2{}^2 + a_3{}^2b_1{}^2 - 2a_1a_3b_1b_3$$

$$+ a_1{}^2b_3{}^2 + a_1{}^2b_2{}^2 - 2a_1a_2b_1b_2 + a_2{}^2b_1{}^2$$

$$|\mathbf{A}|^2|\mathbf{B}|^2 - (\mathbf{A} \cdot \mathbf{B})^2 = (a_1{}^2 + a_2{}^2 + a_3{}^2)(b_1{}^2 + b_2{}^2 + b_3{}^2)$$

$$- (a_1b_1 + a_2b_2 + a_3b_3)^2$$

$$= a_1{}^2b_2{}^2 + a_1{}^2b_3{}^2 + a_2{}^2b_1{}^2 + a_2{}^2b_3{}^2 + a_3{}^2b_1{}^2$$

$$+ a_3{}^2b_2{}^2 - 2a_1a_3b_1b_3 - 2a_2a_3b_2b_3 - 2a_1a_2b_1b_2$$

Comparing the two expressions, we conclude that

$$|\mathbf{A} \times \mathbf{B}|^2 = |\mathbf{A}|^2|\mathbf{B}|^2 - (\mathbf{A} \cdot \mathbf{B})^2 \qquad \qquad ●$$

The formula proved in Illustration 4 is useful to us in proving the following theorem, from which we can obtain a geometric interpretation of the cross product.

18.6.6 Theorem   If $\mathbf{A}$ and $\mathbf{B}$ are two vectors in V_3 and θ is the radian measure of the angle between $\mathbf{A}$ and $\mathbf{B}$, then

$$|\mathbf{A} \times \mathbf{B}| = |\mathbf{A}||\mathbf{B}| \sin \theta \qquad \qquad (3)$$

PROOF: From Illustration 4 we have

$$|\mathbf{A} \times \mathbf{B}|^2 = |\mathbf{A}|^2|\mathbf{B}|^2 - (\mathbf{A} \cdot \mathbf{B})^2 \tag{4}$$

From Theorem 18.3.4, if θ is the radian measure of the angle between $\mathbf{A}$ and $\mathbf{B}$, we have

$$\mathbf{A} \cdot \mathbf{B} = |\mathbf{A}||\mathbf{B}| \cos \theta \tag{5}$$

Substituting from (5) into (4) we get

$$|\mathbf{A} \times \mathbf{B}|^2 = |\mathbf{A}|^2|\mathbf{B}|^2 - |\mathbf{A}|^2|\mathbf{B}|^2 \cos^2 \theta$$
$$= |\mathbf{A}|^2|\mathbf{B}|^2(1 - \cos^2 \theta)$$

So

$$|\mathbf{A} \times \mathbf{B}|^2 = |\mathbf{A}|^2|\mathbf{B}|^2 \sin^2 \theta \tag{6}$$

Because $0 \le \theta \le \pi$, $\sin \theta \ge 0$. Therefore, from Eq. (6), we get

$$|\mathbf{A} \times \mathbf{B}| = |\mathbf{A}||\mathbf{B}| \sin \theta \qquad \blacksquare$$

We consider now a geometric interpretation of $|\mathbf{A} \times \mathbf{B}|$. Let $\overrightarrow{PR}$ be a representation of $\mathbf{A}$ and let $\overrightarrow{PQ}$ be a representation of $\mathbf{B}$. Then the angle between the vectors $\mathbf{A}$ and $\mathbf{B}$ is the angle at P in triangle RPQ (see Fig. 18.6.3). Let the radian measure of this angle be θ. Therefore, the number of square units in the area of the parallelogram having $\overrightarrow{PR}$ and $\overrightarrow{PQ}$ as adjacent sides is $|\mathbf{A}||\mathbf{B}| \sin \theta$ because the altitude of the parallelogram has length $|\mathbf{B}| \sin \theta$ units and the length of the base is $|\mathbf{A}|$ units. So from Eq. (3) it follows that $|\mathbf{A} \times \mathbf{B}|$ square units is the area of this parallelogram.

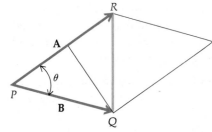

Figure 18.6.3

EXAMPLE 1: Show that the quadrilateral having vertices at $P(1,-2,3), Q(4,3,-1)$, $R(2,2,1)$, and $S(5,7,-3)$ is a parallelogram and find its area.

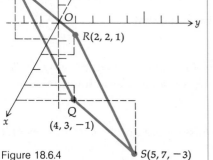

Figure 18.6.4

SOLUTION: Figure 18.6.4 shows the quadrilateral $PQSR$.

$$\mathbf{V}(\overrightarrow{PQ}) = \langle 4-1, 3-(-2), (-1)-3 \rangle = \langle 3, 5, -4 \rangle$$
$$\mathbf{V}(\overrightarrow{PR}) = \langle 2-1, 2-(-2), 1-3 \rangle = \langle 1, 4, -2 \rangle$$
$$\mathbf{V}(\overrightarrow{RS}) = \langle 5-2, 7-2, -3-1 \rangle = \langle 3, 5, -4 \rangle$$
$$\mathbf{V}(\overrightarrow{QS}) = \langle 5-4, 7-3, -3-(-1) \rangle = \langle 1, 4, -2 \rangle$$

Because $\mathbf{V}(\overrightarrow{PQ}) = \mathbf{V}(\overrightarrow{RS})$ and $\mathbf{V}(\overrightarrow{PR}) = \mathbf{V}(\overrightarrow{QS})$, it follows that $\overrightarrow{PQ}$ is parallel to $\overrightarrow{RS}$ and $\overrightarrow{PR}$ is parallel to $\overrightarrow{QS}$. Therefore, $PQSR$ is a parallelogram.

Let $\mathbf{A} = \mathbf{V}(\overrightarrow{PR})$ and $\mathbf{B} = \mathbf{V}(\overrightarrow{PQ})$, then

$$\mathbf{A} \times \mathbf{B} = (\mathbf{i} + 4\mathbf{j} - 2\mathbf{k}) \times (3\mathbf{i} + 5\mathbf{j} - 4\mathbf{k})$$
$$= 3(\mathbf{i} \times \mathbf{i}) + 5(\mathbf{i} \times \mathbf{j}) - 4(\mathbf{i} \times \mathbf{k}) + 12(\mathbf{j} \times \mathbf{i}) + 20(\mathbf{j} \times \mathbf{j})$$
$$- 16(\mathbf{j} \times \mathbf{k}) - 6(\mathbf{k} \times \mathbf{i}) - 10(\mathbf{k} \times \mathbf{j}) + 8(\mathbf{k} \times \mathbf{k})$$
$$= 3(\mathbf{0}) + 5(\mathbf{k}) - 4(-\mathbf{j}) + 12(-\mathbf{k}) + 20(\mathbf{0}) - 16(\mathbf{i})$$
$$- 6(\mathbf{j}) - 10(-\mathbf{i}) + 8(\mathbf{0})$$

$$= -6\mathbf{i} - 2\mathbf{j} - 7\mathbf{k}$$

Hence,

$$|\mathbf{A} \times \mathbf{B}| = \sqrt{36 + 4 + 49} = \sqrt{89}$$

The area of the parallelogram is therefore $\sqrt{89}$ square units.

The following theorem, which gives a method for determining if two vectors in V_3 are parallel, follows from Theorem 18.6.6.

18.6.7 Theorem   If $\mathbf{A}$ and $\mathbf{B}$ are two vectors in V_3, $\mathbf{A}$ and $\mathbf{B}$ are parallel if and only if $\mathbf{A} \times \mathbf{B} = \mathbf{0}$.

PROOF: If either $\mathbf{A}$ or $\mathbf{B}$ is the zero vector, then from Theorem 18.6.2, $\mathbf{A} \times \mathbf{B} = \mathbf{0}$. Because the zero vector is parallel to any vector, the theorem holds.

If neither $\mathbf{A}$ nor $\mathbf{B}$ is the zero vector, $|\mathbf{A}| \neq 0$ and $|\mathbf{B}| \neq 0$. Therefore, from Eq. (3), $|\mathbf{A} \times \mathbf{B}| = 0$ if and only if $\sin \theta = 0$. Because $|\mathbf{A} \times \mathbf{B}| = 0$ if and only if $\mathbf{A} \times \mathbf{B} = \mathbf{0}$ and $\sin \theta = 0$ $(0 \leq \theta \leq \pi)$ if and only if $\theta = 0$ or π, we can conclude that

$$\mathbf{A} \times \mathbf{B} = \mathbf{0} \quad \text{if and only if} \quad \theta = 0 \text{ or } \pi$$

However, from Theorem 18.3.6, two nonzero vectors are parallel if and only if the radian measure of the angle between the two vectors is 0 or π. Thus, the theorem follows.   ■

The product $\mathbf{A} \cdot (\mathbf{B} \times \mathbf{C})$ is called the *triple scalar product* of the vectors $\mathbf{A}$, $\mathbf{B}$, and $\mathbf{C}$. Actually, the parentheses are not needed because $\mathbf{A} \cdot \mathbf{B}$ is a scalar, and therefore $\mathbf{A} \cdot \mathbf{B} \times \mathbf{C}$ can be interpreted only in one way.

18.6.8 Theorem   If $\mathbf{A}$, $\mathbf{B}$, and $\mathbf{C}$ are vectors in V_3, then

$$\mathbf{A} \cdot \mathbf{B} \times \mathbf{C} = \mathbf{A} \times \mathbf{B} \cdot \mathbf{C} \qquad (7)$$

Theorem 18.6.8 can be proved by letting $\mathbf{A} = \langle a_1, a_2, a_3 \rangle$, $\mathbf{B} = \langle b_1, b_2, b_3 \rangle$, and $\mathbf{C} = \langle c_1, c_2, c_3 \rangle$ and then by showing that the number on the left side of (7) is the same as the number on the right. The details are left as an exercise (see Exercise 17).

● ILLUSTRATION 5:   We verify Theorem 18.6.8 if $\mathbf{A} = \langle 1, -1, 2 \rangle$, $\mathbf{B} = \langle 3, 4, -2 \rangle$, and $\mathbf{C} = \langle -5, 1, -4 \rangle$.

$$\mathbf{B} \times \mathbf{C} = (3\mathbf{i} + 4\mathbf{j} - 2\mathbf{k}) \times (-5\mathbf{i} + \mathbf{j} - 4\mathbf{k})$$

$$= 3\mathbf{k} - 12(-\mathbf{j}) - 20(-\mathbf{k}) - 16\mathbf{i} + 10\mathbf{j} - 2(-\mathbf{i})$$

$$= -14\mathbf{i} + 22\mathbf{j} + 23\mathbf{k}$$

$$\mathbf{A} \cdot (\mathbf{B} \times \mathbf{C}) = \langle 1, -1, 2 \rangle \cdot \langle -14, 22, 23 \rangle = -14 - 22 + 46$$

$$= 10$$

$$\mathbf{A} \times \mathbf{B} = (\mathbf{i} - \mathbf{j} + 2\mathbf{k}) \times (3\mathbf{i} + 4\mathbf{j} - 2\mathbf{k})$$

$$= 4\mathbf{k} - 2(-\mathbf{j}) - 3(-\mathbf{k}) + 2\mathbf{i} + 6\mathbf{j} + 8\,(-\mathbf{i})$$

$$= -6\mathbf{i} + 8\mathbf{j} + 7\mathbf{k}$$

$$(\mathbf{A} \times \mathbf{B}) \cdot \mathbf{C} = \langle -6, 8, 7 \rangle \cdot \langle -5, 1, -4 \rangle$$

$$= 30 + 8 - 28$$

$$= 10$$

This verifies the theorem for these three vectors.   •

18.6.9 Theorem   If **A** and **B** are two vectors in V_3, then the vector $\mathbf{A} \times \mathbf{B}$ is orthogonal to both **A** and **B**.

PROOF: From Theorem 18.6.8 we have

$$\mathbf{A} \cdot \mathbf{A} \times \mathbf{B} = \mathbf{A} \times \mathbf{A} \cdot \mathbf{B}$$

From Theorem 18.6.2(i), $\mathbf{A} \times \mathbf{A} = \mathbf{0}$. Therefore, from the above equation we have

$$\mathbf{A} \cdot \mathbf{A} \times \mathbf{B} = \mathbf{0} \cdot \mathbf{B} = 0$$

Because the dot product of **A** and $\mathbf{A} \times \mathbf{B}$ is zero, it follows from Definition 18.3.7 that **A** and $\mathbf{A} \times \mathbf{B}$ are orthogonal.
We also have from Theorem 18.6.8 that

$$\mathbf{A} \times \mathbf{B} \cdot \mathbf{B} = \mathbf{A} \cdot \mathbf{B} \times \mathbf{B}$$

Again applying Theorem 18.6.2(i), we get $\mathbf{B} \times \mathbf{B} = \mathbf{0}$, and so from the above equation we have

$$\mathbf{A} \times \mathbf{B} \cdot \mathbf{B} = \mathbf{A} \cdot \mathbf{0} = 0$$

Therefore, since the dot product of $\mathbf{A} \times \mathbf{B}$ and **B** is zero, $\mathbf{A} \times \mathbf{B}$ and **B** are orthogonal and the theorem is proved.   ■

From Theorem 18.6.9 we can conclude that if representations of the vectors **A**, **B**, and $\mathbf{A} \times \mathbf{B}$ have the same initial point, then the representation of $\mathbf{A} \times \mathbf{B}$ is perpendicular to the plane formed by the representations of **A** and **B**.

EXAMPLE 2:   Given the points $P(-1, -2, -3), Q(-2, 1, 0)$, and $R(0, 5, 1)$, find a unit vector

SOLUTION: Let $\mathbf{A} = \mathbf{V}(\overrightarrow{PQ})$ and $\mathbf{B} = \mathbf{V}(\overrightarrow{PR})$. Then

$$\mathbf{A} = \langle -2 - (-1), 1 - (-2), 0 - (-3) \rangle = \langle -1, 3, 3 \rangle$$

whose representations are perpendicular to the plane through the points P, Q, and R.

$$B = \langle 0 - (-1), 5 - (-2), 1 - (-3)\rangle = \langle 1, 7, 4\rangle$$

The plane through P, Q, and R is the plane formed by $\overrightarrow{PQ}$ and $\overrightarrow{PR}$, which are, respectively, representations of vectors **A** and **B**. Therefore, any representation of the vector **A** × **B** is perpendicular to this plane.

$$\mathbf{A} \times \mathbf{B} = (-\mathbf{i} + 3\mathbf{j} + 3\mathbf{k}) \times (\mathbf{i} + 7\mathbf{j} + 4\mathbf{k}) = -9\mathbf{i} + 7\mathbf{j} - 10\mathbf{k}$$

The desired vector is a unit vector parallel to **A** × **B**. To find this unit vector we apply Theorem 18.2.9 and divide **A** × **B** by |**A** × **B**|, and we obtain

$$\frac{\mathbf{A} \times \mathbf{B}}{|\mathbf{A} \times \mathbf{B}|} = -\frac{9}{\sqrt{230}}\mathbf{i} + \frac{7}{\sqrt{230}}\mathbf{j} - \frac{10}{\sqrt{230}}\mathbf{k}$$

EXAMPLE 3: Find an equation of the plane through the points $P(1, 3, 2)$, $Q(3, -2, 2)$, and $R(2, 1, 3)$.

SOLUTION: $\mathbf{V}(\overrightarrow{QR}) = -\mathbf{i} + 3\mathbf{j} + \mathbf{k}$ and $\mathbf{V}(\overrightarrow{PR}) = \mathbf{i} - 2\mathbf{j} + \mathbf{k}$. A normal vector to the required plane is the cross product $\mathbf{V}(\overrightarrow{QR}) \times \mathbf{V}(\overrightarrow{PR})$, which is

$$(-\mathbf{i} + 3\mathbf{j} + \mathbf{k}) \times (\mathbf{i} - 2\mathbf{j} + \mathbf{k}) = 5\mathbf{i} + 2\mathbf{j} - \mathbf{k}$$

So if $P_0 = (1, 3, 2)$ and $\mathbf{N} = \langle 5, 2, -1\rangle$, from Theorem 18.4.2 we have as an equation of the required plane

$$5(x - 1) + 2(y - 3) - (z - 2) = 0$$

or, equivalently,

$$5x + 2y - z - 9 = 0$$

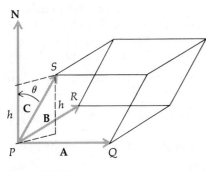

Figure 18.6.5

A geometric interpretation of the triple scalar product is obtained by considering a parallelepiped having edges $\overrightarrow{PQ}$, $\overrightarrow{PR}$, and $\overrightarrow{PS}$, and letting $\mathbf{A} = \mathbf{V}(\overrightarrow{PQ})$, $\mathbf{B} = \mathbf{V}(\overrightarrow{PR})$, and $\mathbf{C} = \mathbf{V}(\overrightarrow{PS})$. See Fig. 18.6.5. The vector **A** × **B** is a normal vector to the plane of $\overrightarrow{PQ}$ and $\overrightarrow{PR}$. The vector $-(\mathbf{A} \times \mathbf{B})$ is also a normal vector to this plane. We are not certain which of the two vectors, $(\mathbf{A} \times \mathbf{B})$ or $-(\mathbf{A} \times \mathbf{B})$, makes the smaller angle with **C**. Let **N** be the one of the two vectors $(\mathbf{A} \times \mathbf{B})$ or $-(\mathbf{A} \times \mathbf{B})$ that makes an angle of radian measure $\theta < \frac{1}{2}\pi$ with **C**. Then the representations of **N** and **C** having their initial points at P are on the same side of the plane of $\overrightarrow{PQ}$ and $\overrightarrow{PR}$ as shown in Fig. 18.6.5. The area of the base of the parallelepiped is |**A** × **B**| square units. If h units is the length of the altitude of the parallelepiped, and if V cubic units is the volume of the parallelepiped,

$$V = |\mathbf{A} \times \mathbf{B}|h \tag{8}$$

Consider now the dot product $\mathbf{N} \cdot \mathbf{C}$. By Theorem 18.3.4, $\mathbf{N} \cdot \mathbf{C} = |\mathbf{N}||\mathbf{C}| \cos \theta$. But $h = |\mathbf{C}| \cos \theta$, and so $\mathbf{N} \cdot \mathbf{C} = |\mathbf{N}|h$. Because **N** is either $(\mathbf{A} \times \mathbf{B})$ or $-(\mathbf{A} \times \mathbf{B})$, it follows that $|\mathbf{N}| = |\mathbf{A} \times \mathbf{B}|$. Hence, we have

$$\mathbf{N} \cdot \mathbf{C} = |\mathbf{A} \times \mathbf{B}|h \tag{9}$$

Comparing Eqs. (8) and (9) we have

$$\mathbf{N} \cdot \mathbf{C} = V$$

It follows that the measure of the volume of the parallelepiped is either $(\mathbf{A} \times \mathbf{B}) \cdot \mathbf{C}$ or $-(\mathbf{A} \times \mathbf{B}) \cdot \mathbf{C}$; that is, the measure of the volume of the parallelepiped is the absolute value of the triple scalar product $\mathbf{A} \times \mathbf{B} \cdot \mathbf{C}$.

EXAMPLE 4: Find the volume of the parallelepiped having vertices $P(5, 4, 5), Q(4, 10, 6), R(1, 8, 7)$, and $S(2, 6, 9)$ and edges $\overrightarrow{PQ}, \overrightarrow{PR}$, and $\overrightarrow{PS}$.

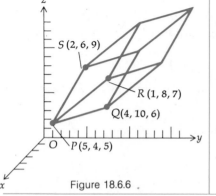

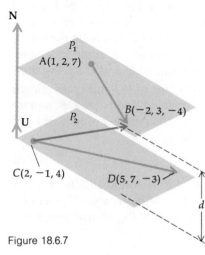

Figure 18.6.6

SOLUTION: Figure 18.6.6 shows the parallelepiped. Let $\mathbf{A} = \mathbf{V}(\overrightarrow{PQ}) = \langle -1, 6, 1 \rangle$, $\mathbf{B} = \mathbf{V}(\overrightarrow{PR}) = \langle -4, 4, 2 \rangle$, and $\mathbf{C} = \mathbf{V}(\overrightarrow{PS}) = \langle -3, 2, 4 \rangle$. Then

$$\mathbf{A} \times \mathbf{B} = (-\mathbf{i} + 6\mathbf{j} + \mathbf{k}) \times (-4\mathbf{i} + 4\mathbf{j} + 2\mathbf{k}) = 8\mathbf{i} - 2\mathbf{j} + 20\mathbf{k}$$

Therefore,

$$(\mathbf{A} \times \mathbf{B}) \cdot \mathbf{C} = \langle 8, -2, 20 \rangle \cdot \langle -3, 2, 4 \rangle = -24 - 4 + 80 = 52$$

Thus, the volume is 52 cubic units.

EXAMPLE 5: Find the distance between the two skew lines, l_1 and l_2, of Example 5 in Sec. 18.5.

Figure 18.6.7

SOLUTION: Because l_1 and l_2 are skew lines, there are parallel planes P_1 and P_2 containing the lines l_1 and l_2, respectively. See Fig. 18.6.7. Let d units be the distance between planes P_1 and P_2. The distance between l_1 and l_2 is also d units. A normal vector to the two planes is $\mathbf{N} = \mathbf{V}(\overrightarrow{AB}) \times \mathbf{V}(\overrightarrow{CD})$. Let $\mathbf{U}$ be a unit normal vector in the direction of $\mathbf{N}$. Then

$$\mathbf{U} = \frac{\mathbf{V}(\overrightarrow{AB}) \times \mathbf{V}(\overrightarrow{CB})}{|\mathbf{V}(\overrightarrow{AB}) \times \mathbf{V}(\overrightarrow{CD})|}$$

Now we take two points, one in each plane (e.g., B and C). Then the scalar projection of $\mathbf{V}(\overrightarrow{CB})$ on $\mathbf{N}$ is $\mathbf{V}(\overrightarrow{CB}) \cdot \mathbf{U}$, and

$$d = |\mathbf{V}(\overrightarrow{CB}) \cdot \mathbf{U}| = \left| \mathbf{V}(\overrightarrow{CB}) \cdot \frac{\mathbf{V}(\overrightarrow{AB}) \times \mathbf{V}(\overrightarrow{CD})}{|\mathbf{V}(\overrightarrow{AB}) \times \mathbf{V}(\overrightarrow{CD})|} \right|$$

Performing the computations required, we have

$$\mathbf{V}(\overrightarrow{AB}) = -3\mathbf{i} + \mathbf{j} - 11\mathbf{k} \qquad \mathbf{V}(\overrightarrow{CD}) = 3\mathbf{i} + 8\mathbf{j} - 7\mathbf{k}$$

$$N = V(\overrightarrow{AB}) \times V(\overrightarrow{CD}) = \begin{vmatrix} i & j & k \\ -3 & 1 & -11 \\ 3 & 8 & -7 \end{vmatrix} = 27(3i - 2j - k)$$

$$U = \frac{27(3i - 2j - k)}{\sqrt{27^2(3^2 + 2^2 + 1^2)}} = \frac{3i - 2j - k}{\sqrt{14}}$$

Finally, $V(\overrightarrow{CB}) = -4i + 4j - 8k$, and so

$$d = |V(\overrightarrow{CB}) \cdot U| = \frac{1}{\sqrt{14}} |-12 - 8 + 8| = \frac{12}{\sqrt{14}} = \frac{6}{7}\sqrt{14}$$

Exercises 18.6

In Exercises 1 through 12, let $A = \langle 1, 2, 3 \rangle$, $B = \langle 4, -3, -1 \rangle$, $C = \langle -5, -3, 5 \rangle$, $D = \langle -2, 1, 6 \rangle$, $E = \langle 4, 0, -7 \rangle$, and $F = \langle 0, 2, 1 \rangle$.

1. Find $A \times B$

2. Find $D \times E$

3. Find $(C \times D) \cdot (E \times F)$

4. Find $(C \times E) \cdot (D \times F)$

5. Verify Theorem 18.6.3 for vectors A and B.

6. Verify Theorem 18.6.4 for vectors A, B, and C.

7. Verify Theorem 18.6.5(i) for vectors A and B and $c = 3$.

8. Verify Theorem 18.6.5(ii) for vectors A and B and $c = 3$.

9. Verify Theorem 18.6.8 for vectors A, B, and C.

10. Find $(A \times B) \times C$ and $A \times (B \times C)$.

11. Find $(A + B) \times (C - D)$ and $(D - C) \times (A + B)$ and verify they are equal.

12. Find $|A \times B||C \times D|$.

13. Prove Theorem 18.6.2(ii) and (iii).

14. Prove Theorem 18.6.4.

15. Prove Theorem 18.6.5(i).

16. Prove Theorem 18.6.5(ii).

17. Prove Theorem 18.6.8.

18. Given the two unit vectors

$$A = \tfrac{4}{9}i + \tfrac{7}{9}j - \tfrac{4}{9}k \quad \text{and} \quad B = -\tfrac{2}{3}i + \tfrac{2}{3}j + \tfrac{1}{3}k$$

If θ is the radian measure of the angle between A and B, find $\sin \theta$ in two ways: (a) by using the cross product (formula (3) of this section); (b) by using the dot product and a trigonometric identity.

19. Follow the instructions of Exercise 18 for the two unit vectors:

$$A = \frac{1}{\sqrt{3}}i - \frac{1}{\sqrt{3}}j + \frac{1}{\sqrt{3}}k \quad \text{and} \quad B = \frac{1}{3\sqrt{3}}i + \frac{5}{3\sqrt{3}}j + \frac{1}{3\sqrt{3}}k$$

20. Show that the quadrilateral having vertices at $(1, 1, 3)$, $(-2, 1, -1)$, $(-5, 4, 0)$, and $(-8, 4, -4)$ is a parallelogram and find its area.

21. Show that the quadrilateral having vertices at $(1, -2, 3)$, $(4, 3, -1)$, $(2, 2, 1)$, and $(5, 7, -3)$ is a parallelogram and find its area.

22. Find the area of the parallelogram $PQRS$ if $\mathbf{V}(\overrightarrow{PQ}) = 3\mathbf{i} - 2\mathbf{j}$ and $\mathbf{V}(\overrightarrow{PS}) = 3\mathbf{j} + 4\mathbf{k}$.

23. Find the area of the triangle having vertices at $(0, 2, 2)$, $(8, 8, -2)$, and $(9, 12, 6)$.

24. Find the area of the triangle having vertices at $(4, 5, 6)$, $(4, 4, 5)$, and $(3, 5, 5)$.

25. Let $\overrightarrow{OP}$ be the position representation of vector $\mathbf{A}$, $\overrightarrow{OQ}$ be the position representation of vector $\mathbf{B}$, and $\overrightarrow{OR}$ be the position representation of vector $\mathbf{C}$. Prove that the area of triangle PQR is $\frac{1}{2}|(\mathbf{B} - \mathbf{A}) \times (\mathbf{C} - \mathbf{A})|$.

26. Find a unit vector whose representations are perpendicular to the plane containing $\overrightarrow{PQ}$ and $\overrightarrow{PR}$ if $\overrightarrow{PQ}$ is a representation of the vector $\mathbf{i} + 3\mathbf{j} - 2\mathbf{k}$ and $\overrightarrow{PR}$ is a representation of the vector $2\mathbf{i} - \mathbf{j} - \mathbf{k}$.

27. Given the points $P(5, 2, -1)$, $Q(2, 4, -2)$, and $R(11, 1, 4)$. Find a unit vector whose representations are perpendicular to the plane through points P, Q, and R.

28. Find the volume of the parallelepiped having edges $\overrightarrow{PQ}$, $\overrightarrow{PR}$, and $\overrightarrow{PS}$ if the points P, Q, R, and S are, respectively, $(1, 3, 4)$, $(3, 5, 3)$, $(2, 1, 6)$, and $(2, 2, 5)$.

29. Find the volume of the parallelepiped $PQRS$ if the vectors $\mathbf{V}(\overrightarrow{PQ})$, $\mathbf{V}(\overrightarrow{PR})$, and $\mathbf{V}(\overrightarrow{PS})$ are, respectively, $\mathbf{i} + 3\mathbf{j} + 2\mathbf{k}$, $2\mathbf{i} + \mathbf{j} - \mathbf{k}$, and $\mathbf{i} - 2\mathbf{j} + \mathbf{k}$.

30. If $\mathbf{A}$ and $\mathbf{B}$ are any two vectors in V_3, prove that $(\mathbf{A} - \mathbf{B}) \times (\mathbf{A} + \mathbf{B}) = 2(\mathbf{A} \times \mathbf{B})$.

In Exercises 31 and 32, use the cross product to find an equation of the plane containing the given three points.

31. $(-2, 2, 2)$, $(-8, 1, 6)$, $(3, 4, -1)$ 32. $(a, b, 0)$, $(a, 0, c)$, $(0, b, c)$

In Exercises 33 and 34, find the perpendicular distance between the two given skew lines.

33. $\dfrac{x-1}{5} = \dfrac{y-2}{3} = \dfrac{z+1}{2}$ and $\dfrac{x+2}{4} = \dfrac{y+1}{2} = \dfrac{z-3}{-3}$

34. $\dfrac{x+1}{2} = \dfrac{y+2}{-4} = \dfrac{z-1}{-3}$ and $\dfrac{x-1}{5} = \dfrac{y-1}{3} = \dfrac{z+1}{2}$

35. Let P, Q, and R be three noncollinear points in R^3 and $\overrightarrow{OP}$, $\overrightarrow{OQ}$, and $\overrightarrow{OR}$ be the position representations of vectors $\mathbf{A}$, $\mathbf{B}$, and $\mathbf{C}$, respectively. Prove that the representations of the vector $\mathbf{A} \times \mathbf{B} + \mathbf{B} \times \mathbf{C} + \mathbf{C} \times \mathbf{A}$ are perpendicular to the plane containing the points P, Q, and R.

18.7 CYLINDERS AND SURFACES OF REVOLUTION

As mentioned previously, the graph of an equation in three variables is a *surface*. A surface is represented by an equation if the coordinates of every point on the surface satisfy the equation and if every point whose coordinates satisfy the equation lies on the surface. We have already discussed two kinds of surfaces, a plane and a sphere. Another kind of surface that is fairly simple is a cylinder. You are probably familiar with right-circular cylinders from previous experience. We now consider a more general cylindrical surface.

18.7.1 Definition

A *cylinder* is a surface that is generated by a line moving along a given plane curve in such a way that it always remains parallel to a fixed line not lying in the plane of the given curve. The moving line is called a *generator* of the cylinder and the given plane curve is called a *directrix* of the cylinder. Any position of a generator is called a *ruling* of the cylinder.

We confine ourselves to cylinders having a directrix in a coordinate

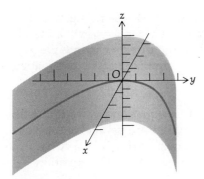

Figure 18.7.1

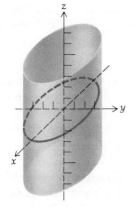

Figure 18.7.2

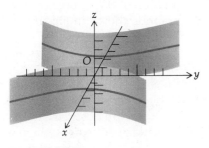

Figure 18.7.3

plane and rulings perpendicular to that plane. If the rulings of a cylinder are perpendicular to the plane of a directrix, the cylinder is said to be perpendicular to the plane.

The familiar right-circular cylinder is one for which a directrix is a circle in a plane perpendicular to the cylinder.

● ILLUSTRATION 1: In Fig. 18.7.1, we show a cylinder whose directrix is the parabola $y^2 = 8x$ in the xy plane and whose rulings are parallel to the z axis. This cylinder is called a *parabolic cylinder*. An *elliptic cylinder* is shown in Fig. 18.7.2; its directrix is the ellipse $9x^2 + 16y^2 = 144$ in the xy plane and its rulings are parallel to the z axis. Figure 18.7.3 shows a *hyperbolic cylinder* having as a directrix the hyperbola $25x^2 - 4y^2 = 100$ in the xy plane and rulings parallel to the z axis. ●

Let us consider the problem of finding an equation of a cylinder having a directrix in a coordinate plane and rulings parallel to the coordinate axis not in that plane. To be specific, we take the directrix in the xy plane and the rulings parallel to the z axis. Refer to Fig. 18.7.4. Suppose that an equation of the directrix in the xy plane is $y = f(x)$. If the point $(x_0, y_0, 0)$ in the xy plane satisfies this equation, any point (x_0, y_0, z) in three-dimensional space, where z is any real number, will satisfy the same equation because z does not appear in the equation. The points having representations (x_0, y_0, z) all lie on the line parallel to the z axis through the point $(x_0, y_0, 0)$. This line is a ruling of the cylinder. Hence, any point whose x and y coordinates satisfy the equation $y = f(x)$ lies on the cylinder. Conversely, if the point $P(x, y, z)$ lies on the cylinder (see Fig. 18.7.5), then the point $(x, y, 0)$ lies on the directrix of the cylinder in the xy plane, and hence the x and y coordinates of P satisfy the equation $y = f(x)$. Therefore, if $y = f(x)$ is considered as an equation of a graph in

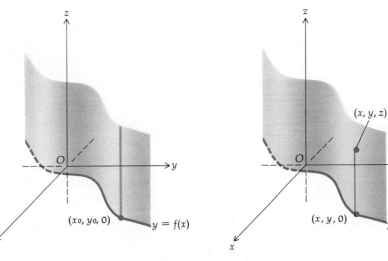

Figure 18.7.4

Figure 18.7.5

three-dimensional space, the graph is a cylinder whose rulings are parallel to the z axis and which has as a directrix the curve $y = f(x)$ in the plane $z = 0$. A similar discussion pertains when the directrix is in either of the other coordinate planes. The results are summarized in the following theorem.

18.7.2 Theorem   In three-dimensional space, the graph of an equation in two of the three variables x, y, and z is a cylinder whose rulings are parallel to the axis associated with the missing variable and whose directrix is a curve in the plane associated with the two variables appearing in the equation.

• ILLUSTRATION 2: It follows from Theorem 18.7.2 that an equation of the parabolic cylinder of Fig. 18.7.1 is $y^2 = 8x$, considered as an equation in R^3. Similarly, equations of the elliptic cylinder of Fig. 18.7.2 and the hyperbolic cylinder of Fig. 18.7.3 are, respectively, $9x^2 + 16y^2 = 144$ and $25x^2 - 4y^2 = 100$, both considered as equations in R^3.   •

A *cross section* of a surface in a plane is the set of all points of the surface which lie in the given plane. If a plane is parallel to the plane of the directrix of a cylinder, the cross section of the cylinder is the same as the directrix. For example, the cross section of the elliptic cylinder of Fig. 18.7.2 in any plane parallel to the xy plane is an ellipse.

EXAMPLE 1:   Draw a sketch of the graph of each of the following equations: (a) $y = \ln z$; (b) $z^2 = x^3$.

SOLUTION: (a) The graph is a cylinder whose directrix in the yz plane is the curve $y = \ln z$ and whose rulings are parallel to the x axis. A sketch of the graph is shown in Fig. 18.7.6.

(b) The graph is a cylinder whose directrix is in the xz plane and whose rulings are parallel to the y axis. An equation of the directrix is the curve $z^2 = x^3$ in the xz plane. A sketch of the graph is shown in Fig. 18.7.7.

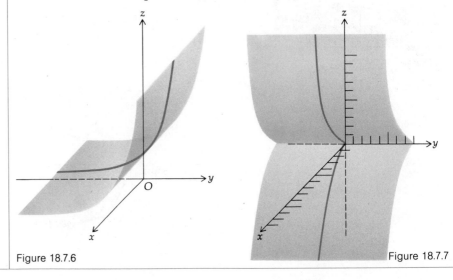

Figure 18.7.6

Figure 18.7.7

18.7.3 Definition If a plane curve is revolved about a fixed line lying in the plane of the curve, the surface generated is called a *surface of revolution*. The fixed line is called the *axis* of the surface of revolution, and the plane curve is called the *generating curve*.

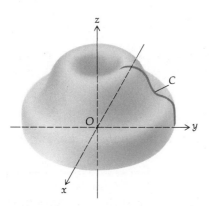

Figure 18.7.8

Figure 18.7.8 shows a surface of revolution whose generating curve is the curve C in the yz plane and whose axis is the z axis. A sphere is a particular example of a surface of revolution because a sphere can be generated by revolving a semicircle about a diameter.

● ILLUSTRATION 3: Figure 18.7.9 shows a sphere which can be generated by revolving the semicircle $y^2 + z^2 = r^2$, $z \geq 0$, about the y axis. Another example of a surface of revolution is a right-circular cylinder for which the generating curve and the axis are parallel straight lines. If the generating curve is the line $z = k$ in the xz plane and the axis is the x axis, we obtain the right-circular cylinder shown in Fig. 18.7.10. ●

We now find an equation of the surface generated by revolving about the y axis the curve in the yz plane having the two-dimensional equation

$$z = f(y) \tag{1}$$

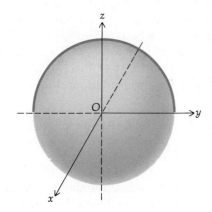

Figure 18.7.9

Refer to Fig. 18.7.11. Let $P(x, y, z)$ be any point on the surface of revolution. Through P, pass a plane perpendicular to the y axis. Denote the point of intersection of this plane with the y axis by $Q(0, y, 0)$, and let $P_0(0, y, z)$ be the point of intersection of the plane with the generating curve. Because the cross section of the surface with the plane through P is a circle, P is on the surface if and only if

$$|\overline{QP}|^2 = |\overline{QP_0}|^2 \tag{2}$$

Because $|\overline{QP}| = \sqrt{x^2 + z^2}$ and $|\overline{QP_0}| = z_0$, we obtain from (2)

$$x^2 + z^2 = z_0{}^2 \tag{3}$$

The point P_0 is on the generating curve, and so its coordinates must satisfy Eq. (1). Therefore, we have

$$z_0 = f(y) \tag{4}$$

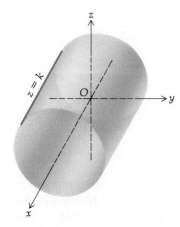

Figure 18.7.10

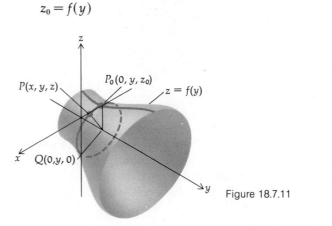

Figure 18.7.11

From Eqs. (3) and (4), we conclude that the point P is on the surface of revolution if and only if

$$x^2 + z^2 = [f(y)]^2 \qquad (5)$$

Equation (5) is the desired equation of the surface of revolution. Because (5) is equivalent to

$$\pm\sqrt{x^2 + z^2} = f(y)$$

we can obtain (5) by replacing z in (1) by $\pm\sqrt{x^2 + z^2}$.

In a similar manner we can show that if the curve in the yz plane having the two-dimensional equation

$$y = g(z) \qquad (6)$$

is revolved about the z axis, an equation of the surface of revolution generated is obtained by replacing y in (6) by $\pm\sqrt{x^2 + y^2}$. Analogous remarks hold when a curve in any coordinate plane is revolved about either one of the coordinate axes in that plane. In summary, the graphs of any of the following equations are surfaces of revolution having the indicated axis: $x^2 + y^2 = [F(z)]^2$—z axis; $x^2 + z^2 = [F(y)]^2$—y axis; $y^2 + z^2 = [F(x)]^2$—x axis. In each case, cross sections of the surface in planes perpendicular to the axis are circles having centers on the axis.

EXAMPLE 2: Find an equation of the surface of revolution generated by revolving the parabola $y^2 = 4x$ in the xy plane about the x axis. Draw a sketch of the graph of the surface.

SOLUTION: In the equation of the parabola, we replace y by $\pm\sqrt{y^2 + z^2}$ and obtain

$$y^2 + z^2 = 4x$$

A sketch of the graph is shown in Fig. 18.7.12. Note that the same surface is generated if the parabola $z^2 = 4x$ in the xz plane is revolved about the x axis.

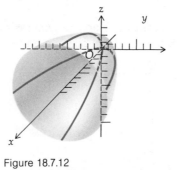

Figure 18.7.12

The surface obtained in Example 2 is called a *paraboloid of revolution*. If an ellipse is revolved about one of its axes, the surface obtained is called an *ellipsoid of revolution*. A *hyperboloid of revolution* is obtained when a hyperbola is revolved about an axis.

EXAMPLE 3:   Draw a sketch of the surface $x^2 + z^2 - 4y^2 = 0$, if $y \geq 0$.

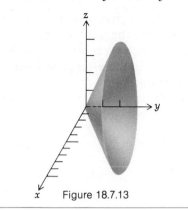

x   Figure 18.7.13

SOLUTION: The given equation is of the form $x^2 + z^2 = [F(y)]^2$, and so its graph is a surface of revolution having the y axis as axis. If we solve the given equation for y, we obtain

$$2y = \pm \sqrt{x^2 + z^2}$$

Hence, the generating curve can be either the straight line $2y = x$ in the xy plane or the straight line $2y = z$ in the yz plane. By drawing sketches of the two possible generating curves and using the fact that cross sections of the surface in planes perpendicular to the y axis are circles having centers on the y axis, we obtain the surface shown in Fig. 18.7.13 (note that because $y \geq 0$ we have only one nappe of the cone).

The surface obtained in Example 3 is called a *right-circular cone*.

Exercises 18.7

In Exercises 1 through 8, draw a sketch of the cylinder having the given equation.

1. $4x^2 + 9y^2 = 36$ 2. $x^2 - z^2 = 4$ 3. $y = |z|$ 4. $z = \sin y$

5. $z = 2x^2$ 6. $x^2 = y^3$ 7. $y = \cosh x$ 8. $z^2 = 4y^2$

In Exercises 9 through 14, find an equation of the surface of revolution generated by revolving the given plane curve about the indicated axis. Draw a sketch of the surface.

9. $x^2 = 4y$ in the xy plane, about the y axis.

10. $x^2 = 4y$ in the xy plane, about the x axis.

11. $x^2 + 4z^2 = 16$ in the xz plane, about the x axis.

12. $x^2 + 4z^2 = 16$ in the xz plane, about the z axis.

13. $y = \sin x$ in the xy plane, about the x axis.

14. $y^2 = z^3$ in the yz plane, about the z axis.

In Exercises 15 through 18, find a generating curve and the axis for the given surface of revolution. Draw a sketch of the surface.

15. $x^2 + y^2 - z^2 = 4$ 16. $y^2 + z^2 = e^{2x}$ 17. $x^2 + z^2 = |y|$ 18. $4x^2 + 9y^2 + 4z^2 = 36$

19. The tractrix

$$x = t - a \tanh \frac{t}{a} \qquad y = a \operatorname{sech} \frac{t}{a}$$

from $x = -a$ to $x = 2a$ is revolved about the x axis. Draw a sketch of the surface of revolution.

18.8 QUADRIC SURFACES

The graph of a second-degree equation in three variables x, y, and z is called a *quadric surface*. These surfaces correspond to the conics in the plane.

The simplest types of quadric surfaces are the parabolic, elliptic, and hyperbolic cylinders, which were discussed in the preceding section. There are six other types of quadric surfaces, which we now consider. We choose the coordinate axes so the equations are in their simplest form. In our discussion of each of these surfaces, we refer to the cross sections of the surfaces in planes parallel to the coordinate planes. These cross sections help to visualize the surface.

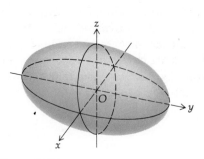

Figure 18.8.1

The ellipsoid

$$\frac{x^2}{a^2} + \frac{y^2}{b^2} + \frac{z^2}{c^2} = 1 \tag{1}$$

where a, b, and c are positive (see Fig. 18.8.1).

If in Eq. (1) we replace z by zero, we obtain the cross section of the ellipsoid in the xy plane, which is the ellipse $x^2/a^2 + y^2/b^2 = 1$. To obtain the cross sections of the surface with the planes $z = k$, we replace z by k in the equation of the ellipsoid and get

$$\frac{x^2}{a^2} + \frac{y^2}{b^2} = 1 - \frac{k^2}{c^2}$$

If $|k| < c$, the cross section is an ellipse and the lengths of the semiaxes decrease to zero as $|k|$ increases to the value c. If $|k| = c$, the intersection of a plane $z = k$ with the ellipsoid is the single point $(0, 0, k)$. If $|k| > c$, there is no intersection. We may have a similar discussion if we consider cross sections formed by planes parallel to either of the other coordinate planes.

The numbers a, b, and c are the lengths of the semiaxes of the ellipsoid. If any two of these three numbers are equal, we have an ellipsoid of revolution, which is also called a *spheroid*. If we have a spheroid and the third number is greater than the two equal numbers, the spheroid is said to be *prolate*. A prolate spheroid is shaped like a football. An *oblate* spheroid is obtained if the third number is less than the two equal numbers. If all three numbers a, b, and c in the equation of an ellipsoid are equal, the ellipsoid is a *sphere*.

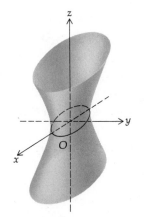

Figure 18.8.2

The elliptic hyperboloid of one sheet

$$\frac{x^2}{a^2} + \frac{y^2}{b^2} - \frac{z^2}{c^2} = 1 \tag{2}$$

where a, b, and c are positive (see Fig. 18.8.2).

The cross sections in the planes $z = k$ are ellipses $x^2/a^2 + y^2/b^2 = 1 + k^2/c^2$. When $k = 0$, the lengths of the semiaxes of the ellipse are smallest,

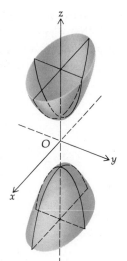

Figure 18.8.3

and these lengths increase as $|k|$ increases. The cross sections in the planes $x = k$ are hyperbolas $y^2/b^2 - z^2/c^2 = 1 - k^2/a^2$. If $|k| < a$, the transverse axis of the hyperbola is parallel to the y axis, and if $|k| > a$, the transverse axis is parallel to the z axis. If $k = a$, the hyperbola degenerates into two straight lines: $y/b - z/c = 0$ and $y/b + z/c = 0$. In an analogous manner, the cross sections in the planes $y = k$ are also hyperbolas. The axis of this hyperboloid is the z axis.

If $a = b$, the surface is a hyperboloid of revolution for which the axis is the line containing the conjugate axis.

The elliptic hyperboloid of two sheets

$$-\frac{x^2}{a^2} - \frac{y^2}{b^2} + \frac{z^2}{c^2} = 1 \tag{3}$$

where a, b, and c are positive (see Fig. 18.8.3).

Replacing z by k in Eq. (3), we obtain $x^2/a^2 + y^2/b^2 = k^2/c^2 - 1$. If $|k| < c$, there is no intersection of the plane $z = k$ with the surface; hence, there are no points of the surface between the planes $z = -c$ and $z = c$. If $|k| = c$, the intersection of the plane $z = k$ with the surface is the single point $(0, 0, k)$. When $|k| > c$, the cross section of the surface in the plane $z = k$ is an ellipse and the lengths of the semiaxes of the ellipse increase as $|k|$ increases.

The cross sections of the surface in the planes $x = k$ are the hyperbolas $z^2/c^2 - y^2/b^2 = 1 + k^2/a^2$ whose transverse axes are parallel to the z axis. In a similar fashion, the cross sections in the planes $y = k$ are the hyperbolas given by $z^2/c^2 - x^2/a^2 = 1 + k^2/b^2$ for which the transverse axes are also parallel to the z axis.

If $a = b$, the surface is a hyperboloid of revolution in which the axis is the line containing the transverse axis of the hyperbola.

Each of the above three quadric surfaces is symmetric with respect to each of the coordinate planes and symmetric with respect to the origin. Their graphs are called *central quadrics* and their center is at the origin. The graph of any equation of the form

$$\pm\frac{x^2}{a^2} \pm \frac{y^2}{b^2} \pm \frac{z^2}{c^2} = 1$$

where a, b, and c are positive, is a central quadric.

EXAMPLE 1: Draw a sketch of the graph of the equation

$$4x^2 - y^2 + 25z^2 = 100$$

and name the surface.

SOLUTION: The given equation can be written as

$$\frac{x^2}{25} - \frac{y^2}{100} + \frac{z^2}{4} = 1$$

which is of the form of Eq. (2) with y and z interchanged. Hence, the surface is an elliptic hyperboloid of one sheet whose axis is the y axis. The cross sections in the planes $y = k$ are the ellipses $x^2/25 + z^2/4 = 1 + k^2/100$. The cross sections in the planes $x = k$ are the hyperbolas $z^2/4 - y^2/100 = 1 - k^2/25$, and the cross sections in the planes $z = k$ are the hyperbolas $x^2/25 - y^2/100 = 1 - k^2/4$. A sketch of the surface is shown in Fig. 18.8.4.

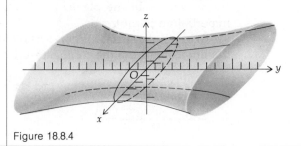

Figure 18.8.4

EXAMPLE 2:   Draw a sketch of the graph of the equation

$$4x^2 - 25y^2 - z^2 = 100$$

and name the surface.

SOLUTION: The given equation can be written as

$$\frac{x^2}{25} - \frac{y^2}{4} - \frac{z^2}{100} = 1$$

which is of the form of Eq. (3) with x and z interchanged; thus, the surface is an elliptic hyperboloid of two sheets whose axis is the x axis. The cross sections in the planes $x = k$, where $|k| > 5$, are the ellipses $y^2/4 + z^2/100 = k^2/25 - 1$. The planes $x = k$, where $|k| < 5$, do not intersect the surface. The cross sections in the planes $y = k$ are the hyperbolas $x^2/25 - z^2/100 = 1 + k^2/4$, and the cross sections in the planes $z = k$ are the hyperbolas $x^2/25 - y^2/4 = 1 + k^2/100$. The required sketch is shown in Fig. 18.8.5.

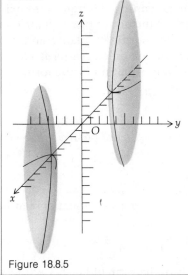

Figure 18.8.5

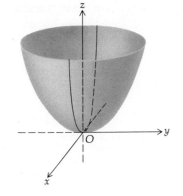

Figure 18.8.6

The following two quadrics are called noncentral quadrics.

The elliptic paraboloid

$$\frac{x^2}{a^2} + \frac{y^2}{b^2} = \frac{z}{c} \tag{4}$$

where a and b are positive and $c \neq 0$. Figure 18.8.6 shows the surface if $c > 0$.

Substituting k for z in Eq. (4), we obtain $x^2/a^2 + y^2/b^2 = k/c$. When $k = 0$, this equation becomes $x^2/a^2 + y^2/b^2 = 0$, which represents a single point, the origin. If $k \neq 0$ and k and c have the same sign, the equation is that of an ellipse. So we conclude that cross sections of the surface in the planes $z = k$, where k and c have the same sign, are ellipses and the lengths of the semiaxes increase as $|k|$ increases. If k and c have opposite signs, the planes $z = k$ do not intersect the surface. The cross sections of the surface with the planes $x = k$ and $y = k$ are parabolas. When $c > 0$, the parabolas open upward, as shown in Fig. 18.8.6; when $c < 0$, the parabolas open downward.

If $a = b$, the surface is a paraboloid of revolution.

The hyperbolic paraboloid

$$\frac{y^2}{b^2} - \frac{x^2}{a^2} = \frac{z}{c} \tag{5}$$

where a and b are positive and $c \neq 0$. The surface is shown in Fig. 18.8.7 for $c > 0$.

The cross sections of the surface in the planes $z = k$, where $k \neq 0$, are hyperbolas having their transverse axes parallel to the y axis if k and c have the same sign and parallel to the x axis if k and c have opposite signs. The cross section of the surface in the plane $z = 0$ consists of two straight lines through the origin. The cross sections in the planes $x = k$ are parabolas opening upward if $c > 0$ and opening downward if $c < 0$. The cross sections in the planes $y = k$ are parabolas opening downward if $c > 0$ and opening upward if $c < 0$.

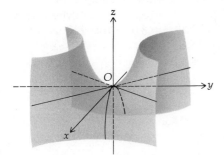

Figure 18.8.7

EXAMPLE 3:   Draw a sketch of the graph of the equation

$$3y^2 + 12z^2 = 16x$$

and name the surface.

SOLUTION: The given equation can be written as

$$\frac{y^2}{16} + \frac{z^2}{4} = \frac{x}{3}$$

which is of the form of Eq. (4) with x and z interchanged. Hence, the graph of the equation is an elliptic paraboloid whose axis is the x axis. The cross sections in the planes $x = k > 0$ are the ellipses $y^2/16 + z^2/4 = k/3$, and the planes $x = k < 0$ do not intersect the surface. The cross sections in the planes $y = k$ are the parabolas $12z^2 = 16x - 3k^2$, and the cross sections in the planes $z = k$ are the parabolas $3y^2 = 16x - 12k^2$. A sketch of the elliptic paraboloid is shown in Fig. 18.8.8.

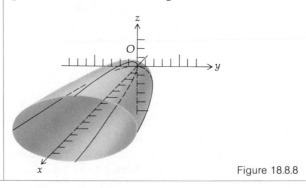

Figure 18.8.8

EXAMPLE 4:   Draw a sketch of the graph of the equation

$$3y^2 - 12z^2 = 16x$$

and name the surface.

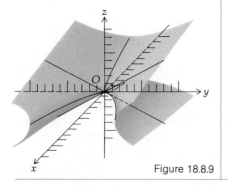

Figure 18.8.9

SOLUTION: Writing the given equation as

$$\frac{y^2}{16} - \frac{z^2}{4} = \frac{x}{3}$$

we see it is of the form of Eq. (5) with x and z interchanged. The surface is therefore a hyperbolic paraboloid. The cross sections in the planes $x = k \neq 0$ are the hyperbolas $y^2/16 - z^2/4 = k/3$. The cross section in the yz plane ($x = 0$) consists of the two lines $y = 2z$ and $y = -2z$. In the planes $z = k$, the cross sections are the parabolas $3y^2 = 16x + 12k^2$; in the planes $y = k$, the cross sections are the parabolas $12z^2 = 3k^2 - 16x$. Figure 18.8.9 shows a sketch of the hyperbolic paraboloid.

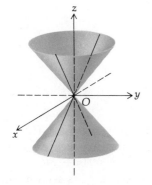

Figure 18.8.10

The elliptic cone

$$\frac{x^2}{a^2} + \frac{y^2}{b^2} - \frac{z^2}{c^2} = 0 \tag{6}$$

where a, b, and c are positive (see Fig. 18.8.10).

The intersection of the plane $z = 0$ with the surface is a single point, the origin. The cross sections of the surface in the planes $z = k$, where $k \neq 0$, are ellipses, and the lengths of the semiaxes increase as k increases. Cross sections in the planes $x = 0$ and $y = 0$ are pairs of intersecting lines. In the planes $x = k$ and $y = k$, where $k \neq 0$, the cross sections are hyperbolas.

EXAMPLE 5:   Draw a sketch of the graph of the equation

$$4x^2 - y^2 + 25z^2 = 0$$

and name the surface.

SOLUTION: The given equation can be written as

$$\frac{x^2}{25} - \frac{y^2}{100} + \frac{z^2}{4} = 0$$

which is of the form of Eq. (6) with y and z interchanged. Therefore, the surface is an elliptic cone having the y axis as its axis. The surface intersects the xz plane ($y = 0$) at the origin only. The intersection of the surface with the yz plane ($x = 0$) is the pair of intersecting lines $y = \pm 5z$, and the intersection with the xy plane ($z = 0$) is the pair of intersecting lines $y = \pm 2x$. The cross sections in the planes $y = k \neq 0$ are the ellipses $x^2/25 + z^2/4 = k^2/100$. In the planes $x = k \neq 0$ and $z = k \neq 0$, the cross sections are, respectively, the hyperbolas $y^2/100 - z^2/4 = k^2/25$ and $y^2/100 - x^2/25 = k^2/4$. A sketch of the surface is shown in Fig. 18.8.11.

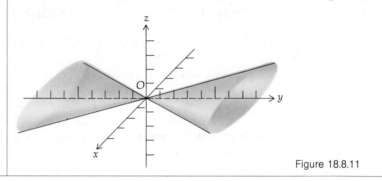

Figure 18.8.11

The general equation of the second degree in x, y, and z is of the form

$$ax^2 + by^2 + cz^2 + dxy + exz + fyz + gx + hy + iz + j = 0$$

where $a, b, \ldots, j$ are constants. It can be shown that by translation and rotation of the three-dimensional coordinate axes (the study of which is beyond the scope of this book) this equation can be reduced to one of the following two forms:

$$Ax^2 + By^2 + Cz^2 + J = 0 \qquad (7)$$

or

$$Ax^2 + By^2 + Iz = 0 \qquad (8)$$

Graphs of the equations of the second degree will either be one of the above six types of quadrics or else will degenerate into a cylinder, plane, line, point, or the empty set.

The nondegenerate curves associated with equations of the form (7) are the central quadrics and the elliptic cone, whereas those associated with equations of the form (8) are the noncentral quadrics. Following are examples of some degenerate cases:

$$x^2 - y^2 = 0; \text{ two planes, } x - y = 0 \text{ and } x + y = 0$$

$z^2 = 0$; one plane, the xy plane

$x^2 + y^2 = 0$; one line, the z axis

$x^2 + y^2 + z^2 = 0$; a single point, the origin

$x^2 + y^2 + z^2 + 1 = 0$; the empty set

Exercises 18.8

In Exercises 1 through 12, draw a sketch of the graph of the given equation and name the surface.

1. $4x^2 + 9y^2 + z^2 = 36$

2. $4x^2 - 9y^2 - z^2 = 36$

3. $4x^2 + 9y^2 - z^2 = 36$

4. $4x^2 - 9y^2 + z^2 = 36$

5. $x^2 = y^2 - z^2$

6. $x^2 = y^2 + z^2$

7. $\dfrac{x^2}{36} + \dfrac{z^2}{25} = 4y$

8. $\dfrac{y^2}{25} + \dfrac{x^2}{36} = 4$

9. $\dfrac{x^2}{36} - \dfrac{z^2}{25} = 9y$

10. $x^2 = 2y + 4z$

11. $x^2 + 16z^2 = 4y^2 - 16$

12. $9y^2 - 4z^2 + 18x = 0$

13. Find the values of k for which the intersection of the plane $x + ky = 1$ and the elliptic hyperboloid of two sheets $y^2 - x^2 - z^2 = 1$ is (a) an ellipse and (b) a hyperbola.

14. Find the vertex and focus of the parabola which is the intersection of the plane $y = 2$ with the hyperbolic paraboloid

$$\frac{y^2}{16} - \frac{x^2}{4} = \frac{z}{9}$$

15. Find the area of the plane section formed by the intersection of the plane $y = 3$ with the solid bounded by the ellipsoid

$$\frac{x^2}{9} + \frac{y^2}{25} + \frac{z^2}{4} = 1$$

16. Show that the intersection of the hyperbolic paraboloid $y^2/b^2 - x^2/a^2 = z/c$ and the plane $z = bx + ay$ consists of two intersecting straight lines.

17. Use the method of parallel plane sections to find the volume of the solid bounded by the ellipsoid $x^2/a^2 + y^2/b^2 + z^2/c^2 = 1$. (The measure of the area of the region enclosed by the ellipse having semiaxes a and b is πab.)

18.9 CURVES IN R^3

We consider vector-valued functions in three-dimensional space.

18.9.1 Definition   Let f_1, f_2, and f_3 be three real-valued functions of a real variable t. Then for every number t in the domain common to f_1, f_2, and f_3 there is a vector $\mathbf{R}$ defined by

$$\mathbf{R}(t) = f_1(t)\mathbf{i} + f_2(t)\mathbf{j} + f_3(t)\mathbf{k} \tag{1}$$

and $\mathbf{R}$ is called a *vector-valued function.*

The graph of a vector-valued function in three-dimensional space is obtained analogously to the way we obtained the graph of a vector-valued function in two dimensions in Sec. 17.4. As t assumes all values in the domain of $\mathbf{R}$, the terminal point of the position representation of the vector $\mathbf{R}(t)$ traces a curve C, and this curve is called the graph of (1). A point on the curve C has the cartesian representation (x, y, z), where

$$x = f_1(t) \qquad y = f_2(t) \qquad z = f_3(t) \tag{2}$$

Equations (2) are called *parametric equations* of C, whereas Eq. (1) is called a *vector equation* of C. By eliminating t from Eqs. (2) we obtain two equations in $x, y,$ and z. These equations are called *cartesian equations* of C. Each cartesian equation is an equation of a surface, and curve C is the intersection of the two surfaces. The equations of any two surfaces containing C may be taken as the cartesian equations defining C.

● ILLUSTRATION 1: We draw a sketch of the curve having the vector equation

$$\mathbf{R}(t) = a \cos t\,\mathbf{i} + b \sin t\,\mathbf{j} + t\mathbf{k}$$

Parametric equations of the given curve are

$$x = a \cos t \qquad y = b \sin t \qquad z = t$$

To eliminate t from the first two equations, we write them as

$$x^2 = a^2 \cos^2 t \quad \text{and} \quad y^2 = b^2 \sin^2 t$$

from which we get

$$\frac{x^2}{a^2} = \cos^2 t \quad \text{and} \quad \frac{y^2}{b^2} = \sin^2 t$$

Adding corresponding members of these two equations, we obtain

$$\frac{x^2}{a^2} + \frac{y^2}{b^2} = 1$$

Therefore, the curve lies entirely on the elliptical cylinder whose directrix is an ellipse in the xy plane and whose rulings are parallel to the z axis. Table 18.9.1 gives sets of values of $x, y,$ and z for specific values of t. A sketch of the curve is shown in Fig. 18.9.1. ●

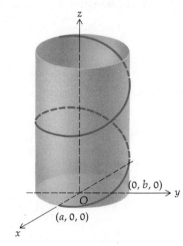

Figure 18.9.1

Table 18.9.1

t	x	y	z
0	a	0	0
$\dfrac{\pi}{4}$	$\dfrac{a}{\sqrt{2}}$	$\dfrac{b}{\sqrt{2}}$	$\dfrac{\pi}{4}$
$\dfrac{\pi}{2}$	0	b	$\dfrac{\pi}{2}$
$\dfrac{3\pi}{4}$	$-\dfrac{a}{\sqrt{2}}$	$\dfrac{b}{\sqrt{2}}$	$\dfrac{3\pi}{4}$
π	$-a$	0	π
$\dfrac{3\pi}{2}$	0	$-b$	$\dfrac{3\pi}{2}$

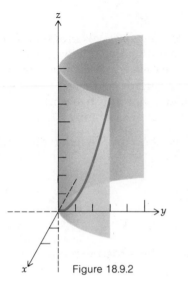

Figure 18.9.2

The curve of Illustration 1 is called a *helix*. If $a = b$, the helix is called a *circular helix* and it lies on the right-circular cylinder $x^2 + y^2 = a^2$.

● ILLUSTRATION 2: The curve having the vector equation

$$\mathbf{R}(t) = t\mathbf{i} + t^2\mathbf{j} + t^3\mathbf{k}$$

is called a *twisted cubic*. Parametric equations of the twisted cubic are

$$x = t \qquad y = t^2 \qquad z = t^3$$

Eliminating t from the first two of these equations yields $y = x^2$, which is a cylinder whose directrix in the xy plane is a parabola. The twisted cubic lies on this cylinder. Figure 18.9.2 shows a sketch of the cylinder and the portion of the twisted cubic from $t = 0$ to $t = 2$. ●

Many of the definitions and theorems pertaining to vector-valued functions in two dimensions can be extended to vector-valued functions in three dimensions.

18.9.2 Definition   If $\mathbf{R}(t) = f_1(t)\mathbf{i} + f_2(t)\mathbf{j} + f_3(t)\mathbf{k}$, then

$$\lim_{t \to t_1} \mathbf{R}(t) = \lim_{t \to t_1} f_1(t)\mathbf{i} + \lim_{t \to t_1} f_2(t)\mathbf{j} + \lim_{t \to t_1} f_3(t)\mathbf{k}$$

if $\lim_{t \to t_1} f_1(t)$, $\lim_{t \to t_1} f_2(t)$, and $\lim_{t \to t_1} f_3(t)$ all exist.

18.9.3 Definition   The vector-valued function $\mathbf{R}$ is continuous at t_1 if and only if

(i) $\mathbf{R}(t_1)$ exists;

(ii) $\lim_{t \to t_1} \mathbf{R}(t)$ exists;

(iii) $\lim_{t \to t_1} \mathbf{R}(t) = \mathbf{R}(t_1)$.

18.9.4 Definition   The derivative of the vector-valued function $\mathbf{R}$ is a vector-valued function, denoted by $\mathbf{R}'$ and defined by

$$\mathbf{R}'(t) = \lim_{\Delta t \to 0} \frac{\mathbf{R}(t + \Delta t) - \mathbf{R}(t)}{\Delta t}$$

if this limit exists.

18.9.5 Theorem   If $\mathbf{R}$ is the vector-valued function defined by

$$\mathbf{R}(t) = f_1(t)\mathbf{i} + f_2(t)\mathbf{j} + f_3(t)\mathbf{k}$$

and $\mathbf{R}'(t)$ exists, then

$$\mathbf{R}'(t) = f_1'(t)\mathbf{i} + f_2'(t)\mathbf{j} + f_3'(t)\mathbf{k}$$

The proof of Theorem 18.9.5 is left as an exercise (see Exercise 9).

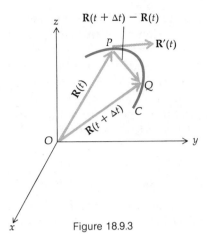

Figure 18.9.3

The geometric interpretation for the derivative of **R** is the same as that for the derivative of a vector-valued function in R^2. Figure 18.9.3 shows a portion of the curve C, which is the graph of **R**. In the figure $\overrightarrow{OP}$ is the position representation of $\mathbf{R}(t)$, $\overrightarrow{OQ}$ is the position representation of $\mathbf{R}(t + \Delta t)$, and so $\overrightarrow{PQ}$ is a representation of the vector $\mathbf{R}(t + \Delta t) - \mathbf{R}(t)$. As Δt approaches zero, the vector $[\mathbf{R}(t + \Delta t) - \mathbf{R}(t)]/\Delta t$ has a representation approaching a directed line segment tangent to the curve C at P.

The definition of the unit tangent vector is analogous to Definition 17.8.1 for vectors in the plane. So if $\mathbf{T}(t)$ denotes the unit tangent vector to curve C having vector equation (1), then

$$\mathbf{T}(t) = \frac{D_t\mathbf{R}(t)}{|D_t\mathbf{R}(t)|} \tag{3}$$

● ILLUSTRATION 3: We find the unit tangent vector for the twisted cubic of Illustration 2.

Because $\mathbf{R}(t) = t\mathbf{i} + t^2\mathbf{j} + t^3\mathbf{k}$,

$$D_t\mathbf{R}(t) = \mathbf{i} + 2t\mathbf{j} + 3t^2\mathbf{k}$$

and

$$|D_t\mathbf{R}(t)| = \sqrt{1 + 4t^2 + 9t^4}$$

From Eq. (3), we have, then,

$$\mathbf{T}(t) = \frac{1}{\sqrt{1 + 4t^2 + 9t^4}}(\mathbf{i} + 2t\mathbf{j} + 3t^2\mathbf{k})$$

Therefore, in particular,

$$\mathbf{T}(1) = \frac{1}{\sqrt{14}}\mathbf{i} + \frac{2}{\sqrt{14}}\mathbf{j} + \frac{3}{\sqrt{14}}\mathbf{k}$$

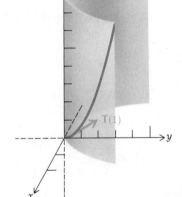

Figure 18.9.4

Figure 18.9.4 shows the representation of $\mathbf{T}(1)$ at the point $(1, 1, 1)$.   ●

Theorems 17.5.6, 17.5.7, and 17.5.8 regarding derivatives of sums and products of two-dimensional vector-valued functions also hold for vectors in three dimensions. The following theorem regarding the derivative of the cross product of two vector-valued functions is similar to the corresponding formula for the derivative of the product of real-valued functions; however, it is important to maintain the correct order of the vector-valued functions because the cross product is not commutative.

18.9.6 Theorem   If **R** and **Q** are vector-valued functions, then

$$D_t[\mathbf{R}(t) \times \mathbf{Q}(t)] = \mathbf{R}(t) \times \mathbf{Q}'(t) + \mathbf{R}'(t) \times \mathbf{Q}(t)$$

for all values of t for which $\mathbf{R}'(t)$ and $\mathbf{Q}'(t)$ exist.

The proof of Theorem 18.9.6 is left as an exercise (see Exercise 10).

We can define the length of an arc of a curve C in three-dimensional space in exactly the same way as we defined the length of an arc of a curve in the plane (see Definition 17.6.1). If C is the curve having parametric equations (2), f_1', f_2', f_3' are continuous on the closed interval $[a, b]$, and no two values of t give the same point (x, y, z) on C, then we can prove (as we did for the plane) a theorem similar to Theorem 17.6.3, which states that the length of arc, L units, of the curve C from the point $(f_1(a), f_2(a), f_3(a))$ to the point $(f_1(b), f_2(b), f_3(b))$ is determined by

$$L = \int_a^b \sqrt{[f_1'(t)]^2 + [f_2'(t)]^2 + [f_3'(t)]^2}\ dt \qquad (4)$$

If s is the measure of the length of arc of C from the fixed point $(f_1(t_0), f_2(t_0), f_3(t_0))$ to the variable point $(f_1(t), f_2(t), f_3(t))$ and s increases as t increases, then s is a function of t and is given by

$$s = \int_{t_0}^t \sqrt{[f_1'(u)]^2 + [f_2'(u)]^2 + [f_3'(u)]^2}\ du \qquad (5)$$

As we showed in Sec. 17.6 for plane curves, we can show that if (1) is a vector equation of C, then

$$D_t s = |D_t \mathbf{R}(t)| \qquad (6)$$

and the length of arc, L units, given by (4), also can be determined by

$$L = \int_a^b |D_t \mathbf{R}(t)|\ dt \qquad (7)$$

EXAMPLE 1: Given the circular helix $\mathbf{R}(t) = a \cos t\mathbf{i} + a \sin t\mathbf{j} + t\mathbf{k}$, where $a > 0$, find the length of arc from $t = 0$ to $t = 2\pi$.

SOLUTION: $D_t \mathbf{R}(t) = -a \sin t\mathbf{i} + a \cos t\mathbf{j} + \mathbf{k}$. So from (7) we obtain

$$L = \int_0^{2\pi} \sqrt{(-a \sin t)^2 + (a \cos t)^2 + 1}\ dt$$

$$= \int_0^{2\pi} \sqrt{a^2 + 1}\ dt = 2\pi \sqrt{a^2 + 1}$$

Thus, the length of arc is $2\pi\sqrt{a^2 + 1}$ units.

The definitions of the *curvature vector* $\mathbf{K}(t)$ and the *curvature* $K(t)$ at a point P on a curve C in R^3 are the same as for plane curves given in Definition 17.9.1. Hence, if $\mathbf{T}(t)$ is the unit tangent vector to C at P and s is the measure of the arc length from an arbitrarily chosen point on C to P, where s increases as t increases, then

$$\mathbf{K}(t) = D_s \mathbf{T}(t)$$

or, equivalently,

$$\mathbf{K}(t) = \frac{D_t \mathbf{T}(t)}{|D_t \mathbf{R}(t)|} \qquad (8)$$

and

$$K(t) = |D_s\mathbf{T}(t)|$$

or, equivalently,

$$K(t) = \left| \frac{D_t\mathbf{T}(t)}{|D_t\mathbf{R}(t)|} \right| \qquad (9)$$

Taking the dot product of $\mathbf{K}(t)$ and $\mathbf{T}(t)$ and using (8), we get

$$\mathbf{K}(t) \cdot \mathbf{T}(t) = \frac{D_t\mathbf{T}(t)}{|D_t\mathbf{R}(t)|} \cdot \mathbf{T}(t) = \frac{1}{|D_t\mathbf{R}(t)|} D_t\mathbf{T}(t) \cdot \mathbf{T}(t) \qquad (10)$$

Theorem 17.5.11 states that if a vector-valued function in a plane has a constant magnitude, it is orthogonal to its derivative. This theorem and its proof also hold for vectors in three dimensions. Therefore, because $|\mathbf{T}(t)| = 1$, we can conclude from (10) that $\mathbf{K}(t) \cdot \mathbf{T}(t) = 0$. And so the curvature vector and the unit tangent vector of a curve at a point are orthogonal.

We define the *unit normal vector* as the unit vector having the same direction as the curvature vector, provided that the curvature vector is not the zero vector. So if $\mathbf{N}(t)$ denotes the unit normal vector to a curve C at a point P, then if $\mathbf{K}(t) \neq \mathbf{0}$,

$$\mathbf{N}(t) = \frac{\mathbf{K}(t)}{|\mathbf{K}(t)|} \qquad (11)$$

From (11) and the previous discussion, it follows that the unit normal vector and the unit tangent vector are orthogonal. Thus, the angle between these two vectors has a radian measure of $\frac{1}{2}\pi$, and we have from Theorem 18.6.6,

$$|\mathbf{T}(t) \times \mathbf{N}(t)| = |\mathbf{T}(t)||\mathbf{N}(t)| \sin \tfrac{1}{2}\pi = (1)(1)(1) = 1$$

Therefore, the cross product of $\mathbf{T}(t)$ and $\mathbf{N}(t)$ is a unit vector. By Theorem 18.6.9 $\mathbf{T}(t) \times \mathbf{N}(t)$ is orthogonal to both $\mathbf{T}(t)$ and $\mathbf{N}(t)$; hence, the vector $\mathbf{B}(t)$, defined by

$$\mathbf{B}(t) = \mathbf{T}(t) \times \mathbf{N}(t) \qquad (12)$$

is a unit vector orthogonal to $\mathbf{T}(t)$ and $\mathbf{N}(t)$ and is called the *unit binormal vector* to the curve C at P.

The three mutually orthogonal unit vectors, $\mathbf{T}(t)$, $\mathbf{N}(t)$, and $\mathbf{B}(t)$, of a curve C are called the *moving trihedral* of C (see Fig. 18.9.5).

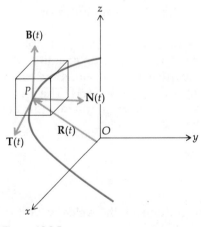

Figure 18.9.5

EXAMPLE 2: Find the moving trihedral and the curvature at any point of the circular helix of Example 1.

SOLUTION: A vector equation of the circular helix is

$$\mathbf{R}(t) = a \cos t\mathbf{i} + a \sin t\mathbf{j} + t\mathbf{k}$$

So $D_t\mathbf{R}(t) = -a \sin t\mathbf{i} + a \cos t\mathbf{j} + \mathbf{k}$ and $|D_t\mathbf{R}(t)| = \sqrt{a^2 + 1}$. From (3) we get

$$\mathbf{T}(t) = \frac{1}{\sqrt{a^2 + 1}} (-a \sin t\mathbf{i} + a \cos t\mathbf{j} + \mathbf{k})$$

So

$$D_t\mathbf{T}(t) = \frac{1}{\sqrt{a^2+1}}(-a\cos t\mathbf{i} - a\sin t\mathbf{j})$$

Applying (8), we obtain

$$\mathbf{K}(t) = \frac{1}{a^2+1}(-a\cos t\mathbf{i} - a\sin t\mathbf{j})$$

The curvature, then, is given by

$$K(t) = |\mathbf{K}(t)| = \frac{a}{a^2+1}$$

and so the curvature of the circular helix is constant. From (11) we get

$$\mathbf{N}(t) = -\cos t\mathbf{i} - \sin t\mathbf{j}$$

Applying (12), we have

$$\mathbf{B}(t) = \frac{1}{\sqrt{a^2+1}}(-a\sin t\mathbf{i} + a\cos t\mathbf{j} + \mathbf{k}) \times (-\cos t\mathbf{i} - \sin t\mathbf{j})$$

$$= \frac{1}{\sqrt{a^2+1}}(\sin t\mathbf{i} - \cos t\mathbf{j} + a\mathbf{k})$$

A thorough study of curves and surfaces by means of calculus forms the subject of *differential geometry*. The use of the calculus of vectors further enhances this subject. The previous discussion has been but a short introduction.

We now consider briefly the motion of a particle along a curve in three-dimensional space. If the parameter t in the vector equation (1) measures time, then the position at t of a particle moving along the curve C, having vector equation (1), is the point $P(f_1(t), f_2(t), f_3(t))$. The *velocity vector*, $\mathbf{V}(t)$, and the *acceleration vector*, $\mathbf{A}(t)$, are defined as in the plane. The vector $\mathbf{R}(t)$ is called the *position vector*, and

$$\mathbf{V}(t) = D_t\mathbf{R}(t) \tag{13}$$

and

$$\mathbf{A}(t) = D_t\mathbf{V}(t) = D_t{}^2\mathbf{R}(t) \tag{14}$$

The *speed* of the particle at t is the magnitude of the velocity vector. By applying (6) we can write

$$|\mathbf{V}(t)| = D_t s$$

EXAMPLE 3.   A particle is moving along the curve having parametric equations $x = 3t$, $y = t^2$, and $z = \frac{2}{3}t^3$. Find the velocity and acceleration vectors and the speed

SOLUTION: A vector equation of the curve is

$$\mathbf{R}(t) = 3t\mathbf{i} + t^2\mathbf{j} + \tfrac{2}{3}t^3\mathbf{k}$$

Therefore,

$$\mathbf{V}(t) = D_t\mathbf{R}(t) = 3\mathbf{i} + 2t\mathbf{j} + 2t^2\mathbf{k}$$

of the particle at $t = 1$. Draw a sketch of a portion of the curve at $t = 1$, and draw representations of the velocity and acceleration vectors there.

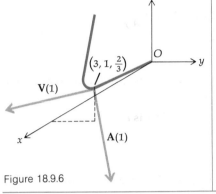

Figure 18.9.6

and

$$A(t) = D_t V(t) = 2j + 4tk$$

Also,

$$|V(t)| = \sqrt{9 + 4t^2 + 4t^4}$$

So when $t = 1$, $V = 3i + 2j + 2k$, $A = 2j + 4k$, and $|V(1)| = \sqrt{17}$. The required sketch is shown in Fig. 18.9.6.

Exercises 18.9

In Exercises 1 through 4, find the unit tangent vector for the curve having the given vector equation.

1. $R(t) = (t + 1)i - t\,j + (1 - 2t)k$

2. $R(t) = \sin 2ti + \cos 2tj + 2t^{3/2}k$

3. $R(t) = e^t \cos ti + e^t \sin tj + e^tk$

4. $R(t) = t^2i + (t + \frac{1}{3}t^3)j + (t - \frac{1}{3}t^3)k$

In Exercises 5 through 8, find the length of arc of the curve from t_1 to t_2.

5. $R(t) = (t + 1)i - t^2j + (1 - 2t)k$; $t_1 = -1$; $t_2 = 2$.

6. The curve of Exercise 2; $t_1 = 0$; $t_2 = 1$.

7. The curve of Exercise 3; $t_1 = 0$; $t_2 = 3$.

8. The curve of Exercise 4; $t_1 = 0$; $t_2 = 1$.

9. Prove Theorem 18.9.5.

10. Prove Theorem 18.9.6.

11. Write a vector equation of the curve of intersection of the surfaces $y = e^x$ and $z = xy$.

12. Prove that the unit tangent vector of the circular helix of Example 1 makes an angle of constant radian measure with the unit vector k.

13. Find the moving trihedral and the curvature at the point where $t = 1$ on the twisted cubic of Illustration 2.

14. Find the moving trihedral and the curvature at any point of the curve $R(t) = \cosh ti + \sinh tj + tk$.

In Exercises 15 through 18, find the moving trihedral and the curvature of the given curve at $t = t_1$, if they exist.

15. The curve of Exercise 5; $t_1 = -1$.

16. The curve of Exercise 2; $t_1 = 0$.

17. The curve of Exercise 3; $t_1 = 0$.

18. The curve of Exercise 4; $t_1 = 1$.

In Exercises 19 through 22, a particle is moving along the given curve. Find the velocity vector, the acceleration vector, and the speed at $t = t_1$. Draw a sketch of a portion of the curve at $t = t_1$ and draw the velocity and acceleration vectors there.

19. The circular helix of Example 1; $t_1 = \frac{1}{2}\pi$.

20. $x = t$, $y = \frac{1}{2}t^2$, $z = \frac{1}{3}t^3$; $t_1 = 2$.

21. $x = e^{2t}$, $y = e^{-2t}$, $z = te^{2t}$; $t_1 = 1$.

22. $x = 1/2(t^2 + 1)$, $y = \ln(1 + t^2)$, $z = \tan^{-1} t$; $t_1 = 1$.

23. Prove that if the speed of a moving particle is constant, its acceleration vector is always orthogonal to its velocity vector.

24. Prove that for the twisted cubic of Illustration 2, if $t \neq 0$, no two of the vectors $\mathbf{R}(t)$, $\mathbf{V}(t)$, and $\mathbf{A}(t)$ are orthogonal.

25. Prove that if $\mathbf{R}(t) = f_1(t)\mathbf{i} + f_2(t)\mathbf{j} + f_3(t)\mathbf{k}$ is a vector equation of curve C, and $K(t)$ is the curvature of C, then

$$K(t) = \frac{|D_t\mathbf{R}(t) \times D_t^2\mathbf{R}(t)|}{|D_t\mathbf{R}(t)|^3}$$

26. Use the formula of Exercise 25 to show that the curvature of the circular helix of Example 1 is $a/(a^2 + 1)$.

In Exercises 27 and 28, find the curvature of the given curve at the indicated point.

27. $x = t$, $y = t^2$, $z = t^3$; the origin.   28. $x = e^t$, $y = e^{-t}$, $z = t$; $t = 0$.

29. Prove that if $\mathbf{R}(t) = f_1(t)\mathbf{i} + f_2(t)\mathbf{j} + f_3(t)\mathbf{k}$ is a vector equation of curve C, $K(t)$ is the curvature of C at a point P, and s units is the arc length measured from an arbitrarily chosen point on C to P, then

$$D_s\mathbf{R}(t) \cdot D_s^3\mathbf{R}(t) = -[K(t)]^2$$

18.10 CYLINDRICAL AND SPHERICAL COORDINATES

Cylindrical and *spherical coordinates* are generalizations of polar coordinates to three-dimensional space. The cylindrical coordinate representation of a point P is (r, θ, z), where r and θ are the polar coordinates of the projection of P on a polar plane and z is the directed distance from this polar plane to P. See Fig. 18.10.1.

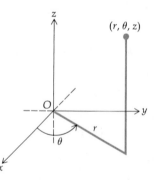

Figure 18.10.1

EXAMPLE 1:   Draw a sketch of the graph of each of the following equations where c is a constant: (a) $r = c$; (b) $\theta = c$; (c) $z = c$.

SOLUTION: (a) For a point $P(r, \theta, z)$ on the graph of $r = c$, θ and z can have any values and r is a constant. The graph is a right-circular cylinder having radius $|c|$ and the z axis as its axis. A sketch of the graph is shown in Fig. 18.10.2.

(b) For all points $P(r, \theta, z)$ on the graph of $\theta = c$, r and z can assume any value while θ remains constant. The graph is a plane through the z axis. See Fig. 18.10.3 for a sketch of the graph.

(c) The graph of $z = c$ is a plane parallel to the polar plane at a directed distance of c units from it. Figure 18.10.4 shows a sketch of the graph.

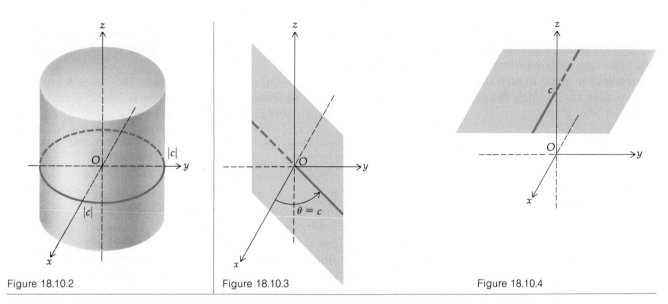

Figure 18.10.2

Figure 18.10.3

Figure 18.10.4

Figure 18.10.5

The name "cylindrical coordinates" comes from the fact that the graph of $r = c$ is a right-circular cylinder as in Example 1(a). Cylindrical coordinates are often used in a physical problem when there is an axis of symmetry.

Suppose that a cartesian-coordinate system and a cylindrical-coordinate system are placed so the xy plane is the polar plane of the cylindrical-coordinate system and the positive side of the x axis is the polar axis as shown in Fig. 18.10.5. Then the point P has (x, y, z) and (r, θ, z) as two sets of coordinates which are related by the equations

$$x = r \cos \theta \qquad y = r \sin \theta \qquad z = z \tag{1}$$

and

$$r^2 = x^2 + y^2 \qquad \tan \theta = \frac{y}{x} \ \text{ if } x \neq 0 \qquad z = z \tag{2}$$

EXAMPLE 2: Find an equation in cartesian coordinates of the following surfaces whose equations are given in cylindrical coordinates and identify the surface:
(a) $r = 6 \sin \theta$;
(b) $r(3 \cos \theta + 2 \sin \theta) + 6z = 0$.

SOLUTION: (a) Multiplying on both sides of the equation by r, we get $r^2 = 6r \sin \theta$. Because $r^2 = x^2 + y^2$ and $r \sin \theta = y$, we have $x^2 + y^2 = 6y$. This equation can be written in the form $x^2 + (y - 3)^2 = 9$, which shows that its graph is a right-circular cylinder whose cross section in the xy plane is the circle with its center at $(0, 3)$ and radius 3.

(b) Replacing $r \cos \theta$ by x and $r \sin \theta$ by y, we get the equation $3x + 2y + 6z = 0$. Hence, the graph is a plane through the origin and has $\langle 3, 2, 6 \rangle$ as a normal vector.

EXAMPLE 3:   Find an equation in cylindrical coordinates for each of the following surfaces whose equations are given in cartesian coordinates and identify the surface: (a) $x^2 + y^2 = z$; (b) $x^2 - y^2 = z$.

SOLUTION: (a) The equation is similar to Eq. (4) of Sec. 18.8, and so the graph is an elliptic paraboloid. If $x^2 + y^2$ is replaced by r^2, the equation becomes $r^2 = z$.

(b) The equation is similar to Eq. (5) of Sec. 18.8 with x and y interchanged. The graph is therefore a hyperbolic paraboloid having the z axis as its axis. When we replace x by $r \cos \theta$ and y by $r \sin \theta$, the equation becomes $r^2 \cos^2 \theta - r^2 \sin^2 \theta = z$; and because $\cos^2 \theta - \sin^2 \theta = \cos 2\theta$, we can write this as $z = r^2 \cos 2\theta$.

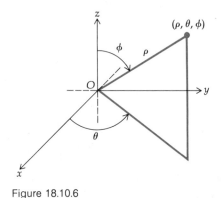

Figure 18.10.6

In a spherical-coordinate system there is a polar plane and an axis perpendicular to the polar plane, with the origin of the z axis at the pole of the polar plane. A point is located by three numbers, and the spherical-coordinate representation of a point P is (ρ, θ, ϕ), where $\rho = |\overline{OP}|$, θ is the radian measure of the polar angle of the projection of P on the polar plane, and ϕ is the nonnegative radian measure of the smallest angle measured from the positive side of the z axis to the line OP. See Fig. 18.10.6. The origin has the spherical-coordinate representation $(0, \theta, \phi)$, where θ and ϕ may have any values. If the point $P(\rho, \theta, \phi)$ is not the origin, then $\rho > 0$ and $0 \leq \phi \leq \pi$, where $\phi = 0$ if P is on the positive side of the z axis and $\phi = \pi$ if P is on the negative side of the z axis.

EXAMPLE 4:   Draw a sketch of the graph of each of the following equations where c is a constant: (a) $\rho = c$, and $c > 0$; (b) $\theta = c$; (c) $\phi = c$, and $0 < c < \pi$.

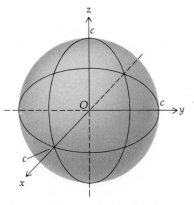

Figure 18.10.7

SOLUTION: (a) Every point $P(\rho, \theta, \phi)$ on the graph of $\rho = c$ has the same value of ρ, θ may be any number, and $0 \leq \phi \leq \pi$. It follows that the graph is a sphere of radius c and has its center at the pole. Figure 18.10.7 shows a sketch of the sphere.

(b) For any point $P(\rho, \theta, \phi)$ on the graph of $\theta = c$, ρ may be any nonnegative number, ϕ may be any number in the closed interval $[0, \pi]$, and θ is constant. The graph is a half plane containing the z axis and is obtained by rotating about the z axis through an angle of c radians that half of the xz plane for which $x \geq 0$. Figure 18.10.8 shows sketches of the half planes for $\theta = \frac{1}{4}\pi$, $\theta = \frac{2}{3}\pi$, $\theta = \frac{4}{3}\pi$, and $\theta = -\frac{1}{6}\pi$.

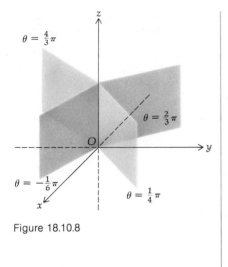

$\theta = \frac{4}{3}\pi$

$\theta = \frac{2}{3}\pi$

O

y

$\theta = -\frac{1}{6}\pi$

x

$\theta = \frac{1}{4}\pi$

Figure 18.10.8

(c) The graph of $\phi = c$ contains all the points $P(\rho, \theta, \phi)$ for which ρ is any nonnegative number, θ is any number, and ϕ is the constant c. The graph is half of a cone having its vertex at the origin and the z axis as its axis. Figure 18.10.9a and b each show a sketch of the half cone for $0 < c < \frac{1}{2}\pi$ and $\frac{1}{2}\pi < c < \pi$, respectively.

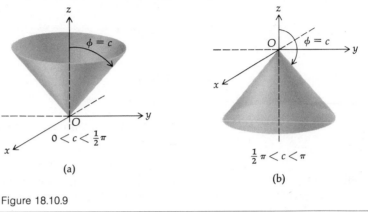

(a)

(b)

Figure 18.10.9

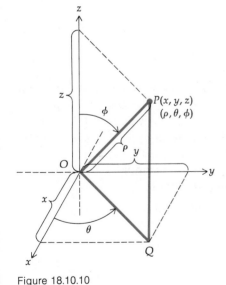

Figure 18.10.10

Because the graph of $\rho = c$ is a sphere as seen in Example 4(a), we have the name "spherical coordinates." In a physical problem when there is a point that is a center of symmetry, spherical coordinates are often used.

By placing a spherical-coordinate system and a cartesian-coordinate system together as shown in Fig. 18.10.10, we obtain relationships between the spherical coordinates and the cartesian coordinates of a point P from

$$x = |\overline{OQ}| \cos \theta \qquad y = |\overline{OQ}| \sin \theta \qquad z = |\overline{QP}|$$

Because $|\overline{OQ}| = \rho \sin \phi$ and $|\overline{QP}| = \rho \cos \phi$, these equations become

$$x = \rho \sin \phi \cos \theta \qquad y = \rho \sin \phi \sin \theta \qquad z = \rho \cos \phi \qquad (3)$$

By squaring each of the equations in (3) and adding, we have

$$x^2 + y^2 + z^2 = \rho^2 \sin^2 \phi \cos^2 \theta + \rho^2 \sin^2 \phi \sin^2 \theta + \rho^2 \cos^2 \phi$$

$$= \rho^2 \sin^2 \phi (\cos^2 \theta + \sin^2 \theta) + \rho^2 \cos^2 \phi$$

$$= \rho^2 (\sin^2 \phi + \cos^2 \phi)$$

$$= \rho^2$$

EXAMPLE 5: Find an equation in cartesian coordinates of the following surfaces whose equations

SOLUTION: (a) Because $z = \rho \cos \phi$, the equation becomes $z = 4$. Hence, the graph is a plane parallel to the xy plane and 4 units above it.

(b) For spherical coordinates $\rho \geq 0$ and $\sin \phi \geq 0$ (because $0 \leq$

are given in spherical coordinates and identify the surface: (a) $\rho \cos \phi = 4$; (b) $\rho \sin \phi = 4$.

$\phi \leq \pi$); therefore, if we square on both sides of the given equation, we obtain the equivalent equation $\rho^2 \sin^2 \phi = 16$, which in turn is equivalent to

$$\rho^2(1 - \cos^2 \phi) = 16$$

or

$$\rho^2 - \rho^2 \cos^2 \phi = 16$$

Replacing ρ^2 by $x^2 + y^2 + z^2$ and $\rho \cos \phi$ by z, we get

$$x^2 + y^2 + z^2 - z^2 = 16$$

or, equivalently,

$$x^2 + y^2 = 16$$

Therefore, the graph is the right-circular cylinder having the z axis as its axis and radius 4.

EXAMPLE 6: Find an equation in spherical coordinates for: (a) the elliptic paraboloid of Example 3(a); and (b) the plane of Example 2(b).

SOLUTION: (a) A cartesian equation of the elliptic paraboloid of Example 3(a) is $x^2 + y^2 = z$. Replacing x by $\rho \sin \phi \cos \theta$, y by $\rho \sin \phi \sin \theta$, and z by $\rho \cos \phi$, we get

$$\rho^2 \sin^2 \phi \cos^2 \theta + \rho^2 \sin^2 \phi \sin^2 \theta = \rho \cos \phi$$

or, equivalently,

$$\rho^2 \sin^2 \phi(\cos^2 \theta + \sin^2 \theta) = \rho \cos \phi$$

which is equivalent to the two equations

$$\rho = 0 \quad \text{and} \quad \rho \sin^2 \phi = \cos \phi$$

The origin is the only point whose coordinates satisfy $\rho = 0$. Because the origin $(0, \theta, \frac{1}{2}\pi)$ lies on $\rho \sin^2 \phi = \cos \phi$, we can disregard the equation $\rho = 0$. Furthermore, $\sin \phi \neq 0$ because there is no value of ϕ for which both $\sin \phi$ and $\cos \phi$ are 0. Therefore, the equation $\rho \sin^2 \phi = \cos \phi$ can be written as $\rho = \csc^2 \phi \cos \phi$, or, equivalently, $\rho = \csc \phi \cot \phi$.

(b) A cartesian equation of the plane of Example 2(b) is $3x + 2y + 6z = 0$. By using Eqs. (3) this equation becomes

$$3\rho \sin \phi \cos \theta + 2\rho \sin \phi \sin \theta + 6\rho \cos \phi = 0$$

Exercises 18.10

1. Find the cartesian coordinates of the point having the given cylindrical coordinates:

   (a) $(3, \frac{1}{2}\pi, 5)$ (b) $(7, \frac{2}{3}\pi, -4)$ (c) $(1, 1, 1)$

2. Find a set of cylindrical coordinates of the point having the given cartesian coordinates:

   (a) $(4, 4, -2)$ (b) $(-3\sqrt{3}, 3, 6)$ (c) $(1, 1, 1)$

3. Find the cartesian coordinates of the point having the given spherical coordinates:

(a) $(4, \frac{1}{6}\pi, \frac{1}{4}\pi)$ (b) $(4, \frac{1}{2}\pi, \frac{1}{3}\pi)$ (c) $(\sqrt{6}, \frac{1}{3}\pi, \frac{3}{4}\pi)$

4. Find a set of spherical coordinates of the point having the given cartesian coordinates:

(a) $(1, -1, -\sqrt{2})$ (b) $(-1, \sqrt{3}, 2)$ (c) $(2, 2, 2)$

5. Find a set of cylindrical coordinates of the point having the given spherical coordinates:

(a) $(4, \frac{2}{3}\pi, \frac{5}{6}\pi)$ (b) $(\sqrt{2}, \frac{3}{4}\pi, \pi)$ (c) $(2\sqrt{3}, \frac{1}{3}\pi, \frac{1}{4}\pi)$

6. Find a set of spherical coordinates of the point having the given cylindrical coordinates:

(a) $(3, \frac{1}{6}\pi, 3)$ (b) $(3, \frac{1}{2}\pi, 2)$ (c) $(2, \frac{5}{6}\pi, -4)$

In Exercises 7 through 10, find an equation in cylindrical coordinates of the given surface and identify the surface.

7. $x^2 + y^2 + 4z^2 = 16$ 8. $x^2 - y^2 = 9$

9. $x^2 - y^2 = 3z^2$ 10. $x^2 + y^2 = z^2$

In Exercises 11 through 14, find an equation in spherical coordinates of the given surface and identify the surface.

11. $x^2 + y^2 + z^2 - 9z = 0$ 12. $x^2 + y^2 = z^2$

13. $x^2 + y^2 = 9$ 14. $x^2 + y^2 = 2z$

In Exercises 15 through 18, find an equation in cartesian coordinates for the surface whose equation is given in cylindrical coordinates. In Exercises 15 and 16, identify the surface.

15. (a) $r = 4$; (b) $\theta = \frac{1}{4}\pi$ 16. $r = 3 \cos \theta$

17. $r^2 \cos 2\theta = z^3$ 18. $z^2 \sin^3 \theta = r^3$

In Exercises 19 through 22, find an equation in cartesian coordinates for the surface whose equation is given in spherical coordinates. In Exercises 19 and 20, identify the surface.

19. (a) $\rho = 9$; (b) $\theta = \frac{1}{4}\pi$; (c) $\phi = \frac{1}{4}\pi$ 20. $\rho = 9 \sec \phi$

21. $\rho = 2 \tan \theta$ 22. $\rho = 6 \sin \phi \sin \theta + 3 \cos \phi$

23. A curve C in R^3 has the following parametric equations in cylindrical coordinates:

$$r = F_1(t) \qquad \theta = F_2(t) \qquad z = F_3(t)$$

Use formula (4) of Sec. 18.9 and formulas (1) of this section to prove that if L units is the length of arc of C from the point where $t = a$ to the point where $t = b$, then

$$L = \int_a^b \sqrt{(D_t r)^2 + r^2(D_t \theta)^2 + (D_t z)^2} \; dt$$

24. A curve C in R^3 has the following parametric equations in spherical coordinates:

$$\rho = G_1(t) \qquad \theta = G_2(t) \qquad \phi = G_3(t)$$

Use formula (4) of Sec. 18.9 and formulas (3) of this section to prove that if L units is the length of arc of C from the point where $t = a$ to the point where $t = b$, then

$$L = \int_a^b \sqrt{(D_t \rho)^2 + \rho^2 \sin^2 \phi (D_t \theta)^2 + \rho^2(D_t \phi)^2} \; dt$$

25. (a) Show that parametric equations for the circular helix of Example 1, Sec. 18.9, are

$$r = a \qquad \theta = t \qquad z = t$$

(b) Use the formula of Exercise 23 to find the length of arc of the circular helix of part (a) from $t = 0$ to $t = 2\pi$. Check your result with that of Example 1, Sec. 18.9.

26. A *conical helix* winds around a cone in a way similar to that in which a circular helix winds around a cylinder. Use the formula of Exercise 24 to find the length of arc from $t = 0$ to $t = 2\pi$ of the conical helix having parametric equations

$$\rho = t \qquad \theta = t \qquad \phi = \tfrac{1}{4}\pi$$

Review Exercises (Chapter 18)

1. Draw a sketch of the graph of $x = 3$ in R^1, R^2, and R^3.

2. Draw a sketch of the set of points satisfying the simultaneous equations $x = 6$ and $y = 3$ in R^2 and R^3.

In Exercises 3 through 11, describe in words the set of points in R^3 satisfying the given equation or the given pair of equations. Draw a sketch of the graph.

3. $\begin{cases} y = 0 \\ z = 0 \end{cases}$

4. $\begin{cases} x = z \\ y = z \end{cases}$

5. $\begin{cases} x^2 + z^2 = 4 \\ y = 0 \end{cases}$

6. $x^2 + z^2 = 4$

7. $x = y$

8. $y^2 - z^2 = 0$

9. $x^2 + y^2 = 9z$

10. $x^2 + y^2 = z^2$

11. $x^2 - y^2 = z^2$

In Exercises 12 through 17, let $\mathbf{A} = -\mathbf{i} + 3\mathbf{j} + 2\mathbf{k}$, $\mathbf{B} = 2\mathbf{i} + \mathbf{j} - 4\mathbf{k}$, $\mathbf{C} = \mathbf{i} + 2\mathbf{j} - 2\mathbf{k}$, $\mathbf{D} = 3\mathbf{j} - \mathbf{k}$, $\mathbf{E} = 5\mathbf{i} - 2\mathbf{j}$, and find the indicated vector or scalar.

12. $3\mathbf{A} - 2\mathbf{B} + \mathbf{C}$

13. $6\mathbf{C} + 4\mathbf{D} - \mathbf{E}$

14. $2\mathbf{B} \cdot \mathbf{C} + 3\mathbf{D} \cdot \mathbf{E}$

15. $\mathbf{D} \cdot \mathbf{B} \times \mathbf{C}$

16. $(\mathbf{A} \times \mathbf{C}) - (\mathbf{D} \times \mathbf{E})$

17. $|\mathbf{A} \times \mathbf{B}||\mathbf{D} \times \mathbf{E}|$

In Exercises 18 through 23, there is only one way that a meaningful expression can be obtained by inserting parentheses. Insert the parentheses and find the indicated vector or scalar if $\mathbf{A} = \langle 3, -2, 4 \rangle$, $\mathbf{B} = \langle -5, 7, 2 \rangle$, and $\mathbf{C} = \langle 4, 6, -1 \rangle$.

18. $\mathbf{B} \cdot \mathbf{A} - \mathbf{C}$

19. $\mathbf{A} + \mathbf{B} \cdot \mathbf{C}$

20. $\mathbf{A} \cdot \mathbf{B} \, \mathbf{C}$

21. $\mathbf{A} \, \mathbf{B} \cdot \mathbf{C}$

22. $\mathbf{A} \times \mathbf{B} \cdot \mathbf{C} \times \mathbf{A}$

23. $\mathbf{A} \times \mathbf{B} \cdot \mathbf{A} + \mathbf{B} - \mathbf{C}$

24. If $\mathbf{A}$ is any vector, prove that $\mathbf{A} = (\mathbf{A} \cdot \mathbf{i})\mathbf{i} + (\mathbf{A} \cdot \mathbf{j})\mathbf{j} + (\mathbf{A} \cdot \mathbf{k})\mathbf{k}$.

25. Find an equation of the sphere concentric with the sphere $x^2 + y^2 + z^2 + 4x + 2y - 6z + 10 = 0$ and containing the point $(-4, 2, 5)$.

26. Find an equation of the surface of revolution generated by revolving the ellipse $9x^2 + 4z^2 = 36$ in the xz plane about the x axis. Draw a sketch of the surface.

27. Determine the value of c so that the vectors $3\mathbf{i} + c\mathbf{j} - 3\mathbf{k}$ and $5\mathbf{i} - 4\mathbf{j} + \mathbf{k}$ are orthogonal.

28. Show that there are representations of the three vectors $\mathbf{A} = 5\mathbf{i} + \mathbf{j} - 3\mathbf{k}$, $\mathbf{B} = \mathbf{i} + 3\mathbf{j} - 2\mathbf{k}$, and $\mathbf{C} = -4\mathbf{i} + 2\mathbf{j} + \mathbf{k}$ which form a triangle.

29. Find the distance from the origin to the plane through the point $(-6, 3, -2)$ and having $5\mathbf{i} - 3\mathbf{j} + 4\mathbf{k}$ as a normal vector.

30. Find an equation of the plane containing the points $(1, 7, -3)$ and $(3, 1, 2)$ and which does not intersect the x axis.

31. Find an equation of the plane through the three points $(-1, 2, 1)$, $(1, 4, 0)$, and $(1, -1, 3)$ by two methods: (a) using the cross product; (b) without using the cross product.

32. Find two unit vectors orthogonal to $\mathbf{i} - 3\mathbf{j} + 4\mathbf{k}$ and whose representations are parallel to the yz plane.

33. Find the distance from the point $P(4, 6, -4)$ to the line through the two points $A(2, 2, 1)$ and $B(4, 3, -1)$.

34. Find the distance from the plane $9x - 2y + 6z + 44 = 0$ to the point $(-3, 2, 0)$.

35. If θ is the radian measure of the angle between the vectors $\mathbf{A} = 2\mathbf{i} + \mathbf{j} + \mathbf{k}$ and $\mathbf{B} = 4\mathbf{i} - 3\mathbf{j} + 5\mathbf{k}$ find $\cos \theta$ in two ways: (a) by using the dot product; (b) by using the cross product and a trigonometric identity.

36. Prove that the lines

$$\frac{x-1}{1} = \frac{y+2}{2} = \frac{z-2}{2} \quad \text{and} \quad \frac{x-2}{2} = \frac{y-5}{3} = \frac{z-5}{1}$$

are skew lines and find the distance between them.

37. Find symmetric and parametric equations of the line through the origin and perpendicular to each of the lines of Exercise 36.

38. Find the area of the parallelogram two of whose sides are the position representations of the vectors $2\mathbf{j} - 3\mathbf{k}$ and $5\mathbf{i} + 4\mathbf{k}$.

39. Find the volume of the parallelepiped having vertices at $(1, 3, 0)$, $(2, -1, 3)$, $(-2, 2, -1)$, and $(-1, 1, 2)$.

40. Find the length of the arc of the curve

$$x = t \cos t \qquad y = t \sin t \qquad z = t$$

from $t = 0$ to $t = \frac{1}{2}\pi$.

41. A particle is moving along the curve of Exercise 40. Find the velocity vector, the acceleration vector, and the speed at $t = \frac{1}{2}\pi$. Draw a sketch of a portion of the curve at $t = \frac{1}{2}\pi$ and draw the representations of the velocity and acceleration vectors there.

42. Find the unit tangent vector and the curvature at any point on the curve having the vector equation

$$\mathbf{R}(t) = e^t\mathbf{i} + e^{-t}\mathbf{j} + 2t\mathbf{k}$$

43. Find an equation in cylindrical coordinates of the graph of each of the equations: (a) $(x + y)^2 + 1 = z$; (b) $25x^2 + 4y^2 = 100$.

44. Find an equation in spherical coordinates of the graph of each of the equations: (a) $x^2 + y^2 + 4z^2 = 4$; (b) $4x^2 - 4y^2 + 9z^2 = 36$.

45. If $\mathbf{R}$, $\mathbf{Q}$, and $\mathbf{W}$ are three vector-valued functions whose derivatives with respect to t exist, prove that

$$D_t[\mathbf{R}(t) \cdot \mathbf{Q}(t) \times \mathbf{W}(t)] = D_t\mathbf{R}(t) \cdot \mathbf{Q}(t) \times \mathbf{W}(t) + \mathbf{R}(t) \cdot D_t\mathbf{Q}(t) \times \mathbf{W}(t) + \mathbf{R}(t) \cdot \mathbf{Q}(t) \times D_t\mathbf{W}(t)$$

19

Differential calculus
of functions
# of several variables

19.1 FUNCTIONS OF MORE THAN ONE VARIABLE

In this section we extend the concept of a function to functions of n variables, and in succeeding sections we extend to functions of n variables the concepts of the *limit* of a function, *continuity* of a function, and *derivative* of a function. A thorough treatment of these topics belongs to a course in advanced calculus. In this book we confine most of our discussion of functions of more than one variable to those of two and three variables; however, we make the definitions for functions of n variables and then show the applications of these definitions to functions of two and three variables. We also show that when each of these definitions is applied to a function of one variable we have the definition previously given.

To extend the concept of a function to functions of any number of variables, we must first consider points in n-dimensional number space. Just as we denoted a point in R^1 by a real number x, a point in R^2 by an ordered pair of real numbers (x, y), and a point in R^3 by an ordered triple of real numbers (x, y, z), we represent a point in n-dimensional number space, R^n, by an ordered n-tuple of real numbers customarily denoted by $P = (x_1, x_2, \ldots, x_n)$. In particular, if $n = 1$, we let $P = x$; if $n = 2$, $P = (x, y)$; if $n = 3$, $P = (x, y, z)$; if $n = 6$, $P = (x_1, x_2, x_3, x_4, x_5, x_6)$.

19.1.1 Definition

The set of all ordered n-tuples of real numbers is called the *n-dimensional number space* and is denoted by R^n. Each ordered n-tuple $(x_1, x_2, \ldots, x_n)$ is called a *point* in the n-dimensional number space.

19.1.2 Definition

A *function of n variables* is a set of ordered pairs of the form (P, w) in which no two distinct ordered pairs have the same first element. P is a point in n-dimensional number space and w is a real number. The set of all possible values of P is called the *domain* of the function, and the set of all possible values of w is called the *range* of the function.

From this definition, we see that the domain of a function of n variables is a set of points in R^n and that the range is a set of real numbers or, equivalently, a set of points in R^1. When $n = 1$, we have a function of one variable; thus, the domain is a set of points in R^1 or, equivalently, a set of real numbers, and the range is a set of real numbers. Hence, we see that Definition 1.7.1 is a special case of Definition 19.1.2. If $n = 2$, we have a function of two variables, and the domain is a set of points in R^2 or, equivalently, a set of ordered pairs of real numbers (x, y). The range is a set of real numbers.

● ILLUSTRATION 1: Let the function f of two variables x and y be the set of all ordered pairs of the form (P, z) such that

$$z = \sqrt{25 - x^2 - y^2}$$

The domain of f is the set of all ordered pairs (x, y) for which $25 - x^2 - y^2 \geq 0$. This is the set of all points in the xy plane on the circle $x^2 + y^2 = 25$ and in the interior region bounded by the circle.

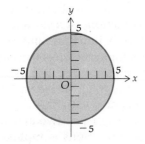

Figure 19.1.1

Because $z = \sqrt{25 - (x^2 + y^2)}$, we see that $0 \le z \le 5$; therefore, the range of f is the set of all real numbers in the closed interval $[0, 5]$. In Fig. 19.1.1 we have a sketch showing as a shaded region in R^2 the set of points in the domain of f.   ●

● ILLUSTRATION 2: The function g of two variables x and y is the set of all ordered pairs of the form (P, z) such that

$$z = \frac{\sqrt{x^2 + y^2 - 25}}{y}$$

The domain of g consists of all ordered pairs (x, y) for which $x^2 + y^2 \ge 25$ and $y \ne 0$. This is the set of points, not on the x axis, which are either on the circle $x^2 + y^2 = 25$ or in the exterior region bounded by the circle. Figure 19.1.2 is a sketch showing as a shaded region in R^2 the set of points in the domain of g.   ●

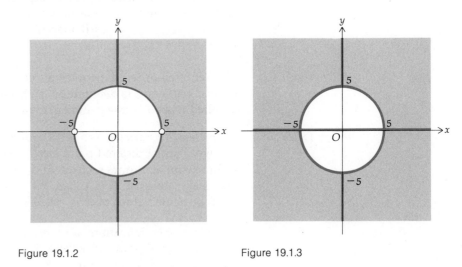

Figure 19.1.2   Figure 19.1.3

● ILLUSTRATION 3: The function F of two variables x and y is the set of all ordered pairs of the form (P, z) such that

$$z = y\sqrt{x^2 + y^2 - 25}$$

If $y = 0$, then $z = 0$ regardless of the value of x. However, if $y \ne 0$, then $x^2 + y^2 - 25$ must be nonnegative in order for z to be defined. Therefore, the domain of F consists of all ordered pairs (x, y) for which either $y = 0$ or $x^2 + y^2 - 25 \ge 0$. This is the set of all points on the circle $x^2 + y^2 = 25$, all points in the exterior region bounded by the circle, and all points on the x axis for which $-5 < x < 5$ In Fig. 19.1.3 we have a sketch showing as a shaded region in R^2 the set of points in the domain of F.   ●

● ILLUSTRATION 4: The function G of two variables x and y is the set of all

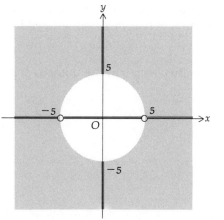

Figure 19.1.4

ordered pairs of the form (P, z) such that

$$z = \frac{y}{\sqrt{x^2 + y^2 - 25}}$$

If $y = 0$, then $z = 0$ provided that $x^2 + y^2 - 25 \neq 0$. If $y \neq 0$, then $x^2 + y^2 - 25$ must be positive in order for z to be defined. Hence, the domain of G consists of all ordered pairs (x, y) for which $x^2 + y^2 - 25 > 0$ and those for which $y = 0$ and $x \neq \pm 5$. These are all the points in the exterior region bounded by the circle $x^2 + y^2 = 25$ and the points on the x axis for which $-5 < x < 5$. Figure 19.1.4 is a sketch showing as a shaded region in R^2 the set of points in the domain of G.

If f is a function of n variables, then according to Definition 19.1.2, f is a set of ordered pairs of the form (P, w), where $P = (x_1, x_2, \ldots , x_n)$ is a point in R^n and w is a real number. We denote the particular value of w, which corresponds to a point P, by the symbol $f(P)$ or $f(x_1, x_2, \ldots , x_n)$. In particular, if $n = 2$ and we let $P = (x, y)$, we can denote the function value by either $f(P)$ or $f(x, y)$. Similarly, if $n = 3$ and $P = (x, y, z)$, we denote the function value by either $f(P)$ or $f(x, y, z)$. Note that if $n = 1$, $P = x$; hence, if f is a function of one variable, $f(P) = f(x)$. Therefore, this notation is consistent with our notation for function values of one variable.

A function f of n variables can be defined by the equation

$$w = f(x_1, x_2, \ldots , x_n)$$

The variables $x_1, x_2, \ldots , x_n$ are called the *independent variables*, and w is called the *dependent variable*.

● ILLUSTRATION 5: Let f be the function of Illustration 1; that is,

$$f(x, y) = \sqrt{25 - x^2 - y^2}$$

Then

$$f(3, -4) = \sqrt{25 - (3)^2 - (-4)^2} = \sqrt{25 - 9 - 16} = 0$$
$$f(-2, 1) = \sqrt{25 - (-2)^2 - (1)^2} = \sqrt{25 - 4 - 1} = 2\sqrt{5}$$
$$f(u, 3v) = \sqrt{25 - u^2 - (3v)^2} = \sqrt{25 - u^2 - 9v^2}$$

●

EXAMPLE 1:   The domain of a function g is the set of all ordered triples of real numbers (x, y, z) such that

$$g(x, y, z) = x^2 - 5xz + yz^2$$

Find (a) $g(1, 4, -2)$;
(b) $g(2a, -b, 3c)$; (c) $g(x^2, y^2, z^2)$;
(d) $g(y, z, -x)$.

SOLUTION:

(a) $g(1, 4, -2) = 1^2 - 5(1)(-2) + 4(-2)^2 = 1 + 10 + 16 = 27$

(b) $g(2a, -b, 3c) = (2a)^2 - 5(2a)(3c) + (-b)(3c)^2$

$$= 4a^2 - 30ac - 9bc^2$$

(c) $g(x^2, y^2, z^2) = (x^2)^2 - 5(x^2)(z^2) + (y^2)(z^2)^2 = x^4 - 5x^2z^2 + y^2z^4$

(d) $g(y, z, -x) = y^2 - 5y(-x) + z(-x)^2 = y^2 + 5xy + x^2z$

19.1.3 Definition   If f is a function of a single variable and g is a function of two variables, then the *composite function* $f \circ g$ is the function of two variables defined by

$$(f \circ g)(x, y) = f(g(x, y))$$

and the domain of $f \circ g$ is the set of all points (x, y) in the domain of g such that $g(x, y)$ is in the domain of f.

EXAMPLE 2:   Given $f(t) = \ln t$ and $g(x, y) = x^2 + y$, find $h(x, y)$ if $h = f \circ g$, and find the domain of h.

SOLUTION:

$$h(x, y) = (f \circ g)(x, y) = f(g(x, y))$$
$$= f(x^2 + y)$$
$$= \ln(x^2 + y)$$

The domain of g is the set of all points in R^2, and the domain of f is $(0, +\infty)$. Therefore, the domain of h is the set of all points (x, y) for which $x^2 + y > 0$.

Definition 19.1.3 can be extended to a composite function of n variables as follows.

19.1.4 Definition   If f is a function of a single variable and g is a function of n variables, then the *composite function* $f \circ g$ is the function of n variables defined by

$$(f \circ g)(x_1, x_2, \ldots, x_n) = f(g(x_1, x_2, \ldots, x_n))$$

and the domain of $f \circ g$ is the set of all points $(x_1, x_2, \ldots, x_n)$ in the domain of g such that $g(x_1, x_2, \ldots, x_n)$ is in the domain of f.

EXAMPLE 3:   Given $F(x) = \sin^{-1} x$ and $G(x, y, z) = \sqrt{x^2 + y^2 + z^2 - 4}$, find the function $F \circ G$ and its domain.

SOLUTION:

$$(F \circ G)(x, y, z) = F(G(x, y, z))$$
$$= F(\sqrt{x^2 + y^2 + z^2 - 4})$$
$$= \sin^{-1} \sqrt{x^2 + y^2 + z^2 - 4}$$

The domain of G is the set of all points (x, y, z) in R^3 such that $x^2 + y^2 + z^2 - 4 \geq 0$, and the domain of F is $[-1, 1]$. So the domain of $F \circ G$ is the set of all points (x, y, z) in R^3 such that $0 \leq x^2 + y^2 + z^2 - 4 \leq 1$ or, equivalently, $4 \leq x^2 + y^2 + z^2 \leq 5$.

A *polynomial function* of two variables x and y is a function f such that $f(x, y)$ is the sum of terms of the form $cx^n y^m$, where c is a real number and n and m are nonnegative integers. The *degree* of the polynomial function is determined by the largest sum of the exponents of x and y appearing in any one term. Hence, the function f defined by

$$f(x, y) = 6x^3 y^2 - 5xy^3 + 7x^2 y - 2x^2 + y$$

is a polynomial function of degree 5.

A *rational function* of two variables is a function h such that $h(x, y) = f(x, y)/g(x, y)$, where f and g are two polynomial functions. For example, the function f defined by

$$f(x, y) = \frac{x^2 y^2}{x^2 + y^2}$$

is a rational function.

The graph of a function f of a single variable consists of the set of points (x, y) in R^2 for which $y = f(x)$. Similarly, the graph of a function of two variables is a set of points in R^3.

19.1.5 Definition   If f is a function of two variables, then the *graph* of f is the set of all points. (x, y, z) in R^3 for which (x, y) is a point in the domain of f and $z = f(x, y)$.

Hence, the graph of a function f of two variables is a surface which is the set of all points in three-dimensional space whose cartesian coordinates are given by the ordered triples of real numbers (x, y, z). Because the domain of f is a set of points in the xy plane, and because for each ordered pair (x, y) in the domain of f there corresponds a unique value of z, no line perpendicular to the xy plane can intersect the graph of f in more than one point.

● ILLUSTRATION 6: The function of Illustration 1 is the function f which is the set of all ordered pairs of the form (P, z) such that

$$z = \sqrt{25 - x^2 - y^2}$$

So the graph of f is the hemisphere on and above the xy plane having a radius of 5 and its center at the origin. A sketch of the graph of this hemisphere is shown in Fig. 19.1.5. ●

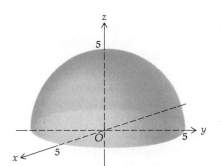

Figure 19.1.5

EXAMPLE 4:   Draw a sketch of the graph of the function f having function values $f(x, y) = x^2 + y^2$.

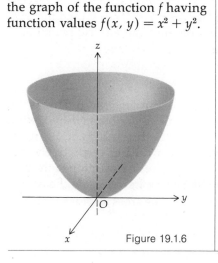

x Figure 19.1.6

SOLUTION: The graph of f is the surface having the equation $z = x^2 + y^2$. The trace of the surface in the xy plane is found by using the equation $z = 0$ simultaneously with the equation of the surface. We obtain $x^2 + y^2 = 0$, which is the origin. The traces in the xz and yz planes are found by using the equations $y = 0$ and $x = 0$, respectively, with the equation $z = x^2 + y^2$. We obtain the parabolas $z = x^2$ and $z = y^2$. The cross section of the surface in a plane $z = k$, parallel to the xy plane, is a circle with its center on the z axis and radius $\sqrt{k}$. With this information we have the required sketch shown in Fig. 19.1.6.

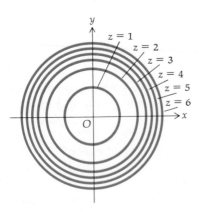

Figure 19.1.7

There is another useful method of representing a function of two variables geometrically. It is a method similar to that of representing a three-dimensional landscape by a two-dimensional topographical map. Suppose that the surface $z = f(x, y)$ is intersected by the plane $z = k$, and the curve of intersection is projected onto the xy plane. This projected curve has $f(x, y) = k$ as an equation, and the curve is called the *level curve* (or *contour curve*) of the function f at k. Each point on the level curve corresponds to the unique point on the surface which is k units above it if k is positive, or k units below it if k is negative. By considering different values for the constant k, we obtain a set of level curves. This set of curves is called a *contour map*. The set of all possible values of k is the range of the function f, and each level curve, $f(x, y) = k$, in the contour map consists of the points (x, y) in the domain of f having equal function values of k. For example, for the function f of Example 4, the level curves are circles with the center at the origin. The particular level curves for $z = 1, 2, 3, 4, 5,$ and 6 are shown in Fig. 19.1.7.

A contour map shows the variation of z with x and y. The level curves are usually shown for values of z at constant intervals, and the values of z are changing more rapidly when the level curves are close together than when they are far apart; that is, when the level curves are close together, the surface is steep, and when the level curves are far apart the elevation of the surface is changing slowly. On a two-dimensional topographical map of a landscape, a general notion of its steepness is obtained by considering the spacing of its level curves. Also on a topographical map if the path of a level curve is followed, the elevation remains constant.

To illustrate a use of level curves, suppose that the temperature at any point of a flat metal plate is given by the function f; that is, if t degrees is the temperature, then at the point (x, y), $t = f(x, y)$. Then the curves having equations of the form $f(x, y) = k$, where k is a constant, are curves on which the temperature is constant. These are the level curves of f and are called *isothermals*. Furthermore, if V volts gives the amount of electric potential at any point (x, y) of the xy plane, and $V = f(x, y)$, then the level curves of f are called *equipotential curves* because the electric potential at each point of such a curve is the same.

EXAMPLE 5: Let f be the function for which $f(x, y) = 8 - x^2 - 2y$. Draw a sketch of the graph of f and a contour map of f showing the level curves of f at $10, 8, 6, 4, 2, 0, -2, -4, -6,$ and -8.

SOLUTION: A sketch of the graph of f is shown in Fig. 19.1.8. This is the surface $z = 8 - x^2 - 2y$. The trace in the xy plane is obtained by setting $z = 0$, which gives the parabola $x^2 = -2(y - 4)$. Setting $y = 0$ and $x = 0$, we obtain the traces in the xz and yz planes, which are, respectively, the parabola $x^2 = -(z - 8)$ and the line $2y + z = 8$. The cross section of the surface made by the plane $z = k$ is a parabola having its vertex on the line $2y + z = 8$ in the yz plane and opening to the left. The cross sections for $z = 8, 6, 4, 2, -2, -4, -6,$ and -8 are shown in the figure.

The level curves of f are the parabolas $x^2 = -2(y - 4 + \frac{1}{2}k)$. The con-

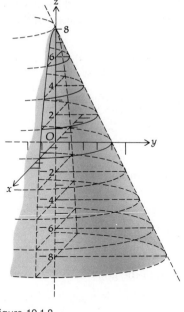

Figure 19.1.8

tour map of f with sketches of the required level curves is shown in Fig. 19.1.9.

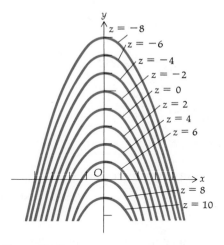

Figure 19.1.9

Extending the notion of the graph of a function to a function of n variables, we have the following definition.

19.1.6 Definition   If f is a function of n variables, then the *graph* of f is the set of all points $(x_1, x_2, \ldots, x_n, w)$ in R^{n+1} for which $(x_1, x_2, \ldots, x_n)$ is a point in the domain of f and $w = f(x_1, x_2, \ldots, x_n)$.

Analogous to level curves for a function of two variables is a similar situation for functions of three variables. If f is a function whose domain is a set of points in R^3, then if k is a number in the range of f, the graph of the equation $f(x, y, z) = k$ is a surface. This surface is called the *level surface* of f at k. Every surface in three-dimensional space can be considered as a level surface of some function of three variables. For example, if the function g is defined by the equation $g(x, y, z) = x^2 + y^2 - z$, then the surface shown in Fig. 19.1.6 is the level surface of g at 0. Similarly, the surface having equation $z - x^2 - y^2 + 5 = 0$ is the level surface of g at 5.

Exercises 19.1

1. Let the function f of two variables x and y be the set of all ordered pairs of the form (P, z) such that $z = (x + y)/(x - y)$. Find: (a) $f(-3, 4)$; (b) $f(x^2, y^2)$; (c) $[f(x, y)]^2$; (d) $f(-x, y) - f(x, -y)$; (e) the domain of f; (f) the range of f. Draw a sketch showing as a shaded region in R^2 the set of points not in the domain of f.

2. Let the function g of three variables, x, y, and z, be the set of all ordered pairs of the form (P, w) such that $w =$

$\sqrt{4 - x^2 - y^2 - z^2}$. Find: (a) $g(1, -1, -1)$; (b) $g(-a, 2b, \frac{1}{2}c)$; (c) $g(y, -x, -y)$; (d) the domain of g; (e) the range of g; (f) $[g(x, y, z)]^2 - [g(x + 2, y + 2, z)]^2$. Draw a sketch showing as a shaded solid in R^3 the set of points in the domain of g.

In Exercises 3 through 11, find the domain and range of the function f and draw a sketch showing as a shaded region in R^2 the set of points in the domain of f.

3. $f(x, y) = \dfrac{\sqrt{25 - x^2 - y^2}}{x}$

4. $f(x, y) = x\sqrt{25 - x^2 - y^2}$

5. $f(x, y) = \dfrac{x}{\sqrt{25 - x^2 - y^2}}$

6. $f(x, y) = \sqrt{\dfrac{x - y}{x + y}}$

7. $f(x, y) = \dfrac{x^2 - y^2}{x - y}$

8. $f(x, y) = \dfrac{x + y}{xy}$

9. $f(x, y) = \dfrac{x}{|y|}$

10. $f(x, y) = \sin^{-1}(x + y)$

11. $f(x, y) = \ln(xy - 1)$

In Exercises 12 through 14, find the domain and range of the function f.

12. $f(x, y, z) = (x + y)\sqrt{z - 2}$

13. $f(x, y, z) = \sin^{-1} x + \cos^{-1} y + \tan^{-1} z$

14. $f(x, y, z) = |x|e^{y/z}$

In Exercises 15 through 20, find the domain and range of the function f and draw a sketch of the graph.

15. $f(x, y) = 4x^2 + 9y^2$

16. $f(x, y) = \sqrt{x + y}$

17. $f(x, y) = 16 - x^2 - y^2$

18. $f(x, y) = \sqrt{100 - 25x^2 - 4y^2}$

19. $f(x, y) = \sqrt{10 - x - y^2}$

20. $f(x, y) = \begin{cases} 2 & \text{if } x \neq y \\ 0 & \text{if } x = y \end{cases}$

In Exercises 21 through 26, draw a sketch of a contour map of the function f showing the level curves of f at the given numbers.

21. The function of Exercise 15 at 36, 25, 16, 9, 4, 1, and 0.

22. The function of Exercise 16 at 5, 4, 3, 2, 1, and 0.

23. The function of Exercise 17 at 8, 4, 0, -4, and -8.

24. The function of Exercise 18 at 10, 8, 6, 5, and 0.

25. The function f for which $f(x, y) = \frac{1}{2}(x^2 + y^2)$ at 8, 6, 4, 2, and 0.

26. The function f for which $f(x, y) = (x - 3)/(y + 2)$ at 4, 2, 1, $\frac{1}{2}$, $\frac{1}{4}$, 0, $-\frac{1}{4}$, $-\frac{1}{2}$, -1, -2, and -4.

In Exercises 27 and 28, a function f and a function g are defined. Find $h(x, y)$ if $h = f \circ g$, and also find the domain of h.

27. $f(t) = \sin^{-1} t$; $g(x, y) = \sqrt{1 - x^2 - y^2}$

28. $f(t) = \tan^{-1} t$; $g(x, y) = \sqrt{x^2 - y^2}$

29. Given $f(x, y) = x - y$, $g(t) = \sqrt{t}$, $h(s) = s^2$. Find (a) $(g \circ f)(5, 1)$; (b) $f(h(3), g(9))$; (c) $f(g(x), h(y))$; (d) $g((h \circ f)(x, y))$; (e) $(g \circ h)(f(x, y))$.

30. Given $f(x, y) = x/y^2$, $g(x) = x^2$, $h(x) = \sqrt{x}$. Find (a) $(h \circ f)(2, 1)$; (b) $f(g(2), h(4))$; (c) $f(g(\sqrt{x}), h(x^2))$; (d) $h((g \circ f)(x, y))$; (e) $(h \circ g)(f(x, y))$.

31. The electric potential at a point (x, y) of the xy plane is V volts and $V = 4/\sqrt{9 - x^2 - y^2}$. Draw the equipotential curves for $V = 16, 12, 8, 4, 1, \frac{1}{2}$, and $\frac{1}{4}$.

32. The temperature at a point (x, y) of a flat metal plate is t degrees and $t = 4x^2 + 2y^2$. Draw the isothermals for $t = 12, 8, 4, 1$, and 0.

33. For the production of a certain commodity, if x is the number of machines used and y is the number of man-hours, the number of units of the commodity produced is $f(x, y)$ and $f(x, y) = 6xy$. Such a function f is called a production function and the level curves of f are called constant product curves. Draw the constant product curves for this function f at 30, 24, 18, 12, 6, and 0.

In Exercises 34 and 35, draw sketches of the level surfaces of the function f at the given numbers.

34. $f(x, y, z) = x^2 + y^2 + z^2$ at 9, 4, 1, and 0.

35. $f(x, y, z) = x^2 + y^2 - 4z$ at 8, 4, 0, -4, and -8.

19.2 LIMITS OF FUNCTIONS OF MORE THAN ONE VARIABLE

In R^1 the distance between two points is the absolute value of the difference of two real numbers. That is, $|x - a|$ is the distance between the points x and a. In R^2 the distance between the two points $P(x, y)$ and $P_0(x_0, y_0)$ is given by $\sqrt{(x - x_0)^2 + (y - y_0)^2}$. In R^3 the distance between the two points $P(x, y, z)$ and $P_0(x_0, y_0, z_0)$ is given by

$$\sqrt{(x - x_0)^2 + (y - y_0)^2 + (z - z_0)^2}$$

In R^n we define the distance between two points analogously as follows.

19.2.1 Definition If $P(x_1, x_2, \ldots, x_n)$ and $A(a_1, a_2, \ldots, a_n)$ are two points in R^n, then the distance between P and A, denoted by $\|P - A\|$, is given by

$$\|P - A\| = \sqrt{(x_1 - a_1)^2 + (x_2 - a_2)^2 + \cdots + (x_n - a_n)^2} \tag{1}$$

If in R^1 we take $P = x$ and $A = a$, (1) becomes

$$\|x - a\| = \sqrt{(x - a)^2} = |x - a| \tag{2}$$

If in R^2 we take $P = (x, y)$ and $A = (x_0, y_0)$, (1) becomes

$$\|(x, y) - (x_0, y_0)\| = \sqrt{(x - x_0)^2 + (y - y_0)^2} \tag{3}$$

And, if in R^3 we take $P = (x, y, z)$ and $A = (x_0, y_0, z_0)$, (1) becomes

$$\|(x, y, z) - (x_0, y_0, z_0)\| = \sqrt{(x - x_0)^2 + (y - y_0)^2 + (z - z_0)^2} \tag{4}$$

$\|P - A\|$ is read as "the distance between P and A." It is a nonnegative number.

19.2.2 Definition If A is a point in R^n and r is a positive number, then the *open ball* $B(A; r)$ is defined to be the set of all points P in R^n such that $\|P - A\| < r$.

19.2.3 Definition If A is a point in R^n and r is a positive number, then the *closed ball* $B[A; r]$ is defined to be the set of all points P in R^n such that $\|P - A\| \leq r$.

To illustrate these definitions, we show what they mean in R^1, R^2, and R^3. First of all, if a is a point in R^1, then the open ball $B(a; r)$ is the set of all points x in R^1 such that

$$|x - a| < r \tag{5}$$

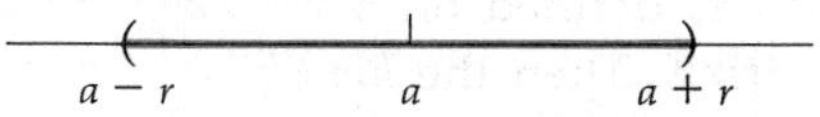

The set of all points x satisfying (5) is the set of all points in the open interval $(a - r, a + r)$; so the open ball $B(a; r)$ in R^1 (see Fig. 19.2.1) is simply an open interval having its midpoint at a and its endpoints at

open ball $B(a; r)$ in R_1

Figure 19.2.1

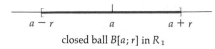

closed ball $B[a;r]$ in R_1

Figure 19.2.2

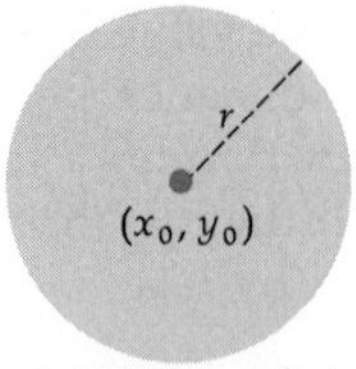

open ball $B((x_0, y_0); r)$ in R_2

Figure 19.2.3

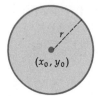

closed ball $B[(x_0, y_0); r]$ in R_2

Figure 19.2.4

$a - r$ and $a + r$. The closed ball $B[a; r]$ in R^1 (Fig. 19.2.2) is the closed interval $[a - r, a + r]$.

If (x_0, y_0) is a point in R^2, then the open ball $B((x_0, y_0); r)$ is the set of all points (x, y) in R^2 such that

$$\|(x, y) - (x_0, y_0)\| < r \tag{6}$$

From (3) we see that (6) is equivalent to

$$\sqrt{(x - x_0)^2 + (y - y_0)^2} < r$$

So the open ball $B((x_0, y_0); r)$ in R^2 (Fig. 19.2.3) consists of all points in the interior region bounded by the circle having its center at (x_0, y_0) and radius r. An open ball in R^2 is sometimes called an *open disk*. The closed ball, or closed disk, $B[(x_0, y_0); r]$ in R^2 (Fig. 19.2.4) is the set of all points in the open ball $B((x_0, y_0); r)$ and on the circle having its center at (x_0, y_0) and radius r.

If (x_0, y_0, z_0) is a point in R^3, then the open ball $B((x_0, y_0, z_0); r)$ is the set of all points (x, y, z) in R^3 such that

$$\|(x, y, z) - (x_0, y_0, z_0)\| < r \tag{7}$$

From (4) and (7) we see that the open ball $B((x_0, y_0, z_0); r)$ in R^3 (Fig. 19.2.5) consists of all points in the interior region bounded by the sphere having its center at P_0 and radius r. Similarly, the closed ball $B[(x_0, y_0, z_0); r]$ in R^3 (Fig. 19.2.6) consists of all points in the open ball $B((x_0, y_0, z_0); r)$ and on the sphere having its center at (x_0, y_0, z_0) and radius r. We are now in a position to define what is meant by the limit of a function of n variables.

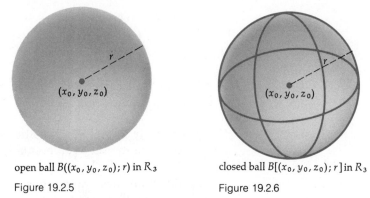

open ball $B((x_0, y_0, z_0); r)$ in R_3

Figure 19.2.5

closed ball $B[(x_0, y_0, z_0); r]$ in R_3

Figure 19.2.6

19.2.4 Definition   Let f be a function of n variables which is defined on some open ball $B(A; r)$, except possibly at the point A itself. Then the *limit of $f(P)$ as P approaches A is L*, written as

$$\lim_{P \to A} f(P) = L \tag{8}$$

if for any $\epsilon > 0$, however small, there exists a $\delta > 0$ such that

$$|f(P) - L| < \epsilon \quad \text{whenever} \quad 0 < \|P - A\| < \delta \tag{9}$$

If f is a function of one variable and if in the above definition we take $A = a$ in R^1 and $P = x$, then (8) becomes

$$\lim_{x \to a} f(x) = L$$

and (9) becomes

$$|f(x) - L| < \epsilon \quad \text{whenever} \quad 0 < |x - a| < \delta$$

So we see that the definition (2.1.1) of the limit of a function of one variable is a special case of Definition 19.2.4.

We now state the definition of the limit of a function of two variables. It is the special case of Definition 19.2.4, where A is the point (x_0, y_0) and P is the point (x, y).

19.2.5 Definition   Let f be a function of two variables which is defined on some open disk $B((x_0, y_0); r)$, except possibly at the point (x_0, y_0) itself. Then

$$\lim_{(x,y) \to (x_0, y_0)} f(x, y) = L$$

if for any $\epsilon > 0$, however small, there exists a $\delta > 0$ such that

$$|f(x, y) - L| < \epsilon \quad \text{whenever} \quad 0 < \sqrt{(x - x_0)^2 + (y - y_0)^2} < \delta \tag{10}$$

In words, Definition 19.2.5 states that the function values $f(x, y)$ approach a limit L as the point (x, y) approaches the point (x_0, y_0) if the absolute value of the difference between $f(x, y)$ and L can be made arbitrarily small by taking the point (x, y) sufficiently close to (x_0, y_0) but not equal to (x_0, y_0). Note that in Definition 19.2.5 nothing is said about the function value at the point (x_0, y_0); that is, it is not necessary that the function be defined at (x_0, y_0) in order for $\lim_{(x,y) \to (x_0, y_0)} f(x, y)$ to exist.

A geometric interpretation of Definition 19.2.5 is illustrated in Fig. 19.2.7. The portion above the open disk $B((x_0, y_0); r)$ of the surface having equation $z = f(x, y)$ is shown. We see that $f(x, y)$ on the z axis will lie between $L - \epsilon$ and $L + \epsilon$ whenever the point (x, y) in the xy plane is in the open disk $B((x_0, y_0); \delta)$. Another way of stating this is that $f(x, y)$ on the z axis can be restricted to lie between $L - \epsilon$ and $L + \epsilon$ by restricting the point (x, y) in the xy plane to be in the open disk $B((x_0, y_0); \delta)$.

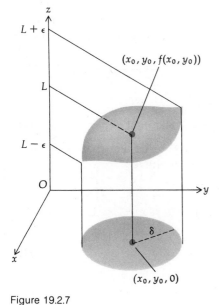

Figure 19.2.7

● ILLUSTRATION 1: We apply Definition 19.2.5 to prove that

$$\lim_{(x,y) \to (1,3)} (2x + 3y) = 11$$

We wish to show that for any $\epsilon > 0$ there exists a $\delta > 0$ such that

$$|(2x + 3y) - 11| < \epsilon \quad \text{whenever} \quad 0 < \sqrt{(x-1)^2 + (y-3)^2} < \delta$$

Applying the triangle inequality, we get

$$|2x + 3y - 11| = |2x - 2 + 3y - 9| \leq 2|x - 1| + 3|y - 3|$$

Because

$$|x - 1| \leq \sqrt{(x-1)^2 + (y-3)^2} \quad \text{and} \quad |y - 3| \leq \sqrt{(x-1)^2 + (y-3)^2}$$

we can conclude that

$$2|x - 1| + 3|y - 3| < 2\delta + 3\delta$$

whenever

$$0 < \sqrt{(x-1)^2 + (y-3)^2} < \delta$$

So if we take $\delta = \frac{1}{5}\epsilon$, we have

$$|2x + 3y - 11| \leq 2|x - 1| + 3|y - 3| < 5\delta = \epsilon$$

whenever

$$0 < \sqrt{(x-1)^2 + (y-3)^2} < \delta$$

This proves that $\lim\limits_{(x,y) \to (1,3)} (2x + 3y) = 11$.   •

EXAMPLE 1: Prove that

$$\lim\limits_{(x,y) \to (1,2)} (3x^2 + y) = 5$$

by applying Definition 19.2.5.

SOLUTION: We wish to show that for any $\epsilon > 0$ there exists a $\delta > 0$ such that

$$|(3x^2 + y) - 5| < \epsilon \quad \text{whenever} \quad 0 < \sqrt{(x-1)^2 + (y-2)^2} < \delta$$

Applying the triangle inequality, we get

$$|3x^2 + y - 5| = |3x^2 - 3 + y - 2| \leq 3|x - 1||x + 1| + |y - 2| \qquad (11)$$

If we require the δ, for which we are looking, to be less than or equal to 1, then $|x - 1| < \delta \leq 1$ and $|y - 2| < \delta \leq 1$ whenever

$$0 < \sqrt{(x-1)^2 + (y-2)^2} < \delta \leq 1$$

Furthermore, whenever $|x - 1| < 1$, then $-1 < x - 1 < 1$, and so $1 < x + 1 < 3$. Hence,

$$3|x - 1||x + 1| + |y - 2| < 3 \cdot \delta \cdot 3 + \delta = 10\delta \qquad (12)$$

whenever

$$0 < \sqrt{(x-1)^2 + (y-2)^2} < \delta \leq 1$$

So if for any $\epsilon > 0$ we take $\delta = \min(1, \frac{1}{10}\epsilon)$, then we have from (11) and (12)

$$|3x^2 + y - 5| < 10\delta \leq \epsilon \quad \text{whenever} \quad 0 < \sqrt{(x-1)^2 + (y-2)^2} < \delta$$

This proves that $\lim\limits_{(x,y) \to (1,2)} (3x^2 + y) = 5$.

We now introduce the concept of an "accumulation point," which we need in order to continue the discussion of limits of functions of two variables.

19.2.6 Definition   A point P_0 is said to be an *accumulation point* of a set S of points in R^n if every open ball $B(P_0; r)$ contains infinitely many points of S.

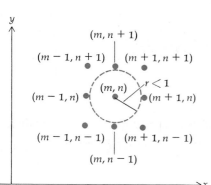

Figure 19.2.8

• ILLUSTRATION 2: If S is the set of all points in R^2 on the positive side of the x axis, the origin will be an accumulation point of S because no matter how small we take the value of r, every open disk having its center at the origin and radius r will contain infinitely many points of S. This is an example of a set having an accumulation point for which the accumulation point is not a point of the set. Any point of this set S also will be an accumulation point of S.   •

• ILLUSTRATION 3: If S is the set of all points in R^2 for which the cartesian coordinates are positive integers, then this set has no accumulation point. This can be seen by considering the point (m, n), where m and n are positive integers. Then an open disk having its center at (m, n) and radius less than 1 will contain no points of S other than (m, n); therefore, Definition 19.2.6 will not be satisfied (see Fig. 19.2.8).   •

We now consider the limit of a function of two variables as a point (x, y) approaches a point (x_0, y_0), where (x, y) is restricted to a specific set of points.

19.2.7 Definition   Let f be a function defined on a set of points S in R^2, and let (x_0, y_0) be an accumulation point of S. Then the *limit of $f(x, y)$ as (x, y) approaches (x_0, y_0) in S is L*, written as

$$\lim_{\substack{(x,y)\to(x_0,y_0)\\(P \text{ in } S)}} f(x, y) = L \tag{13}$$

if for any $\epsilon > 0$, however small, there exists a $\delta > 0$ such that

$$|f(x, y) - L| < \epsilon \quad \text{whenever} \quad 0 < \|(x, y) - (x_0, y_0)\| < \delta$$

and (x, y) is in S.

A special case of (13) occurs when S is a set of points on a curve containing (x_0, y_0). In such cases the limit in (13) becomes the limit of a function of one variable. For example, consider $\lim_{(x,y)\to(0,0)} f(x, y)$. Then if S_1 is the set of all points on the positive side of the x axis, we have

$$\lim_{\substack{(x,y)\to(0,0)\\(P \text{ in } S_1)}} f(x, y) = \lim_{x\to 0^+} f(x, 0)$$

If S_2 is the set of all points on the negative side of the y axis,

$$\lim_{\substack{(x,y)\to(0,0)\\(P\text{ in }S_2)}} f(x,y) = \lim_{y\to 0^-} f(0,y)$$

If S_3 is the set of all points on the x axis,

$$\lim_{\substack{(x,y)\to(0,0)\\(P\text{ in }S_3)}} f(x,y) = \lim_{x\to 0} f(x,0)$$

If S_4 is the set of all points on the parabola $y = x^2$,

$$\lim_{\substack{(x,y)\to(0,0)\\(P\text{ in }S_4)}} f(x,y) = \lim_{x\to 0} f(x,x^2)$$

19.2.8 Theorem   Suppose that the function f is defined for all points on an open disk having its center at (x_0, y_0), except possibly at (x_0, y_0) itself, and

$$\lim_{(x,y)\to(x_0,y_0)} f(x,y) = L$$

Then if S is any set of points in R^2 having (x_0, y_0) as an accumulation point,

$$\lim_{\substack{(x,y)\to(x_0,y_0)\\(P\text{ in }S)}} f(x,y)$$

exists and always has the value L.

PROOF: Because $\lim_{(x,y)\to(x_0,y_0)} f(x,y) = L$, then by Definition 19.2.5, for any $\epsilon > 0$ there exists a $\delta > 0$ such that

$$|f(x,y) - L| < \epsilon \quad \text{whenever} \quad 0 < \|(x,y) - (x_0, y_0)\| < \delta$$

The above will be true if we further restrict (x,y) by the requirement that (x,y) be in a set S, where S is any set of points having (x_0, y_0) as an accumulation point. Therefore, by Definition 19.2.7,

$$\lim_{\substack{(x,y)\to(x_0,y_0)\\(P\text{ in }S)}} f(x,y) = L$$

and L does not depend on the set S through which (x,y) is approaching (x_0, y_0). This proves the theorem.   ∎

The following is an immediate consequence of Theorem 19.2.8.

19.2.9 Theorem   If the function f has different limits as (x,y) approaches (x_0, y_0) through two distinct sets of points having (x_0, y_0) as an accumulation point, then $\lim_{(x,y)\to(x_0,y_0)} f(x,y)$ does not exist.

PROOF: Let S_1 and S_2 be two distinct sets of points in R^2 having (x_0, y_0)

as an accumulation point and let

$$\lim_{\substack{(x,y)\to(x_0,y_0)\\(P \text{ in } S_1)}} f(x, y) = L_1 \quad \text{and} \quad \lim_{\substack{(x,y)\to(x_0,y_0)\\(P \text{ in } S_2)}} f(x, y) = L_2$$

Now assume that $\lim\limits_{(x,y)\to(x_0,y_0)} f(x, y)$ exists. Then by Theorem 19.2.8 L_1 must equal L_2, but by hypothesis $L_1 \neq L_2$, and so we have a contradiction. Therefore, $\lim\limits_{(x,y)\to(x_0,y_0)} f(x, y)$ does not exist.   ■

EXAMPLE 2: Given

$$f(x, y) = \frac{xy}{x^2 + y^2}$$

find $\lim\limits_{(x,y)\to(0,0)} f(x, y)$ if it exists.

SOLUTION: Let S_1 be the set of all points on the x axis. Then

$$\lim_{\substack{(x,y)\to(0,0)\\(P \text{ in } S_1)}} f(x, y) = \lim_{x\to 0} f(x, 0) = \lim_{x\to 0} \frac{0}{x^2 + 0} = 0$$

Let S_2 be the set of all points on the line $y = x$. Then

$$\lim_{\substack{(x,y)\to(0,0)\\(P \text{ in } S_2)}} f(x, y) = \lim_{x\to 0} \frac{x^2}{x^2 + x^2} = \lim_{x\to 0} \frac{1}{2} = \frac{1}{2}$$

Because

$$\lim_{\substack{(x,y)\to(0,0)\\(P \text{ in } S_1)}} f(x, y) \neq \lim_{\substack{(x,y)\to(0,0)\\(P \text{ in } S_2)}} f(x, y)$$

it follows from Theorem 19.2.9 that $\lim\limits_{(x,y)\to(0,0)} f(x, y)$ does not exist.

In the solution of Example 2, instead of taking S_1 to be the set of all the points on the x axis, we could just as well have restricted the points of S_1 to be on the positive side of the x axis because the origin is an accumulation point of this set.

EXAMPLE 3: Given

$$f(x, y) = \frac{3x^2 y}{x^2 + y^2}$$

find $\lim\limits_{(x,y)\to(0,0)} f(x, y)$ if it exists.

SOLUTION: Let S_1 be the set of all points on the x axis. Then

$$\lim_{\substack{(x,y)\to(0,0)\\(P \text{ in } S_1)}} f(x, y) = \lim_{x\to 0} \frac{0}{x^2 + 0} = 0$$

Let S_2 be the set of all points on any line through the origin; that is, for any point (x, y) in S_2, $y = mx$.

$$\lim_{\substack{(x,y)\to(0,0)\\(P \text{ in } S_2)}} f(x, y) = \lim_{x\to 0} \frac{3x^2(mx)}{x^2 + m^2 x^2} = \lim_{x\to 0} \frac{3mx}{1 + m^2} = 0$$

Even though we obtain the same limit of 0, if (x, y) approaches $(0, 0)$ through a set of points on any line through the origin, we cannot conclude that $\lim\limits_{(x,y)\to(0,0)} f(x, y)$ exists and is zero (see Example 4). However, let us attempt to prove that $\lim\limits_{(x,y)\to(0,0)} f(x, y) = 0$. From Definition 19.2.5, if we can show that for any $\epsilon > 0$ there exists a $\delta > 0$ such that

$$\left|\frac{3x^2y}{x^2+y^2}\right| < \epsilon \quad \text{whenever} \quad 0 < \sqrt{x^2+y^2} < \delta \tag{14}$$

then we have proved that $\lim\limits_{(x,y)\to(0,0)} f(x, y) = 0$.

Because $x^2 \le x^2 + y^2$ and $|y| \le \sqrt{x^2+y^2}$, we have

$$\left|\frac{3x^2y}{x^2+y^2}\right| = \frac{3x^2|y|}{x^2+y^2} \le \frac{3(x^2+y^2)\sqrt{x^2+y^2}}{x^2+y^2} = 3\sqrt{x^2+y^2}$$

So if $\delta = \tfrac{1}{3}\epsilon$, we can conclude that

$$\left|\frac{3x^2y}{x^2+y^2}\right| < \epsilon \quad \text{whenever} \quad 0 < \sqrt{x^2+y^2} < \delta$$

which is (14). Hence, we have proved that $\lim\limits_{(x,y)\to(0,0)} f(x, y) = 0$.

EXAMPLE 4:   Given

$$f(x, y) = \frac{x^2y}{x^4+y^2}$$

find $\lim\limits_{(x,y)\to(0,0)} f(x, y)$ if it exists.

SOLUTION: Let S_1 be the set of all points on either the x axis or the y axis. So if (x, y) is in S_1, $xy = 0$. Therefore,

$$\lim_{\substack{(x,y)\to(0,0)\\(P \text{ in } S_1)}} f(x, y) = 0$$

Let S_2 be the set of all points on any line through the origin; so if (x, y) is a point in S_2, $y = mx$. We have, then,

$$\lim_{\substack{(x,y)\to(0,0)\\(P \text{ in } S_2)}} f(x, y) = \lim_{x\to 0} \frac{mx^3}{x^4+m^2x^2} = \lim_{x\to 0} \frac{mx}{x^2+m^2} = 0$$

Let S_3 be the set of all points on the parabola $y = x^2$. Then

$$\lim_{\substack{(x,y)\to(0,0)\\(P \text{ in } S_3)}} f(x, y) = \lim_{x\to 0} \frac{x^4}{x^4+x^4} = \lim_{x\to 0} \frac{1}{2} = \frac{1}{2}$$

Because

$$\lim_{\substack{(x,y)\to(0,0)\\(P \text{ in } S_3)}} f(x, y) \ne \lim_{\substack{(x,y)\to(0,0)\\(P \text{ in } S_1)}} f(x, y)$$

it follows that $\lim\limits_{(x,y)\to(0,0)} f(x, y)$ does not exist.

EXAMPLE 5:   Given

$$f(x, y) = \begin{cases} (x+y)\sin\dfrac{1}{x} & \text{if } x \ne 0 \\ 0 & \text{if } x = 0 \end{cases}$$

find $\lim\limits_{(x,y)\to(0,0)} f(x, y)$ if it exists.

SOLUTION: Let S_1 be the set of all points on the y axis. Then

$$\lim_{\substack{(x,y)\to(0,0)\\(P \text{ in } S_1)}} f(x, y) = \lim_{x\to 0} 0 = 0$$

Let S_2 be the set of all points on any line through the origin except points on the y axis; that is, if (x, y) is a point in S_2, $y = kx$, where $x \ne 0$. Then

$$\lim_{\substack{(x,y)\to(0,0) \\ (P \text{ in } S_2)}} f(x, y) = \lim_{x\to 0} (x + kx) \sin\frac{1}{x}$$

To find the above limit we make use of the fact that $\lim_{x\to 0} (x + kx) = 0$. Because $\lim_{x\to 0} \sin(1/x)$ does not exist, we cannot apply the theorem about the limit of a product. However, because $\lim_{x\to 0} (x + kx) = 0$, it follows that for any $\epsilon > 0$ there exists a $\delta > 0$ such that

$$|x + kx| < \epsilon \quad \text{whenever} \quad 0 < |x| < \delta$$

The δ is, in fact, $\epsilon/|1 + k|$. But

$$\left|(x + kx) \sin\frac{1}{x}\right| = |x + kx| \left|\sin\frac{1}{x}\right| \le |x + kx| \cdot 1$$

Hence, for any $\epsilon > 0$ there exists a $\delta > 0$ such that

$$\left|(x + kx) \sin\frac{1}{x}\right| < \epsilon \quad \text{whenever} \quad 0 < |x| < \delta$$

Thus,

$$\lim_{\substack{(x,y)\to(0,0) \\ (P \text{ in } S_2)}} f(x, y) = 0 \tag{15}$$

Let S_3 be the set of all points (x, y) for which $y = kx^n$, where n is any positive integer and $x \ne 0$. Then by an argument similar to that used for proving (15) it follows that

$$\lim_{\substack{(x,y)\to(0,0) \\ (P \text{ in } S_3)}} f(x, y) = \lim_{x\to 0} (x + kx^n) \sin\frac{1}{x} = 0$$

We now attempt to find a $\delta > 0$ for any $\epsilon > 0$ such that

$$|f(x, y) - 0| < \epsilon \quad \text{whenever} \quad 0 < \|(x, y) - (0, 0)\| < \delta \tag{16}$$

which will prove that $\lim_{(x,y)\to(0,0)} f(x, y) = 0$. We distinguish two cases: $x = 0$ and $x \ne 0$.

Case 1: If $x = 0$, $|f(x, y) - 0| = |0 - 0| = 0$, which is less than ϵ for any $\delta > 0$.

Case 2: If $x \ne 0$, $|f(x, y) - 0| = |(x + y) \sin(1/x)|$.

$$\left|(x + y) \sin\frac{1}{x}\right| = |x + y| \left|\sin\frac{1}{x}\right|$$
$$\le |x + y|(1)$$
$$\le |x| + |y|$$
$$\le \sqrt{x^2 + y^2} + \sqrt{x^2 + y^2}$$

$$= 2\sqrt{x^2 + y^2}$$

Then

$$\left| (x + y) \sin \frac{1}{x} \right| < 2 \cdot \tfrac{1}{2}\epsilon \quad \text{whenever} \quad 0 < \sqrt{x^2 + y^2} < \tfrac{1}{2}\epsilon$$

So take $\delta = \tfrac{1}{2}\epsilon$.

Therefore, in both cases we have found a $\delta > 0$ for any $\epsilon > 0$ such that (16) holds, and this proves that $\lim\limits_{(x,y)\to(0,0)} f(x, y) = 0$.

The limit theorems of Chapter 2 and their proofs, with minor modifications, apply to functions of several variables. We use these theorems without restating them and their proofs.

● ILLUSTRATION 4: By applying the limit theorems on sums and products, we have

$$\lim_{(x,y)\to(-2,1)} (x^3 + 2x^2y - y^2 + 2) = (-2)^3 + 2(-2)^2(1) - (1)^2 + 2 = 1 \quad ●$$

Analogous to Theorem 2.6.5 for functions of a single variable is the following theorem regarding the limit of a composite function of two variables.

19.2.10 Theorem If g is a function of two variables and $\lim\limits_{(x,y)\to(x_0,y_0)} g(x, y) = b$, and f is a function of a single variable continuous at b, then

$$\lim_{(x,y)\to(x_0,y_0)} (f \circ g)(x, y) = f(b)$$

or, equivalently,

$$\lim_{(x,y)\to(x_0,y_0)} f(g(x, y)) = f\left(\lim_{(x,y)\to(x_0,y_0)} g(x, y) \right)$$

The proof of this theorem is similar to the proof of Theorem 2.6.5 and is left as an exercise (see Exercise 20).

EXAMPLE 6: Use Theorem 19.2.10 to find $\lim\limits_{(x,y)\to(2,1)} \ln(xy - 1)$.

SOLUTION: Let g be the function such that $g(x, y) = xy - 1$, and f be the function such that $f(t) = \ln t$.

$$\lim_{(x,y)\to(2,1)} (xy - 1) = 1$$

and because f is continuous at 1, we use Theorem 19.2.10 and get

$$\lim_{(x,y)\to(2,1)} \ln(xy - 1) = \ln\left(\lim_{(x,y)\to(2,1)} (xy - 1) \right)$$

$$= \ln 1$$

$$= 0$$

Exercises 19.2

In Exercises 1 through 6, establish the limit by finding a $\delta > 0$ for any $\epsilon > 0$ so that Definition 19.2.5 holds.

1. $\lim\limits_{(x,y)\to(3,2)} (3x - 4y) = 1$

2. $\lim\limits_{(x,y)\to(2,4)} (5x - 3y) = -2$

3. $\lim\limits_{(x,y)\to(1,1)} (x^2 + y^2) = 2$

4. $\lim\limits_{(x,y)\to(2,3)} (2x^2 - y^2) = -1$

5. $\lim\limits_{(x,y)\to(2,4)} (x^2 + 2x - y) = 4$

6. $\lim\limits_{(x,y)\to(3,-1)} (x^2 + y^2 - 4x + 2y) = -4$

In Exercises 7 through 12, prove that for the given function f, $\lim\limits_{(x,y)\to(0,0)} f(x, y)$ does not exist.

7. $f(x, y) = \dfrac{x^2 - y^2}{x^2 + y^2}$

8. $f(x, y) = \dfrac{x^2}{x^2 + y^2}$

9. $f(x, y) = \dfrac{x^3 + y^3}{x^2 + y}$

10. $f(x, y) = \dfrac{x^4 + 3x^2y^2 + 2xy^3}{(x^2 + y^2)^2}$

11. $f(x, y) = \dfrac{x^4 y^4}{(x^2 + y^4)^3}$

12. $f(x, y) = \dfrac{x^2 y^2}{x^3 + y^3}$

In Exercises 13 through 16, prove that $\lim\limits_{(x,y)\to(0,0)} f(x, y)$ exists.

13. $f(x, y) = \dfrac{xy}{\sqrt{x^2 + y^2}}$

14. $f(x, y) = \dfrac{x^3 + y^3}{x^2 + y^2}$

15. $f(x, y) = \begin{cases} (x + y) \sin \dfrac{1}{x} \sin \dfrac{1}{y} & \text{if } x \neq 0 \text{ and } y \neq 0 \\ 0 & \text{if either } x = 0 \text{ or } y = 0 \end{cases}$

16. $f(x, y) = \begin{cases} \dfrac{1}{x} \sin (xy) & \text{if } x \neq 0 \\ y & \text{if } x = 0 \end{cases}$

In Exercises 17 through 19, evaluate the given limit by the use of limit theorems.

17. $\lim\limits_{(x,y)\to(2,3)} (3x^2 + xy - 2y^2)$

18. $\lim\limits_{(x,y)\to(-2,4)} y \sqrt[3]{x^3 + 2y}$

19. $\lim\limits_{(x,y)\to(0,0)} \dfrac{e^x + e^y}{\cos x + \sin y}$

20. Prove Theorem 19.2.10

In Exercises 21 through 23, show the application of Theorem 19.2.10 to find the indicated limit.

21. $\lim\limits_{(x,y)\to(2,2)} \tan^{-1} \dfrac{y}{x}$

22. $\lim\limits_{(x,y)\to(-2,3)} [\![5x + \tfrac{1}{2} y^2]\!]$

23. $\lim\limits_{(x,y)\to(4,2)} \sqrt{\dfrac{1}{3x - 4y}}$

In Exercises 24 through 29, determine if the indicated limit exists.

24. $\lim\limits_{(x,y)\to(0,0)} \dfrac{x^2 y^2}{x^4 + y^4}$

25. $\lim\limits_{(x,y)\to(0,0)} \dfrac{x^2 y^2}{x^2 + y^2}$

26. $\lim\limits_{(x,y)\to(2,-2)} \dfrac{\sin(x + y)}{x + y}$

27. $\lim\limits_{(x,y)\to(0,0)} \dfrac{x^2 + y}{x^2 + y^2}$

28. $f(x, y) = \begin{cases} \dfrac{xy}{x^2 + y^2} + y \sin \dfrac{1}{x} & \text{if } x \neq 0 \\ 0 & \text{if } x = 0 \end{cases}$ $\lim\limits_{(x,y)\to(0,0)} f(x, y)$

29. $f(x, y) = \begin{cases} x \sin \dfrac{1}{y} + y \sin \dfrac{1}{x} & \text{if } x \neq 0 \text{ and } y \neq 0 \\ 0 & \text{if either } x = 0 \text{ or } y = 0 \end{cases}$ $\lim\limits_{(x,y)\to(0,0)} f(x, y)$

30. (a) Give a definition, similar to Definition 19.2.5, of the limit of a function of three variables as a point (x, y, z) approaches a point (x_0, y_0, z_0). (b) Give a definition, similar to Definition 19.2.7, of the limit of a function of three variables as a point (x, y, z) approaches a point (x_0, y_0, z_0) in a specific set of points S in R^3.

31. (a) State and prove a theorem similar to Theorem 19.2.8 for a function f of three variables. (b) State and prove a theorem similar to Theorem 19.2.9 for a function f of three variables.

In Exercises 32 through 36, use the definitions and theorems of Exercises 30 and 31 to prove that $\lim\limits_{(x,y,z)\to(0,0,0)} f(x,y,z)$ does not exist.

32. $f(x, y, z) = \dfrac{x^4 + yx^3 + z^2x^2}{x^4 + y^4 + z^4}$

33. $f(x, y, z) = \dfrac{x^2 + y^2 - z^2}{x^2 + y^2 + z^2}$

34. $f(x, y, z) = \dfrac{x^3 + yz^2}{x^4 + y^2 + z^4}$

35. $f(x, y, z) = \dfrac{x^2y^2z^2}{x^6 + y^6 + z^6}$

In Exercises 36 and 37, use the definition in Exercise 30(a) to prove that $\lim\limits_{(x,y,z)\to(0,0,0)} f(x,y,z)$ exists.

36. $f(x, y, z) = \dfrac{y^3 + xz^2}{x^2 + y^2 + z^2}$

37. $f(x, y, z) = \begin{cases} (x + y + z)\sin\dfrac{1}{x}\sin\dfrac{1}{y} & \text{if } x \neq 0 \text{ and } y \neq 0 \\ 0 & \text{if either } x = 0 \text{ or } y = 0 \end{cases}$

19.3 CONTINUITY OF FUNCTIONS OF MORE THAN ONE VARIABLE

We define continuity of a function of n variables at a point in R^n.

19.3.1 Definition   Suppose that f is a function of n variables and A is a point in R^n. Then f is said to be *continuous* at the point A if and only if the following three conditions are satisfied:

(i) $f(A)$ exists;
(ii) $\lim\limits_{P \to A} f(P)$ exists;
(iii) $\lim\limits_{P \to A} f(P) = f(A)$.

If one or more of these three conditions fails to hold at the point A, then f is said to be *discontinuous* at A.

Definition 2.5.1 of continuity of a function of one variable at a number a is a special case of Definition 19.3.1.

If f is a function of two variables, A is the point (x_0, y_0), and P is a point (x, y), then Definition 19.3.1 becomes the following.

19.3.2 Definition   The function f of two variables x and y is said to be *continuous* at the point (x_0, y_0) if and only if the following three conditions are satisfied:

(i) $f(x_0, y_0)$ exists;
(ii) $\lim\limits_{(x,y)\to(x_0,y_0)} f(x, y)$ exists;
(iii) $\lim\limits_{(x,y)\to(x_0,y_0)} f(x, y) = f(x_0, y_0)$.

EXAMPLE 1:   Given

$f(x, y) = \begin{cases} \dfrac{3x^2y}{x^2 + y^2} & \text{if } (x, y) \neq (0, 0) \\ 0 & \text{if } (x, y) = (0, 0) \end{cases}$

SOLUTION: We check the three conditions of Definition 19.3.2 at the point $(0, 0)$.

(i) $f(0, 0) = 0$. Therefore, condition (i) holds.

determine if f is continuous at $(0, 0)$.

(ii) $\displaystyle\lim_{(x,y)\to(0,0)} f(x, y) = \lim_{(x,y)\to(0,0)} \frac{3x^2y}{x^2 + y^2} = 0$, which was proved in Example 3, Sec. 19.2.

(iii) $\displaystyle\lim_{(x,y)\to(0,0)} f(x, y) = f(0, 0)$.

So we conclude that f is continuous at $(0, 0)$.

EXAMPLE 2:   Let the function f be defined by

$$f(x, y) = \begin{cases} \dfrac{xy}{x^2 + y^2} & \text{if } (x, y) \neq (0, 0) \\ 0 & \text{if } (x, y) = (0, 0) \end{cases}$$

Determine if f is continuous at $(0, 0)$.

SOLUTION: Checking the conditions of Definition 19.3.2, we have the following.

(i) $f(0, 0) = 0$ and so condition (i) holds.
(ii) When $(x, y) \neq (0, 0)$, $f(x, y) = xy/(x^2 + y^2)$. In Example 2, Sec. 19.2, we showed that $\displaystyle\lim_{(x,y)\to(0,0)} xy/(x^2 + y^2)$ does not exist and so $\displaystyle\lim_{(x,y)\to(0,0)} f(x, y)$ does not exist. Therefore, condition (ii) fails to hold.

We conclude that f is discontinuous at $(0, 0)$.

If a function f of two variables is discontinuous at the point (x_0, y_0) but $\displaystyle\lim_{(x,y)\to(x_0,y_0)} f(x, y)$ exists, then f is said to have a *removable discontinuity* at (x_0, y_0) because if f is redefined at (x_0, y_0) so that $f(x_0, y_0) = \displaystyle\lim_{(x,y)\to(x_0,y_0)} f(x, y)$, then f becomes continuous at (x_0, y_0). If the discontinuity is not removable, it is called an *essential discontinuity*.

● ILLUSTRATION 1: (a) If $g(x, y) = 3x^2y/(x^2 + y^2)$, then g is discontinuous at the origin because $g(0, 0)$ is not defined. However, in Example 3, Sec. 19.2, we showed that $\displaystyle\lim_{(x,y)\to(0,0)} 3x^2y/(x^2 + y^2) = 0$. Therefore, the discontinuity is removable if $g(0, 0)$ is defined to be 0. (Refer to Example 1.)

(b) Let $h(x, y) = xy/(x^2 + y^2)$. Then h is discontinuous at the origin because $h(0, 0)$ is not defined. In Example 2, Sec. 19.2, we showed that $\displaystyle\lim_{(x,y)\to(0,0)} xy/(x^2 + y^2)$ does not exist. Therefore, the discontinuity is essential. (Refer to Example 2.)   ●

The theorems about continuity for functions of a single variable can be extended to functions of two variables.

19.3.3 Theorem   If f and g are two functions which are continuous at the point (x_0, y_0), then

(i) $f + g$ is continuous at (x_0, y_0);
(ii) $f - g$ is continuous at (x_0, y_0);
(iii) fg is continuous at (x_0, y_0);
(iv) f/g is continuous at (x_0, y_0), provided that $g(x_0, y_0) \neq 0$.

The proof of this theorem is analogous to the proof of the corresponding theorem (2.6.1) for functions of one variable, and hence it is omitted.

19.3.4 Theorem A polynomial function of two variables is continuous at every point in R^2.

PROOF: Every polynomial function is the sum of products of the functions defined by $f(x, y) = x$, $g(x, y) = y$, and $h(x, y) = c$, where c is a real number. Because f, g, and h are continuous at every point in R^2, the theorem follows by repeated applications of Theorem 19.3.3, parts (i) and (iii). ∎

19.3.5 Theorem A rational function of two variables is continuous at every point in its domain.

PROOF: A rational function is the quotient of two polynomial functions f and g which are continuous at every point in R^2 by Theorem 19.3.4. If (x_0, y_0) is any point in the domain of f/g, then $g(x_0, y_0) \neq 0$; so by Theorem 19.3.3(iv) f/g is continuous there. ∎

EXAMPLE 3: Let the function f be defined by

$$f(x, y) = \begin{cases} x^2 + y^2 & \text{if } x^2 + y^2 \leq 1 \\ 0 & \text{if } x^2 + y^2 > 1 \end{cases}$$

Discuss the continuity of f. What is the region of continuity of f?

SOLUTION: The function f is defined at all points in R^2. Therefore, condition (i) of Definition 19.3.2 holds for every point (x_0, y_0).

Consider the points (x_0, y_0) if $x_0^2 + y_0^2 \neq 1$. If $x_0^2 + y_0^2 < 1$, then

$$\lim_{(x,y) \to (x_0,y_0)} f(x, y) = \lim_{(x,y) \to (x_0,y_0)} (x^2 + y^2) = x_0^2 + y_0^2 = f(x_0, y_0)$$

If $x_0^2 + y_0^2 > 1$, then

$$\lim_{(x,y) \to (x_0,y_0)} f(x, y) = \lim_{(x,y) \to (x_0,y_0)} 0 = 0 = f(x_0, y_0)$$

Thus, f is continuous at all points (x_0, y_0) for which $x_0^2 + y_0^2 \neq 1$.

To determine the continuity of f at points (x_0, y_0) for which $x_0^2 + y_0^2 = 1$, we determine if $\lim_{(x,y) \to (x_0,y_0)} f(x, y)$ exists and equals 1.

Let S_1 be the set of all points (x, y) such that $x^2 + y^2 \leq 1$. Then

$$\lim_{\substack{(x,y) \to (x_0,y_0) \\ (P \text{ in } S_1)}} f(x, y) = \lim_{\substack{(x,y) \to (x_0,y_0) \\ (P \text{ in } S_1)}} (x^2 + y^2) = x_0^2 + y_0^2 = 1$$

Let S_2 be the set of all points (x, y) such that $x^2 + y^2 > 1$. Then

$$\lim_{\substack{(x,y) \to (x_0,y_0) \\ (P \text{ in } S_2)}} f(x, y) = \lim_{\substack{(x,y) \to (x_0,y_0) \\ (P \text{ in } S_2)}} 0 = 0$$

Because

$$\lim_{\substack{(x,y) \to (x_0,y_0) \\ (P \text{ in } S_1)}} f(x, y) \neq \lim_{\substack{(x,y) \to (x_0,y_0) \\ (P \text{ in } S_2)}} f(x, y)$$

we conclude that $\lim_{(x,y) \to (x_0,y_0)} f(x, y)$ does not exist. Hence, f is discontinuous at all points (x_0, y_0) for which $x_0^2 + y_0^2 = 1$. The region of continuity of f consists of all points in the xy plane except those on the circle $x^2 + y^2 = 1$.

19.3.6 Definition   The function f of n variables is said to be *continuous on an open ball* if it is continuous at every point of the open ball.

As an illustration of the above definition, the function of Example 3 is continuous on every open disk that does not contain a point of the circle $x^2 + y^2 = 1$.

The following theorem states that a continuous function of a continuous function is continuous. It is analogous to Theorem 2.6.6.

19.3.7 Theorem   Suppose that f is a function of a single variable and g is a function of two variables. Suppose further that g is continuous at (x_0, y_0) and f is continuous at $g(x_0, y_0)$. Then the composite function $f \circ g$ is continuous at (x_0, y_0).

The proof of this theorem, which makes use of Theorem 19.2.10, is similar to the proof of Theorem 2.6.6 and is left as an exercise (see Exercise 7).

● ILLUSTRATION 2: Let

$$h(x, y) = \ln(xy - 1)$$

We discuss the continuity of h. If g is the function defined by $g(x, y) = xy - 1$, g is continuous at all points in R^2. The natural logarithmic function is continuous on its entire domain, which is the set of all positive numbers. So if f is the function defined by $f(t) = \ln t$, f is continuous for all $t > 0$. Then the function h is the composite function $f \circ g$ and, by Theorem 19.3.7, is continuous at all points (x, y) in R^2 for which $xy - 1 > 0$ or, equivalently, $xy > 1$. The shaded region of Fig. 19.3.1 is the region of continuity of h.   ●

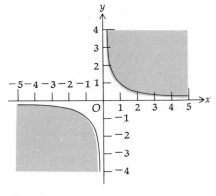

Figure 19.3.1

EXAMPLE 4:   Given that

$$f(x, y) = \frac{y}{\sqrt{x^2 + y^2 - 25}}$$

discuss the continuity of f and draw a sketch showing as a shaded region in R the region of continuity of f.

SOLUTION: This is the same function as the function G of Illustration 4 in Sec. 19.1. We saw there that the domain of this function is the set of all points in the exterior region bounded by the circle $x^2 + y^2 = 25$ and the points on the x axis for which $-5 < x < 5$.

The function f is the quotient of the functions g and h for which $g(x, y) = y$ and $h(x, y) = \sqrt{x^2 + y^2 - 25}$. The function g is a polynomial function and therefore is continuous everywhere. It follows from Theorem 19.3.7 that h is continuous at all points in R^2 for which $x^2 + y^2 > 25$. Therefore, by Theorem 19.3.3(iv) we conclude that f is continuous at all points in the exterior region bounded by the circle $x^2 + y^2 = 25$.

Now consider the points on the x axis for which $-5 < x < 5$, that is, the points $(a, 0)$ where $-5 < a < 5$. If S_1 is the set of points on the line $x = a$, $(a, 0)$ is an accumulation point of S_1, but

$$\lim_{\substack{(x,y) \to (a,0) \\ (P \text{ in } S_1)}} f(x, y) = \lim_{y \to 0} \frac{y}{\sqrt{a^2 + y^2 - 25}}$$

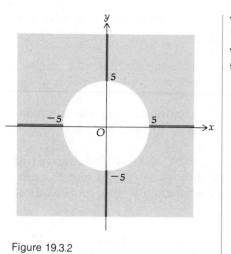

Figure 19.3.2

which does not exist because $y/\sqrt{a^2 + y^2 - 25}$ is not defined if $|y| \leq \sqrt{25 - a^2}$. Therefore, f is discontinuous at the points on the x axis for which $-5 < x < 5$. The shaded region of Fig. 19.3.2 is the region of continuity of f.

Exercises 19.3

In Exercises 1 through 6, discuss the continuity of f.

1. $f(x, y) = \begin{cases} \dfrac{xy}{\sqrt{x^2 + y^2}} & \text{if } (x, y) \neq (0, 0) \\ 0 & \text{if } (x, y) = (0, 0) \end{cases}$ (HINT: See Exercise 13, Exercises 19.2)

2. $f(x, y) = \begin{cases} \dfrac{x^2 y}{x^4 + y^2} & \text{if } (x, y) \neq (0, 0) \\ 0 & \text{if } (x, y) = (0, 0) \end{cases}$ (HINT: See Example 4, Sec. 19.2.)

3. $f(x, y) = \begin{cases} \dfrac{x + y}{x^2 + y^2} & \text{if } (x, y) \neq (0, 0) \\ 0 & \text{if } (x, y) = (0, 0) \end{cases}$

4. $f(x, y) = \begin{cases} \dfrac{x^3 + y^3}{x^2 + y^2} & \text{if } (x, y) \neq (0, 0) \\ 0 & \text{if } (x, y) = (0, 0) \end{cases}$

5. $f(x, y) = \begin{cases} \dfrac{xy}{|x| + |y|} & \text{if } (x, y) \neq (0, 0) \\ 0 & \text{if } (x, y) = (0, 0) \end{cases}$

6. $f(x, y) = \begin{cases} \dfrac{x^2 y^2}{|x^3| + |y^3|} & \text{if } (x, y) \neq (0, 0) \\ 0 & \text{if } (x, y) = (0, 0) \end{cases}$

7. Prove Theorem 19.3.7.

In Exercises 8 through 17, determine the region of continuity of f and draw a sketch showing as a shaded region in R^2 the region of continuity of f.

8. $f(x, y) = \dfrac{y}{\sqrt{x^2 - y^2 - 4}}$

9. $f(x, y) = \dfrac{xy}{\sqrt{16 - x^2 - y^2}}$

10. $f(x, y) = \dfrac{x^2 + y^2}{\sqrt{9 - x^2 - y^2}}$

11. $f(x, y) = \dfrac{x}{\sqrt{4x^2 + 9y^2 - 36}}$

12. $f(x, y) = \ln(x^2 + y^2 - 9) - \ln(1 - x^2 - y^2)$

13. $f(x, y) = x \ln(xy)$

14. $f(x, y) = \sin^{-1}(xy)$

15. $f(x, y) = \tan^{-1}\dfrac{x}{y} + \sec^{-1}(xy)$

16. $f(x, y) = \begin{cases} \dfrac{x^2 - y^2}{x - y} & \text{if } x \neq y \\ x - y & \text{if } x = y \end{cases}$

17. $f(x, y) = \begin{cases} \dfrac{\sin(x + y)}{x + y} & \text{if } x + y \neq 0 \\ 1 & \text{if } x + y = 0 \end{cases}$

In Exercises 18 through 21, prove that the function is discontinuous at the origin. Then determine if the discontinuity is removable or essential. If the discontinuity is removable, define $f(0, 0)$ so that the discontinuity is removed.

18. $f(x, y) = \dfrac{\sqrt{xy}}{x + y}$

19. $f(x, y) = (x + y) \sin \dfrac{x}{y}$

20. $f(x, y) = \dfrac{x^2 y^2}{x^2 + y^2}$

21. $f(x, y) = \dfrac{x^3 y^2}{x^6 + y^4}$

22. (a) Give a definition of continuity at a point for a function of three variables, similar to Definition 19.3.2. (b) State theorems for functions of three variables similar to Theorems 19.3.3 and 19.3.7. (c) Define a polynomial function of three variables and a rational function of three variables.

In Exercises 23 through 26, use the definitions and theorems of Exercise 22 to discuss the continuity of the given function.

23. $f(x, y, z) = \dfrac{xz}{\sqrt{x^2 + y^2 + z^2 - 1}}$

24. $f(x, y, z) = \ln(36 - 4x^2 - y^2 - 9z^2)$

25. $f(x, y, z) = \begin{cases} \dfrac{3xyz}{x^2 + y^2 + z^2} & \text{if } (x, y, z) \neq (0, 0, 0) \\ 0 & \text{if } (x, y, z) = (0, 0, 0) \end{cases}$

26. $f(x, y, z) = \begin{cases} \dfrac{xz - y^2}{x^2 + y^2 + z^2} & \text{if } (x, y, z) \neq (0, 0, 0) \\ 0 & \text{if } (x, y, z) = (0, 0, 0) \end{cases}$

19.4 PARTIAL DERIVATIVES

We now discuss differentiation of real-valued functions of n variables. The discussion is reduced to the one-dimensional case by treating a function of n variables as a function of one variable at a time and holding the others fixed. This leads to the concept of a "partial derivative." We first define the partial derivative of a function of two variables.

19.4.1 Definition Let f be a function of two variables, x and y. The *partial derivative of f with respect to x* is that function, denoted by $D_1 f$, such that its function value at any point (x, y) in the domain of f is given by

$$D_1 f(x, y) = \lim_{\Delta x \to 0} \frac{f(x + \Delta x, y) - f(x, y)}{\Delta x} \tag{1}$$

if this limit exists. Similarly, the *partial derivative of f with respect to y* is that function, denoted by $D_2 f$, such that its function value at any point (x, y) in the domain of f is given by

$$D_2 f(x, y) = \lim_{\Delta y \to 0} \frac{f(x, y + \Delta y) - f(x, y)}{\Delta y} \tag{2}$$

if this limit exists.

The process of finding a partial derivative is called *partial differentiation*.

$D_1 f$ is read as "D sub 1 of f," and this denotes the partial-derivative function. $D_1 f(x, y)$ is read as "D sub 1 of f of x and y," and this denotes the partial-derivative function value at the point (x, y). Other notations for the partial-derivative function $D_1 f$ are f_1, f_x, and $\partial f / \partial x$. Other notations for the partial-derivative function value $D_1 f(x, y)$ are $f_1(x, y)$, $f_x(x, y)$, and $\partial f(x, y) / \partial x$. Similarly, other notations for $D_2 f$ are f_2, f_y, and $\partial f / \partial y$; other notations for $D_2 f(x, y)$ are $f_2(x, y)$, $f_y(x, y)$, and $\partial f(x, y) / \partial y$. If $z = f(x, y)$, we can write $\partial z / \partial x$ for $D_1 f(x, y)$. A partial derivative cannot be thought of as a ratio of ∂z and ∂x because neither of these symbols has a separate meaning. The notation dy/dx can be regarded as the quotient of two differentials when y is a function of the single variable x, but there is not a similar interpretation for $\partial z / \partial x$.

EXAMPLE 1: Given

$$f(x, y) = 3x^2 - 2xy + y^2$$

find $D_1 f(x, y)$ and $D_2 f(x, y)$ by applying Definition 19.4.1.

SOLUTION:

$$D_1 f(x, y) = \lim_{\Delta x \to 0} \frac{f(x + \Delta x, y) - f(x, y)}{\Delta x}$$

$$= \lim_{\Delta x \to 0} \frac{3(x + \Delta x)^2 - 2(x + \Delta x)y + y^2 - (3x^2 - 2xy + y^2)}{\Delta x}$$

$$= \lim_{\Delta x \to 0} \frac{3x^2 + 6x\,\Delta x + 3(\Delta x)^2 - 2xy - 2y\,\Delta x + y^2 - 3x^2 + 2xy - y^2}{\Delta x}$$

$$= \lim_{\Delta x \to 0} \frac{6x\,\Delta x + 3(\Delta x)^2 - 2y\,\Delta x}{\Delta x}$$

$$= \lim_{\Delta x \to 0} (6x + 3\,\Delta x - 2y)$$

$$= 6x - 2y$$

$$D_2 f(x, y) = \lim_{\Delta y \to 0} \frac{f(x, y + \Delta y) - f(x, y)}{\Delta y}$$

$$= \lim_{\Delta y \to 0} \frac{3x^2 - 2x(y + \Delta y) + (y + \Delta y)^2 - (3x^2 - 2xy + y^2)}{\Delta y}$$

$$= \lim_{\Delta y \to 0} \frac{3x^2 - 2xy - 2x\,\Delta y + y^2 + 2y\,\Delta y + (\Delta y)^2 - 3x^2 + 2xy - y^2}{\Delta y}$$

$$= \lim_{\Delta y \to 0} \frac{-2x\,\Delta y + 2y\,\Delta y + (\Delta y)^2}{\Delta y}$$

$$= \lim_{\Delta y \to 0} (-2x + 2y + \Delta y)$$

$$= -2x + 2y$$

If (x_0, y_0) is a particular point in the domain of f, then

$$D_1 f(x_0, y_0) = \lim_{\Delta x \to 0} \frac{f(x_0 + \Delta x, y_0) - f(x_0, y_0)}{\Delta x} \qquad (3)$$

if this limit exists, and

$$D_2f(x_0, y_0) = \lim_{\Delta y \to 0} \frac{f(x_0, y_0 + \Delta y) - f(x_0, y_0)}{\Delta y} \tag{4}$$

if this limit exists.

● ILLUSTRATION 1: We apply formula (3) to find $D_1f(3, -2)$ for the function f of Example 1.

$$D_1f(3, -2) = \lim_{\Delta x \to 0} \frac{f(3 + \Delta x, -2) - f(3, -2)}{\Delta x}$$

$$= \lim_{\Delta x \to 0} \frac{3(3 + \Delta x)^2 - 2(3 + \Delta x)(-2) + (-2)^2 - (27 + 12 + 4)}{\Delta x}$$

$$= \lim_{\Delta x \to 0} \frac{27 + 18\,\Delta x + 3(\Delta x)^2 + 12 + 4\,\Delta x + 4 - 43}{\Delta x}$$

$$= \lim_{\Delta x \to 0} (18 + 3\,\Delta x + 4)$$

$$= 22 \qquad ●$$

Alternate formulas to (3) and (4) for $D_1f(x_0, y_0)$ and $D_2f(x_0, y_0)$ are given by

$$D_1f(x_0, y_0) = \lim_{x \to x_0} \frac{f(x, y_0) - f(x_0, y_0)}{x - x_0} \tag{5}$$

if this limit exists, and

$$D_2f(x_0, y_0) = \lim_{y \to y_0} \frac{f(x_0, y) - f(x_0, y_0)}{y - y_0} \tag{6}$$

if this limit exists.

● ILLUSTRATION 2: We apply formula (5) to find $D_1f(3, -2)$ for the function f of Example 1.

$$D_1f(3, -2) = \lim_{x \to 3} \frac{f(x, -2) - f(3, -2)}{x - 3}$$

$$= \lim_{x \to 3} \frac{3x^2 + 4x + 4 - 43}{x - 3}$$

$$= \lim_{x \to 3} \frac{3x^2 + 4x - 39}{x - 3}$$

$$= \lim_{x \to 3} \frac{(3x + 13)(x - 3)}{x - 3}$$

$$= \lim_{x \to 3} (3x + 13)$$

$$= 22 \qquad ●$$

● ILLUSTRATION 3: In Example 1, we showed that

$$D_1f(x, y) = 6x - 2y$$

Therefore,

$$D_1f(3, -2) = 18 + 4$$
$$= 22$$

This result agrees with those of Illustrations 1 and 2.   ●

To distinguish derivatives of functions of more than one variable from derivatives of functions of one variable, we call the latter derivatives *ordinary derivatives*.

Comparing Definition 19.4.1 with the definition of an ordinary derivative (3.3.1), we see that $D_1f(x, y)$ is the ordinary derivative of f if f is considered as a function of one variable x (i.e., y is held constant), and $D_2f(x, y)$ is the ordinary derivative of f if f is considered as a function of one variable y (and x is held constant). So the results in Example 1 could have been obtained more easily by applying the theorems for ordinary differentiation if we consider y constant when finding $D_1f(x, y)$ and if we consider x constant when finding $D_2f(x, y)$. The following example illustrates this.

EXAMPLE 2:   Given $f(x, y) = 3x^3 - 4x^2y + 3xy^2 + 7x - 8y$, find $D_1f(x, y)$ and $D_2f(x, y)$.

SOLUTION: Considering f as a function of x and holding y constant, we have

$$D_1f(x, y) = 9x^2 - 8xy + 3y^2 + 7$$

Considering f as a function of y and holding x constant, we have

$$D_2f(x, y) = -4x^2 + 6xy - 8$$

EXAMPLE 3:   Given

$$f(x, y) = \begin{cases} \dfrac{xy(x^2 - y^2)}{x^2 + y^2} & \text{if } (x, y) \neq (0, 0) \\ 0 & \text{if } (x, y) = (0, 0) \end{cases}$$

find: (a) $f_1(0, y)$; (b) $f_2(x, 0)$.

SOLUTION: (a) If $y \neq 0$, from (5) we have

$$f_1(0, y) = \lim_{x \to 0} \frac{f(x, y) - f(0, y)}{x - 0}$$

$$= \lim_{x \to 0} \frac{\dfrac{xy(x^2 - y^2)}{x^2 + y^2} - 0}{x}$$

$$= \lim_{x \to 0} \frac{y(x^2 - y^2)}{x^2 + y^2}$$

$$= -\frac{y^3}{y^2}$$

$$= -y$$

If $y = 0$, we have

$$f_1(0, 0) = \lim_{x \to 0} \frac{f(x, 0) - f(0, 0)}{x - 0} = \lim_{x \to 0} \frac{0 - 0}{x} = 0$$

Because $f_1(0, y) = -y$ if $y \neq 0$ and $f_1(0, 0) = 0$, we can conclude that $f_1(0, y) = -y$ for all y.

(b) If $x \neq 0$, from (6) we have

$$f_2(x, 0) = \lim_{y \to 0} \frac{f(x, y) - f(x, 0)}{y - 0}$$

$$= \lim_{y \to 0} \frac{\dfrac{xy(x^2 - y^2)}{x^2 + y^2} - 0}{y}$$

$$= \lim_{y \to 0} \frac{x(x^2 - y^2)}{x^2 + y^2}$$

$$= \frac{x^3}{x^2}$$

$$= x$$

If $x = 0$, we have

$$f_2(0, 0) = \lim_{y \to 0} \frac{f(0, y) - f(0, 0)}{y - 0} = \lim_{y \to 0} \frac{0 - 0}{y} = 0$$

Because $f_2(x, 0) = x$, if $x \neq 0$ and $f_2(0, 0) = 0$, we can conclude that $f_2(x, 0) = x$ for all x.

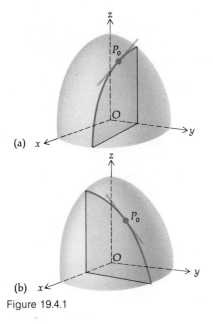

(a)

(b)

Figure 19.4.1

Geometric interpretations of the partial derivatives of a function of two variables are similar to those of a function of one variable. The graph of a function f of two variables is a surface having equation $z = f(x, y)$. If y is held constant (say, $y = y_0$), then $z = f(x, y_0)$ is the equation of the trace of this surface in the plane $y = y_0$. The curve can be represented by the two equations

$$y = y_0 \quad \text{and} \quad z = f(x, y) \tag{7}$$

because the curve is the intersection of these two surfaces.

Then $D_1 f(x_0, y_0)$ is the slope of the tangent line to the curve given by Eqs. (7) at the point $P_0(x_0, y_0, f(x_0, y_0))$ in the plane $y = y_0$. In an analogous fashion, $D_2 f(x_0, y_0)$ represents the slope of the tangent line to the curve having equations

$$x = x_0 \quad \text{and} \quad z = f(x, y)$$

at the point P_0 in the plane $x = x_0$. Figure 19.4.1a and b shows the portions of the curves and the tangent lines.

EXAMPLE 4:   Find the slope of the tangent line to the curve of intersection of the surface $z = \frac{1}{2}\sqrt{24 - x^2 - 2y^2}$ with the plane $y = 2$ at the point $(2, 2, \sqrt{3})$.

SOLUTION: The required slope is the value of $\partial z/\partial x$ at the point $(2, 2, \sqrt{3})$.

$$\frac{\partial z}{\partial x} = \frac{-x}{2\sqrt{24 - x^2 - 2y^2}}$$

So at $(2, 2, \sqrt{3})$,

$$\frac{\partial z}{\partial x} = \frac{-2}{2\sqrt{12}} = -\frac{1}{2\sqrt{3}}$$

A partial derivative can be interpreted as a rate of change. Actually, every derivative is a measure of a rate of change. If f is a function of the two variables x and y, the partial derivative of f with respect to x at the point $P_0(x_0, y_0)$ gives the instantaneous rate of change, at P_0, of $f(x, y)$ per unit change in x (x alone varies and y is held fixed at y_0). Similarly, the partial derivative of f with respect to y at P_0 gives the instantaneous rate of change, at P_0, of $f(x, y)$ per unit change in y.

EXAMPLE 5:   According to the *ideal gas law* for a confined gas, if P pounds per square unit is the pressure, V cubic units is the volume, and T degrees is the temperature, we have the formula

$$PV = kT \qquad (8)$$

where k is a constant of proportionality. Suppose that the volume of gas in a certain container is 100 in.^{3} and the temperature is 90°, and $k = 8$.

(a) Find the instantaneous rate of change of P per unit change in T if V remains fixed at 100. (b) Use the result of part (a) to approximate the change in the pressure if the temperature is increased to 92°. (c) Find the instantaneous rate of change of V per unit change in P if T remains fixed at 90. (d) Suppose that the temperature is held constant. Use the result of part (c) to find the approximate change in the vol-

SOLUTION: Substituting $V = 100$, $T = 90$, and $k = 8$ in Eq. (8), we obtain $P = 7.2$. (a) Solving Eq. (8) for P when $k = 8$, we get

$$P = \frac{8T}{V}$$

Therefore,

$$\frac{\partial P}{\partial T} = \frac{8}{V}$$

When $T = 90$ and $V = 100$, $\partial P/\partial T = 0.08$, which is the answer required.

(b) From the result of part (a) when T is increased by 2 (and V remains fixed) an approximate increase in P is $2(0.08) = 0.16$. We conclude, then, that if the temperature is increased from 90° to 92°, the increase in the pressure is approximately 0.16 lb/in.^{2}.

(c) Solving Eq. (8) for V when $k = 8$, we obtain

$$V = \frac{8T}{P}$$

Therefore,

$$\frac{\partial V}{\partial P} = -\frac{8T}{P^2}$$

When $T = 90$ and $P = 7.2$,

$$\frac{\partial V}{\partial P} = -\frac{8(90)}{(7.2)^2} = -\frac{125}{9}$$

ume necessary to produce the same change in the pressure as obtained in part (b).

which is the instantaneous rate of change of V per unit change in P when $T = 90$ and $P = 7.2$ if T remains fixed at 90.

(d) If P is to be increased by 0.16 and T is held fixed, then from the result of part (c) the change in V should be approximately $(0.16)(-\frac{125}{9}) = -\frac{20}{9}$. Hence, the volume should be decreased by approximately $\frac{20}{9}$ in.^{3} if the pressure is to be increased from 7.2 lb/in.^{2} to 7.36 lb/in.^{2}.

We now extend the concept of partial derivative to functions of n variables.

19.4.2 Definition Let $P(x_1, x_2, \ldots, x_n)$ be a point in R^n, and let f be a function of the n variables $x_1, x_2, \ldots, x_n$. Then the partial derivative of f with respect to x_k is that function, denoted by $D_k f$, such that its function value at any point P in the domain of f is given by

$$D_k f(x_1, x_2, \ldots, x_n) =$$

$$\lim_{\Delta x_k \to 0} \frac{f(x_1, x_2, \ldots, x_{k-1}, x_k + \Delta x_k, x_{k+1}, \ldots, x_n) - f(x_1, x_2, \ldots, x_n)}{\Delta x_k}$$

if this limit exists.

In particular, if f is a function of the three variables x, y, and z, then the partial derivatives of f are given by

$$D_1 f(x, y, z) = \lim_{\Delta x \to 0} \frac{f(x + \Delta x, y, z) - f(x, y, z)}{\Delta x}$$

$$D_2 f(x, y, z) = \lim_{\Delta y \to 0} \frac{f(x, y + \Delta y, z) - f(x, y, z)}{\Delta y}$$

and

$$D_3 f(x, y, z) = \lim_{\Delta z \to 0} \frac{f(x, y, z + \Delta z) - f(x, y, z)}{\Delta z}$$

if these limits exist.

EXAMPLE 6: **Given**

$$f(x, y, z) = x^2 y + yz^2 + z^3$$

verify that $xf_1(x, y, z) + yf_2(x, y, z) + zf_3(x, y, z) = 3f(x, y, z)$.

SOLUTION: Holding y and z constant, we get

$$f_1(x, y, z) = 2xy$$

Holding x and z constant, we obtain

$$f_2(x, y, z) = x^2 + z^2$$

Holding x and y constant, we get

$$f_3(x, y, z) = 2yz + 3z^2$$

Therefore,

$$xf_1(x, y, z) + yf_2(x, y, z) + zf_3(x, y, z) = x(2xy) + y(x^2 + z^2) + z(2yz + 3z^2)$$

$$= 2x^2y + x^2y + yz^2 + 2yz^2 + 3z^3$$
$$= 3(x^2y + yz^2 + z^3)$$
$$= 3f(x, y, z)$$

Exercises 19.4

In Exercises 1 through 6, apply Definition 19.4.1 to find each of the partial derivatives.

1. $f(x, y) = 6x + 3y - 7; D_1f(x, y)$ 2. $f(x, y) = 4x^2 - 3xy; D_1f(x, y)$ 3. $f(x, y) = 3xy + 6x - y^2; D_2f(x, y)$

4. $f(x, y) = xy^2 - 5y + 6; D_2f(x, y)$ 5. $f(x, y) = \sqrt{x^2 + y^2}; D_1f(x, y)$ 6. $f(x, y) = \dfrac{x + 2y}{x^2 - y}; D_2f(x, y)$

In Exercises 7 through 10, apply Definition 19.4.2 to find each of the partial derivatives.

7. $f(x, y, z) = x^2y - 3xy^2 + 2yz; D_2f(x, y, z)$ 8. $f(x, y, z) = x^2 + 4y^2 + 9z^2; D_1f(x, y, z)$

9. $f(x, y, z, r, t) = xyr + yzt + yrt + zrt; D_4f(x, y, z, r, t)$

10. $f(r, s, t, u, v, w) = 3r^2st + st^2v - 2tuv^2 - tvw + 3uw^2; D_5f(r, s, t, u, v, w)$

11. Given $f(x, y) = x^2 - 9y^2$. Find $D_1f(2, 1)$ by (a) applying formula (3); (b) applying formula (5); (c) applying formula (1) and then replacing x and y by 2 and 1, respectively.

12. For the function in Exercise 11, find $D_2f(2, 1)$ by (a) applying formula (4); (b) applying formula (6); (c) applying formula (2) and then replacing x and y by 2 and 1, respectively.

In Exercises 13 through 24, find the indicated partial derivatives by holding all but one of the variables constant and applying theorems for ordinary differentiation.

13. $f(x, y) = 4y^3 + \sqrt{x^2 + y^2}; D_1f(x, y)$

14. $f(x, y) = \dfrac{x + y}{\sqrt{y^2 - x^2}}; D_2f(x, y)$

15. $f(\theta, \phi) = \sin 3\theta \cos 2\phi; D_2f(\theta, \phi)$

16. $f(r, \theta) = r^2 \cos \theta - 2r \tan \theta; D_2f(r, \theta)$

17. $z = e^{y/x} \ln \dfrac{x^2}{y}; \dfrac{\partial z}{\partial y}$ 18. $r = e^{-\theta} \cos(\theta + \phi); \dfrac{\partial r}{\partial \theta}$

19. $u = (x^2 + y^2 + z^2)^{-1/2}; \dfrac{\partial u}{\partial z}$ 20. $u = \tan^{-1}(xyzw); \dfrac{\partial u}{\partial w}$

21. $f(x, y, z) = 4xyz + \ln(2xyz); f_3(x, y, z)$

22. $f(x, y, z) = e^{xy} \sinh 2z - e^{xy} \cosh 2z; f_3(x, y, z)$

23. $f(x, y, z) = e^{xyz} + \tan^{-1} \dfrac{3xy}{z^2}; f_2(x, y, z)$

24. $f(r, \theta, \phi) = 4r^2 \sin \theta + 5e^r \cos \theta \sin \phi - 2 \cos \phi; f_2(r, \theta, \phi)$

In Exercises 25 and 26, find $f_x(x, y)$ and $f_y(x, y)$.

25. $f(x, y) = \displaystyle\int_x^y \ln \sin t \, dt$

26. $f(x, y) = \displaystyle\int_x^y e^{\cos t} \, dt$

27. Given $u = \sin \dfrac{r}{t} + \ln \dfrac{t}{r}$. Verify $t \dfrac{\partial u}{\partial t} + r \dfrac{\partial u}{\partial r} = 0$.   28. Given $w = x^2y + y^2z + z^2x$. Verify $\dfrac{\partial w}{\partial x} + \dfrac{\partial w}{\partial y} + \dfrac{\partial w}{\partial z} = (x + y + z)^2$.

29. Given $f(x, y) = \begin{cases} \dfrac{x^3 + y^3}{x^2 + y^2} & \text{if } (x, y) \neq (0, 0) \\ 0 & \text{if } (x, y) = (0, 0) \end{cases}$

Find (a) $f_1(0, 0)$; (b) $f_2(0, 0)$.

30. Given $f(x, y) = \begin{cases} \dfrac{x^2 - xy}{x + y} & \text{if } (x, y) \neq (0, 0) \\ 0 & \text{if } (x, y) = (0, 0) \end{cases}$

Find (a) $f_1(0, y)$ if $y \neq 0$; (b) $f_1(0, 0)$.

31. For the function of Exercise 30 find (a) $f_2(x, 0)$ if $x \neq 0$; (b) $f_2(0, 0)$.

32. Find the slope of the tangent line to the curve of intersection of the surface $36x^2 - 9y^2 + 4z^2 + 36 = 0$ with the plane $x = 1$ at the point $(1, \sqrt{12}, -3)$. Interpret this slope as a partial derivative.

33. Find the slope of the tangent line to the curve of intersection of the surface $z = x^2 + y^2$ with the plane $y = 1$ at the point $(2, 1, 5)$. Draw a sketch. Interpret this slope as a partial derivative.

34. Find equations of the tangent line to the curve of intersection of the surface $x^2 + y^2 + z^2 = 9$ with the plane $y = 2$ at the point $(1, 2, 2)$.

35. The temperature at any point (x, y) of a flat plate is T degrees and $T = 54 - \frac{2}{3}x^2 - 4y^2$. If distance is measured in feet, find the rate of change of the temperature with respect to the distance moved along the plate in the directions of the positive x and y axes, respectively, at the point $(3, 1)$.

36. Use the ideal gas law for a confined gas (see Example 5) to show that

$$\frac{\partial V}{\partial T} \cdot \frac{\partial T}{\partial P} \cdot \frac{\partial P}{\partial V} = -1$$

37. If V dollars is the present value of an ordinary annuity of equal payments of $100 per year for t years at an interest rate of $100i$ percent per year, then

$$V = 100 \left[\frac{1 - (1 + i)^{-t}}{i} \right]$$

(a) Find the instantaneous rate of change of V per unit change in i if t remains fixed at 8. (b) Use the result of part (a) to find the approximate change in the present value if the interest rate changes from 6% to 7% and the time remains fixed at 8 years. (c) Find the instantaneous rate of change of V per unit change in t if i remains fixed at 0.06. (d) Use the result of part (c) to find the approximate change in the present value if the time is decreased from 8 to 7 years and the interest rate remains fixed at 6%.

19.5 DIFFERENTIABILITY AND THE TOTAL DIFFERENTIAL

In Sec. 3.6 in the proof of the chain rule we showed that if f is a differentiable function of the single variable x and $y = f(x)$, then the increment Δy of the dependent variable can be expressed as

$$\Delta y = f'(x) \Delta x + \eta \Delta x$$

where η is a function of Δx and $\eta \to 0$ as $\Delta x \to 0$.

From the above it follows that if the function f is differentiable at x_0, the increment of f at x_0, denoted by $\Delta f(x_0)$, is given by

$$\Delta f(x_0) = f'(x_0) \Delta x + \eta \Delta x \tag{1}$$

where $\lim_{\Delta x \to 0} \eta = 0$.

For functions of two or more variables we use an equation corresponding to Eq. (1) to define *differentiability* of a function. And from the definition we determine criteria for a function to be differentiable at a point. We give the details for a function of two variables and begin by defining the increment of such a function.

19.5.1 Definition   If f is a function of two variables x and y, then the *increment of f* at the point (x_0, y_0), denoted by $\Delta f(x_0, y_0)$, is given by

$$\Delta f(x_0, y_0) = f(x_0 + \Delta x, y_0 + \Delta y) - f(x_0, y_0) \qquad (2)$$

Figure 19.5.1 illustrates Eq. (2) for a function which is continuous on an open disk containing the points (x_0, y_0) and $(x_0 + \Delta x, y_0 + \Delta y)$. The figure shows a portion of the surface $z = f(x, y)$. $\Delta f(x_0, y_0) = \overline{QR}$, where Q is the point $(x_0 + \Delta x, y_0 + \Delta y, f(x_0, y_0))$ and R is the point $(x_0 + \Delta x, y_0 + \Delta y, f(x_0 + \Delta x, y_0 + \Delta y))$.

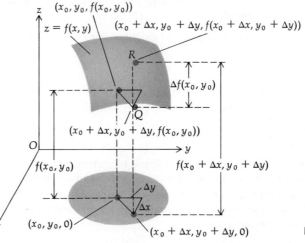

Figure 19.5.1

● ILLUSTRATION 1: For the function f defined by

$$f(x, y) = 3x - xy^2$$

we find the increment of f at any point (x_0, y_0).

$$\Delta f(x_0, y_0) = f(x_0 + \Delta x, y_0 + \Delta y) - f(x_0, y_0)$$
$$= 3(x_0 + \Delta x) - (x_0 + \Delta x)(y_0 + \Delta y)^2 - (3x_0 - x_0 y_0^2)$$
$$= 3x_0 + 3\,\Delta x - x_0 y_0^2 - y_0^2\,\Delta x - 2x_0 y_0\,\Delta y - 2y_0\,\Delta x\,\Delta y$$
$$\qquad - x_0(\Delta y)^2 - \Delta x(\Delta y)^2 - 3x_0 + x_0 y_0^2$$
$$= 3\,\Delta x - y_0^2\,\Delta x - 2x_0 y_0\,\Delta y - 2y_0\,\Delta x\,\Delta y - x_0(\Delta y)^2 - \Delta x(\Delta y)^2 \; ●$$

19.5.2 Definition   If f is a function of two variables x and y and the increment of f at (x_0, y_0) can be written as

$$\Delta f(x_0, y_0) = D_1 f(x_0, y_0)\,\Delta x + D_2 f(x_0, y_0)\,\Delta y + \epsilon_1\,\Delta x + \epsilon_2\,\Delta y \qquad (3)$$

where ϵ_1 and ϵ_2 are functions of Δx and Δy such that $\epsilon_1 \to 0$ and $\epsilon_2 \to 0$ as $(\Delta x, \Delta y) \to (0, 0)$, then f is said to be *differentiable* at (x_0, y_0).

• ILLUSTRATION 2: We use Definition 19.5.2 to prove that the function of Illustration 1 is differentiable at all points in R^2. We must show that for all points (x_0, y_0) in R^2 we can find an ϵ_1 and an ϵ_2 such that

$$\Delta f(x_0, y_0) - D_1 f(x_0, y_0) \, \Delta x - D_2 f(x_0, y_0) \, \Delta y = \epsilon_1 \, \Delta x + \epsilon_2 \, \Delta y$$

and $\epsilon_1 \to 0$ and $\epsilon_2 \to 0$ as $(\Delta x, \Delta y) \to (0, 0)$.

Because $f(x, y) = 3x - xy^2$,

$$D_1 f(x_0, y_0) = 3 - y_0^2 \quad \text{and} \quad D_2 f(x_0, y_0) = -2x_0 y_0$$

Using these values and the value of $\Delta f(x_0, y_0)$ from Illustration 1, we have

$$\Delta f(x_0, y_0) - D_1 f(x_0, y_0) \, \Delta x - D_2 f(x_0, y_0) \, \Delta y = -x_0 (\Delta y)^2 - 2y_0 \, \Delta x \, \Delta y - \Delta x (\Delta y)^2$$

The right side of the above equation can be written in the following ways:

$$[-2y_0 \, \Delta y - (\Delta y)^2] \, \Delta x + (-x_0 \, \Delta y) \, \Delta y$$

or

$$(-2y_0 \, \Delta y) \, \Delta x + (-\Delta x \, \Delta y - x_0 \, \Delta y) \, \Delta y$$

or

$$[-(\Delta y)^2] \, \Delta x + (-2y_0 \, \Delta x - x_0 \, \Delta y) \, \Delta y$$

or

$$0 \cdot \Delta x + [-2y_0 \, \Delta x - \Delta x \, \Delta y - x_0 \, \Delta y] \, \Delta y$$

So we have four possible pairs of values for ϵ_1 and ϵ_2:

$$\epsilon_1 = -2y_0 \, \Delta y - (\Delta y)^2 \quad \text{and} \quad \epsilon_2 = -x_0 \, \Delta y$$

or

$$\epsilon_1 = -2y_0 \, \Delta y \qquad \text{and} \quad \epsilon_2 = -\Delta x \, \Delta y - x_0 \, \Delta y$$

or

$$\epsilon_1 = -(\Delta y)^2 \qquad \text{and} \quad \epsilon_2 = -2y_0 \, \Delta x - x_0 \, \Delta y$$

or

$$\epsilon_1 = 0 \qquad \text{and} \quad \epsilon_2 = -2y_0 \, \Delta x - \Delta x \, \Delta y - x_0 \, \Delta y$$

For each pair, we see that

$$\lim_{(\Delta x, \Delta y) \to (0,0)} \epsilon_1 = 0 \quad \text{and} \quad \lim_{(\Delta x, \Delta y) \to (0,0)} \epsilon_2 = 0$$

It should be noted that it is only necessary to find one pair of values for ϵ_1 and ϵ_2.   •

19.5.3 Theorem   If a function f of two variables is differentiable at a point, it is continuous at that point.

PROOF: If f is differentiable at the point (x_0, y_0), it follows from Definition 19.5.2 that

$$f(x_0 + \Delta x, y_0 + \Delta y) - f(x_0, y_0) = D_1 f(x_0, y_0)\ \Delta x + D_2 f(x_0, y_0)\ \Delta y$$
$$+ \epsilon_1\ \Delta x + \epsilon_2\ \Delta y$$

where $\epsilon_1 \to 0$ and $\epsilon_2 \to 0$ as $(\Delta x, \Delta y) \to (0, 0)$. Therefore,

$$f(x_0 + \Delta x, y_0 + \Delta y) = f(x_0, y_0) + D_1 f(x_0, y_0)\ \Delta x + D_2 f(x_0, y_0)\ \Delta y$$
$$+ \epsilon_1\ \Delta x + \epsilon_2\ \Delta y$$

Taking the limit on both sides of the above as $(\Delta x, \Delta y) \to (0,0)$, we obtain

$$\lim_{(\Delta x, \Delta y) \to (0,0)} f(x_0 + \Delta x, y_0 + \Delta y) = f(x_0, y_0) \qquad (4)$$

If we let $x_0 + \Delta x = x$ and $y_0 + \Delta y = y$, "$(\Delta x, \Delta y) \to (0, 0)$" is equivalent to "$(x, y) \to (x_0, y_0)$." Thus, we have from (4)

$$\lim_{(x,y) \to (x_0, y_0)} f(x, y) = f(x_0, y_0)$$

which proves that f is continuous at (x_0, y_0). ∎

Theorem 19.5.3 states that for a function of two variables *differentiability implies continuity*. However, the mere existence of the partial derivatives $D_1 f$ and $D_2 f$ at a point does not imply differentiability at that point. The following example illustrates this.

EXAMPLE 1:   Given

$$f(x, y) = \begin{cases} \dfrac{xy}{x^2 + y^2} & \text{if } (x, y) \neq (0, 0) \\ 0 & \text{if } (x, y) = (0, 0) \end{cases}$$

prove that $D_1 f(0, 0)$ and $D_2 f(0, 0)$ exist but that f is not differentiable at $(0, 0)$.

SOLUTION:

$$D_1 f(0, 0) = \lim_{x \to 0} \frac{f(x, 0) - f(0, 0)}{x - 0} = \lim_{x \to 0} \frac{0 - 0}{x} = 0$$

$$D_2 f(0, 0) = \lim_{y \to 0} \frac{f(0, y) - f(0, 0)}{y - 0} = \lim_{y \to 0} \frac{0 - 0}{y} = 0$$

Therefore, both $D_1 f(0, 0)$ and $D_2 f(0, 0)$ exist.

In Example 2 of Sec. 19.2 we showed that for this function

$$\lim_{(x,y) \to (0,0)} f(x, y)$$

does not exist; hence, f is not continuous at $(0, 0)$. Because f is not continuous at $(0, 0)$, it follows from Theorem 19.5.3 that f is not differentiable there.

Before stating a theorem that gives conditions for which a function will be differentiable at a point, we consider a theorem needed in its proof. It is the mean-value theorem for a function of a single variable applied to a function of two variables.

19.5.4 Theorem Let f be a function of two variables defined for all x in the closed interval $[a, b]$ and all y in the closed interval $[c, d]$.

(i) If $D_1f(x, y_0)$ exists for some y_0 in $[c, d]$ and for all x in $[a, b]$, then there is a number ξ_1 in the open interval (a, b) such that

$$f(b, y_0) - f(a, y_0) = (b - a)D_1f(\xi_1, y_0) \tag{5}$$

(ii) If $D_2f(x_0, y)$ exists for some x_0 in $[a, b]$ and for all y in $[c, d]$, then there is a number ξ_2 in the open interval (c, d) such that

$$f(x_0, d) - f(x_0, c) = (d - c)D_2f(x_0, \xi_2) \tag{6}$$

Before proving this theorem, we interpret it geometrically. For part (i) refer to Fig. 19.5.2, which shows the portion of the surface $z = f(x, y)$ above the rectangular region in the xy plane bounded by the lines $x = a$, $x = b, y = c$, and $y = d$. The plane $y = y_0$ intersects the surface in the curve represented by the two equations $y = y_0$ and $z = f(x, y)$. The slope of the line through the points $A(a, y_0, f(a, y_0))$ and $B(b, y_0, f(b, y_0))$ is

$$\frac{f(b, y_0) - f(a, y_0)}{b - a}$$

Theorem 19.5.4(i) states that there is some point $(\xi_1, y_0, f(\xi_1, y_0))$ on the curve between the points A and B where the tangent line is parallel to the secant line through A and B; that is, there is some number ξ_1 in (a, b) such that $D_1f(\xi_1, y_0) = [f(b, y_0) - f(a, y_0)]/(b - a)$, and this is illustrated in the figure, for which $D_1f(\xi_1, y_0) < 0$.

Figure 19.5.3 illustrates part (ii) of Theorem 19.5.4. The plane $x = x_0$ intersects the surface $z = f(x, y)$ in the curve represented by the two equations $x = x_0$ and $z = f(x, y)$. The slope of the line through the points

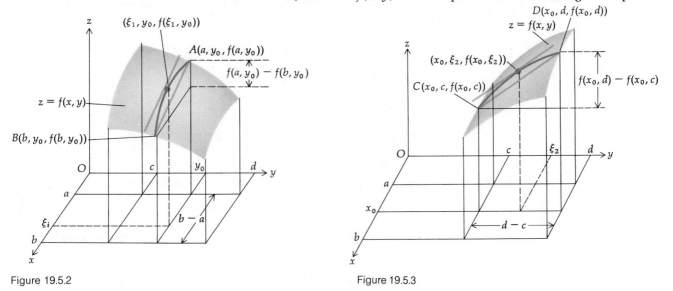

Figure 19.5.2   Figure 19.5.3

$C(x_0, c, f(x_0, c))$ and $D(x_0, d, f(x_0, d))$ is $[f(x_0, d) - f(x_0, c)]/(d - c)$, and Theorem 19.5.4(ii) states that there is some point $(x_0, \xi_2, f(x_0, \xi_2))$ on the curve between the points C and D where the tangent line is parallel to the secant line through C and D; that is, there is some number ξ_2 in (c, d) such that $D_2 f(x_0, \xi_2) = [f(x_0, d) - f(x_0, c)]/(d - c)$.

PROOF OF THEOREM 19.5.4(i): Let g be the function of one variable x defined by

$$g(x) = f(x, y_0)$$

Then

$$g'(x) = D_1 f(x, y_0)$$

Because $D_1 f(x, y_0)$ exists for all x in $[a, b]$, it follows that $g'(x)$ exists for all x in $[a, b]$, and therefore g is continuous on $[a, b]$. So by the mean-value theorem (4.7.2) for ordinary derivatives there exists a number ξ_1 in (a, b) such that

$$g'(\xi_1) = \frac{g(b) - g(a)}{b - a}$$

or, equivalently,

$$D_1 f(\xi_1, y_0) = \frac{f(b, y_0) - f(a, y_0)}{b - a}$$

from which we obtain

$$f(b, y_0) - f(a, y_0) = (b - a)D_1 f(\xi_1, y_0)$$

The proof of part (ii) is similar to the proof of part (i) and is left as an exercise (see Exercise 11). ∎

Equation (5) can be written in the form

$$f(x_0 + h, y_0) - f(x_0, y_0) = hD_1 f(\xi_1, y_0) \tag{7}$$

where ξ_1 is between x_0 and $x_0 + h$ and h is either positive or negative (see Exercise 12).

Equation (6) can be written in the form

$$f(x_0, y_0 + k) - f(x_0, y_0) = kD_2 f(x_0, \xi_2) \tag{8}$$

where ξ_2 is between y_0 and $y_0 + k$ and k is either positive or negative (see Exercise 13).

EXAMPLE 2: Given

$$f(x, y) = \frac{2xy}{3 + x}$$

SOLUTION: By Theorem 19.5.4, there is a number ξ_1 in the open interval $(2, 5)$ such that

$$f(5, 4) - f(2, 4) = (5 - 2)D_1 f(\xi_1, 4)$$

find a ξ_1 required by Theorem 19.5.4 if x is in $[2, 5]$ and $y = 4$.

So

$$5 - \frac{16}{5} = 3 \cdot \frac{24}{(3 + \xi_1)^2}$$

$$\frac{9}{5} = \frac{72}{(3 + \xi_1)^2}$$

$$(3 + \xi_1)^2 = 40$$

Therefore,

$$3 + \xi_1 = \pm 2\sqrt{10}$$

But because $2 < \xi_1 < 5$, we take only the "+" sign and obtain

$$\xi_1 = 2\sqrt{10} - 3$$

The following theorem states that a function having continuous partial derivatives at a point is necessarily differentiable at the point.

19.5.5 Theorem   Let f be a function of two variables x and y. Suppose that D_1f and D_2f exist on an open disk $B(P_0; r)$, where P_0 is the point (x_0, y_0). Then if D_1f and D_2f are continuous at P_0, f is differentiable at P_0.

PROOF: Choose the point $(x_0 + \Delta x, y_0 + \Delta y)$ so that it is in $B(P_0; r)$. Then

$$\Delta f(x_0, y_0) = f(x_0 + \Delta x, y_0 + \Delta y) - f(x_0, y_0)$$

Subtracting and adding $f(x_0 + \Delta x, y_0)$ to the right side of the above equation, we get

$$\Delta f(x_0, y_0) = [f(x_0 + \Delta x, y_0 + \Delta y) - f(x_0 + \Delta x, y_0)]$$
$$+ [f(x_0 + \Delta x, y_0) - f(x_0, y_0)] \quad (9)$$

Because D_1f and D_2f exist on $B(P_0; r)$ and $(x_0 + \Delta x, y_0 + \Delta y)$ is in $B(P_0; r)$, it follows from (8) that

$$f(x_0 + \Delta x, y_0 + \Delta y) - f(x_0 + \Delta x, y_0) = (\Delta y)D_2f(x_0 + \Delta x, \xi_2) \quad (10)$$

where ξ_2 is between y_0 and $y_0 + \Delta y$.
From (7) it follows that

$$f(x_0 + \Delta x, y_0) - f(x_0, y_0) = (\Delta x)D_1f(\xi_1, y_0) \quad (11)$$

where ξ_1 is between x_0 and $x_0 + \Delta x$.
Substituting from (10) and (11) in (9), we obtain

$$\Delta f(x_0, y_0) = (\Delta y)D_2f(x_0 + \Delta x, \xi_2) + (\Delta x)D_1f(\xi_1, y_0) \quad (12)$$

Because $(x_0 + \Delta x, y_0 + \Delta y)$ is in $B(P_0; r)$, ξ_2 is between y_0 and $y_0 + \Delta y$, and D_2f is continuous at P_0, it follows that

$$\lim_{(\Delta x, \Delta y) \to (0,0)} D_2f(x_0 + \Delta x, \xi_2) = D_2f(x_0, y_0) \tag{13}$$

and, because ξ_1 is between x_0 and $x_0 + \Delta x$ and D_1f is continuous at P_0, it follows that

$$\lim_{(\Delta x, \Delta y) \to (0,0)} D_1f(\xi_1, y_0) = D_1f(x_0, y_0) \tag{14}$$

If we let

$$\epsilon_1 = D_1f(\xi_1, y_0) - D_1f(x_0, y_0) \tag{15}$$

it follows from Eq. (14) that

$$\lim_{(\Delta x, \Delta y) \to (0,0)} \epsilon_1 = 0 \tag{16}$$

and if we let

$$\epsilon_2 = D_2f(x_0 + \Delta x, \xi_2) - D_2f(x_0, y_0) \tag{17}$$

it follows from Eq. (13) that

$$\lim_{(\Delta x, \Delta y) \to (0,0)} \epsilon_2 = 0 \tag{18}$$

Substituting from Eqs. (15) and (17) into (12), we get

$$\Delta f(x_0, y_0) = \Delta y[D_2f(x_0, y_0) + \epsilon_2] + \Delta x[D_1f(x_0, y_0) + \epsilon_1]$$

from which we obtain

$$\Delta f(x_0, y_0) = D_1f(x_0, y_0)\, \Delta x + D_2f(x_0, y_0)\, \Delta y + \epsilon_1\, \Delta x + \epsilon_2\, \Delta y \tag{19}$$

From Eqs. (16), (18), and (19) we see that Definition 19.5.2 holds; so f is differentiable at (x_0, y_0).

A function satisfying the hypothesis of Theorem 19.5.5 is said to be *continuously differentiable* at the point P_0.

EXAMPLE 3: Given

$$f(x, y) = \begin{cases} \dfrac{x^2 y^2}{x^2 + y^2} & \text{if } (x, y) \neq (0, 0) \\ 0 & \text{if } (x, y) = (0, 0) \end{cases}$$

use Theorem 19.5.5 to prove that f is differentiable at $(0, 0)$.

SOLUTION: To find D_1f we consider two cases: $(x, y) = (0, 0)$ and $(x, y) \neq (0, 0)$. If $(x, y) = (0, 0)$, we have

$$D_1f(0, 0) = \lim_{x \to 0} \frac{f(x, 0) - f(0, 0)}{x - 0} = \lim_{x \to 0} \frac{0 - 0}{x} = 0$$

If $(x, y) \neq (0, 0)$, $f(x, y) = x^2y^2/(x^2 + y^2)$. To find $D_1f(x, y)$ we can use the theorem for the ordinary derivative of a quotient and consider y as a constant. We have

$$D_1f(x, y) = \frac{2xy^2(x^2 + y^2) - 2x(x^2y^2)}{(x^2 + y^2)^2}$$

$$= \frac{2xy^4}{(x^2 + y^2)^2}$$

The function D_1f is therefore defined by

$$D_1f(x, y) = \begin{cases} \dfrac{2xy^4}{(x^2 + y^2)^2} & \text{if } (x, y) \neq (0, 0) \\ 0 & \text{if } (x, y) = (0, 0) \end{cases}$$

In the same manner we obtain the function D_2f defined by

$$D_2f(x, y) = \begin{cases} \dfrac{2x^4y}{(x^2 + y^2)^2} & \text{if } (x, y) \neq (0, 0) \\ 0 & \text{if } (x, y) = (0, 0) \end{cases}$$

Both D_1f and D_2f exist on every open disk having its center at the origin. It remains to show that D_1f and D_2f are continuous at $(0, 0)$.

Because $D_1f(0, 0) = 0$, D_1f will be continuous at $(0, 0)$ if

$$\lim_{(x,y)\to(0,0)} D_1f(x, y) = 0$$

Therefore, we must show that for any $\epsilon > 0$ there exists a $\delta > 0$ such that

$$\left| \frac{2xy^4}{(x^2 + y^2)^2} \right| < \epsilon \quad \text{whenever} \quad 0 < \sqrt{x^2 + y^2} < \delta \tag{20}$$

$$\left| \frac{2xy^4}{(x^2 + y^2)^2} \right| = \frac{2|x|y^4}{(x^2 + y^2)^2} \leq \frac{2\sqrt{x^2 + y^2}(\sqrt{x^2 + y^2})^4}{(x^2 + y^2)^2} = 2\sqrt{x^2 + y^2}$$

Therefore,

$$\left| \frac{2xy^4}{(x^2 + y^2)^2} \right| < 2\delta \quad \text{whenever} \quad 0 < \sqrt{x^2 + y^2} < \delta$$

So if we take $\delta = \frac{1}{2}\epsilon$, we have (20). Hence, D_1f is continuous at $(0, 0)$. In the same way we show that D_2f is continuous at $(0, 0)$. It follows from Theorem 19.5.5 that f is differentiable at $(0, 0)$.

If we refer back to Eq. (3), the expression involving the first two terms on the right side, $D_1f(x_0, y_0) \, \Delta x + D_2f(x_0, y_0) \, \Delta y$, is called the *principal part* of $\Delta f(x_0, y_0)$ or the "total differential" of the function f at (x_0, y_0). We make this as a formal definition.

19.5.6 Definition   If f is a function of two variables x and y, and f is differentiable at (x, y), then the *total differential* of f is the function df having function values given by

$$df(x, y, \Delta x, \Delta y) = D_1f(x, y) \, \Delta x + D_2f(x, y) \, \Delta y \tag{21}$$

Note that df is a function of the four variables x, y, Δx, and Δy. If

$z = f(x, y)$, we sometimes write dz in place of $df(x, y, \Delta x, \Delta y)$, and then Eq. (21) is written as

$$dz = D_1f(x, y)\ \Delta x + D_2f(x, y)\ \Delta y \tag{22}$$

If in particular $f(x, y) = x$, then $z = x$, $D_1f(x, y) = 1$, and $D_2f(x, y) = 0$, and so Eq. (22) gives $dz = \Delta x$. Because $z = x$, we have for this function $dx = \Delta x$. In a similar fashion, if we take $f(x, y) = y$, then $z = y$, $D_1f(x, y) = 0$, and $D_2f(x, y) = 1$, and so Eq. (22) gives $dz = \Delta y$. Because $z = y$, we have for this function $dy = \Delta y$. Hence, we define the differentials of the independent variables as $dx = \Delta x$ and $dy = \Delta y$. Then Eq. (22) can be written as

$$dz = D_1f(x, y)\ dx + D_2f(x, y)\ dy \tag{23}$$

and at the point (x_0, y_0), we have

$$dz = D_1f(x_0, y_0)\ dx + D_2f(x_0, y_0)\ dy \tag{24}$$

In Eq. (3), letting $\Delta z = \Delta f(x_0, y_0)$, $dx = \Delta x$, and $dy = \Delta y$, we have

$$\Delta z = D_1f(x_0, y_0)\ dx + D_2f(x_0, y_0)\ dy + \epsilon_1\ dx + \epsilon_2\ dy \tag{25}$$

Comparing Eqs. (24) and (25), we see that when dx (i.e., Δx) and dy (i.e., Δy) are close to zero, and because then ϵ_1 and ϵ_2 also will be close to zero, we can conclude that dz is an approximation to Δz. Because dz is often easier to calculate than Δz, we make use of the fact that $dz \approx \Delta z$ in certain situations. Before showing this in an example, we write Eq. (23) with the notation $\partial z/\partial x$ and $\partial z/\partial y$ instead of $D_1f(x, y)$ and $D_2f(x, y)$, respectively:

$$dz = \frac{\partial z}{\partial x}\ dx + \frac{\partial z}{\partial y}\ dy \tag{26}$$

EXAMPLE 4:   A closed metal can in the shape of a right-circular cylinder is to have an inside height of 6 in., an inside radius of 2 in., and a thickness of 0.1 in. If the cost of the metal to be used is 10 cents per in.³, find by differentials the approximate cost of the metal to be used in the manufacture of the can.

SOLUTION: The formula for the volume of a right-circular cylinder, where the volume is V in.³, the radius is r in., and the height is h in., is

$$V = \pi r^2 h \tag{27}$$

The exact volume of metal in the can is the difference between the volumes of two right-circular cylinders for which $r = 2.1$, $h = 6.2$, and $r = 2$, $h = 6$, respectively.

ΔV would give us the exact volume of metal, but because we only want an approximate value, we find dV instead. Using (26), we have

$$dV = \frac{\partial V}{\partial r}\ dr + \frac{\partial V}{\partial h}\ dh \tag{28}$$

From Eq. (27) it follows that

$$\frac{\partial V}{\partial r} = 2\pi rh \quad \text{and} \quad \frac{\partial V}{\partial h} = \pi r^2$$

Substituting these values into Eq. (28) gives

$$dV = 2\pi rh \, dr + \pi r^2 \, dh$$

Because $r = 2$, $h = 6$, $dr = 0.1$, and $dh = 0.2$, we have

$$dV = 2\pi(2)(6)(0.1) + \pi(2)^2(0.2)$$

$$= 3.2\pi$$

Hence, $\Delta V \approx 3.2\pi$, and so there is approximately 3.2π in.^{3} of metal in the can. Because the cost of the metal is 10 cents per in.^{3} and $10 \cdot 3.2\pi = 32\pi \approx 100.53$, the approximate cost of the metal to be used in the manufacture of the can is \$1.

We conclude this section by extending the concepts of differentiability and the total differential to a function of n variables.

19.5.7 Definition If f is a function of the n variables $x_1, x_2, \ldots, x_n$, and $\bar{P}$ is the point $(\bar{x}_1, \bar{x}_2, \ldots, \bar{x}_n)$, then the *increment of f at $\bar{P}$* is given by

$$\Delta f(\bar{P}) = f(\bar{x}_1 + \Delta x_1, \bar{x}_2 + \Delta x_2, \ldots, \bar{x}_n + \Delta x_n) - f(\bar{P}) \tag{29}$$

19.5.8 Definition If f is a function of the n variables $x_1, x_2, \ldots, x_n$, and the increment of f at the point $\bar{P}$ can be written as

$$\Delta f(\bar{P}) = D_1 f(\bar{P}) \, \Delta x_1 + D_2 f(\bar{P}) \, \Delta x_2 + \cdots + D_n f(\bar{P}) \, \Delta x_n$$

$$+ \epsilon_1 \, \Delta x_1 + \epsilon_2 \, \Delta x_2 + \cdots + \epsilon_n \, \Delta x_n \tag{30}$$

where $\epsilon_1 \to 0$, $\epsilon_2 \to 0$, $\ldots$, $\epsilon_n \to 0$, as

$$(\Delta x_1, \Delta x_2, \ldots, \Delta x_n) \to (0, 0, \ldots, 0)$$

then f is said to be *differentiable* at $\bar{P}$.

Analogously to Theorem 19.5.5, it can be proved that sufficient conditions for a function f of n variables to be differentiable at a point $\bar{P}$ are that $D_1 f, D_2 f, \ldots, D_n f$ all exist on an open ball $B(\bar{P}; r)$ and that $D_1 f, D_2 f, \ldots, D_n f$ are all continuous at $\bar{P}$. As was the case for functions of two variables, it follows that for functions of n variables differentiability implies continuity. However, the existence of the partial derivatives $D_1 f, D_2 f, \ldots, D_n f$ at a point does not imply differentiability of the function at the point.

19.5.9 Definition If f is a function of the n variables $x_1, x_2, \ldots, x_n$ and f is differentiable at P, then the *total differential* of f is the function df having function values given by

$$df(P, \Delta x_1, \Delta x_2, \ldots, \Delta x_n) = D_1 f(P) \, \Delta x_1 + D_2 f(P) \, \Delta x_2 + \cdots + D_n f(P) \, \Delta x_n \tag{31}$$

Letting $w = f(x_1, x_2, \ldots, x_n)$, defining $dx_1 = \Delta x_1$, $dx_2 = \Delta x_2$, $\ldots$, $dx_n = \Delta x_n$, and using the notation $\partial w / \partial x_i$ instead of $D_i f(P)$, we can write Eq. (31) as

$$dw = \frac{\partial w}{\partial x_1} \, dx_1 + \frac{\partial w}{\partial x_2} \, dx_2 + \cdots + \frac{\partial w}{\partial x_n} \, dx_n \tag{32}$$

EXAMPLE 5:   The dimensions of a box are measured to be 10 in., 12 in., and 15 in., and the measurements are correct to 0.02 in. Find approximately the greatest error if the volume of the box is calculated from the given measurements. Also find the approximate percent error.

SOLUTION: Letting V in.^{3} be the volume of a box whose dimensions are x in., y in., and z in., we have the formula

$$V = xyz$$

The exact value of the error would be found from ΔV; however, we use dV as an approximation to ΔV. Using Eq. (32) for three independent variables, we have

$$dV = \frac{\partial V}{\partial x} \, dx + \frac{\partial V}{\partial y} \, dy + \frac{\partial V}{\partial z} \, dz$$

and so

$$dV = yz \, dx + xz \, dy + xy \, dz \tag{33}$$

From the given information $|\Delta x| \leq 0.02$, $|\Delta y| \leq 0.02$, and $|\Delta z| \leq 0.02$. To find the greatest error in the volume we take the greatest error in the measurements of the three dimensions. So taking $dx = 0.02$, $dy = 0.02$, $dz = 0.02$, and $x = 10$, $y = 12$, $z = 15$, we have from Eq. (33)

$$dV = (12)(15)(0.02) + (10)(15)(0.02) + (10)(12)(0.02)$$

$$= 9$$

So, $\Delta V \approx 9$, and therefore the greatest possible error in the calculation of the volume from the given measurements is approximately 9 in.^{3}.

The relative error is found by dividing the error by the actual value. Hence, the relative error in computing the volume from the given measurements is $\Delta V / V \approx dV / V = \frac{9}{1800} = \frac{1}{200} = 0.005$. So the approximate percent error is 0.5%.

Exercises 19.5

1. If $f(x, y) = 3x^2 + 2xy - y^2$, $\Delta x = 0.03$, and $\Delta y = -0.02$, find (a) the increment of f at $(1, 4)$ and (b) the total differential of f at $(1, 4)$.

2. If $f(x, y) = xye^{xy}$, $\Delta x = -0.1$, and $\Delta y = 0.2$, find (a) the increment of f at $(2, -4)$ and (b) the total differential of f at $(2, -4)$.

3. If $f(x, y, z) = xy + \ln(yz)$, $\Delta x = 0.02$, $\Delta y = 0.04$, and $\Delta z = -0.03$, find (a) the increment of f at $(4, 1, 5)$ and (b) the total differential of f at $(4, 1, 5)$.

4. If $f(x, y, z) = x^2y + 2xyz - z^3$, $\Delta x = 0.01$, $\Delta y = 0.03$, and $\Delta z = -0.01$, find (a) the increment of f at $(-3, 0, 2)$ and (b) the total differential of f at $(-3, 0, 2)$.

In Exercises 5 through 8, prove that f is differentiable at all points in its domain by doing each of the following: (a) Find $\Delta f(x_0, y_0)$ for the given function; (b) find an ϵ_1 and an ϵ_2 so that Eq. (3) holds; (c) show that the ϵ_1 and the ϵ_2 found in part (b) both approach zero as $(\Delta x, \Delta y) \to (0, 0)$.

5. $f(x, y) = x^2y - 2xy$

6. $f(x, y) = 2x^2 + 3y^2$

7. $f(x, y) = \dfrac{x^2}{y}$

8. $f(x, y) = \dfrac{y}{x}$

9. Given $f(x, y) = \begin{cases} x + y - 2 & \text{if } x = 1 \text{ or } y = 1 \\ 2 & \text{if } x \neq 1 \text{ and } y \neq 1 \end{cases}$

   Prove that $D_1f(1, 1)$ and $D_2f(1, 1)$ exist, but f is not differentiable at $(1, 1)$.

10. Given $f(x, y) = \begin{cases} \dfrac{3x^2y^2}{x^4 + y^4} & \text{if } (x, y) \neq (0, 0) \\ 0 & \text{if } (x, y) = (0, 0) \end{cases}$

   Prove that $D_1f(0, 0)$ and $D_2f(0, 0)$ exist, but f is not differentiable at $(0, 0)$.

11. Prove Theorem 19.5.4(ii).

12. Show that Eq. (5) may be written in the form (7) where ξ_1 is between x_0 and $x_0 + h$.

13. Show that Eq. (6) may be written in the form (8) where ξ_2 is between y_0 and $y_0 + k$.

In Exercises 14 through 17, use Theorem 19.5.4 to find either a ξ_1 or a ξ_2, whichever applies.

14. $f(x, y) = x^2 + 3xy - y^2$; x is in $[1, 3]$; $y = 4$

15. $f(x, y) = x^3 - y^2$; x is in $[2, 6]$; $y = 3$

16. $f(x, y) = \dfrac{4x}{x + y}$; y is in $[-2, 2]$; $x = 4$

17. $f(x, y) = \dfrac{2x - y}{2y + x}$; y is in $[0, 4]$; $x = 2$

18. Given $f(x, y) = \begin{cases} \dfrac{3x^2y}{x^2 + y^2} & \text{if } (x, y) \neq (0, 0) \\ 0 & \text{if } (x, y) = (0, 0) \end{cases}$

   This function is continuous at $(0, 0)$ (see Example 3, Sec. 19.2, and Illustration 1, Sec. 19.3). Prove that $D_1f(0, 0)$ and $D_2f(0, 0)$ exist but D_1f and D_2f are not continuous at $(0, 0)$.

19. Given $f(x, y) = \begin{cases} \dfrac{xy(x^2 - y^2)}{x^2 + y^2} & \text{if } (x, y) \neq (0, 0) \\ 0 & \text{if } (x, y) = (0, 0) \end{cases}$

   Prove that f is differentiable at $(0, 0)$ by using Theorem 19.5.5.

In Exercises 20 and 21, prove that f is differentiable at all points in R^3 by doing each of the following: (a) Find $\Delta f(x_0, y_0, z_0)$; (b) find an ϵ_1, ϵ_2, and ϵ_3, so that Eq. (30) holds; (c) show that the ϵ_1, ϵ_2, and ϵ_3 found in (b) all approach zero as $(\Delta x, \Delta y, \Delta z)$ approaches $(0, 0, 0)$.

20. $f(x, y, z) = 2x^2z - 3yz^2$

21. $f(x, y, z) = xy - xz + z^2$

22. Given $f(x, y, z) = \begin{cases} \dfrac{xy^2z}{x^4 + y^4 + z^4} & \text{if } (x, y, z) \neq (0, 0, 0) \\ 0 & \text{if } (x, y, z) = (0, 0, 0) \end{cases}$

   (a) Show that $D_1f(0, 0, 0)$, $D_2f(0, 0, 0)$, and $D_3f(0, 0, 0)$ exist; (b) make use of the fact that differentiability implies continuity to prove that f is not differentiable at $(0, 0, 0)$.

23. Given $f(x, y, z) = \begin{cases} \dfrac{xyz^2}{x^2 + y^2 + z^2} & \text{if } (x, y, z) \neq (0, 0, 0) \\ 0 & \text{if } (x, y, z) = (0, 0, 0) \end{cases}$

Prove that f is differentiable at $(0, 0, 0)$.

24. Use the total differential to find approximately the greatest error in calculating the area of a right triangle from the lengths of the legs if they are measured to be 6 in. and 8 in., respectively, with a possible error of 0.1 in. for each measurement. Also find the approximate percent error.

25. Find approximately, by using the total differential, the greatest error in calculating the length of the hypotenuse of the right triangle from the measurements of Exercise 24. Also find the approximate percent error.

26. If the ideal gas law (see Example 5, Sec. 19.4) is used to find P when T and V are given, but there is an error of 0.3% in measuring T and an error of 0.8% in measuring V, find approximately the greatest percent error in P.

27. The specific gravity s of an object is given by the formula

$$s = \frac{A}{A - W}$$

where A is the number of pounds in the weight of the object in air and W is the number of pounds in the weight of the object in water. If the weight of an object in air is read as 20 lb with a possible error of 0.01 lb and its weight in water is read as 12 lb with a possible error of 0.02 lb, find approximately the largest possible error in calculating s from these measurements. Also find the largest possible relative error.

28. A wooden box is to be made of lumber that is $\frac{2}{3}$ in. thick. The inside length is to be 6 ft, the inside width is to be 3 ft, the inside depth is to be 4 ft, and the box is to have no top. Use the total differential to find the approximate amount of lumber to be used in the box.

29. A company has contracted to manufacture 10,000 closed wooden crates having dimensions 3 ft, 4 ft, and 5 ft. The cost of the wood to be used is 5¢ per square foot. If the machines that are used to cut the pieces of wood have a possible error of 0.05 ft in each dimension, find approximately, by using the total differential, the greatest possible error in the estimate of the cost of the wood.

In Exercises 30 through 33, we show that a function may be differentiable at a point even though it is not continuously differentiable there. Hence, the conditions of Theorem 19.5.5 are sufficient but not necessary for differentiability. The function f in these exercises is defined by

$$f(x, y) = \begin{cases} (x^2 + y^2) \sin \dfrac{1}{\sqrt{x^2 + y^2}} & \text{if } (x, y) \neq (0, 0) \\ 0 & \text{if } (x, y) = (0, 0) \end{cases}$$

30. Find $\Delta f(0, 0)$.   31. Find $D_1 f(x, y)$ and $D_2 f(x, y)$.

32. Prove that f is differentiable at $(0, 0)$ by using Definition 19.5.2 and the results of Exercises 30 and 31.

33. Prove that $D_1 f$ and $D_2 f$ are not continuous at $(0, 0)$.

19.6 THE CHAIN RULE In Sec. 3.6 we had the following chain rule (Theorem 3.6.1) for functions of a single variable: If y is a function of u, defined by $y = f(u)$, and $D_u y$ exists; and u is a function of x, defined by $u = g(x)$, and $D_x u$ exists; then y is a function of x, and $D_x y$ exists and is given by

$$D_x y = D_u y \, D_x u$$

or, equivalently,

$$\frac{dy}{dx} = \frac{dy}{du}\frac{du}{dx}$$ (1)

We now consider the chain rule for a function of two variables, where each of these variables is also a function of two variables.

19.6.1 Theorem
The Chain Rule

If u is a differentiable function of x and y, defined by $u = f(x, y)$, and $x = F(r, s)$, $y = G(r, s)$, and $\partial x/\partial r$, $\partial x/\partial s$, $\partial y/\partial r$, and $\partial y/\partial s$ all exist, then u is a function of r and s and

$$\frac{\partial u}{\partial r} = \left(\frac{\partial u}{\partial x}\right)\left(\frac{\partial x}{\partial r}\right) + \left(\frac{\partial u}{\partial y}\right)\left(\frac{\partial y}{\partial r}\right)$$ (2)

$$\frac{\partial u}{\partial s} = \left(\frac{\partial u}{\partial x}\right)\left(\frac{\partial x}{\partial s}\right) + \left(\frac{\partial u}{\partial y}\right)\left(\frac{\partial y}{\partial s}\right)$$ (3)

PROOF: We prove (2). The proof of (3) is similar.

If s is held fixed and r is changed by an amount Δr, then x is changed by an amount Δx and y is changed by an amount Δy. So we have

$$\Delta x = F(r + \Delta r, s) - F(r, s)$$ (4)

and

$$\Delta y = G(r + \Delta r, s) - G(r, s)$$ (5)

Because f is differentiable,

$$\Delta f(x, y) = D_1 f(x, y)\,\Delta x + D_2 f(x, y)\,\Delta y + \epsilon_1\,\Delta x + \epsilon_2\,\Delta y$$ (6)

where ϵ_1 and ϵ_2 both approach zero as $(\Delta x, \Delta y)$ approaches $(0, 0)$. Furthermore, we require that $\epsilon_1 = 0$ and $\epsilon_2 = 0$ when $\Delta x = \Delta y = 0$. We make this requirement so that ϵ_1 and ϵ_2, which are functions of Δx and Δy, will be continuous at $(\Delta x, \Delta y) = (0, 0)$.

If in (6) we replace $\Delta f(x, y)$ by Δu, $D_1 f(x, y)$ by $\partial u/\partial x$, and $D_2 f(x, y)$ by $\partial u/\partial y$ and divide on both sides by Δr ($\Delta r \neq 0$), we obtain

$$\frac{\Delta u}{\Delta r} = \frac{\partial u}{\partial x}\frac{\Delta x}{\Delta r} + \frac{\partial u}{\partial y}\frac{\Delta y}{\Delta r} + \epsilon_1\frac{\Delta x}{\Delta r} + \epsilon_2\frac{\Delta y}{\Delta r}$$

Taking the limit on both sides of the above as Δr approaches zero, we get

$$\lim_{\Delta r \to 0}\frac{\Delta u}{\Delta r} = \frac{\partial u}{\partial x}\lim_{\Delta r \to 0}\frac{\Delta x}{\Delta r} + \frac{\partial u}{\partial y}\lim_{\Delta r \to 0}\frac{\Delta y}{\Delta r} + \left(\lim_{\Delta r \to 0}\epsilon_1\right)\lim_{\Delta r \to 0}\frac{\Delta x}{\Delta r} + \left(\lim_{\Delta r \to 0}\epsilon_2\right)\lim_{\Delta r \to 0}\frac{\Delta y}{\Delta r}$$ (7)

Because u is a function of x and y and both x and y are functions of r and s, u is a function of r and s. Because s is held fixed and r is changed by an amount Δr, we have

$$\lim_{\Delta r \to 0} \frac{\Delta u}{\Delta r} = \lim_{\Delta r \to 0} \frac{u(r + \Delta r, s) - u(r, s)}{\Delta r} = \frac{\partial u}{\partial r} \tag{8}$$

Also,

$$\lim_{\Delta r \to 0} \frac{\Delta x}{\Delta r} = \lim_{\Delta r \to 0} \frac{F(r + \Delta r, s) - F(r, s)}{\Delta r} = \frac{\partial x}{\partial r} \tag{9}$$

and

$$\lim_{\Delta r \to 0} \frac{\Delta y}{\Delta r} = \lim_{\Delta r \to 0} \frac{G(r + \Delta r, s) - G(r, s)}{\Delta r} = \frac{\partial y}{\partial r} \tag{10}$$

Because $\partial x / \partial r$ and $\partial y / \partial r$ exist, F and G are each continuous with respect to the variable r. (NOTE: The existence of the partial derivatives of a function does not imply continuity with respect to all of the variables simultaneously, as we saw in the preceding section, but as with functions of a single variable it does imply continuity of the function with respect to each variable separately.) Hence, we have from (4)

$$\lim_{\Delta r \to 0} \Delta x = \lim_{\Delta r \to 0} [F(r + \Delta r, s) - F(r, s)]$$

$$= F(r, s) - F(r, s)$$

$$= 0$$

and from (5)

$$\lim_{\Delta r \to 0} \Delta y = \lim_{\Delta r \to 0} [G(r + \Delta r, s) - G(r, s)]$$

$$= G(r, s) - G(r, s)$$

$$= 0$$

Therefore, as Δr approaches zero, both Δx and Δy approach zero. And because both ϵ_1 and ϵ_2 approach zero as $(\Delta x, \Delta y)$ approaches $(0, 0)$, we can conclude that

$$\lim_{\Delta r \to 0} \epsilon_1 = 0 \quad \text{and} \quad \lim_{\Delta r \to 0} \epsilon_2 = 0 \tag{11}$$

Now it is possible that for certain values of Δr, $\Delta x = \Delta y = 0$. Because we required in such a case that $\epsilon_1 = \epsilon_2 = 0$, the limits in (11) are still zero. Substituting from (8), (9), (10), and (11) into (7), we obtain

$$\frac{\partial u}{\partial r} = \left(\frac{\partial u}{\partial x}\right)\left(\frac{\partial x}{\partial r}\right) + \left(\frac{\partial u}{\partial y}\right)\left(\frac{\partial y}{\partial r}\right)$$

which proves (2). ∎

EXAMPLE 1: Given

$$u = \ln \sqrt{x^2 + y^2}$$

SOLUTION:

$$\frac{\partial u}{\partial x} = \frac{x}{x^2 + y^2} \qquad \frac{\partial u}{\partial y} = \frac{y}{x^2 + y^2} \qquad \frac{\partial x}{\partial r} = e^s$$

$x = re^s$, and $y = re^{-s}$, find $\partial u/\partial r$ and $\partial u/\partial s$.

$$\frac{\partial x}{\partial s} = re^s \qquad \frac{\partial y}{\partial r} = e^{-s} \qquad \frac{\partial y}{\partial s} = -re^{-s}$$

From (2) we get

$$\frac{\partial u}{\partial r} = \frac{x}{x^2 + y^2}\,(e^s) + \frac{y}{x^2 + y^2}\,(e^{-s}) = \frac{xe^s + ye^{-s}}{x^2 + y^2}$$

From (3) we get

$$\frac{\partial u}{\partial s} = \frac{x}{x^2 + y^2}\,(re^s) + \frac{y}{x^2 + y^2}\,(-re^{-s}) = \frac{r(xe^s - ye^{-s})}{x^2 + y^2}$$

As mentioned earlier the symbols $\partial u/\partial r$, $\partial u/\partial s$, $\partial u/\partial x$, $\partial u/\partial y$, and so forth must not be considered as fractions. The symbols ∂u, ∂x, and so on have no meaning by themselves. For functions of one variable, the chain rule, given by Eq. (1), is easily remembered by thinking of an ordinary derivative as the quotient of two differentials, but there is no similar interpretation for partial derivatives.

Another troublesome notational problem arises when considering u as a function of x and y and then as a function of r and s. If $u = f(x, y)$, $x = F(r, s)$, and $y = G(r, s)$, then $u = f(F(r, s), G(r, s))$. [Note that it is incorrect to write $u = f(r, s)$.]

● ILLUSTRATION 1: In Example 1,

$$u = f(x, y) = \ln\sqrt{x^2 + y^2}$$

$$x = F(r, s) = re^s$$

$$y = G(r, s) = re^{-s}$$

and so

$$u = f(F(r, s), G(r, s)) = \ln\sqrt{r^2 e^{2s} + r^2 e^{-2s}}$$

$$[f(r, s) = \ln\sqrt{r^2 + s^2} \neq u.]$$ ●

If we let $f(F(r, s), G(r, s)) = h(r, s)$, then Eqs. (2) and (3) can be written respectively as

$$h_1(r, s) = f_1(x, y)F_1(r, s) + f_2(x, y)G_1(r, s)$$

and

$$h_2(r, s) = f_1(x, y)F_2(r, s) + f_2(x, y)G_2(r, s)$$

In the statement of Theorem 19.6.1 the independent variables are r and s, and u is the dependent variable. The variables x and y can be called the intermediate variables. We now extend the chain rule to n intermediate variables and m independent variables.

19.6.2 Theorem
The General Chain Rule

Suppose that u is a differentiable function of the n variables $x_1, x_2, \ldots,$ x_n, and each of these variables is in turn a function of the m variables

$y_1, y_2, \ldots, y_m$. Suppose further that each of the partial derivatives $\partial x_i/\partial y_j$ $(i = 1, 2, \ldots, n; j = 1, 2, \ldots, m)$ exists. Then u is a function of $y_1, y_2, \ldots, y_m$, and

$$\frac{\partial u}{\partial y_1} = \left(\frac{\partial u}{\partial x_1}\right)\left(\frac{\partial x_1}{\partial y_1}\right) + \left(\frac{\partial u}{\partial x_2}\right)\left(\frac{\partial x_2}{\partial y_1}\right) + \cdots + \left(\frac{\partial u}{\partial x_n}\right)\left(\frac{\partial x_n}{\partial y_1}\right)$$

$$\frac{\partial u}{\partial y_2} = \left(\frac{\partial u}{\partial x_1}\right)\left(\frac{\partial x_1}{\partial y_2}\right) + \left(\frac{\partial u}{\partial x_2}\right)\left(\frac{\partial x_2}{\partial y_2}\right) + \cdots + \left(\frac{\partial u}{\partial x_n}\right)\left(\frac{\partial x_n}{\partial y_2}\right)$$

$$\vdots$$

$$\frac{\partial u}{\partial y_m} = \left(\frac{\partial u}{\partial x_1}\right)\left(\frac{\partial x_1}{\partial y_m}\right) + \left(\frac{\partial u}{\partial x_2}\right)\left(\frac{\partial x_2}{\partial y_m}\right) + \cdots + \left(\frac{\partial u}{\partial x_n}\right)\left(\frac{\partial x_n}{\partial y_m}\right)$$

The proof is an extension of the proof of Theorem 19.6.1.

Note that in the general chain rule, there are as many terms on the right side of each equation as there are intermediate variables.

EXAMPLE 2: Given

$$u = xy + xz + yz$$

$x = r$, $y = r \cos t$, and $z = r \sin t$, find $\partial u/\partial r$ and $\partial u/\partial t$.

SOLUTION: By applying the chain rule, we obtain

$$\frac{\partial u}{\partial r} = \left(\frac{\partial u}{\partial x}\right)\left(\frac{\partial x}{\partial r}\right) + \left(\frac{\partial u}{\partial y}\right)\left(\frac{\partial y}{\partial r}\right) + \left(\frac{\partial u}{\partial z}\right)\left(\frac{\partial z}{\partial r}\right)$$

$$= (y + z)(1) + (x + z)(\cos t) + (x + y)(\sin t)$$

$$= y + z + x \cos t + z \cos t + x \sin t + y \sin t$$

$$= r \cos t + r \sin t + r \cos t + (r \sin t)(\cos t) + r \sin t + (r \cos t)(\sin t)$$

$$= 2r(\cos t + \sin t) + r(2 \sin t \cos t)$$

$$= 2r(\cos t + \sin t) + r \sin 2t$$

$$\frac{\partial u}{\partial t} = \left(\frac{\partial u}{\partial x}\right)\left(\frac{\partial x}{\partial t}\right) + \left(\frac{\partial u}{\partial y}\right)\left(\frac{\partial y}{\partial t}\right) + \left(\frac{\partial u}{\partial z}\right)\left(\frac{\partial z}{\partial t}\right)$$

$$= (y + z)(0) + (x + z)(-r \sin t) + (s + y)(r \cos t)$$

$$= (r + r \sin t)(-r \sin t) + (r + r \cos t)(r \cos t)$$

$$= -r^2 \sin t - r^2 \sin^2 t + r^2 \cos t + r^2 \cos^2 t$$

$$= r^2(\cos t - \sin t) + r^2(\cos^2 t - \sin^2 t)$$

$$= r^2(\cos t - \sin t) + r^2 \cos 2t$$

Now suppose that u is a differentiable function of the two variables x and y, and both x and y are differentiable functions of the single variable t. Then u is a function of the single variable t, and so instead of the partial derivative of u with respect to t, we have the ordinary derivative of u with respect to t, which is given by

$$\frac{du}{dt} = \left(\frac{\partial u}{\partial x}\right)\left(\frac{dx}{dt}\right) + \left(\frac{\partial u}{\partial y}\right)\left(\frac{dy}{dt}\right) \tag{12}$$

We call du/dt given by Eq. (12) the *total derivative* of u with respect to t. If u is a differentiable function of the n variables $x_1, x_2, \ldots , x_n$ and each x_i is a differentiable function of the single variable t, then u is a function of t and the total derivative of u with respect to t is given by

$$\frac{du}{dt} = \left(\frac{\partial u}{\partial x_1}\right)\left(\frac{dx_1}{dt}\right) + \left(\frac{\partial u}{\partial x_2}\right)\left(\frac{dx_2}{dt}\right) + \cdots + \left(\frac{\partial u}{\partial x_n}\right)\left(\frac{dx_n}{dt}\right)$$

EXAMPLE 3: Given

$$u = x^2 + 2xy + y^2$$

$x = t \cos t$, and $y = t \sin t$, find du/dt by two methods: (a) using the chain rule; (b) expressing u in terms of t before differentiating.

SOLUTION: (a) $\partial u/\partial x = 2x + 2y$; $\partial u/\partial y = 2x + 2y$; $dx/dt = \cos t - t \sin t$; $dy/dt = \sin t + t \cos t$. So from (12) we have

$$\frac{du}{dt} = (2x + 2y)(\cos t - t \sin t) + (2x + 2y)(\sin t + t \cos t)$$

$$= 2(x + y)(\cos t - t \sin t + \sin t + t \cos t)$$

$$= 2(t \cos t + t \sin t)(\cos t - t \sin t + \sin t + t \cos t)$$

$$= 2t(\cos^2 t - t \sin t \cos t + \sin t \cos t + t \cos^2 t + \sin t \cos t$$

$$- t \sin^2 t + \sin^2 t + t \sin t \cos t)$$

$$= 2t[1 + 2 \sin t \cos t + t(\cos^2 t - \sin^2 t)]$$

$$= 2t(1 + \sin 2t + t \cos 2t)$$

(b) $u = (t \cos t)^2 + 2(t \cos t)(t \sin t) + (t \sin t)^2$

$$= t^2 \cos^2 t + t^2(2 \sin t \cos t) + t^2 \sin^2 t$$

$$= t^2 + t^2 \sin 2t$$

So

$$\frac{du}{dt} = 2t + 2t \sin 2t + 2t^2 \cos 2t$$

EXAMPLE 4: If f is a differentiable function and a and b are constants, prove that $z = f(\frac{1}{2}bx^2 - \frac{1}{3}ay^3)$ satisfies the partial differential equation

$$ay^2 \frac{\partial z}{\partial x} + bx \frac{\partial z}{\partial y} = 0$$

SOLUTION: Let $u = \frac{1}{2}bx^2 - \frac{1}{3}ay^3$. We wish to show that $z = f(u)$ satisfies the given equation. By the chain rule we get

$$\frac{\partial z}{\partial x} = \frac{dz}{du}\frac{\partial u}{\partial x} = f'(u)(bx) \quad \text{and} \quad \frac{\partial z}{\partial y} = \frac{dz}{du}\frac{\partial u}{\partial y} = f'(u)(-ay^2)$$

Therefore,

$$ay^2 \frac{\partial z}{\partial x} + bx \frac{\partial z}{\partial y} = ay^2[f'(u)(bx)] + bx[f'(u)(-ay^2)] = 0$$

which is what we wished to prove.

EXAMPLE 5:   Use the ideal gas law (see Example 5, Sec. 19.4) with $k = 10$ to find the rate at which the temperature is changing at the instant when the volume of the gas is 120 in.³ and the gas is under a pressure of 8 lb/in.² if the volume is increasing at the rate of 2 in.³/sec and the pressure is decreasing at the rate of 0.1 lb/in.² per sec.

SOLUTION: Let $t =$ the number of seconds in the time that has elapsed since the volume of the gas started to increase;
$T =$ the number of degrees in the temperature at t sec;
$P =$ the number of pounds per square inch in the pressure at t sec;
$V =$ the number of cubic inches in the volume of the gas at t sec.

$$PV = 10T \quad \text{and so} \quad T = \frac{PV}{10}$$

At the given instant, $P = 8$, $V = 120$, $dP/dt = -0.1$, and $dV/dt = 2$. Using the chain rule, we obtain

$$\frac{dT}{dt} = \frac{\partial T}{\partial P}\frac{dP}{dt} + \frac{\partial T}{\partial V}\frac{dV}{dt}$$

$$= \frac{V}{10}\frac{dP}{dt} + \frac{P}{10}\frac{dV}{dt}$$

$$= \tfrac{120}{10}(-0.1) + \tfrac{8}{10}(2)$$

$$= -1.2 + 1.6$$

$$= 0.4$$

Therefore the temperature is increasing at the rate of 0.4 degree per second at the given instant.

Exercises 19.6

In Exercises 1 through 4, find the indicated partial derivative by two methods: (a) Use the chain rule; (b) make the substitutions for x and y before differentiating.

1. $u = x^2 - y^2$; $x = 3r - s$; $y = r + 2s$; $\dfrac{\partial u}{\partial r}$; $\dfrac{\partial u}{\partial s}$

2. $u = 3x^2 + xy - 2y^2 + 3x - y$; $x = 2r - 3s$; $y = r + s$; $\dfrac{\partial u}{\partial r}$; $\dfrac{\partial u}{\partial s}$

3. $u = e^{u/x}$; $x = 2r \cos t$; $y = 4r \sin t$; $\dfrac{\partial u}{\partial r}$; $\dfrac{\partial u}{\partial t}$

4. $u = x^2 + y^2$; $x = \cosh r \cos t$; $y = \sinh r \sin t$; $\dfrac{\partial u}{\partial r}$; $\dfrac{\partial u}{\partial t}$

In Exercises 5 through 10, find the indicated partial derivative by using the chain rule.

5. $u = \sin^{-1}(3x + y)$; $x = r^2 e^s$; $y = \sin rs$; $\dfrac{\partial u}{\partial r}$; $\dfrac{\partial u}{\partial s}$

6. $u = xe^{-y}$; $x = \tan^{-1}(rst)$; $y = \ln(3rs + 5st)$; $\dfrac{\partial u}{\partial r}$; $\dfrac{\partial u}{\partial s}$; $\dfrac{\partial u}{\partial t}$

7. $u = \cosh \dfrac{y}{x}$; $x = 3r^2 s$; $y = 6se^r$; $\dfrac{\partial u}{\partial r}$; $\dfrac{\partial u}{\partial s}$

8. $u = xy + xz + yz$; $x = rs$; $y = r^2 - s^2$; $z = (r - s)^2$; $\dfrac{\partial u}{\partial r}$; $\dfrac{\partial u}{\partial s}$

9. $u = x^2 + y^2 + z^2$; $x = r \sin \phi \cos \theta$; $y = r \sin \phi \sin \theta$; $z = r \cos \phi$; $\dfrac{\partial u}{\partial r}$; $\dfrac{\partial u}{\partial \phi}$; $\dfrac{\partial u}{\partial \theta}$

10. $u = x^2 yz$; $x = \dfrac{r}{s}$; $y = re^s$; $z = re^{-s}$; $\dfrac{\partial u}{\partial r}$; $\dfrac{\partial u}{\partial s}$

In Exercises 11 through 14, find the total derivative du/dt by two methods: (a) Use the chain rule; (b) make the substitutions for x and y or for x, y, and z before differentiating.

11. $u = ye^x + xe^y$; $x = \cos t$; $y = \sin t$

12. $u = \ln xy + y^2$; $x = e^t$; $y = e^{-t}$

13. $u = \sqrt{x^2 + y^2 + z^2}$; $x = \tan t$; $y = \cos t$; $z = \sin t$; $0 < t < \frac{1}{2}\pi$

14. $u = \dfrac{t + e^x}{y - e^{t'}}$; $x = 3 \sin t$; $y = \ln t$

In Exercises 15 through 18, find the total derivative du/dt by using the chain rule; do not express u as a function of t before differentiating.

15. $u = \tan^{-1}\left(\dfrac{y}{x}\right)$; $x = \ln t$; $y = e^t$

16. $u = xy + xz + yz$; $x = t \cos t$; $y = t \sin t$; $z = t$

17. $u = \dfrac{x + t}{y + t}$; $x = \ln t$; $y = \ln \dfrac{1}{t}$

18. $u = \ln(x^2 + y^2 + t^2)$; $x = t \sin t$; $y = \cos t$

In Exercises 19 through 22, assume that the given equation defines z as a function of x and y. Differentiate implicitly to find $\partial z/\partial x$ and $\partial z/\partial y$.

19. $3x^2 + y^2 + z^2 - 3xy + 4xz - 15 = 0$

20. $z = (x^2 + y^2) \sin xz$

21. $ye^{xyz} \cos 3xz = 5$

22. $ze^{yz} + 2xe^{xz} - 4e^{xy} = 3$

23. If f is a differentiable function of the variable u, let $u = bx - ay$ and prove that $z = f(bx - ay)$ satisfies the equation $a(\partial z/\partial x) + b(\partial z/\partial y) = 0$, where a and b are constants.

24. If f is a differentiable function of two variables u and v, let $u = x - y$ and $v = y - x$ and prove that $z = f(x - y, y - x)$ satisfies the equation $\partial z/\partial x + \partial z/\partial y = 0$.

25. If f is a differentiable function of x and y and $u = f(x, y)$, $x = r \cos \theta$, and $y = r \sin \theta$, show that

$$\frac{\partial u}{\partial x} = \frac{\partial u}{\partial r} \cos \theta - \frac{\partial u}{\partial \theta} \frac{\sin \theta}{r}$$

$$\frac{\partial u}{\partial y} = \frac{\partial u}{\partial r} \sin \theta + \frac{\partial u}{\partial \theta} \frac{\cos \theta}{r}$$

26. If f and g are differentiable functions of x and y and $u = f(x, y)$ and $v = g(x, y)$, such that $\partial u/\partial x = \partial v/\partial y$ and $\partial u/\partial y = -\partial v/\partial x$, then if $x = r \cos \theta$ and $y = r \sin \theta$, show that

$$\frac{\partial u}{\partial r} = \frac{1}{r}\frac{\partial v}{\partial \theta} \quad \text{and} \quad \frac{\partial v}{\partial r} = -\frac{1}{r}\frac{\partial u}{\partial \theta}$$

27. Suppose f is a differentiable function of x and y and $u = f(x, y)$. Then if $x = \cosh v \cos w$ and $y = \sinh v \sin w$, express $\partial u/\partial v$ and $\partial u/\partial w$ in terms of $\partial u/\partial x$ and $\partial u/\partial y$.

28. Suppose f is a differentiable function of x, y, and z and $u = f(x, y, z)$. Then if $x = r \sin \phi \cos \theta$, $y = r \sin \phi \sin \theta$, and $z = r \cos \phi$, express $\partial u/\partial r$, $\partial u/\partial \phi$, and $\partial u/\partial \theta$ in terms of $\partial u/\partial x$, $\partial u/\partial y$, and $\partial u/\partial z$.

29. At a given instant, the length of one leg of a right triangle is 10 ft and it is increasing at the rate of 1 ft/min and the length of the other leg of the right triangle is 12 ft and it is decreasing at the rate of 2 ft/min. Find the rate of change of the measure of the acute angle opposite the leg of length 12 ft at the given instant.

30. A vertical wall makes an angle of radian measure $\frac{2}{3}\pi$ with the ground. A ladder of length 20 ft is leaning against the wall and its top is sliding down the wall at the rate of 3 ft/sec. How fast is the area of the triangle formed by the ladder, the wall, and the ground changing when the ladder makes an angle of $\frac{1}{6}\pi$ radians with the ground?

31. A quantity of gas obeys the ideal gas law (see Example 5, Sec. 19.4) with $k = 12$, and the gas is in a container which is being heated at a rate of 3° per second. If at the instant when the temperature is 300°, the pressure is 6 lb/in.² and is decreasing at the rate of 0.1 lb/in.² per second, find the rate of change of the volume at that instant.

32. Water is flowing into a tank in the form of a right-circular cylinder at the rate of $\frac{4}{5}\pi$ ft³/min. The tank is stretching in such a way that even though it remains cylindrical, its radius is increasing at the rate of 0.002 ft/min. How fast is the surface of the water rising when the radius is 2 ft and the volume of water in the tank is 20π ft³?

19.7 HIGHER-ORDER PARTIAL DERIVATIVES

If f is a function of two variables, then in general D_1f and D_2f are also functions of two variables. And if the partial derivatives of these functions exist, they are called second partial derivatives of f. In contrast, D_1f and D_2f are called first partial derivatives of f. There are four second partial derivatives of a function of two variables. If f is a function of the two variables x and y, the notations

$$D_2(D_1f) \qquad D_{12}f \qquad f_{12} \qquad f_{xy} \qquad \frac{\partial^2 f}{\partial y\, \partial x}$$

all denote the second partial derivative of f, which we obtain by first partial-differentiating f with respect to x and then partial-differentiating the result with respect to y. This second partial derivative is defined by

$$f_{12}(x, y) = \lim_{\Delta y \to 0} \frac{f_1(x, y + \Delta y) - f_1(x, y)}{\Delta y} \tag{1}$$

if this limit exists. The notations

$$D_1(D_1f) \qquad D_{11}f \qquad f_{11} \qquad f_{xx} \qquad \frac{\partial^2 f}{\partial x^2}$$

all denote the second partial derivative of f, which is obtained by partial-differentiating twice with respect to x. We have the definition

$$f_{11}(x, y) = \lim_{\Delta x \to 0} \frac{f_1(x + \Delta x, y) - f_1(x, y)}{\Delta x} \tag{2}$$

if this limit exists. We define the other two second partial derivatives in an analogous way and obtain

$$f_{21}(x, y) = \lim_{\Delta x \to 0} \frac{f_2(x + \Delta x, y) - f_2(x, y)}{\Delta x} \tag{3}$$

and

$$f_{22}(x, y) = \lim_{\Delta y \to 0} \frac{f_2(x, y + \Delta y) - f_2(x, y)}{\Delta y} \tag{4}$$

if these limits exist.

The definitions of higher-order partial derivatives are similar. Again we have various notations for a specific derivative. For example,

$$D_{112}f \qquad f_{112} \qquad f_{xxy} \qquad \frac{\partial^3 f}{\partial y\, \partial x\, \partial x} \qquad \frac{\partial^3 f}{\partial y\, \partial x^2}$$

all stand for the third partial derivative of f, which is obtained by partial-differentiating twice with respect to x and then once with respect to y.

Note that in the subscript notation, the order of partial differentiation is from left to right; in the notation $\partial^3 f/\partial y\, \partial x\, \partial x$, the order is from right to left.

EXAMPLE 1:   Given

$$f(x, y) = e^x \sin y + \ln xy$$

find: (a) $D_{11}f(x, y)$; (b) $D_{12}f(x, y)$; (c) $\partial^3 f/\partial x\, \partial y^2$.

SOLUTION:

$$D_1 f(x, y) = e^x \sin y + \frac{1}{xy} y = e^x \sin y + \frac{1}{x}$$

So (a) $D_{11}f(x, y) = e^x \sin y - 1/x^2$; and (b) $D_{12}f(x, y) = e^x \cos y$. (c) To find $\partial^3 f/\partial x\, \partial y^2$, we partial-differentiate twice with respect to y and then once with respect to x. This gives us

$$\frac{\partial f}{\partial y} = e^x \cos y + \frac{1}{y} \qquad \frac{\partial^2 f}{\partial y^2} = -e^x \sin y - \frac{1}{y^2} \qquad \frac{\partial^3 f}{\partial x\, \partial y^2} = -e^x \sin y$$

Higher-order partial derivatives of a function of n variables have definitions which are analogous to the definitions of higher-order partial derivatives of a function of two variables. If f is a function of n variables, there may be n^2 second partial derivatives of f at a particular point. That is, for a function of three variables, if all the second-order partial derivatives exist, there are nine of them: $f_{11}, f_{12}, f_{13}, f_{21}, f_{22}, f_{23}, f_{31}, f_{32},$ and f_{33}.

EXAMPLE 2:   Given

$$f(x, y, z) = \sin(xy + 2z)$$

find $D_{132}f(x, y, z)$.

SOLUTION:

$$D_1 f(x, y, z) = y \cos(xy + 2z)$$

$$D_{13}f(x, y, z) = -2y \sin(xy + 2z)$$

$$D_{132}f(x, y, z) = -2 \sin(xy + 2z) - 2xy \cos(xy + 2z)$$

EXAMPLE 3:   Given

$$f(x, y) = x^3 y - y \cosh xy$$

find: (a) $D_{12}f(x, y)$; (b) $D_{21}f(x, y)$.

SOLUTION:

(a) $D_1 f(x, y) = 3x^2 y - y^2 \sinh xy$

$\quad D_{12}f(x, y) = 3x^2 - 2y \sinh xy - xy^2 \cosh xy$

(b) $D_2 f(x, y) = x^3 - \cosh xy - xy \sinh xy$

$\quad D_{21}f(x, y) = 3x^2 - y \sinh xy - y \sinh xy - xy^2 \cosh xy$

$\qquad\qquad\quad = 3x^2 - 2y \sinh xy - xy^2 \cosh xy$

We see from the above results that for the function of Example 3 the "mixed" partial derivatives $D_{12}f(x, y)$ and $D_{21}f(x, y)$ are equal. So for this particular function, when finding the second partial derivative with respect to x and then y, the order of differentiation is immaterial. This condition holds for many functions. However, the following example shows that it is not always true.

EXAMPLE 4:   Let f be the function defined by

$$f(x, y) = \begin{cases} (xy)\dfrac{x^2 - y^2}{x^2 + y^2} & \text{if } (x, y) \neq (0, 0) \\ 0 & \text{if } (x, y) = (0, 0) \end{cases}$$

Find $f_{12}(0, 0)$ and $f_{21}(0, 0)$.

SOLUTION: In Example 3, Sec. 19.4, we showed that for this function

$$f_1(0, y) = -y \qquad \text{for all } y \tag{5}$$

and

$$f_2(x, 0) = x \qquad \text{for all } x \tag{6}$$

From formula (1) we obtain

$$f_{12}(0, 0) = \lim_{\Delta y \to 0} \frac{f_1(0, 0 + \Delta y) - f_1(0, 0)}{\Delta y}$$

But from (5), $f_1(0, \Delta y) = -\Delta y$ and $f_1(0, 0) = 0$, and so we have

$$f_{12}(0, 0) = \lim_{\Delta y \to 0} \frac{-\Delta y - 0}{\Delta y} = \lim_{\Delta y \to 0} (-1) = -1$$

From formula (3), we get

$$f_{21}(0, 0) = \lim_{\Delta x \to 0} \frac{f_2(0 + \Delta x, 0) - f_2(0, 0)}{\Delta x}$$

From (6), $f_2(\Delta x, 0) = \Delta x$ and $f_2(0, 0) = 0$. Therefore,

$$f_{21}(0, 0) = \lim_{\Delta x \to 0} \frac{\Delta x - 0}{\Delta x} = \lim_{\Delta x \to 0} 1 = 1$$

For the function in Example 4 we see that the mixed partial derivatives $f_{12}(x, y)$ and $f_{21}(x, y)$ are not equal at $(0, 0)$. A set of conditions for which $f_{12}(x_0, y_0) = f_{21}(x_0, y_0)$ is given by Theorem 19.7.1, which follows. The function of Example 4 does not satisfy the hypothesis of this theorem because both f_{12} and f_{21} are discontinuous at $(0, 0)$. It is left as an exercise to show this (see Exercise 20).

19.7.1 Theorem   Suppose that f is a function of two variables x and y defined on an open disk $B((x_0, y_0); r)$ and f_x, f_y, f_{xy}, and f_{yx} also are defined on B. Furthermore, suppose that f_{xy} and f_{yx} are continuous on B. Then

$$f_{xy}(x_0, y_0) = f_{yx}(x_0, y_0)$$

PROOF: Consider a square having its center at (x_0, y_0) and the length of its side $2|h|$ such that $0 < \sqrt{2}|h| < r$. Then all the points in the interior of the square and on the sides of the square are in the open disk B (see Fig. 19.7.1). So the points $(x_0 + h, y_0 + h)$, $(x_0 + h, y_0)$, and $(x_0, y_0 + h)$ are in B. Let Δ be defined by

$$\Delta = f(x_0 + h, y_0 + h) - f(x_0 + h, y_0) - f(x_0, y_0 + h) + f(x_0, y_0) \tag{7}$$

Consider the function G defined by

$$G(x) = f(x, y_0 + h) - f(x, y_0) \tag{8}$$

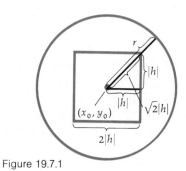

Figure 19.7.1

Then

$$G(x + h) = f(x + h, y_0 + h) - f(x + h, y_0)$$

So (7) can be written as

$$\Delta = G(x_0 + h) - G(x_0) \tag{9}$$

From (8) we obtain

$$G'(x) = f_x(x, y_0 + h) - f_x(x, y_0) \tag{10}$$

Now, because $f_x(x, y_0 + h)$ and $f_x(x, y_0)$ are defined on B, $G'(x)$ exists if x is in the closed interval having endpoints at x_0 and $x_0 + h$. Hence, G is continuous if x is in this closed interval. By the mean-value theorem (4.7.2) there is a number c_1 between x_0 and $x_0 + h$ such that

$$G(x_0 + h) - G(x_0) = hG'(c_1) \tag{11}$$

Substituting from (11) into (9), we get

$$\Delta = hG'(c_1) \tag{12}$$

From (12) and (10) we obtain

$$\Delta = h[f_x(c_1, y_0 + h) - f_x(c_1, y_0)] \tag{13}$$

Now if g is the function defined by

$$g(y) = f_x(c_1, y) \tag{14}$$

we can write (13) as

$$\Delta = h[g(y_0 + h) - g(y_0)] \tag{15}$$

From (14) we obtain

$$g'(y) = f_{xy}(c_1, y) \tag{16}$$

Because $f_{xy}(c_1, y)$ is defined on B, $g'(y)$ exists if y is in the closed interval having endpoints at y_0 and $y_0 + h$; hence, g is continuous if y is in this closed interval. Therefore, by the mean-value theorem there is a number d_1 between y_0 and $y_0 + h$ such that

$$g(y_0 + h) - g(y_0) = hg'(d_1) \tag{17}$$

Substituting from (17) into (15), we get $\Delta = h^2 g'(d_1)$; so from (16) it follows that

$$\Delta = h^2 f_{xy}(c_1, d_1) \tag{18}$$

for some point (c_1, d_1) in the open disk B. We define a function ϕ by

$$\phi(y) = f(x_0 + h, y) - f(x_0, y) \tag{19}$$

and so $\phi(y + h) = f(x_0 + h, y + h) - f(x_0, y + h)$. Therefore, (7) can be written as

$$\Delta = \phi(y_0 + h) - \phi(y_0) \tag{20}$$

From (19) we get

$$\phi'(y) = f_y(x_0 + h, y) - f_y(x_0, y) \tag{21}$$

ϕ' exists if y is in the closed interval having y_0 and $y_0 + h$ as endpoints because by hypothesis each term on the right side of (21) exists on B. Therefore, ϕ is continuous on this closed interval. So by the mean-value theorem there is a number d_2 between y_0 and $y_0 + h$ such that

$$\phi(y_0 + h) - \phi(y_0) = h\phi'(d_2) \tag{22}$$

From (20), (21), and (22) it follows that

$$\Delta = h[f_y(x_0 + h, d_2) - f_y(x_0, d_2)] \tag{23}$$

Define the function χ by

$$\chi(x) = f_y(x, d_2) \tag{24}$$

and write (23) as

$$\Delta = h[\chi(x_0 + h) - \chi(x_0)] \tag{25}$$

From (24) we get

$$\chi'(x) = f_{yx}(x, d_2) \tag{26}$$

and by the mean-value theorem we conclude that there is a number c_2 between x_0 and $x_0 + h$ such that

$$\chi(x_0 + h) - \chi(x_0) = h\chi'(c_2) \tag{27}$$

From (25), (26), and (27) we obtain

$$\Delta = h^2 f_{yx}(c_2, d_2) \tag{28}$$

Equating the right sides of (18) and (28), we get

$$h^2 f_{xy}(c_1, d_1) = h^2 f_{yx}(c_2, d_2)$$

and because $h \neq 0$, we can divide by h^2, which gives

$$f_{xy}(c_1, d_1) = f_{yx}(c_2, d_2) \tag{29}$$

where (c_1, d_1) and (c_2, d_2) are in B.

Because c_1 and c_2 are each between x_0 and $x_0 + h$, we can write $c_1 = x_0 + \epsilon_1 h$, where $0 < \epsilon_1 < 1$, and $c_2 = x_0 + \epsilon_2 h$, where $0 < \epsilon_2 < 1$. Similarly, because both d_1 and d_2 are between y_0 and $y_0 + h$, we can write $d_1 = y_0 + \epsilon_3 h$, where $0 < \epsilon_3 < 1$, and $d_2 = y_0 + \epsilon_4 h$, where $0 < \epsilon_4 < 1$. Making these substitutions in (29) gives

$$f_{xy}(x_0 + \epsilon_1 h, y_0 + \epsilon_3 h) = f_{yx}(x_0 + \epsilon_2 h, y_0 + \epsilon_4 h) \tag{30}$$

Because f_{xy} and f_{yx} are continuous on B, upon taking the limit on both sides of (30) as h approaches zero, we obtain

$$f_{xy}(x_0, y_0) = f_{yx}(x_0, y_0) \qquad\blacksquare$$

As a result of the above theorem, if the function f of two variables has continuous partial derivatives on some open disk, then the order of partial differentiation can be changed without affecting the result; that is,

$$D_{112}f = D_{121}f = D_{211}f$$

$$D_{1122}f = D_{1212}f = D_{1221}f = D_{2112}f = D_{2121}f = D_{2211}f$$

and so forth. In particular, assuming that all of the partial derivatives are continuous on some open disk, we can prove that $D_{211}f = D_{112}f$ by applying Theorem 19.7.1 repeatedly. Doing this, we have

$$D_{211}f = D_1(D_{21}f) = D_1(D_{12}f) = D_1[D_2(D_1f)] = D_2[D_1(D_1f)]$$

$$= D_2(D_{11}f) = D_{112}f$$

EXAMPLE 5: Given that $u = f(x, y)$, $x = F(r, s)$, and $y = G(r, s)$, and assuming that $f_{xy} = f_{yx}$, prove by using the chain rule that

$$\frac{\partial^2 u}{\partial r^2} = f_{xx}(x, y)[F_r(r, s)]^2$$

$$+ 2f_{xy}(x, y)F_r(r, s)G_r(r, s)$$
$$+ f_{yy}(x, y)[G_r(r, s)]^2$$
$$+ f_x(x, y)F_{rr}(r, s)$$
$$+ f_y(x, y)G_{rr}(r, s)$$

SOLUTION: From the chain rule (Theorem 19.6.1) we have

$$\frac{\partial u}{\partial r} = f_x(x, y)F_r(r, s) + f_y(x, y)G_r(r, s)$$

Taking the partial derivative again with respect to r, and using the formula for the derivative of a product and the chain rule, we obtain

$$\frac{\partial^2 u}{\partial r^2} = [f_{xx}(x, y)F_r(r, s) + f_{xy}(x, y)G_r(r, s)]F_r(r, s) + f_x(x, y)F_{rr}(r, s)$$

$$+ [f_{yx}(x, y)F_r(r, s) + f_{yy}(x, y)G_r(r, s)]G_r(r, s) + f_y(x, y)G_{rr}(r, s)$$

Multiplying and combining terms, and using the fact that $f_{xy}(x, y) = f_{yx}(x, y)$, we get

$$\frac{\partial^2 u}{\partial r^2} = f_{xx}(x, y)[F_r(r, s)]^2 + 2f_{xy}(x, y)F_r(r, s)G_r(r, s)$$

$$+ f_{yy}(x, y)[G_r(r, s)]^2 + f_x(x, y)F_{rr}(r, s) + f_y(x, y)G_{rr}(r, s)$$

which is what we wished to prove.

Exercises 19.7

In Exercises 1 through 8, do each of the following: (a) Find $D_{11}f(x, y)$; (b) find $D_{22}f(x, y)$; (c) show that $D_{12}f(x, y) = D_{21}f(x, y)$.

1. $f(x, y) = \dfrac{x^2}{y} - \dfrac{y}{x^2}$

2. $f(x, y) = 2x^3 - 3x^2y + xy^2$

3. $f(x, y) = e^{2x} \sin y$

4. $f(x, y) = e^{-x/y} + \ln \dfrac{y}{x}$

5. $f(x, y) = (x^2 + y^2) \tan^{-1} \dfrac{y}{x}$

6. $f(x, y) = \sin^{-1} \dfrac{3y}{x^2}$

7. $f(x, y) = 4x \sinh y + 3y \cosh x$

8. $f(x, y) = x \cos y - ye^x$

In Exercises 9 through 14, find the indicated partial derivatives.

9. $f(x, y, z) = ye^x + ze^y + e^z$; (a) $f_{xz}(x, y, z)$; (b) $f_{yz}(x, y, z)$

10. $g(x, y, z) = \sin(xyz)$; (a) $g_{23}(x, y, z)$; (b) $g_{12}(x, y, z)$

11. $f(r, s) = 2r^3s + r^2s^2 - 5rs^3$; (a) $f_{121}(r, s)$; (b) $f_{221}(r, s)$

12. $f(u, v) = \ln \cos(u - v)$; (a) $f_{uuv}(u, v)$; (b) $f_{vuv}(u, v)$

13. $g(r, s, t) = \ln(r^2 + 4s^2 - 5t^2)$; (a) $g_{132}(r, s, t)$; (b) $g_{122}(r, s, t)$

14. $f(x, y, z) = \tan^{-1}(3xyz)$; (a) $f_{113}(x, y, z)$; (b) $f_{123}(x, y, z)$

In Exercises 15 through 18, show that $u(x, y)$ satisfies the equation

$$\frac{\partial^2 u}{\partial x^2} + \frac{\partial^2 u}{\partial y^2} = 0$$

which is known as *Laplace's equation* in R^2.

15. $u(x, y) = \ln(x^2 + y^2)$

16. $u(x, y) = e^x \sin y + e^y \cos x$

17. $u(x, y) = \tan^{-1} \dfrac{y}{x} + \dfrac{x}{x^2 + y^2}$

18. $u(x, y) = \tan^{-1} \dfrac{2xy}{x^2 - y^2}$

19. Laplace's equation in R^3 is

$$\frac{\partial^2 u}{\partial x^2} + \frac{\partial^2 u}{\partial y^2} + \frac{\partial^2 u}{\partial z^2} = 0$$

Show that $u(x, y, z) = (x^2 + y^2 + z^2)^{-1/2}$ satisfies this equation.

20. For the function of Example 4, show that f_{12} is discontinuous at $(0, 0)$ and hence that the hypothesis of Theorem 19.7.1 is not satisfied if $(x_0, y_0) = (0, 0)$.

In Exercises 21 through 23, find $f_{12}(0, 0)$ and $f_{21}(0, 0)$, if they exist.

21. $f(x, y) = \begin{cases} \dfrac{2xy}{x^2 + y^2} & \text{if } (x, y) \neq (0, 0) \\ 0 & \text{if } (x, y) = (0, 0) \end{cases}$

22. $f(x, y) = \begin{cases} \dfrac{x^2y^2}{x^4 + y^4} & \text{if } (x, y) \neq (0, 0) \\ 0 & \text{if } (x, y) = (0, 0) \end{cases}$

23. $f(x, y) = \begin{cases} x^2 \tan^{-1} \dfrac{y}{x} - y^2 \tan^{-1} \dfrac{x}{y} & \text{if } x \neq 0 \text{ and } y \neq 0 \\ 0 & \text{if either } x = 0 \text{ or } y = 0 \end{cases}$

24. Given that $u = f(x, y)$, $x = F(t)$, and $y = G(t)$, and assuming that $f_{xy} = f_{yx}$, prove by using the chain rule that

$$\frac{d^2u}{dt^2} = f_{xx}(x, y)[F'(t)]^2 + 2f_{xy}(x, y)F'(t)G'(t) + f_{yy}(x, y)[G'(t)]^2 + f_x(x, y)F''(t) + f_y(x, y)G''(t)$$

25. Given that $u = f(x, y)$, $x = F(r, s)$, and $y = G(r, s)$, and assuming that $f_{xy} = f_{yx}$, prove by using the chain rule that

$$\frac{\partial^2 u}{\partial r \, \partial s} = f_{xx}(x, y)F_r(r, s)F_s(r, s) + f_{xy}(x, y)[F_s(r, s)G_r(r, s) + F_r(r, s)G_s(r, s)]$$
$$+ f_{yy}(x, y)G_r(r, s)G_s(r, s) + f_x(x, y)F_{sr}(r, s) + f_y(x, y)G_{sr}(r, s)$$

26. Given $u = e^y \cos x$, $x = 2t$, $y = t^2$. Find d^2u/dt^2 in three ways: (a) by first expressing u in terms of t; (b) by using the formula of Exercise 24; (c) by using the chain rule.

27. Given $u = 3xy - 4y^2$, $x = 2se^r$, $y = re^{-s}$. Find $\partial^2u/\partial r^2$ in three ways: (a) by first expressing u in terms of r and s; (b) by using the formula of Example 5; (c) by using the chain rule.

28. For u, x, and y as given in Exercise 27, find $\partial^2 u/\partial s \, \partial r$ in three ways: (a) by first expressing u in terms of r and s; (b) by using the formula of Exercise 25; (c) by using the chain rule.

29. Given $u = 9x^2 + 4y^2$, $x = r \cos \theta$, $y = r \sin \theta$. Find $\partial^2 u/\partial r^2$ in three ways: (a) by first expressing u in terms of r and θ; (b) by using the formula of Example 5; (c) by using the chain rule.

30. For u, x, and y as given in Exercise 29, find $\partial^2 u/\partial \theta^2$ in three ways: (a) by first expressing u in terms of r and θ; (b) by using the formula of Example 5; (c) by using the chain rule.

31. For u, x, and y as given in Exercise 29, find $\partial^2 u/\partial r\,\partial\theta$ in three ways: (a) by first expressing u in terms of r and θ; (b) by using the formula of Exercise 25; (c) by using the chain rule.

32. If $u = f(x, y)$ and $v = g(x, y)$, then the equations

$$\frac{\partial u}{\partial x} = \frac{\partial v}{\partial y} \quad \text{and} \quad \frac{\partial v}{\partial x} = -\frac{\partial u}{\partial y}$$

are called the *Cauchy-Riemann equations*. If f and g and their first and second partial derivatives are continuous, prove that if u and v satisfy the Cauchy-Riemann equations, they also satisfy Laplace's equation (see Exercises 15 through 18).

33. The one-dimensional heat-conduction partial differential equation is

$$\frac{\partial u}{\partial t} = k^2 \frac{\partial^2 u}{\partial x^2}$$

Show that if f is a function of x satisfying the equation

$$\frac{d^2 f}{dx^2} + \lambda^2 f(x) = 0$$

and g is a function of t satisfying the equation $dg/dt + k^2\lambda^2 g(t) = 0$, then if $u = f(x)g(t)$, the partial differential equation is satisfied. k and λ are constants.

34. The partial differential equation for a vibrating string is

$$\frac{\partial^2 u}{\partial t^2} = a^2 \frac{\partial^2 u}{\partial x^2}$$

Show that if f is a function of x satisfying the equation $d^2f/dx^2 + \lambda^2 f(x) = 0$ and g is a function of t satisfying the equation $d^2g/dt^2 + a^2\lambda^2 g(t) = 0$, then if $u = f(x)g(t)$, the partial differential equation is satisfied. a and λ are constants.

35. Prove that if f and g are two arbitrary functions of a real variable having continuous second derivatives and $u = f(x + at) + g(x - at)$, then u satisfies the partial differential equation of the vibrating string given in Exercise 34. (HINT: Let $v = x + at$ and $w = x - at$; then u is a function of v and w, and v and w are in turn functions of x and t.)

36. Prove that if f is a function of two variables and all the partial derivatives of f up to the fourth order are continuous on some open disk, then

$$D_{1122}f = D_{2121}f$$

Review Exercises, Chapter 19.

In Exercises 1 through 6, find the indicated partial derivatives.

1. $f(x, y) = \dfrac{x^2 - y}{3y^2}$; $D_1 f(x, y)$, $D_2 f(x, y)$, $D_{12} f(x, y)$

2. $F(x, y, z) = 2xy^2 + 3yz^2 - 5xz^3$; $D_1 f(x, y, z)$, $D_3 f(x, y, z)$, $D_{13} f(x, y, z)$

3. $g(s, t) = \sin(st^2) + te^s$; $D_1 g(s, t)$, $D_2 g(s, t)$, $D_{21} g(s, t)$ 4. $h(x, y) = \tan^{-1}\dfrac{x^3}{y^2}$; $D_1 h(x, y)$, $D_2 h(x, y)$, $D_{11} h(x, y)$

5. $f(u, v, w) = \dfrac{\ln 4uv}{w^2}$; $D_1 f(u, v, w)$, $D_{13} f(u, v, w)$, $D_{131} f(u, v, w)$

6. $f(u, v, w) = w\cos 2v + 3v\sin u - 2uv\tan w$; $D_2 f(u, v, w)$, $D_1 f(u, v, w)$, $D_{131} f(u, v, w)$

In Exercises 7 and 8 find $\partial u/\partial t$ and $\partial u/\partial s$ by two methods.

7. $u = y\ln(x^2 + y^2)$, $x = 2s + 3t$, $y = 3t - 2s$ 8. $u = e^{2x+y}\cos(2y - x)$, $x = 2s^2 - t^2$, $y = s^2 + 2t^2$

9. If $u = xy + x^2$, $x = 4 \cos t$, and $y = 3 \sin t$, find the value of the total derivative du/dt at $t = \frac{1}{4}\pi$ by two methods: (a) Do not express u in terms of t before differentiating; (b) express u in terms of t before differentiating.

10. If $f(x, y, z) = 3xy^2 - 5xz^2 - 2xyz$, $\Delta x = 0.02$, $\Delta y = -0.01$, and $\Delta z = -0.02$, find (a) the increment of f at $(-1, 3, 2)$ and (b) the total differential of f at $(-1, 3, 2)$.

In Exercises 11 through 14, find the domain and range of the function f and draw a sketch showing as a shaded region in R^2 the set of points in the domain of f.

11. $f(x, y) = \sqrt{4x^2 - y}$

12. $f(x, y) = \sin^{-1}\sqrt{1 - x^2 - y^2}$

13. $f(x, y) = \tan^{-1}\sqrt{x^2 - y^2}$

14. $f(x, y) = [\![x]\!] + [\![\sqrt{1 - y^2}]\!]$

In Exercises 15 through 17, find the domain and range of the function f.

15. $f(x, y, z) = \dfrac{xy}{\sqrt{z}}$

16. $f(x, y, z) = \dfrac{xy + xz + yz}{xyz}$

17. $f(x, y, z) = \dfrac{x}{|y| - |z|}$

In Exercises 18 through 20, establish the limit by finding a $\delta > 0$ for any $\epsilon > 0$ so that Definition 19.2.5 holds.

18. $\lim\limits_{(x,y)\to(4,-1)} (4x - 5y) = 21$

19. $\lim\limits_{(x,y)\to(2,-2)} (3x^2 - 4y^2) = -4$

20. $\lim\limits_{(x,y)\to(3,1)} (x^2 - y^2 + 2x - 4y) = 10$

In Exercises 21 and 22, determine if the indicated limit exists.

21. $\lim\limits_{(x,y)\to(0,0)} \dfrac{x^3y^3}{x^2 + y^2}$

22. $\lim\limits_{(x,y)\to(0,0)} \dfrac{x^4 - y^4}{x^4 + y^4}$

In Exercises 23 through 27, discuss the continuity of f.

23. $f(x, y) = \begin{cases} \dfrac{x^3y^3}{x^2 + y^2} & \text{if } (x, y) \neq (0, 0) \\ 0 & \text{if } (x, y) = (0, 0) \end{cases}$ (HINT: See Exercise 21.)

24. $f(x, y) = \begin{cases} \dfrac{x^4 - y^4}{x^4 + y^4} & \text{if } (x, y) \neq (0, 0) \\ 0 & \text{if } (x, y) = (0, 0) \end{cases}$ (HINT: See Exercise 22.)

25. $f(x, y) = \dfrac{x^2 + 4y^2}{x^2 - 4y^2}$

26. $f(x, y) = \dfrac{1}{\cos \frac{1}{2}\pi x} + \dfrac{1}{\cos \frac{1}{2}\pi y}$

27. $f(x, y) = \dfrac{1}{\cos^2 \frac{1}{2}\pi x + \cos^2 \frac{1}{2}\pi y}$

In Exercises 28 and 29, prove that the function f is differentiable at all points in its domain by showing that Definition 19.5.2 holds.

28. $f(x, y) = 3xy^2 - 4x^2 + y^2$

29. $f(x, y) = \dfrac{2x + y}{y^2}$

30. Suppose α is the radian measure of an acute angle of a right triangle and $\sin \alpha$ is determined by a/c, where a in. is the length of the side opposite the angle and c in. is the length of the hypotenuse. If by measurement a is found to be 3.52 and c is found to be 7.14, and there is a possible error of 0.01 in each, find the possible error in the computation of $\sin \alpha$ from these measurements.

31. A painting contractor charges 12¢ per square foot for painting the four walls and ceiling of a room. If the dimensions of the ceiling are measured to be 12 ft and 15 ft, the height of the room is measured to be 10 ft, and these measurements are correct to 0.05 ft, find approximately, by using the total differential, the greatest error in estimating the cost of the job from these measurements.

32. At a given instant, the length of one side of a rectangle is 6 ft and it is increasing at the rate of 1 ft/sec and the length

of another side of the rectangle is 10 ft and it is decreasing at the rate of 2 ft/sec. Find the rate of change of the area of the rectangle at the given instant.

33. If f is a differentiable function of the variable u, let $u = x^2 + y^2$ and prove that $z = xy + f(x^2 + y^2)$ satisfies the equation

$$y \frac{\partial z}{\partial x} - x \frac{\partial z}{\partial y} = y^2 - x^2$$

34. Verify that $u(x, y) = (\sinh x)(\sin y)$ satisfies Laplace's equation in R^2:

$$\frac{\partial^2 u}{\partial x^2} + \frac{\partial^2 u}{\partial y^2} = 0$$

35. Verify that

$$u(x, t) = \sin \frac{n \pi x}{L} e^{(-n^2 \pi^2 k^2/L^2)t}$$

satisfies the one-dimensional heat-conduction partial differential equation:

$$\frac{\partial u}{\partial t} = k^2 \frac{\partial^2 u}{\partial x^2}$$

36. Verify that $u(x, t) = A \cos(kat) \sin(kx)$, where A and k are arbitrary constants, satisfies the partial differential equation for a vibrating string:

$$\frac{\partial^2 u}{\partial t^2} = a^2 \frac{\partial^2 u}{\partial x^2}$$

37. If f is a differentiable function of x and y and $u = f(x, y)$, $x = r \cos \theta$, and $y = r \sin \theta$, show that

$$\left(\frac{\partial u}{\partial r} \right)^2 + \frac{1}{r^2} \left(\frac{\partial u}{\partial \theta} \right)^2 = \left(\frac{\partial u}{\partial x} \right)^2 + \left(\frac{\partial u}{\partial y} \right)^2$$

38. Given

$$f(x, y) = \begin{cases} \dfrac{x^2 y}{x^4 + y^2} & \text{if } (x, y) \neq (0, 0) \\ 0 & \text{if } (x, y) = (0, 0) \end{cases}$$

Prove that $D_1 f(0, 0)$ and $D_2 f(0, 0)$ exist but that f is not differentiable at $(0, 0)$. (HINT: See Example 4, Sec. 19.2, and Exercise 2 in Exercises 19.3.)

39. Given

$$f(x, y, z) = \begin{cases} \dfrac{x^2 y^2 z^2}{(x^2 + y^2 + z^2)^2} & \text{if } (x, y, z) \neq (0, 0, 0) \\ 0 & \text{if } (x, y, z) = (0, 0, 0) \end{cases}$$

Prove that f is differentiable at $(0, 0, 0)$.

40. Let f be the function defined by

$$f(x, y) = \begin{cases} \dfrac{e^{-1/x^2} y}{e^{-2/x^2} + y^2} & \text{if } x \neq 0 \\ 0 & \text{if } x = 0 \end{cases}$$

Prove that f is discontinuous at the origin.

41. For the function of Exercise 40, prove that $D_1 f(0, 0)$ and $D_2 f(0, 0)$ both exist.

Directional derivatives, gradients, applications of partial derivatives, and line integrals

20.1 DIRECTIONAL DERIVATIVES AND GRADIENTS

We now generalize the definition of a partial derivative to obtain the rate of change of a function with respect to any direction. This leads to the concept of a "directional derivative."

Let f be a function of the two variables x and y and let $P(x, y)$ be a point in the xy plane. Suppose that $\mathbf{U}$ is the unit vector making an angle of radian measure θ with the positive side of the x axis. Then

$$\mathbf{U} = \cos \theta \mathbf{i} + \sin \theta \mathbf{j}$$

Figure 20.1.1 shows the representation of $\mathbf{U}$ having its initial point at the point $P(x, y)$.

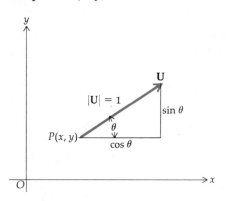

Figure 20.1.1

20.1.1 Definition

Let f be a function of two variables x and y. If $\mathbf{U}$ is the unit vector $\cos \theta \mathbf{i} + \sin \theta \mathbf{j}$, then the *directional derivative* of f in the direction of $\mathbf{U}$, denoted by $D_{\mathbf{U}} f$, is given by

$$D_{\mathbf{U}} f(x, y) = \lim_{h \to 0} \frac{f(x + h \cos \theta, y + h \sin \theta) - f(x, y)}{h}$$

if this limit exists.

The directional derivative gives the rate of change of the function values $f(x, y)$ with respect to the direction of the unit vector $\mathbf{U}$. This is illustrated in Fig. 20.1.2. The equation of the surface S in the figure is $z = f(x, y)$. $P_0(x_0, y_0, z_0)$ is a point on the surface, and the points $R(x_0, y_0, 0)$ and $Q(x_0 + h \cos \theta, y_0 + h \sin \theta, 0)$ are points in the xy plane. The plane through R and Q, parallel to the z axis, makes an angle of θ radians with the positive direction on the x axis. This plane intersects the surface S in the curve C. The directional derivative $D_{\mathbf{U}} f$, evaluated at P_0, is the slope of the tangent line to the curve C at P_0 in the plane of R, Q, and P_0.

If $\mathbf{U} = \mathbf{i}$, then $\cos \theta = 1$ and $\sin \theta = 0$, and we have from Definition 20.1.1

$$D_{\mathbf{i}} f(x, y) = \lim_{h \to 0} \frac{f(x + h, y) - f(x, y)}{h}$$

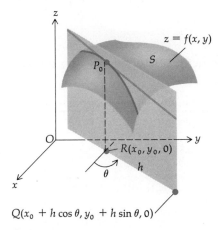

Figure 20.1.2

which is the partial derivative of f with respect to x.

If $\mathbf{U} = \mathbf{j}$, then $\cos \theta = 0$ and $\sin \theta = 1$, and we have

$$D_{\mathbf{j}}f(x, y) = \lim_{h \to 0} \frac{f(x, y + h) - f(x, y)}{h}$$

which is the partial derivative of f with respect to y.

So we see that f_x and f_y are special cases of the directional derivative in the directions of the unit vectors $\mathbf{i}$ and $\mathbf{j}$, respectively.

- ILLUSTRATION 1: We apply Definition 20.1.1 to find $D_{\mathbf{U}}f$ if

$$f(x, y) = 3x^2 - y^2 + 4x$$

and $\mathbf{U}$ is the unit vector in the direction $\frac{1}{6}\pi$. Then $\mathbf{U} = \cos \frac{1}{6}\pi \mathbf{i} + \sin \frac{1}{6}\pi \mathbf{j} = \frac{1}{2}\sqrt{3}\mathbf{i} + \frac{1}{2}\mathbf{j}$. So from Definition 20.1.1 we have

$$D_{\mathbf{U}}f(x, y) = \lim_{h \to 0} \frac{f(x + \frac{1}{2}\sqrt{3}h, y + \frac{1}{2}h) - f(x, y)}{h}$$

$$= \lim_{h \to 0} \frac{3(x + \frac{1}{2}\sqrt{3}h)^2 - (y + \frac{1}{2}h)^2 + 4(x + \frac{1}{2}\sqrt{3}h) - (3x^2 - y^2 + 4x)}{h}$$

$$= \lim_{h \to 0} \frac{3x^2 + 3\sqrt{3}hx + \frac{9}{4}h^2 - y^2 - hy - \frac{1}{4}h^2 + 4x + 2\sqrt{3}h - 3x^2 + y^2 - 4x}{h}$$

$$= \lim_{h \to 0} \frac{3\sqrt{3}hx + \frac{9}{4}h^2 - hy - \frac{1}{4}h^2 + 2\sqrt{3}h}{h}$$

$$= \lim_{h \to 0} (3\sqrt{3}x + \frac{9}{4}h - y - \frac{1}{4}h + 2\sqrt{3})$$

$$= 3\sqrt{3}x - y + 2\sqrt{3} \qquad \bullet$$

We now proceed to obtain a formula that will enable us to calculate a directional derivative in a way that is shorter than if we used the definition. We define g as the function of the single variable t, keeping x, y, and θ fixed such that

$$g(t) = f(x + t \cos \theta, y + t \sin \theta) \tag{1}$$

and let $\mathbf{U} = \cos \theta \mathbf{i} + \sin \theta \mathbf{j}$. Then by the definition of an ordinary derivative we have

$$g'(0) = \lim_{h \to 0} \frac{f(x + (0 + h) \cos \theta, y + (0 + h) \sin \theta) - f(x + 0 \cos \theta, y + 0 \sin \theta)}{h}$$

$$g'(0) = \lim_{h \to 0} \frac{f(x + h \cos \theta, y + h \sin \theta) - f(x, y)}{h}$$

Because the right side of the above is $D_{\mathbf{U}}f(x, y)$, it follows that

$$g'(0) = D_{\mathbf{U}}f(x, y) \tag{2}$$

We now find $g'(t)$ by applying the chain rule to the right side of

(1), which gives

$$g'(t) = f_1(x + t \cos \theta, y + t \sin \theta) \frac{\partial(x + t \cos \theta)}{\partial t}$$

$$+ f_2(x + t \cos \theta, y + t \sin \theta) \frac{\partial(y + t \sin \theta)}{\partial t}$$

$$= f_1(x + t \cos \theta, y + t \sin \theta) \cos \theta$$

$$+ f_2(x + t \cos \theta, y + t \sin \theta) \sin \theta$$

Therefore,

$$g'(0) = f_x(x, y) \cos \theta + f_y(x, y) \sin \theta \tag{3}$$

From (2) and (3) the following theorem is obtained.

20.1.2 Theorem   If f is a differentiable function of x and y, and $\mathbf{U} = \cos \theta \mathbf{i} + \sin \theta \mathbf{j}$, then

$$D_{\mathbf{U}}f(x, y) = f_x(x, y) \cos \theta + f_y(x, y) \sin \theta$$

• ILLUSTRATION 2: For the function f and the unit vector $\mathbf{U}$ of Illustration 1, we find $D_{\mathbf{U}}f$ by Theorem 20.1.2.

Because $f(x, y) = 3x^2 - y^2 + 4x$, $f_x(x, y) = 6x + 4$ and $f_y(x, y) = -2y$. Because $\mathbf{U} = \cos \frac{1}{6}\pi \mathbf{i} + \sin \frac{1}{6}\pi \mathbf{j}$, we have from Theorem 20.1.2

$$D_{\mathbf{U}}f(x, y) = (6x + 4)\tfrac{1}{2}\sqrt{3} + (-2y)\tfrac{1}{2} = 3\sqrt{3}x + 2\sqrt{3} - y$$

which agrees with the result in Illustration 1.   •

The directional derivative can be written as the dot product of two vectors. Because

$$f_x(x, y) \cos \theta + f_y(x, y) \sin \theta = (\cos \theta \mathbf{i} + \sin \theta \mathbf{j}) \cdot [f_x(x, y)\mathbf{i} + f_y(x, y)\mathbf{j}]$$

it follows from Theorem 20.1.2 that

$$D_{\mathbf{U}}f(x, y) = (\cos \theta \mathbf{i} + \sin \theta \mathbf{j}) \cdot [f_x(x, y)\mathbf{i} + f_y(x, y)\mathbf{j}] \tag{4}$$

The second vector on the right side of Eq. (4) is a very important one, and it is called the "gradient" of the function f. The symbol that we use for the gradient of f is ∇f, where ∇ is an inverted capital delta and is read "del." Sometimes the abbreviation *grad f* is used.

20.1.3 Definition   If f is a function of two variables x and y and f_x and f_y exist, then the *gradient* of f, denoted by ∇f (read: "del f"), is defined by

$$\nabla f(x, y) = f_x(x, y)\mathbf{i} + f_y(x, y)\mathbf{j}$$

Using Definition 20.1.3, Eq. (4) can be written as

$$D_{\mathbf{U}}f(x, y) = \mathbf{U} \cdot \nabla f(x, y) \tag{5}$$

Therefore, any directional derivative of a differentiable function can be obtained by dot-multiplying the gradient by a unit vector in the desired direction.

EXAMPLE 1:   If

$$f(x, y) = \frac{x^2}{16} + \frac{y^2}{9}$$

find the gradient of f at the point $(4, 3)$. Also find the rate of change of $f(x, y)$ in the direction $\frac{1}{4}\pi$ at $(4, 3)$.

SOLUTION: Because $f_x(x, y) = \frac{1}{8}x$ and $f_y(x, y) = \frac{2}{9}y$, we have

$$\nabla f(x, y) = \frac{1}{8}x\mathbf{i} + \frac{2}{9}y\mathbf{j}$$

Therefore,

$$\nabla f(4, 3) = \frac{1}{2}\mathbf{i} + \frac{2}{3}\mathbf{j}$$

The rate of change of $f(x, y)$ in the direction $\frac{1}{4}\pi$ at $(4, 3)$ is $D_\mathbf{U}f(4, 3)$, where $\mathbf{U}$ is the unit vector

$$\frac{1}{\sqrt{2}}\mathbf{i} + \frac{1}{\sqrt{2}}\mathbf{j}$$

This is found by dot-multiplying $\nabla f(4, 3)$ by $\mathbf{U}$. We have, then,

$$D_\mathbf{U}f(4, 3) = \left(\frac{1}{\sqrt{2}}\mathbf{i} + \frac{1}{\sqrt{2}}\mathbf{j}\right) \cdot \left(\frac{1}{2}\mathbf{i} + \frac{2}{3}\mathbf{j}\right) = \frac{7}{12}\sqrt{2}$$

If α is the radian measure of the angle between the two vectors $\mathbf{U}$ and ∇f, then

$$\mathbf{U} \cdot \nabla f = |\mathbf{U}||\nabla f| \cos \alpha \qquad (6)$$

From Eqs. (5) and (6) it follows that

$$D_\mathbf{U}f = |\mathbf{U}||\nabla f| \cos \alpha \qquad (7)$$

We see from Eq. (7) that $D_\mathbf{U}f$ will be a maximum when $\cos \alpha = 1$, that is, when $\mathbf{U}$ is in the direction of ∇f; and in this case, $D_\mathbf{U}f = |\nabla f|$. Hence, the gradient of a function is in the direction in which the function has its maximum rate of change. In particular, on a two-dimensional topographical map of a landscape where z units is the elevation at a point (x, y) and $z = f(x, y)$, the direction in which the rate of change of z is the greatest is given by $\nabla f(x, y)$; that is, $\nabla f(x, y)$ points in the direction of steepest ascent. This accounts for the name "gradient" (the grade is steepest in the direction of the gradient).

● ILLUSTRATION 3: In Figure 20.1.3 we have a contour map showing the level curves of the function of Example 1 at 1, 2, and 3. The level curves are ellipses. The figure also shows the representation of $\nabla f(4, 3)$ having its initial point at $(4, 3)$. ●

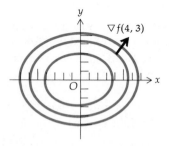

Figure 20.1.3

EXAMPLE 2:   Given

$$f(x, y) = 2x^2 - y^2 + 3x - y$$

SOLUTION: $f_x(x, y) = 4x + 3$ and $f_y(x, y) = -2y - 1$. So,

$$\nabla f(x, y) = (4x + 3)\mathbf{i} + (-2y - 1)\mathbf{j}$$

find the maximum value of $D_U f$ at the point where $x = 1$ and $y = -2$.

Therefore,

$$\nabla f(1, -2) = 7\mathbf{i} + 3\mathbf{j}$$

So the maximum value of $D_U f$ at the point $(1, -2)$ is

$$|\nabla f(1, -2)| = \sqrt{49 + 9} = \sqrt{58}$$

EXAMPLE 3: The temperature at any point (x, y) of a rectangular plate lying in the xy plane is determined by $T(x, y) = x^2 + y^2$. (a) Find the rate of change of the temperature at the point $(3, 4)$ in the direction making an angle of radian measure $\frac{1}{3}\pi$ with the positive x direction; (b) find the direction for which the rate of change of the temperature at the point $(-3, 1)$ is a maximum.

SOLUTION: (a) We wish to find $D_U T(x, y)$, where

$$\mathbf{U} = \cos \tfrac{1}{3}\pi \mathbf{i} + \sin \tfrac{1}{3}\pi \mathbf{j} = \tfrac{1}{2}\mathbf{i} + \tfrac{1}{2}\sqrt{3}\mathbf{j}$$

Because $T(x, y) = x^2 + y^2$, $T_x(x, y) = 2x$, and $T_y(x, y) = 2y$. Hence,

$$\nabla T(x, y) = T_x(x, y)\mathbf{i} + T_y(x, y)\mathbf{j} = 2x\mathbf{i} + 2y\mathbf{j}$$

Therefore,

$$\begin{aligned} D_U T(x, y) &= \mathbf{U} \cdot \nabla T(x, y) \\ &= (\tfrac{1}{2}\mathbf{i} + \tfrac{1}{2}\sqrt{3}\mathbf{j}) \cdot (2x\mathbf{i} + 2y\mathbf{j}) \\ &= x + \sqrt{3}y \end{aligned}$$

Hence,

$$D_U T(3, 4) = 3 + 4\sqrt{3} \approx 3 + 4(1.732) = 9.93$$

So at $(3, 4)$ the temperature is increasing at the rate of 9.93 units per unit change in the distance measured in the direction of $\mathbf{U}$.

(b) $D_U T(-3, 1)$ is a maximum when $\mathbf{U}$ is in the direction of $\nabla T(-3, 1)$. Because $\nabla T(-3, 1) = -6\mathbf{i} + 2\mathbf{j}$, the radian measure of the angle giving the direction of $\nabla T(-3, 1)$ is θ, where $\tan \theta = -\frac{1}{3}$. So $\theta = \pi - \tan^{-1}\frac{1}{3}$. Therefore, the rate of change of the temperature at the point $(-3, 1)$ is a maximum in the direction making an angle of radian measure $\pi - \tan^{-1}\frac{1}{3}$ with the positive side of the x axis.

We extend the definition of a directional derivative to a function of three variables. In three-dimensional space the direction of a vector is determined by its direction cosines. So we let $\cos \alpha$, $\cos \beta$, and $\cos \gamma$ be the direction cosines of the unit vector $\mathbf{U}$; therefore, $\mathbf{U} = \cos \alpha \mathbf{i} + \cos \beta \mathbf{j} + \cos \gamma \mathbf{k}$.

20.1.4 Definition Suppose that f is a function of three variables x, y, and z. If $\mathbf{U}$ is the unit vector $\cos \alpha \mathbf{i} + \cos \beta \mathbf{j} + \cos \gamma \mathbf{k}$, then the directional derivative of f in the direction of $\mathbf{U}$, denoted by $D_U f$, is given by

$$D_U f(x, y, z) = \lim_{h \to 0} \frac{f(x + h \cos \alpha, y + h \cos \beta, z + h \cos \gamma) - f(x, y, z)}{h}$$

if this limit exists.

The directional derivative of a function of three variables gives the rate of change of the function values $f(x, y, z)$ with respect to distance in three-dimensional space measured in the direction of the unit vector **U**.

The following theorem, which gives a method for calculating a directional derivative for a function of three variables, is proved in a manner similar to the proof of Theorem 20.1.2.

20.1.5 Theorem   If f is a differentiable function of x, y, and z and

$$\mathbf{U} = \cos \alpha \mathbf{i} + \cos \beta \mathbf{j} + \cos \gamma \mathbf{k}$$

then

$$D_\mathbf{U} f(x, y, z) = f_x(x, y, z) \cos \alpha + f_y(x, y, z) \cos \beta + f_z(x, y, z) \cos \gamma \quad (8)$$

EXAMPLE 4:   Given $f(x, y, z) =$ $3x^2 + xy - 2y^2 - yz + z^2$, find the rate of change of $f(x, y, z)$ at $(1, -2, -1)$ in the direction of the vector $2\mathbf{i} - 2\mathbf{j} - \mathbf{k}$.

SOLUTION: The unit vector in the direction of $2\mathbf{i} - 2\mathbf{j} - \mathbf{k}$ is given by

$$\mathbf{U} = \tfrac{2}{3}\mathbf{i} - \tfrac{2}{3}\mathbf{j} - \tfrac{1}{3}\mathbf{k}$$

Also,

$$f(x, y, z) = 3x^2 + xy - 2y^2 - yz + z^2$$

So from (8)

$$D_\mathbf{U} f(x, y, z) = \tfrac{2}{3}(6x + y) - \tfrac{2}{3}(x - 4y - z) - \tfrac{1}{3}(-y + 2z)$$

Therefore, the rate of change of $f(x, y, z)$ at $(1, -2, -1)$ in the direction of **U** is given by

$$D_\mathbf{U} f(1, -2, -1) = \tfrac{2}{3}(4) - \tfrac{2}{3}(10) - \tfrac{1}{3}(0) = -4$$

20.1.6 Definition   If f is a function of three variables x, y, and z and the first partial derivatives f_x, f_y, and f_z exist, then the *gradient* of f, denoted by ∇f, is defined by

$$\nabla f(x, y, z) = f_x(x, y, z)\mathbf{i} + f_y(x, y, z)\mathbf{j} + f_z(x, y, z)\mathbf{k}$$

Just as for functions of two variables, it follows from Theorem 20.1.5 and Definition 20.1.6 that if $\mathbf{U} = \cos \alpha \mathbf{i} + \cos \beta \mathbf{j} + \cos \gamma \mathbf{k}$, then

$$D_\mathbf{U} f(x, y, z) = \mathbf{U} \cdot \nabla f(x, y, z) \quad (9)$$

Also, the directional derivative is a maximum when **U** is in the direction of the gradient, and the maximum directional derivative is the magnitude of the gradient.

Applications of the gradient occur in physics in problems in heat conduction and electricity. Suppose that $w = f(x, y, z)$. A level surface of this function f at k is given by

$$f(x, y, z) = k \quad (10)$$

If w is the number of degrees in the temperature at point (x, y, z), then all points on the surface of Eq. (10) have the same temperature of k degrees, and the surface is called an *isothermal surface*. If w is the number of volts in the electric potential at point (x, y, z), then all points on the surface are at the same potential, and the surface is called an *equipotential surface*. The gradient vector at a point gives the direction of greatest rate of change of w. So if the level surface of Eq. (10) is an isothermal surface, $\nabla f(x, y, z)$ gives the direction of the greatest rate of change of temperature at (x, y, z). If Eq. (10) is an equation of an equipotential surface, then $\nabla f(x, y, z)$ gives the direction of the greatest rate of change of potential at (x, y, z).

EXAMPLE 5: If V volts is the electric potential at any point (x, y, z) in three-dimensional space and $V = 1/\sqrt{x^2 + y^2 + z^2}$, find: (a) the rate of change of V at the point $(2, 2, -1)$ in the direction of the vector $2i - 3j + 6k$; and (b) the direction of the greatest rate of change of V at $(2, 2, -1)$.

SOLUTION: Let $f(x, y, z) = 1/\sqrt{x^2 + y^2 + z^2}$.

(a) A unit vector in the direction of $2i - 3j + 6k$ is

$$\mathbf{U} = \tfrac{2}{7}\mathbf{i} - \tfrac{3}{7}\mathbf{j} + \tfrac{6}{7}\mathbf{k}$$

We wish to find $D_U f(2, 2, -1)$.

$$\nabla f(x, y, z) = f_x(x, y, z)\mathbf{i} + f_y(x, y, z)\mathbf{j} + f_z(x, y, z)\mathbf{k}$$

$$= \frac{-x}{(x^2 + y^2 + z^2)^{3/2}}\mathbf{i} + \frac{-y}{(x^2 + y^2 + z^2)^{3/2}}\mathbf{j} + \frac{-z}{(x^2 + y^2 + z^2)^{3/2}}\mathbf{k}$$

Then we have

$$D_U f(2, 2, -1) = \mathbf{U} \cdot \nabla f(2, 2, -1)$$

$$= (\tfrac{2}{7}\mathbf{i} - \tfrac{3}{7}\mathbf{j} + \tfrac{6}{7}\mathbf{k}) \cdot (-\tfrac{2}{27}\mathbf{i} - \tfrac{2}{27}\mathbf{j} + \tfrac{1}{27}\mathbf{k})$$

$$= -\tfrac{4}{189} + \tfrac{6}{189} + \tfrac{6}{189}$$

$$= \tfrac{8}{189}$$

$$\approx 0.042$$

Therefore, at $(2, 2, -1)$ the potential is increasing at the rate of 0.042 volt per unit change in the distance measured in the direction of $\mathbf{U}$.

(b) $\nabla f(2, 2, -1) = -\tfrac{2}{27}\mathbf{i} - \tfrac{2}{27}\mathbf{j} + \tfrac{1}{27}\mathbf{k}$. A unit vector in the direction of $\nabla f(2, 2, -1)$ is

$$\frac{\nabla f(2, 2, -1)}{|\nabla f(2, 2, -1)|} = \frac{-\tfrac{2}{27}\mathbf{i} - \tfrac{2}{27}\mathbf{j} + \tfrac{1}{27}\mathbf{k}}{\tfrac{3}{27}} = -\tfrac{2}{3}\mathbf{i} - \tfrac{2}{3}\mathbf{j} + \tfrac{1}{3}\mathbf{k}$$

The direction cosines of this vector are $-\tfrac{2}{3}$, $-\tfrac{2}{3}$, and $\tfrac{1}{3}$, which give the direction of the greatest rate of change of V at $(2, 2, -1)$.

Exercises 20.1

In Exercises 1 through 4, find the directional derivative of the given function in the direction of the given unit vector $\mathbf{U}$ by using either Definition 20.1.1 or Definition 20.1.4, and then verify your result by applying either Theorem 20.1.2 or Theorem 20.1.5, whichever one applies.

1. $f(x, y) = 2x^2 + 5y^2$; $\mathbf{U} = \cos \frac{1}{4}\pi \mathbf{i} + \sin \frac{1}{4}\pi \mathbf{j}$

2. $g(x, y) = \dfrac{1}{x^2 + y^2}$; $\mathbf{U} = \frac{3}{5}\mathbf{i} - \frac{4}{5}\mathbf{j}$

3. $h(x, y, z) = 3x^2 + y^2 - 4z^2$; $\mathbf{U} = \cos \frac{1}{3}\pi \mathbf{i} + \cos \frac{1}{4}\pi \mathbf{j} + \cos \frac{2}{3}\pi \mathbf{k}$

4. $f(x, y, z) = 6x^2 - 2xy + yz$; $\mathbf{U} = \frac{3}{7}\mathbf{i} + \frac{2}{7}\mathbf{j} + \frac{6}{7}\mathbf{k}$

In Exercises 5 through 10, find the value of the directional derivative at the particular point P_0 for the given function in the direction of $\mathbf{U}$.

5. $g(x, y) = y^2 \tan^2 x$; $\mathbf{U} = -\frac{1}{2}\sqrt{3}\mathbf{i} + \frac{1}{2}\mathbf{j}$; $P_0 = (\frac{1}{3}\pi, 2)$

6. $f(x, y) = xe^{2y}$; $\mathbf{U} = \frac{1}{2}\mathbf{i} + \frac{1}{2}\sqrt{3}\mathbf{j}$; $P_0 = (2, 0)$

7. $h(x, y, z) = \cos(xy) + \sin(yz)$; $\mathbf{U} = -\frac{2}{3}\mathbf{i} + \frac{2}{3}\mathbf{j} + \frac{2}{3}\mathbf{k}$; $P_0 = (2, 0, -3)$

8. $f(x, y, z) = \ln(x^2 + y^2 + z^2)$; $\mathbf{U} = \dfrac{1}{\sqrt{3}}\mathbf{i} - \dfrac{1}{\sqrt{3}}\mathbf{j} - \dfrac{1}{\sqrt{3}}\mathbf{k}$; $P_0 = (1, 3, 2)$

9. $f(x, y) = e^{-3x} \cos 3y$; $\mathbf{U} = \cos(-\frac{1}{12}\pi)\mathbf{i} + \sin(-\frac{1}{12}\pi)\mathbf{j}$; $P_0 = (-\frac{1}{12}\pi, 0)$

10. $g(x, y, z) = \cos 2x \cos 3y \sinh 4z$; $\mathbf{U} = \dfrac{1}{\sqrt{3}}\mathbf{i} - \dfrac{1}{\sqrt{3}}\mathbf{j} + \dfrac{1}{\sqrt{3}}\mathbf{k}$; $P_0 = (\frac{1}{2}\pi, 0, 0)$

In Exercises 11 through 14, a function f, a point P, and a unit vector $\mathbf{U}$ are given. Find (a) the gradient of f at P, and (b) the rate of change of the function value in the direction of $\mathbf{U}$ at P.

11. $f(x, y) = x^2 - 4y$; $P = (-2, 2)$; $\mathbf{U} = \cos \frac{1}{3}\pi \mathbf{i} + \sin \frac{1}{3}\pi \mathbf{j}$

12. $f(x, y) = e^{2xy}$; $P = (2, 1)$; $\mathbf{U} = \frac{4}{5}\mathbf{i} - \frac{3}{5}\mathbf{j}$

13. $f(x, y, z) = y^2 + z^2 - 4xz$; $P = (-2, 1, 3)$; $\mathbf{U} = \frac{2}{7}\mathbf{i} - \frac{6}{7}\mathbf{j} + \frac{3}{7}\mathbf{k}$

14. $f(x, y, z) = 2x^3 + xy^2 + xz^2$; $P = (1, 1, 1)$; $\mathbf{U} = \frac{1}{7}\sqrt{21}\mathbf{j} - \frac{2}{7}\sqrt{7}\mathbf{k}$

15. Draw a contour map showing the level curves of the function of Exercise 11 at $8, 4, 0, -4,$ and -8. Also show the representation of $\nabla f(-2, 2)$ having its initial point at $(-2, 2)$.

16. Draw a contour map showing the level curves of the function of Exercise 12 at $e^8, e^4, 1, e^{-4},$ and e^{-8}. Also show the representation of $\nabla f(2, 1)$ having its initial point at $(2, 1)$.

In Exercises 17 through 20, find $D_\mathbf{U}f$ at the given point P for which $\mathbf{U}$ is a unit vector in the direction of $\overrightarrow{PQ}$. Also at P find $D_\mathbf{U}f$, if $\mathbf{U}$ is a unit vector for which $D_\mathbf{U}f$ is a maximum.

17. $f(x, y) = e^x \tan^{-1} y$; $P(0, 1)$, $Q(3, 5)$

18. $f(x, y) = e^x \cos y + e^y \sin x$; $P(1, 0)$, $Q(-3, 3)$

19. $f(x, y, z) = x - 2y + z^2$; $P(3, 1, -2)$, $Q(10, 7, 4)$

20. $f(x, y, z) = x^2 + y^2 - 4xz$; $P(3, 1, -2)$, $Q(-6, 3, 4)$

21. Find the direction from the point $(1, 3)$ for which the value of f does not change if $f(x, y) = e^{2y} \tan^{-1}(y/3x)$.

22. The density is ρ slugs/ft^2 at any point (x, y) of a rectangular plate in the xy plane and $\rho = 1/\sqrt{x^2 + y^2 + 3}$. (a) Find the rate of change of the density at the point $(3, 2)$ in the direction of the unit vector $\cos \frac{2}{3}\pi \mathbf{i} + \sin \frac{2}{3}\pi \mathbf{j}$. (b) Find the direction and magnitude of the greatest rate of change of ρ at $(3, 2)$.

23. The electric potential is V volts at any point (x, y) in the xy plane and $V = e^{-2x} \cos 2y$. Distance is measured in feet. (a) Find the rate of change of the potential at the point $(0, \frac{1}{4}\pi)$ in the direction of the unit vector $\cos \frac{1}{6}\pi \mathbf{i} + \sin \frac{1}{6}\pi \mathbf{j}$. (b) Find the direction and magnitude of the greatest rate of change of V at $(0, \frac{1}{4}\pi)$.

24. The temperature is T degrees at any point (x, y, z) in three-dimensional space and $T = 60/(x^2 + y^2 + z^2 + 3)$. Distance is measured in inches. (a) Find the rate of change of the temperature at the point $(3, -2, 2)$ in the direction of the vector $-2\mathbf{i} + 3\mathbf{j} - 6\mathbf{k}$. (b) Find the direction and magnitude of the greatest rate of change of T at $(3, -2, 2)$.

25. An equation of the surface of a mountain is $z = 1200 - 3x^2 - 2y^2$, where distance is measured in feet, the x axis points to the east, and the y axis points to the north. A mountain climber is at the point corresponding to $(-10, 5, 850)$. (a) What is the direction of steepest ascent? (b) If the climber moves in the east direction, is he ascending or descending, and what is his rate? (c) If the climber moves in the southwest direction, is he ascending or descending, and what is his rate? (d) In what direction is he traveling a level path?

20.2 TANGENT PLANES AND NORMALS TO SURFACES

Let S be the surface having the equation

$$F(x, y, z) = 0 \tag{1}$$

and suppose that $P_0(x_0, y_0, z_0)$ is a point on S. Then $F(x_0, y_0, z_0) = 0$. Suppose further that C is a curve on S through P_0 and a set of parametric equations of C is

$$x = f(t) \qquad y = g(t) \qquad z = h(t) \tag{2}$$

Let the value of the parameter t at the point P_0 be t_0. A vector equation of C is

$$\mathbf{R}(t) = f(t)\mathbf{i} + g(t)\mathbf{j} + h(t)\mathbf{k} \tag{3}$$

Because curve C is on surface S, we have, upon substituting from (2) in (1),

$$F(f(t), g(t), h(t)) = 0 \tag{4}$$

Let $G(t) = F(f(t), g(t), h(t))$. If F_x, F_y, and F_z are continuous and not all zero at P_0, and if $f'(t_0)$, $g'(t_0)$, and $h'(t_0)$ exist, then the total derivative of F with respect to t at P_0 is given by

$$G'(t_0) = F_x(x_0, y_0, z_0)f'(t_0) + F_y(x_0, y_0, z_0)g'(t_0) + F_z(x_0, y_0, z_0)h'(t_0)$$

which also can be written as

$$G'(t_0) = \nabla F(x_0, y_0, z_0) \cdot D_t \mathbf{R}(t_0)$$

Because $G'(t) = 0$ for all t under consideration (because of (4)), $G'(t_0) = 0$; so it follows from the above that

$$\nabla F(x_0, y_0, z_0) \cdot D_t \mathbf{R}(t_0) = 0 \tag{5}$$

From Sec. 18.9, we know that $D_t \mathbf{R}(t_0)$ has the same direction as the unit tangent vector to curve C at P_0. Therefore, from (5) we can conclude that the gradient vector of F at P_0 is orthogonal to the unit tangent vector of every curve C on S through the point P_0. We are led, then, to the following definition.

20.2.1 Definition   A vector which is orthogonal to the unit tangent vector of every curve C through a point P_0 on a surface S is called a *normal vector* to S at P_0.

From this definition and the preceding discussion we have the following theorem.

20.2.2 Theorem If an equation of a surface S is $F(x, y, z) = 0$, and F_x, F_y, and F_z are continuous and not all zero at the point $P_0(x_0, y_0, z_0)$ on S, then a normal vector to S at P_0 is $\nabla F(x_0, y_0, z_0)$.

We now can define the "tangent plane" to a surface at a point.

20.2.3 Definition If an equation of a surface S is $F(x, y, z) = 0$, then the *tangent plane* of S at a point $P_0(x_0, y_0, z_0)$ is the plane through P_0 having as a normal vector $\nabla F(x_0, y_0, z_0)$.

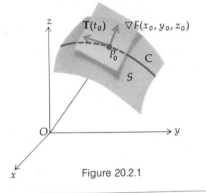

Figure 20.2.1

An equation of the tangent plane of the above definition is

$$F_x(x_0, y_0, z_0)(x - x_0) + F_y(x_0, y_0, z_0)(y - y_0) + F_z(x_0, y_0, z_0)(z - z_0) = 0 \quad (6)$$

Refer to Fig. 20.2.1, which shows the tangent plane to the surface S at P_0 and the representation of the gradient vector having its initial point at P_0.

A vector equation of the tangent plane given by (6) is

$$\nabla F(x_0, y_0, z_0) \cdot [(x - x_0)\mathbf{i} + (y - y_0)\mathbf{j} + (z - z_0)\mathbf{k}] = 0 \quad (7)$$

EXAMPLE 1: Find an equation of the tangent plane to the elliptic paraboloid $4x^2 + y^2 - 16z = 0$ at the point $(2, 4, 2)$.

SOLUTION: Let $F(x, y, z) = 4x^2 + y^2 - 16z$. Then $\nabla F(x, y, z) = 8x\mathbf{i} + 2y\mathbf{j} - 16\mathbf{k}$, and so $\nabla F(2, 4, 2) = 16\mathbf{i} + 8\mathbf{j} - 16\mathbf{k}$. From (7) it follows that an equation of the tangent plane is

$$16(x - 2) + 8(y - 4) - 16(z - 2) = 0$$

$$2x + y - 2z - 4 = 0$$

20.2.4 Definition The *normal line* to a surface S at a point P_0 on S is the line through P_0 having as a set of direction numbers the components of any normal vector to S at P_0.

If an equation of a surface S is $F(x, y, z) = 0$, symmetric equations of the normal line to S at $P_0(x_0, y_0, z_0)$ are

$$\frac{x - x_0}{F_x(x_0, y_0, z_0)} = \frac{y - y_0}{F_y(x_0, y_0, z_0)} = \frac{z - z_0}{F_z(x_0, y_0, z_0)} \quad (8)$$

The denominators in (8) are components of $\nabla F(x_0, y_0, z_0)$, which is a normal vector to S at P_0; thus, (8) follows from Definition 20.2.4. The normal line at a point on a surface is perpendicular to the tangent plane there.

EXAMPLE 2: Find symmetric equations of the normal line to the surface of Example 1 at $(2, 4, 2)$.

SOLUTION: Because $\nabla F(2, 4, 2) = 16\mathbf{i} + 8\mathbf{j} - 16\mathbf{k}$, it follows that symmetric equations of the required normal line are

$$\frac{x - 2}{2} = \frac{y - 4}{1} = \frac{z - 2}{-2}$$

20.2.5 Definition   The *tangent line* to a curve C at a point P_0 is the line through P_0 having as a set of direction numbers the components of the unit tangent vector to C at P_0.

Figure 20.2.2

From Definitions 20.2.3 and 20.2.5 we see that all the tangent lines at the point P_0 to the curves lying on a given surface lie in the tangent plane to the surface at P_0. Refer to Fig. 20.2.2, showing sketches of a surface and the tangent plane at P_0. Some of the curves through P_0 and their tangent lines are also sketched in the figure.

Consider a curve C which is the intersection of two surfaces having equations

$$F(x, y, z) = 0 \qquad (9)$$

and

$$G(x, y, z) = 0 \qquad (10)$$

respectively. We shall show how to obtain equations of the tangent line to C at a point $P_0(x_0, y_0, z_0)$. Because this tangent line lies in each of the tangent planes to the given surfaces at P_0, it is the line of intersection of the two tangent planes. A normal vector at P_0 to the surface having Eq. (9) is given by

$$\mathbf{N}_1 = \nabla F(x_0, y_0, z_0) = F_x(x_0, y_0, z_0)\mathbf{i} + F_y(x_0, y_0, z_0)\mathbf{j} + F_z(x_0, y_0, z_0)\mathbf{k}$$

and a normal vector at P_0 to the surface having Eq. (10) is given by

$$\mathbf{N}_2 = \nabla G(x_0, y_0, z_0) = G_x(x_0, y_0, z_0)\mathbf{i} + G_y(x_0, y_0, z_0)\mathbf{j} + G_z(x_0, y_0, z_0)\mathbf{k}$$

Both $\mathbf{N}_1$ and $\mathbf{N}_2$ are orthogonal to the unit tangent vector to C at P_0; so if $\mathbf{N}_1$ and $\mathbf{N}_2$ are not parallel, it follows from Theorem 18.6.9 that the unit tangent vector has the direction which is the same as, or opposite to, the direction of $\mathbf{N}_1 \times \mathbf{N}_2$. Therefore, the components of $\mathbf{N}_1 \times \mathbf{N}_2$ serve as a set of direction numbers of the tangent line. From this set of direction numbers and the coordinates of P_0 we can obtain symmetric equations of the required tangent line. This is illustrated in the following example.

EXAMPLE 3: Find symmetric equations of the tangent line to the curve of intersection of the surfaces $3x^2 + 2y^2 + z^2 = 49$ and $x^2 + y^2 - 2z^2 = 10$ at the point $(3, -3, 2)$.

SOLUTION: Let $F(x, y, z) = 3x^2 + 2y^2 + z^2 - 49$

and

$$G(x, y, z) = x^2 + y^2 - 2z^2 - 10$$

Then $\nabla F(x, y, z) = 6x\mathbf{i} + 4y\mathbf{j} + 2z\mathbf{k}$ and $\nabla G(x, y, z) = 2x\mathbf{i} + 2y\mathbf{j} - 4z\mathbf{k}$. So

$$\mathbf{N}_1 = \nabla F(3, -3, 2) = 18\mathbf{i} - 12\mathbf{j} + 4\mathbf{k} = 2(9\mathbf{i} - 6\mathbf{j} + 2\mathbf{k})$$

and

$$\mathbf{N}_2 = \nabla G(3, -3, 2) = 6\mathbf{i} - 6\mathbf{j} - 8\mathbf{k} = 2(3\mathbf{i} - 3\mathbf{j} - 4\mathbf{k})$$

$$\mathbf{N}_1 \times \mathbf{N}_2 = 4(9\mathbf{i} - 6\mathbf{j} + 2\mathbf{k}) \times (3\mathbf{i} - 3\mathbf{j} - 4\mathbf{k})$$

$$= 4(30\mathbf{i} + 42\mathbf{j} - 9\mathbf{k})$$

$$= 12(10\mathbf{i} + 14\mathbf{j} - 3\mathbf{k})$$

Therefore, a set of direction numbers of the required tangent line is $[10, 14, -3]$. Symmetric equations of the line are, then,

$$\frac{x-3}{10} = \frac{y+3}{14} = \frac{z-2}{-3}$$

If two surfaces have a common tangent plane at a point, the two surfaces are said to be *tangent* at that point.

Exercises 20.2

In Exercises 1 through 12, find an equation of the tangent plane and equations of the normal line to the given surface at the indicated point.

1. $x^2 + y^2 + z^2 = 17$; $(2, -2, 3)$
2. $4x^2 + y^2 + 2z^2 = 26$; $(1, -2, 3)$
3. $x^2 + y^2 - 3z = 2$; $(-2, -4, 6)$

4. $x^2 + y^2 - z^2 = 6$; $(3, -1, 2)$
5. $y = e^x \cos z$; $(1, e, 0)$
6. $z = e^{3x} \sin 3y$; $(0, \frac{1}{6}\pi, 1)$

7. $x^2 = 12y$; $(6, 3, 3)$
8. $z = x^{1/2} + y^{1/2}$; $(1, 1, 2)$
9. $x^{1/2} + y^{1/2} + z^{1/2} = 4$; $(4, 1, 1)$

10. $zx^2 - xy^2 - yz^2 = 18$; $(0, -2, 3)$
11. $x^{2/3} + y^{2/3} + z^{2/3} = 14$; $(-8, 27, 1)$
12. $x^{1/2} + z^{1/2} = 8$; $(25, 2, 9)$

In Exercises 13 through 18, if the two given surfaces intersect in a curve, find equations of the tangent line to the curve of intersection at the given point; if the two given surfaces are tangent at the given point, prove it.

13. $x^2 + y^2 - z = 8$, $x - y^2 + z^2 = -2$; $(2, -2, 0)$
14. $x^2 + y^2 - 2z + 1 = 0$, $x^2 + y^2 - z^2 = 0$; $(0, 1, 1)$

15. $y = x^2$, $y = 16 - z^2$; $(4, 16, 0)$
16. $x = 2 + \cos \pi yz$, $y = 1 + \sin \pi xz$; $(3, 1, 2)$

17. $x^2 + z^2 + 4y = 0$, $x^2 + y^2 + z^2 - 6z + 7 = 0$; $(0, -1, 2)$
18. $x^2 + y^2 + z^2 = 8$, $yz = 4$; $(0, 2, 2)$

19. Prove that every normal line to the sphere $x^2 + y^2 + z^2 = a^2$ passes through the center of the sphere.

20.3 EXTREMA OF FUNCTIONS OF TWO VARIABLES   An important application of the derivatives of a function of a single variable is in the study of extreme values of a function, which leads to a variety of problems involving maximum and minimum. We discussed this thoroughly in Chapters 4 and 5, where we proved theorems involving the first and second derivatives, which enabled us to determine relative maximum and minimum values of a function of one variable. In extending the theory to functions of two variables, we see that it is similar to the one-variable case; however, more complications arise.

20.3.1 Definition   The function f of two variables is said to have an *absolute maximum value* on a disk B in the xy plane if there is some point (x_0, y_0) in B such that $f(x_0, y_0) \geq f(x, y)$ for all points (x, y) in B. In such a case, $f(x_0, y_0)$ is the absolute maximum value of f on B.

20.3.2 Definition   The function f of two variables is said to have an *absolute minimum value* on a disk B in the xy plane if there is some point (x_0, y_0) in B such that $f(x_0, y_0) \leq f(x, y)$ for all points (x, y) in B. In such a case, $f(x_0, y_0)$ is the absolute minimum value of f on B.

20.3.3 Theorem
The Extreme-Value Theorem
for Functions of Two Variables

Let B be a closed disk in the xy plane, and let f be a function of two variables which is continuous on B. Then there is at least one point in B where f has an absolute maximum value and at least one point in B where f has an absolute minimum value.

The proof of Theorem 20.3.3 is omitted because it is beyond the scope of this book.

20.3.4 Definition   The function f of two variables is said to have a *relative maximum value* at the point (x_0, y_0) if there exists an open disk $B((x_0, y_0); r)$ such that $f(x, y) \leq f(x_0, y_0)$ for all (x, y) in the open disk.

20.3.5 Definition   The function f of two variables is said to have a *relative minimum value* at the point (x_0, y_0) if there exists an open disk $B((x_0, y_0); r)$ such that $f(x, y) \geq f(x_0, y_0)$ for all (x, y) in the open disk.

20.3.6 Theorem   If $f(x, y)$ exists at all points in some open disk $B((x_0, y_0); r)$ and if f has a relative extremum at (x_0, y_0), then if $f_x(x_0, y_0)$ and $f_y(x_0, y_0)$ exist,

$$f_x(x_0, y_0) = f_y(x_0, y_0) = 0$$

PROOF: We prove that if f has a relative maximum value at (x_0, y_0) and if $f_x(x_0, y_0)$ exists, then $f_x(x_0, y_0) = 0$. By the definition of a partial derivative,

$$f_x(x_0, y_0) = \lim_{\Delta x \to 0} \frac{f(x_0 + \Delta x, y_0) - f(x_0, y_0)}{\Delta x}$$

Because f has a relative maximum value at (x_0, y_0), by Definition 20.3.4 it follows that

$$f(x_0 + \Delta x, y_0) - f(x_0, y_0) \leq 0$$

whenever Δx is sufficiently small so that $(x_0 + \Delta x, y_0)$ is in B. If Δx approaches zero from the right, $\Delta x > 0$; therefore,

$$\frac{f(x_0 + \Delta x, y_0) - f(x_0, y_0)}{\Delta x} \leq 0$$

Hence, by Theorem 4.3.4, if $f_x(x_0, y_0)$ exists, $f_x(x_0, y_0) \leq 0$.
Similarly, if Δx approaches zero from the left, $\Delta x < 0$; so

$$\frac{f(x_0 + \Delta x, y_0) - f(x_0, y_0)}{\Delta x} \geq 0$$

Therefore, by Theorem 4.3.5, if $f_x(x_0, y_0)$ exists, $f_x(x_0, y_0) \geq 0$. We conclude, then, that because $f_x(x_0, y_0)$ exists, both inequalities, $f_x(x_0, y_0) \leq 0$ and $f_x(x_0, y_0) \geq 0$, must hold. Consequently, $f_x(x_0, y_0) = 0$.

The proof that $f_y(x_0, y_0) = 0$, if $f_y(x_0, y_0)$ exists and f has a relative maximum value at (x_0, y_0), is analogous and is left as an exercise (see Exercise 13). The proof of the theorem when $f(x_0, y_0)$ is a relative minimum value is also left as an exercise (see Exercise 14).   ■

20.3.7 Definition   A point (x_0, y_0) for which both $f_x(x_0, y_0) = 0$ and $f_y(x_0, y_0) = 0$ is called a *critical point*.

Theorem 20.3.6 states that a necessary condition for a function of two variables to have a relative extremum at a point, where its first partial derivatives exist, is that this point be a critical point. It is possible for a function of two variables to have a relative extremum at a point at which the partial derivatives do not exist, but we do not consider this situation in this book. Furthermore, the vanishing of the first partial derivatives of a function of two variables is not a sufficient condition for the function to have a relative extremum at the point. Such a situation occurs at a point called a *saddle point*.

● ILLUSTRATION 1: A simple example of a function which has a saddle point is the one defined by

$$f(x, y) = y^2 - x^2$$

For this function we see that $f_x(x, y) = -2x$ and $f_y(x, y) = 2y$. Both $f_x(0, 0)$ and $f_y(0, 0)$ equal zero. A sketch of the graph of the function is shown in Fig. 20.3.1, and we see that it is saddle shaped at points close to the origin. It is apparent that this function f does not satisfy either Definition 20.3.4 or 20.3.5 when $(x_0, y_0) = (0, 0)$.   ●

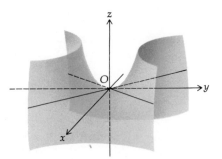

Figure 20.3.1

We have a second-derivative test which gives conditions that guarantee a function to have a relative extremum at a point where the first partial derivatives vanish. However, sometimes it is possible to determine relative extrema of a function by Definitions 20.3.4 and 20.3.5, as shown in the following illustration.

● ILLUSTRATION 2: Let f be the function defined by

$$f(x, y) = 6x - 4y - x^2 - 2y^2$$

We determine if f has any relative extrema.

Because f and its first partial derivatives exist at all (x, y) in R^2, Theorem 20.3.6 is applicable. Differentiating, we get

$$f_x(x, y) = 6 - 2x \quad \text{and} \quad f_y(x, y) = -4 - 4y$$

Setting $f_x(x, y)$ and $f_y(x, y)$ equal to zero, we get $x = 3$ and $y = -1$. The graph (see Fig. 20.3.2 for a sketch) of the equation

$$z = 6x - 4y - x^2 - 2y^2$$

is a paraboloid having a vertical axis, with vertex at $(3, -1, 11)$ and opening downward. We can conclude that $f(x, y) < f(3, -1)$ for all $(x, y) \neq (3, -1)$; hence, by Definition 20.3.4, $f(3, -1) = 11$ is a relative maximum function value. It follows from Definition 20.3.1 that 11 is the absolute maximum function value of f on R^2. ●

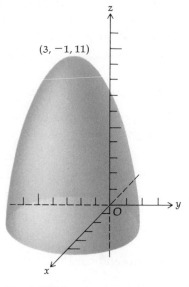

Figure 20.3.2

The basic test for determining relative maxima and minima for functions of two variables is the second-derivative test, which is given in the next theorem.

20.3.8 Theorem
Second-Derivative Test

Let f be a function of two variables such that f and its first- and second-order partial derivatives are continuous on some open disk $B((a, b); r)$. Suppose further that $f_x(a, b) = f_y(a, b) = 0$. Then

(i) f has a relative minimum value at (a, b) if

$$f_{xx}(a, b)f_{yy}(a, b) - f_{xy}^2(a, b) > 0 \quad \text{and} \quad f_{xx}(a, b) > 0$$

(ii) f has a relative maximum value at (a, b) if

$$f_{xx}(a, b)f_{yy}(a, b) - f_{xy}^2(a, b) > 0 \quad \text{and} \quad f_{xx}(a, b) < 0$$

(iii) $f(a, b)$ is not a relative extremum if

$$f_{xx}(a, b)f_{yy}(a, b) - f_{xy}^2(a, b) < 0$$

(iv) We can make no conclusion if

$$f_{xx}(a, b)f_{yy}(a, b) - f_{xy}^2(a, b) = 0$$

PROOF OF (i):   For simplicity of notation, let us define

$$\phi(x, y) = f_{xx}(x, y)f_{yy}(x, y) - f_{xy}^2(x, y)$$

We are given $\phi(a, b) > 0$ and $f_{xx}(a, b) > 0$, and we wish to prove that $f(a, b)$ is a relative minimum function value. Because f_{xx}, f_{xy}, and f_{yy} are continuous on $B((a, b); r)$, it follows that ϕ is also continuous on B. Hence, there exists an open disk $B'((a, b); r')$, where $r' \leq r$, such that $\phi(x, y) > 0$ and $f_{xx}(x, y) > 0$ for every point (x, y) in B'. Let h and k be constants, not both zero, such that the point $(a + h, b + k)$ is in B'. Then the two equations

$$x = a + ht \quad \text{and} \quad y = b + kt \qquad 0 \leq t \leq 1$$

define all the points on the line segment from (a, b) to $(a + h, b + k)$, and all these points are in B'. Let F be the function of one variable defined by

$$F(t) = f(a + ht, b + kt) \tag{1}$$

By Taylor's formula (formula (9), Sec. 15.5), we have

$$F(t) = F(0) + F'(0)t + \frac{F''(\xi)}{2!} t^2 \tag{2}$$

where ξ is between 0 and t. If $t = 1$ in Eq. (2), we get

$$F(1) = F(0) + F'(0) + \tfrac{1}{2}F''(\xi) \tag{3}$$

where $0 < \xi < 1$. Because $F(0) = f(a, b)$ and $F(1) = f(a + h, b + k)$, it follows from Eq. (3) that

$$f(a + h, b + k) = f(a, b) + F'(0) + \tfrac{1}{2}F''(\xi) \tag{4}$$

where $0 < \xi < 1$.

To find $F'(t)$ and $F''(t)$ from (1), we use the chain rule and obtain

$$F'(t) = hf_x(a + ht, b + kt) + kf_y(a + ht, b + kt) \tag{5}$$

and

$$F''(t) = h^2 f_{xx} + hk f_{yx} + hk f_{xy} + k^2 f_{yy}$$

where each second partial derivative is evaluated at $(a + ht, b + kt)$. From Theorem 19.7.1, it follows that $f_{xy}(x, y) = f_{yx}(x, y)$ for all (x, y) in B'. So

$$F''(t) = h^2 f_{xx} + 2hk f_{xy} + k^2 f_{yy} \tag{6}$$

where each second partial derivative is evaluated at $(a + ht, b + kt)$. Substituting 0 for t in Eq. (5) and ξ for t in Eq. (6), we get

$$F'(0) = hf_x(a, b) + kf_y(a, b) = 0 \tag{7}$$

and

$$F''(\xi) = h^2 f_{xx} + 2hk f_{xy} + k^2 f_{yy} \tag{8}$$

where each second partial derivative is evaluated at $(a + h\xi, b + k\xi)$, where $0 < \xi < 1$. Substituting from (7) and (8) into (4), we obtain

$$f(a + h, b + k) - f(a, b) = \tfrac{1}{2}(h^2 f_{xx} + 2hk f_{xy} + k^2 f_{yy}) \tag{9}$$

The terms in parentheses on the right side of Eq. (9) can be written as

$$h^2 f_{xx} + 2hk f_{xy} + k^2 f_{yy} = f_{xx}\left[h^2 + 2hk\frac{f_{xy}}{f_{xx}} + \left(k\frac{f_{xy}}{f_{xx}}\right)^2 - \left(k\frac{f_{xy}}{f_{xx}}\right)^2 + k^2\frac{f_{yy}}{f_{xx}}\right]$$

So from (9) we have

$$f(a + h, b + k) - f(a, b) = \frac{f_{xx}}{2}\left[\left(h + \frac{f_{xy}}{f_{xx}}k\right)^2 + \frac{f_{xx}f_{yy} - f_{xy}^2}{f_{xx}^2}k^2\right] \tag{10}$$

Because $f_{xx}f_{yy} - f_{xy}^2$ evaluated at $(a + h\xi, b + k\xi)$ equals

$$\phi(a + h\xi, b + k\xi) > 0$$

it follows that the expression in brackets on the right side of Eq. (10) is positive. Furthermore, because $f_{xx}(a + h\xi, b + k\xi) > 0$, it follows from Eq. (10) that $f(a + h, b + k) - f(a, b) > 0$. Hence, we have proved that

$$f(a + h, b + k) > f(a, b)$$

for every point $(a + h, b + k) \neq (a, b)$ in B'. Therefore, by Definition 20.3.5, $f(a, b)$ is a relative minimum value of f.

The proof of part (ii) is similar and is left as an exercise (see Exercise 15). The proof of part (iii) is also left as an exercise (see Exercise 16). Part (iv) is included to cover all possible cases. ∎

EXAMPLE 1: Given that f is the function defined by

$$f(x, y) = 2x^4 + y^2 - x^2 - 2y$$

determine the relative extrema of f if there are any.

SOLUTION:

$$f_x(x, y) = 8x^3 - 2x \qquad f_y(x, y) = 2y - 2$$

Setting $f_x(x, y) = 0$, we get $x = -\tfrac{1}{2}$, $x = 0$, and $x = \tfrac{1}{2}$. Setting $f_y(x, y) = 0$, we get $y = 1$. Therefore, f_x and f_y both vanish at the points $(-\tfrac{1}{2}, 1)$, $(0, 1)$, and $(\tfrac{1}{2}, 1)$.

To apply the second-derivative test, we find the second partial derivatives of f and get

$$f_{xx}(x, y) = 24x^2 - 2 \qquad f_{yy}(x, y) = 2 \qquad f_{xy}(x, y) = 0$$

$$f_{xx}(-\tfrac{1}{2}, 1) = 4 > 0$$

and

$$f_{xx}(-\tfrac{1}{2}, 1)f_{yy}(-\tfrac{1}{2}, 1) - f_{xy}^2(-\tfrac{1}{2}, 1) = 4 \cdot 2 - 0 = 8 > 0$$

Hence, by Theorem 20.3.8(i), f has a relative minimum value at $(-\tfrac{1}{2}, 1)$.

$$f_{xx}(0, 1)f_{yy}(0, 1) - f_{xy}{}^2(0, 1) = (-2)(2) - 0 = -4 < 0$$

and so by Theorem 20.3.8(iii), f does not have a relative extremum at $(0, 1)$.

$$f_{xx}(\tfrac{1}{2}, 1) = 4 > 0$$

and

$$f_{xx}(\tfrac{1}{2}, 1)f_{yy}(\tfrac{1}{2}, 1) - f_{xy}{}^2(\tfrac{1}{2}, 1) = 4 \cdot 2 - 0 = 8 > 0$$

Therefore, by Theorem 20.3.8(i) f has a relative minimum value at $(\tfrac{1}{2}, 1)$. Hence, we conclude that f has a relative minimum value of $-\tfrac{9}{8}$ at each of the points $(-\tfrac{1}{2}, 1)$ and $(\tfrac{1}{2}, 1)$.

EXAMPLE 2: Determine the relative dimensions of a rectangular box, without a top and having a specific volume, if the least amount of material is to be used in its manufacture.

SOLUTION: Let $x =$ the number of units in the length of the base of the box;

$y =$ the number of units in the width of the base of the box;

$z =$ the number of units in the depth of the box;

$S =$ the number of square units in the surface area of the box;

$V =$ the number of cubic units in the volume of the box (V is constant).

x, y, and z are in the interval $(0, +\infty)$. Hence, the absolute minimum value of S will be among the relative minimum values of S. We have the equations

$$S = xy + 2xz + 2yz \quad \text{and} \quad V = xyz$$

Solving the second equation for z in terms of the variables x and y and the constant V, we get $z = V/xy$. And substituting this into the first equation gives us

$$S = xy + \frac{2V}{y} + \frac{2V}{x}$$

Differentiating, we get

$$\frac{\partial S}{\partial x} = y - \frac{2V}{x^2} \qquad \frac{\partial S}{\partial y} = x - \frac{2V}{y^2}$$

$$\frac{\partial^2 S}{\partial x^2} = \frac{4V}{x^3} \qquad \frac{\partial^2 S}{\partial y \, \partial x} = 1 \qquad \frac{\partial^2 S}{\partial y^2} = \frac{4V}{y^3}$$

Setting $\partial S/\partial x = 0$ and $\partial S/\partial y = 0$, and solving simultaneously, we get

$$x^2 y - 2V = 0$$

$$xy^2 - 2V = 0$$

from which it follows that $x = \sqrt[3]{2V}$, and $y = \sqrt[3]{2V}$. For these values of x

and y, we have

$$\frac{\partial^2 S}{\partial x^2} = \frac{4V}{(\sqrt[3]{2V})^3} = \frac{4V}{2V} = 2 > 0$$

and

$$\frac{\partial^2 S}{\partial x^2} \frac{\partial^2 S}{\partial y^2} - \left(\frac{\partial^2 S}{\partial y \, \partial x}\right)^2 = \frac{4V}{(\sqrt[3]{2V})^3} \cdot \frac{4V}{(\sqrt[3]{2V})^3} - 1 = 3 > 0$$

From Theorem 20.3.8(i), it follows that S has a relative minimum value and hence an absolute minimum value when $x = \sqrt[3]{2V}$ and $y = \sqrt[3]{2V}$. From these values of x and y we get

$$z = \frac{V}{xy} = \frac{V}{\sqrt[3]{4V^2}} = \frac{\sqrt[3]{2V}}{2}$$

We therefore conclude that the box should have a square base and a depth which is one-half that of the length of a side of the base.

Our discussion of the extrema of functions of two variables can be extended to functions of three or more variables. The definitions of relative extrema and critical point are easily made. For example, if f is a function of the three variables x, y, and z, and $f_x(x_0, y_0, z_0) = f_y(x_0, y_0, z_0) = f_z(x_0, y_0, z_0) = 0$, then (x_0, y_0, z_0) is a critical point of f. Such a point is obtained by solving simultaneously three equations in three unknowns. For a function of n variables, the critical points are found by setting all the n first partial derivatives equal to zero and solving simultaneously the n equations in n unknowns. The extension of Theorem 20.3.8 to functions of three or more variables is given in advanced calculus texts.

In the solution of Example 2 we minimized the function having function values $xy + 2xz + 2yz$, subject to the condition that $x, y,$ and z satisfy the equation $xyz = V$. Compare this with Example 1, in which we found the relative extrema of the function f for which $f(x, y) = 2x^4 + y^2 - x^2 - 2y$. These are essentially two different kinds of problems because in the first case we had an additional condition, called a *constraint* (or *side condition*). Such a problem is called one in *constrained extrema*, whereas that of the second type is called a problem in *free extrema*.

The solution of Example 2 involved obtaining a function of the two variables x and y by replacing z in the first equation by its value from the second equation. Another method that can be used to solve this example is due to Joseph Lagrange, and it is known as the method of *Lagrange multipliers*. The theory behind this method involves theorems known as implicit function theorems, which are studied in advanced calculus. Hence, a proof is not given here. The procedure is outlined and illustrated by examples.

Suppose that we wish to find the critical points of a function f of the three variables $x, y,$ and z, subject to the constraint $g(x, y, z) = 0$. We introduce a new variable, usually denoted by λ, and form the auxiliary function F for which

$$F(x, y, z, \lambda) = f(x, y, z) + \lambda g(x, y, z)$$

The problem then becomes one of finding the critical points of the function F of the four variables x, y, z, and λ. The method is used in the following example.

EXAMPLE 3:   Solve Example 2 by the method of Lagrange multipliers.

SOLUTION: Using the variables x, y, and z and the constant V as defined in the solution of Example 2, let

$$S = f(x, y, z) = xy + 2xz + 2yz$$

and

$$g(x, y, z) = xyz - V$$

We wish to minimize the function f subject to the constraint that

$$g(x, y, z) = 0$$

Let

$$F(x, y, z, \lambda) = f(x, y, z) + \lambda g(x, y, z)$$

$$= xy + 2xz + 2yz + \lambda(xyz - V)$$

Finding the four partial derivatives F_x, F_y, F_z, and F_λ and setting the function values equal to zero, we have

$$F_x(x, y, z, \lambda) = y + 2z + \lambda yz = 0 \tag{11}$$

$$F_y(x, y, z, \lambda) = x + 2z + \lambda xz = 0 \tag{12}$$

$$F_z(x, y, z, \lambda) = 2x + 2y + \lambda xy = 0 \tag{13}$$

$$F_\lambda(x, y, z, \lambda) = xyz - V = 0 \tag{14}$$

Subtracting corresponding members of Eq. (12) from those of Eq. (11) we obtain

$$y - x + \lambda z(y - x) = 0$$

from which we get

$$(y - x)(1 + \lambda z) = 0$$

giving us the two equations

$$y = x \tag{15}$$

and

$$\lambda = -\frac{1}{z} \tag{16}$$

Substituting from Eq. (16) into Eq. (12) we get $x + 2z - x = 0$, giving $z = 0$, which is impossible because z is in the interval $(0, +\infty)$. Substituting from Eq. (15) into Eq. (13) gives

$$2x + 2x + \lambda x^2 = 0$$

$$x(4 + \lambda x) = 0$$

and because $x \neq 0$, we get

$$\lambda = -\frac{4}{x}$$

If in Eq. (12) we take $\lambda = -4/x$, we have

$$x + 2z - \frac{4}{x}(xz) = 0$$

$$x + 2z - 4z = 0$$

$$z = \frac{x}{2} \tag{17}$$

Substituting from Eqs. (15) and (17) into Eq. (14), we get $\frac{1}{2}x^3 - V = 0$, from which it follows that $x = \sqrt[3]{2V}$. From Eqs. (15) and, (17) it follows that $y = \sqrt[3]{2V}$ and $z = \frac{1}{2}\sqrt[3]{2V}$. These results agree with those found in the solution of Example 2.

Note in the solution that the equation $F_\lambda(x, y, z, \lambda) = 0$ is the same as the constraint given by the equation $V = xyz$.

If several constraints are imposed, the method used in Example 3 can be extended by using several multipliers. In particular, if we wish to find critical points of the function having function values $f(x, y, z)$ subject to the two side conditions $g(x, y, z) = 0$ and $h(x, y, z) = 0$, we find the critical points of the function F of the five variables x, y, z, λ, and μ for which

$$F(x, y, z, \lambda, \mu) = f(x, y, z) + \lambda g(x, y, z) + \mu h(x, y, z)$$

The following example illustrates the method.

EXAMPLE 4: Find the relative extrema of the function f if $f(x, y, z) = xz + yz$ and the point (x, y, z) lies on the intersection of the surfaces $x^2 + z^2 = 2$ and $yz = 2$.

SOLUTION: We form the function F for which

$$F(x, y, z, \lambda, \mu) = xz + yz + \lambda(x^2 + z^2 - 2) + \mu(yz - 2)$$

Finding the five partial derivatives and setting them equal to zero, we have

$$F_x(x, y, z, \lambda, \mu) = z + 2\lambda x = 0 \tag{18}$$

$$F_y(x, y, z, \lambda, \mu) = z + \mu z = 0 \tag{19}$$

$$F_z(x, y, z, \lambda, \mu) = x + y + 2\lambda z + \mu y = 0 \tag{20}$$

$$F_\lambda(x, y, z, \lambda, \mu) = x^2 + z^2 - 2 = 0 \tag{21}$$

$$F_\mu(x, y, z, \lambda, \mu) = yz - 2 = 0 \tag{22}$$

From Eq. (19) we obtain $\mu = -1$ and $z = 0$. We reject $z = 0$ because this contradicts Eq. (22). From Eq. (18) we obtain

$$\lambda = -\frac{z}{2x} \tag{23}$$

Substituting from (23) and $\mu = -1$ into Eq. (20), we get

$$x + y - \frac{z^2}{x} - y = 0$$

and so

$$x^2 = z^2 \tag{24}$$

Substituting from Eq. (24) into (21), we have $2x^2 - 2 = 0$, or $x^2 = 1$. This gives two values for x, namely 1 and -1; and for each of these values of x we get, from Eq. (24), the two values 1 and -1 for z. Obtaining the corresponding values for y from Eq. (22), we have four sets of solutions for the five Eqs. (18) through (22). These solutions are

$$x = 1 \qquad y = 2 \qquad z = 1 \qquad \lambda = -\tfrac{1}{2} \qquad \mu = -1$$
$$x = 1 \qquad y = -2 \qquad z = -1 \qquad \lambda = \tfrac{1}{2} \qquad \mu = -1$$
$$x = -1 \qquad y = 2 \qquad z = 1 \qquad \lambda = \tfrac{1}{2} \qquad \mu = -1$$
$$x = -1 \qquad y = -2 \qquad z = -1 \qquad \lambda = -\tfrac{1}{2} \qquad \mu = -1$$

The first and fourth sets of solutions give $f(x, y, z) = 3$, and the second and third sets of solutions give $f(x, y, z) = 1$. Hence, f has a relative maximum function value of 3 and a relative minimum function value of 1.

Exercises 20.3

In Exercises 1 through 6, determine the relative extrema of f, if there are any.

1. $f(x, y) = 18x^2 - 32y^2 - 36x - 128y - 110$

2. $f(x, y) = \dfrac{1}{x} - \dfrac{64}{y} + xy$

3. $f(x, y) = \sin(x + y) + \sin x + \sin y$

4. $f(x, y) = x^3 + y^3 - 18xy$

5. $f(x, y) = 4xy^2 - 2x^2y - x$

6. $f(x, y) = \dfrac{2x + 2y + 1}{x^2 + y^2 + 1}$

In Exercises 7 through 12, use the method of Lagrange multipliers to find the critical points of the given function subject to the indicated constraint.

7. $f(x, y) = x^2 + 2xy + y^2$ with constraint $x - y = 3$

8. $f(x, y) = x^2 + xy + 2y^2 - 2x$ with constraint $x - 2y + 1 = 0$

9. $f(x, y) = 25 - x^2 - y^2$ with constraint $x^2 + y^2 - 4y = 0$

10. $f(x, y) = 4x^2 + 2y^2 + 5$ with constraint $x^2 + y^2 - 2y = 0$

11. $f(x, y, z) = x^2 + y^2 + z^2$ with constraint $3x - 2y + z - 4 = 0$

12. $f(x, y, z) = x^2 + y^2 + z^2$ with constraint $y^2 - x^2 = 1$

13. Prove that $f_y(x_0, y_0) = 0$ if $f_y(x_0, y_0)$ exists and f has a relative maximum value at (x_0, y_0).

14. Prove Theorem 20.3.6 when $f(x_0, y_0)$ is a relative minimum value.

15. Prove Theorem 20.3.8(ii).   16. Prove Theorem 20.3.8(iii).

17. Find three numbers whose sum is $N(N > 0)$ such that their product is as great as possible.

18. Prove that the box having the largest volume that can be placed inside a sphere is in the shape of a cube.

19. Determine the relative dimensions of a rectangular box, without a top, to be made from a given amount of material in order for the box to have the greatest possible volume.

20. A manufacturing plant has two classifications for its workers, A and B. Class A workers earn $14 per run, and class B workers earn $13 per run. For a certain production run, it is determined that in addition to the salaries of the workers, if x class A workers and y class B workers are used, the number of dollars in the cost of the run is $y^3 + x^2 - 8xy + 600$. How many workers of each class should be used so that the cost of the run is a minimum if at least three workers of each class are required for a run?

21. A circular disk is in the shape of the region bounded by the circle $x^2 + y^2 = 1$. If T degrees is the temperature at any point (x, y) of the disk and $T = 2x^2 + y^2 - y$, find the hottest and coldest points on the disk.

22. Find the points on the surface $y^2 - xz = 4$ that are closest to the origin and find the minimum distance.

23. Find the points on the curve of intersection of the ellipsoid $x^2 + 4y^2 + 4z^2 = 4$ and the plane $x - 4y - z = 0$ that are closest to the origin and find the minimum distance.

24. A rectangular box without a top is to be made at a cost of $10 for the material. If the material for the bottom of the box costs 15¢ per square foot and the material for the sides costs 30¢ per square foot, find the dimensions of the box of greatest volume that can be made.

25. A closed rectangular box to contain 16 ft³ is to be made of three kinds of material. The cost of the material for the top and the bottom is 9¢ per ft², the cost of the material for the front and the back is 8¢ per ft², and the cost of the material for the other two sides is 6¢ per ft². Find the dimensions of the box so that the cost of the materials is a minimum.

26. Suppose that T degrees is the temperature at any point (x, y, z) on the sphere $x^2 + y^2 + z^2 = 4$, and $T = 100xy^2z$. Find the points on the sphere where the temperature is the greatest and also the points where the temperature is the least. Also find the temperature at these points.

27. Find the absolute maximum function value of f if $f(x, y, z) = x^2 + y^2 + z^2$ with the two constraints $x - y + z = 0$ and $25x^2 + 4y^2 + 20z^2 = 100$. Use Lagrange multipliers.

28. Find the absolute minimum function value of f if $f(x, y, z) = x^2 + 3y^2 + 2z^2$ with the two constraints $x - 2y - z = 6$ and $x - 3y + 2z = 4$. Use Lagrange multipliers.

20.4 SOME APPLICATIONS OF PARTIAL DERIVATIVES TO ECONOMICS

In Sec. 5.6 we discussed a demand equation giving the relationship between x and p, where p dollars is the price of one unit of a commodity when x units are demanded. In addition to the price of the given commodity, the demand often will depend on the prices of other commodities related to the given one. In particular, let us consider two related commodities for which p dollars is the price per unit of x units of the

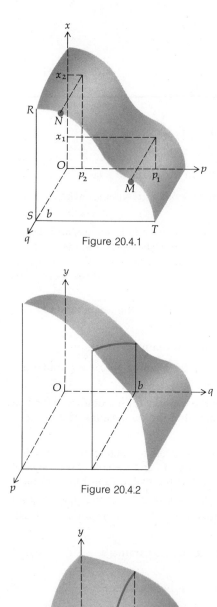

Figure 20.4.1

Figure 20.4.2

Figure 20.4.3

first commodity and q dollars is the price per unit of y units of the second commodity. Then the demand equations for these two commodities can be written, respectively, as

$$\alpha(x, p, q) = 0 \quad \text{and} \quad \beta(y, p, q) = 0$$

or, solving the first equation for x and the second equation for y, as

$$x = f(p, q) \tag{1}$$

and

$$y = g(p, q) \tag{2}$$

The functions f and g in Eqs. (1) and (2) are the demand functions and the graphs of these functions are surfaces. Under normal circumstances x, y, p, and q are nonnegative, and so the surfaces are restricted to the first octant. These surfaces are called *demand surfaces*. Recalling that p dollars is the price of one unit of x units of the first commodity, we note that if the variable q is held constant, then x decreases as p increases and x increases as p decreases. This is illustrated in Fig. 20.4.1, which is a sketch of the demand surface for an equation of type (1) under normal circumstances. The plane $q = b$ intersects the surface in section RST. For any point on the curve RT, q is the constant b. Referring to the points $M(p_1, b, x_1)$ and $N(p_2, b, x_2)$, we see that $x_2 > x_1$ if and only if $p_2 < p_1$; that is, x decreases as p increases and x increases as p decreases.

When q is constant, therefore, as p increases, x decreases; but y may either increase or decrease. If y increases, then a decrease in the demand for one commodity corresponds to an increase in the demand for the other, and the two commodities are said to be *substitutes* (for example, butter and margarine). Now if, when q is constant, y decreases as p increases, then a decrease in the demand for one commodity corresponds to a decrease in the demand for the other, and the two commodities are said to be *complementary* (for example, tires and gasoline).

● ILLUSTRATION 1: Figures 20.4.2 and 20.4.3 each show a sketch of a demand surface for an equation of type (2). In Fig. 20.4.2, we see that when q is constant, y increases as p increases, and so the two commodities are substitutes. In Fig. 20.4.3 the two commodities are complementary because when q is constant, y decreases as p increases. ●

Observe that in Figs. 20.4.1 and 20.4.2, which show the demand surfaces for equations of types (1) and (2), respectively, the p and q axes are interchanged and that the vertical axis in Fig. 20.4.1 is labeled x and in Fig. 20.4.2 it is labeled y.

It is possible that for a fixed value of q, y may increase for some values of p and decrease for other values of p. For example, if the demand surface of Eq. (2) is that shown in Fig. 20.4.4, then for $q = b$, when $p = a_1$, y is increasing, and when $p = a_2$, y is decreasing. This of course means that

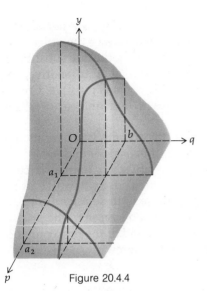

Figure 20.4.4

if the price of the second commodity is held constant, then for some prices of the first commodity the two commodities will be substitutes and for other prices of the first commodity the two commodities will be complementary. These relationships between the two commodities that are determined by the demand surface having equation $y = g(p, q)$ will correspond to similar relationships determined by the demand surface having equation $x = f(p, q)$ for the same fixed values of p and q. An economic example might be one in which investors allocate funds between the stock market and real estate. As stock prices climb, they invest in real estate. Yet once stock prices seem to reach a crash level, investors begin to decrease the amount of real estate purchases with any increase in stock prices in anticipation of a collapse that will affect the real estate market and its values.

The demand functions are now used to define the (partial) "marginal demand."

20.4.1 Definition   Let p dollars be the price of one unit of x units of a first commodity and q dollars be the price of one unit of y units of a second commodity. Suppose that f and g are the respective demand functions for these two commodities so that

$$x = f(p, q) \quad \text{and} \quad y = g(p, q)$$

Then

(i) $\dfrac{\partial x}{\partial p}$ gives the (partial) *marginal demand of x with respect to p*;

(ii) $\dfrac{\partial x}{\partial q}$ gives the (partial) *marginal demand of x with respect to q*;

(iii) $\dfrac{\partial y}{\partial p}$ gives the (partial) *marginal demand of y with respect to p*;

(iv) $\dfrac{\partial y}{\partial q}$ gives the (partial) *marginal demand of y with respect to q*.

Because in normal circumstances if the variable q is held constant, x decreases as p increases and x increases as p decreases, we conclude that $\partial x/\partial p$ is negative. Similarly, $\partial y/\partial q$ is negative in normal circumstances. Two commodities are said to be complementary when a decrease in the demand for one commodity as a result of an increase in its price leads to a decrease in the demand for the other. So when the goods are complementary and q is held constant, both $\partial x/\partial p < 0$ and $\partial y/\partial p < 0$; and when p is held constant, then $\partial x/\partial q < 0$ as well as $\partial y/\partial q < 0$. Therefore, we can conclude that the two commodities are complementary if and only if both $\partial x/\partial q$ and $\partial y/\partial p$ are negative.

When a decrease in the demand for one commodity as a result of an increase in its price leads to an increase in the demand for the other commodity, the goods are substitutes. Hence, when the goods are substitutes, because $\partial x/\partial p$ is always negative, we conclude that $\partial y/\partial p$ is positive; and because $\partial y/\partial q$ is always negative, it follows that $\partial x/\partial q$ is positive. Consequently, the two commodities are substitutes if and only if $\partial x/\partial q$ and $\partial y/\partial p$ are both positive.

If $\partial x/\partial q$ and $\partial y/\partial p$ have opposite signs, the commodities are neither complementary nor substitutes. For example, if $\partial x/\partial q < 0$ and $\partial y/\partial p > 0$, and because $\partial x/\partial p$ and $\partial y/\partial q$ are always negative (in normal circumstances), we have both $\partial x/\partial q < 0$ and $\partial y/\partial q < 0$. Thus, a decrease in the price of the second commodity causes an increase in the demands of both commodities. Because $\partial x/\partial p < 0$ and $\partial y/\partial p > 0$, a decrease in the price of the first commodity causes an increase in the demand of the first commodity and a decrease in the demand of the second commodity.

EXAMPLE 1: Suppose that p dollars is the price per unit of x units of one commodity and q dollars is the price per unit of y units of a second commodity. The demand equations are

$$x = -2p + 3q + 12 \qquad (3)$$

and

$$y = -4q + p + 8 \qquad (4)$$

Find the four marginal demands and determine if the commodities are substitutes or complementary. Also draw sketches of the two demand surfaces.

SOLUTION: If we use Definition 20.4.1, the four marginal demands are given by

$$\frac{\partial x}{\partial p} = -2 \qquad \frac{\partial x}{\partial q} = 3 \qquad \frac{\partial y}{\partial p} = 1 \qquad \frac{\partial y}{\partial q} = -4$$

Because $\partial x/\partial q > 0$ and $\partial y/\partial p > 0$, the two commodities are substitutes.

A sketch of the demand surface of Eq. (3) is shown in Fig. 20.4.5. To draw this sketch we first determine from both equations the permissible values of p and q. Because x and y must be positive or zero, p and q must satisfy the inequalities $-2p + 3q + 12 \geq 0$ and $-4q + p + 8 \geq 0$. Also, p and q are each nonnegative. Hence, the values of p and q are restricted to the quadrilateral $AOBC$. The required demand surface then is the portion in the first octant of the plane defined by Eq. (3) which is above $AOBC$. This is the shaded quadrilateral $ADEC$ in the figure. In Fig. 20.4.6 we have a

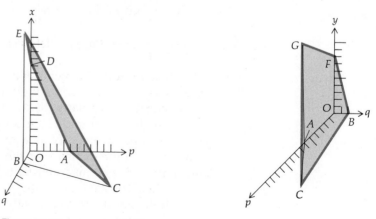

Figure 20.4.5

Figure 20.4.6

sketch of the demand surface defined by Eq. (4). This demand surface is the shaded quadrilateral $BFGC$, that is, the portion in the first octant of the plane defined by Eq. (4) which is above the quadrilateral $AOBC$.

For nonlinear demand functions of two variables, it is often more convenient to represent them geometrically by means of contour maps than by surfaces. The following example is such a case.

EXAMPLE 2: If p dollars is the price of one unit of x units of a first commodity and q dollars is the price of one unit of y units of a second commodity, and the demand equations are given by

$$x = \frac{8}{pq} \quad \text{and} \quad y = \frac{12}{pq}$$

draw sketches of the contour maps of the two demand functions showing the level curves of each function at 6, 4, 2, 1, and $\frac{1}{2}$. Are the commodities substitutes or complementary?

SOLUTION: Let the two demand functions be f and g so that $x = f(p, q) = 8/pq$ and $y = g(p, q) = 12/pq$. Sketches of the contour maps of f and g showing the level curves of these functions at the required numbers are shown in Figs. 20.4.7 and 20.4.8, respectively.

$$\frac{\partial x}{\partial q} = -\frac{8}{pq^2} \quad \text{and} \quad \frac{\partial y}{\partial p} = -\frac{12}{p^2 q}$$

Because $\partial x/\partial q < 0$ and $\partial y/\partial p < 0$, the commodities are complementary.

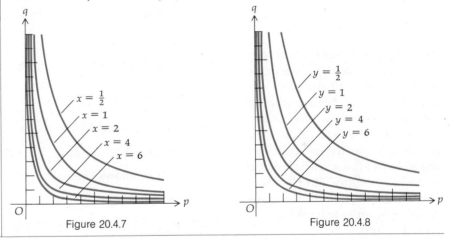

Figure 20.4.7   Figure 20.4.8

EXAMPLE 3: The demand equations for two related commodities are

$$x = 4e^{-pq} \quad \text{and} \quad y = 8e^{p-q}$$

Determine if the commodities are complementary, substitutes, or neither.

SOLUTION:

$$\frac{\partial x}{\partial q} = -4pe^{-pq} \quad \text{and} \quad \frac{\partial y}{\partial p} = 8e^{p-q}$$

Because $\partial x/\partial q < 0$ and $\partial y/\partial p > 0$, the commodities are neither complementary nor substitutes.

If the cost of producing x units of one commodity and y units of another commodity is given by $C(x, y)$, then C is called a *joint-cost function*. The partial derivatives of C are called *marginal cost functions*.

Suppose that a monopolist produces two related commodities whose demand equations are $x = f(p, q)$ and $y = g(p, q)$ and the joint-cost function is C. Because the revenue from the two commodities is given by $px + qy$, then if S is the number of dollars in the profit, we have

$$S = px + qy - C(x, y)$$

To determine the greatest profit that can be earned, we use the demand equations to express S in terms of either p and q or x and y alone and then apply the methods of the preceding section. The following example illustrates the procedure.

EXAMPLE 4:   A monopolist produces two commodities which are substitutes having demand equations

$$x = 8 - p + q$$

and

$$y = 9 + p - 5q$$

where $1000x$ units of the first commodity are demanded if the price is p dollars per unit and $1000y$ units of the second commodity are demanded if the price is q dollars per unit. It costs \$4 to produce each unit of the first commodity and \$2 to produce each unit of the second commodity. Find the demands and prices of the two commodities in order to have the greatest profit.

SOLUTION: When $1000x$ units of the first commodity and $1000y$ units of the second commodity are produced and sold, the number of dollars in the total revenue is $1000px + 1000qy$, and the number of dollars in the total cost of production is $4000x + 2000y$. Hence, if S dollars is the profit, we have

$$S = 1000px + 1000qy - (4000x + 2000y)$$

$$S = 1000p(8 - p + q) + 1000q(9 + p - 5q)$$

$$- 4000(8 - p + q) - 2000(9 + p - 5q)$$

$$S = 1000(-p^2 + 2pq - 5q^2 + 10p + 15q - 50)$$

$$\frac{\partial S}{\partial p} = 1000(-2p + 2q + 10) \qquad \frac{\partial S}{\partial q} = 1000(2p - 10q + 15)$$

Setting $\partial S/\partial p = 0$ and $\partial S/\partial q = 0$, we have

$$-2p + 2q + 10 = 0 \quad \text{and} \quad 2p - 10q + 15 = 0$$

from which it follows that

$$p = \tfrac{65}{8} \quad \text{and} \quad q = \tfrac{25}{8}$$

Hence, $(\tfrac{65}{8}, \tfrac{25}{8})$ is a critical point. Because

$$\frac{\partial^2 S}{\partial p^2} = -2000 \qquad \frac{\partial^2 S}{\partial q^2} = -10{,}000 \qquad \frac{\partial^2 S}{\partial q\, \partial p} = 2000$$

we have

$$\frac{\partial^2 S}{\partial p^2}\frac{\partial^2 S}{\partial q^2} - \left(\frac{\partial^2 S}{\partial q\, \partial p}\right)^2 = (-2000)(-10{,}000) - (2000)^2 > 0$$

Also, $\partial^2 S/\partial p^2 < 0$, and so from Theorem 20.3.8(ii) we conclude that S has a relative maximum value at $(\tfrac{65}{8}, \tfrac{25}{8})$.

Because x, y, p, and q must be nonnegative, we know that

$$8 - p + q \geq 0 \qquad 9 + p - 5q \geq 0 \qquad p \geq 0 \qquad q \geq 0$$

From these inequalities we determine that the region of permissible values is that shaded in Fig. 20.4.9. It follows that S has an absolute maximum

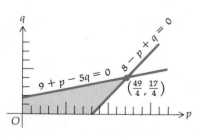

Figure 20.4.9

value at the point $(\frac{65}{8}, \frac{25}{8})$, and the absolute maximum value of S is 14,062.5. From the demand equations we find that when $p = \frac{65}{8}$ and $q = \frac{25}{8}$, $x = 3$ and $y = \frac{3}{2}$.

We therefore conclude that the greatest profit of $14,062.50 is attained when 3000 units of the first commodity are produced and sold at 8.12\frac{1}{2}$ per unit and 1500 units of the second commodity are produced and sold at 3.12\frac{1}{2}$ per unit.

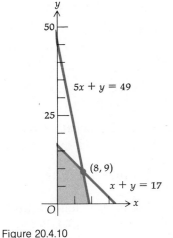

Figure 20.4.10

● ILLUSTRATION 2: In the preceding example, if the demand equations are solved for p and q in terms of x and y, we obtain

$$p = \tfrac{1}{4}(49 - 5x - y) \quad \text{and} \quad q = \tfrac{1}{4}(17 - x - y)$$

Because q and p must be nonnegative as well as x and y, we know that $17 - x - y \geq 0, 49 - 5x - y \geq 0, x \geq 0$, and $y \geq 0$. From these four inequalities we determine that the region of permissible values is that shaded in Fig. 20.4.10. The problem can be solved by considering x and y as the independent variables. You are asked to do this in Exercise 12.   ●

Suppose that in the production of a certain commodity, x is the number of machines, y is the number of man-hours, and z is the number of units of the commodity produced, where z depends on x and y, and $z = f(x, y)$. Such a function f is called a *production function*. Other factors of production may be working capital, materials, and land.

Let us now consider, in general, a commodity involving two factors of production; that is, we have a production function f of two variables. If the amounts of the inputs are given by x and y, and z gives the amount of the output, then $z = f(x, y)$. Suppose that the prices of the two inputs are a dollars and b dollars per unit, respectively, and that the price of the output is c dollars (a, b, and c are constants). This situation could occur if there were so many producers in the market that a change in the output of any particular producer would not affect the price of the commodity. Such a market is called a *perfectly competitive market*. Now if P dollars is the total profit, and because the total profit is obtained by subtracting the total cost from the total revenue, we have

$$P = cz - (ax + by)$$

and because $z = f(x, y)$,

$$P = cf(x, y) - ax - by$$

It is, of course, desired to maximize P. This is illustrated by an example.

EXAMPLE 5:   Suppose that the production of a certain commodity depends on two inputs. The

SOLUTION: If P dollars is the profit,

$$P = 9(100z) - 4(100x) - 100y \tag{5}$$

amounts of these are given by $100x$ and $100y$, whose prices per unit are, respectively, $4 and $1. The amount of the output is given by $100z$, the price per unit of which is $9. Furthermore, the production function f has the function values $f(x, y) = 5 - 1/x - 1/y$. Determine the greatest profit.

Letting $z = f(x, y)$, we get

$$P = 900 \left(5 - \frac{1}{x} - \frac{1}{y}\right) - 400x - 100y$$

x and y are both in the interval $(0, +\infty)$. Hence,

$$\frac{\partial P}{\partial x} = \frac{900}{x^2} - 400 \quad \text{and} \quad \frac{\partial P}{\partial y} = \frac{900}{y^2} - 100$$

Also,

$$\frac{\partial^2 P}{\partial x^2} = -\frac{1800}{x^3} \qquad \frac{\partial^2 P}{\partial y^2} = -\frac{1800}{y^3} \qquad \frac{\partial^2 P}{\partial y \, \partial x} = 0$$

Setting $\partial P/\partial x = 0$ and $\partial P/\partial y = 0$, we have

$$\frac{900}{x^2} - 400 = 0 \quad \text{and} \quad \frac{900}{y^2} - 100 = 0$$

from which we obtain $x = \frac{3}{2}$ and $y = 3$ (we reject the negative result because x and y must be positive). At $(\frac{3}{2}, 3)$

$$\frac{\partial^2 P}{\partial x^2} \cdot \frac{\partial^2 P}{\partial y^2} - \left(\frac{\partial^2 P}{\partial y \, \partial x}\right)^2 = -\left(\frac{1800}{\frac{27}{8}}\right) \cdot \left(-\frac{1800}{27}\right) - (0)^2 > 0$$

From the above and the fact that at $(\frac{3}{2}, 3)$ $\partial^2 P/\partial x^2 < 0$, it follows from Theorem 20.3.8(ii) that P has a relative maximum value at $(\frac{3}{2}, 3)$. Because x and y are both in the interval $(0, +\infty)$, and P is a negative number when x and y are either close to zero or very large, we conclude that the relative maximum value of P is an absolute maximum value. Because $z = f(x, y)$, the value of z at $(\frac{3}{2}, 3)$ is $f(\frac{3}{2}, 3) = 5 - \frac{2}{3} - \frac{1}{3} = 4$. Hence, from Eq. (5)

$$P_{\max} = 900 \cdot 4 - 400 \cdot \frac{3}{2} - 100 \cdot 3 = 2700$$

The greatest profit then is $2700.

EXAMPLE 6: Solve Example 5 by the method of Lagrange multipliers.

SOLUTION: We wish to maximize the function P defined by Eq. (5) subject to the constraint given by the equation $z = 5 - 1/x - 1/y$, which we can write as

$$g(x, y, z) = \frac{1}{x} + \frac{1}{y} + z - 5 = 0 \tag{6}$$

Let

$$F(x, y, z, \lambda) = P(x, y, z) + \lambda g(x, y, z)$$

$$= 900z - 400x - 100y + \lambda \left(\frac{1}{x} + \frac{1}{y} + z - 5\right)$$

We find the four partial derivatives $F_x, F_y, F_z,$ and F_λ and set them equal to zero.

$$F_x(x, y, z, \lambda) = -400 - \frac{\lambda}{x^2} = 0 \qquad F_y(x, y, z, \lambda) = -100 - \frac{\lambda}{y^2} = 0$$

$$F_z(x, y, z, \lambda) = 900 + \lambda = 0 \qquad F_\lambda(x, y, z, \lambda) = \frac{1}{x} + \frac{1}{y} + z - 5 = 0$$

Solving these equations simultaneously, we obtain

$$\lambda = -900 \qquad x = \tfrac{3}{2} \qquad y = 3 \qquad z = 4$$

The values of x, y, and z agree with those found previously, and P is shown to have an absolute maximum value in the same way as before.

In some applications of functions of several variables to problems in economics, the Lagrange multiplier λ is related to marginal concepts, in particular marginal cost and marginal utility of money (for details of this you should consult references in mathematical economics).

Exercises 20.4

In Exercises 1 through 9, demand equations for two related commodities are given. In each exercise, determine the four partial marginal demands. Determine if the commodities are complementary, substitutes, or neither. In Exercises 1 through 6, draw sketches of the two demand surfaces.

1. $x = 14 - p - 2q$, $y = 17 - 2p - q$

2. $x = 5 - 2p + q$, $y = 6 + p - q$

3. $x = -3p + 5q + 15$, $y = 2p - 4q + 10$

4. $x = 9 - 3p + q$, $y = 10 - 2p - 5q$

5. $x = 6 - 3p - 2q$, $y = 2 + p - 2q$

6. $x = -p - 3q + 6$, $y = -2q - p + 8$

7. $x = p^{-0.4}q^{0.5}$, $y = p^{0.4}q^{-1.5}$

8. $pqx = 4$, $p^2qy = 16$

9. $px = q$, $qy = p^2$

10. From the demand equations of Exercise 8, find the two demand functions and draw sketches of the contour maps of these functions showing the level curves of each function at 5, 4, 3, 2, 1, $\tfrac{1}{2}$, $\tfrac{1}{4}$.

11. Follow the instructions of Exercise 10 for the demand equations of Exercise 9.

12. Solve Example 4 of this section by considering x and y as the independent variables. (Refer to Illustration 2.)

13. The demand equations for two commodities that are produced by a monopolist are

$$x = 6 - 2p + q \quad \text{and} \quad y = 7 + p - q$$

where $100x$ is the quantity of the first commodity demanded if the price is p dollars per unit and $100y$ is the quantity of the second commodity demanded if the price is q dollars per unit. Show that the two commodities are substitutes. If it costs \$2 to produce each unit of the first commodity and \$3 to produce each unit of the second commodity, find the quantities demanded and the prices of the two commodities in order to have the greatest profit. Take p and q as the independent variables.

14. Solve Exercise 13 by considering x and y as the independent variables.

15. The production function f for a certain commodity has function values

$$f(x, y) = 4 - \frac{8}{xy}$$

The amounts of the two inputs are given by $100x$ and $100y$, whose prices per unit are, respectively, $10 and $5, and the amount of the output is given by $100z$, whose price per unit is $20. Determine the greatest profit by two methods: (a) without using Lagrange multipliers; (b) using Lagrange multipliers.

16. Solve Exercise 15 if

$$f(x, y) = x + \tfrac{5}{2}y - \tfrac{1}{8}x^2 - \tfrac{1}{4}y^2 - \tfrac{9}{8}$$

the prices per unit of the two inputs are $4 and $8 (instead of $10 and $5, respectively), and the price per unit of the output is $16.

20.5 OBTAINING A FUNCTION FROM ITS GRADIENT

We consider the problem of how to obtain a function if we are given its gradient; that is, we are given

$$\nabla f(x, y) = f_x(x, y)\mathbf{i} + f_y(x, y)\mathbf{j} \tag{1}$$

and we wish to find $f(x, y)$.

● ILLUSTRATION 1: Suppose

$$\nabla f(x, y) = (y^2 + 2x + 4)\mathbf{i} + (2xy + 4y - 5)\mathbf{j} \tag{2}$$

Then because Eq. (1) must be satisfied, it follows that

$$f_x(x, y) = y^2 + 2x + 4 \tag{3}$$

and

$$f_y(x, y) = 2xy + 4y - 5 \tag{4}$$

By integrating both members of Eq. (3) with respect to x, we have

$$f(x, y) = y^2x + x^2 + 4x + g(y) \tag{5}$$

Observe that the "constant" of integration is a function of y and independent of x because we are integrating with respect to x. If we now differentiate both members of Eq. (5) partially with respect to y, we obtain

$$f_y(x, y) = 2xy + g'(y) \tag{6}$$

Equations (4) and (6) give two expressions for $f_y(x, y)$. Hence,

$$2xy + 4y - 5 = 2xy + g'(y)$$

Therefore,

$$g'(y) = 4y - 5$$

$$g(y) = 2y^2 - 5y + C$$

Substituting this value of $g(y)$ into Eq. (5), we have

$$f(x, y) = y^2x + x^2 + 4x + 2y^2 - 5y + C \qquad ●$$

EXAMPLE 1: Find $f(x, y)$ if

$$\nabla f(x, y) = e^{y^2}\cos x\mathbf{i} + 2ye^{y^2}\sin x\mathbf{j}$$

SOLUTION: Because Eq. (1) must hold, we have

$$f_x(x, y) = e^{y^2}\cos x \tag{7}$$

and

$$f_y(x, y) = 2ye^{y^2} \sin x \qquad (8)$$

Integrating both members of Eq. (8) with respect to y, we obtain

$$f(x, y) = e^{y^2} \sin x + g(x) \qquad (9)$$

where $g(x)$ is independent of y. We now partially differentiate both members of Eq. (9) with respect to x and get

$$f_x(x, y) = e^{y^2} \cos x + g'(x) \qquad (10)$$

By equating the right members of Eqs. (7) and (10), we have

$$e^{y^2} \cos x = e^{y^2} \cos x + g'(x)$$

$$g'(x) = 0$$

$$g(x) = C$$

We substitute this value of $g(x)$ into Eq. (9) and obtain

$$f(x, y) = e^{y^2} \sin x + C$$

All vectors of the form $M(x, y)\mathbf{i} + N(x, y)\mathbf{j}$ are not necessarily gradients, as shown in the next illustration.

● ILLUSTRATION 2: We show that there is no function f such that

$$\nabla f(x, y) = 3y\mathbf{i} - 2x\mathbf{j} \qquad (11)$$

Assume that there is such a function. Then it follows that

$$f_x(x, y) = 3y \qquad (12)$$

and

$$f_y(x, y) = -2x \qquad (13)$$

We integrate both members of Eq. (12) with respect to x and obtain

$$f(x, y) = 3xy + g(y)$$

We partially differentiate both members of this equation with respect to y and we have

$$f_y(x, y) = 3x + g'(y) \qquad (14)$$

Equating the right members of Eqs. (13) and (14), we obtain

$$-2x = 3x + g'(y)$$

$$-5x = g'(y)$$

If both members of this equation are differentiated with respect to x, it must follow that

$$-5 = 0$$

which, of course, is not true. Thus, our assumption that $3y\mathbf{i} - 2x\mathbf{j}$ is a gradient leads to a contradiction. ●

We now investigate a condition that must be satisfied in order for a vector to be a gradient.

Suppose that M_y and N_x are continuous on an open disk B in R^2. If

$$M(x, y)\mathbf{i} + N(x, y)\mathbf{j} \tag{15}$$

is a gradient on B, then there is a function f such that

$$f_x(x, y) = M(x, y) \tag{16}$$

and

$$f_y(x, y) = N(x, y) \tag{17}$$

for all (x, y) in B. Because $M_y(x, y)$ exists on B, then from Eq. (16) it follows that

$$M_y(x, y) = f_{xy}(x, y) \tag{18}$$

Furthermore, because $N_x(x, y)$ exists on B, it follows from Eq. (17) that

$$N_x(x, y) = f_{xy}(x, y) \tag{19}$$

Because M_y and N_x are continuous on B, their equivalents f_{xy} and f_{yx} are also continuous on B. Thus, from Theorem 19.7.1 it follows that $f_{xy}(x, y) = f_{yx}(x, y)$ at all points in B. Therefore, the left members of Eqs. (18) and (19) are equal at all points in B. We have proved that if M_y and N_x are continuous on an open disk B in R^2, a necessary condition for vector (15) to be a gradient on B is that

$$M_y(x, y) = N_x(x, y)$$

This equation is also a sufficient condition for vector (15) to be a gradient on B. However, the proof of the sufficiency of the condition involves concepts that are beyond the scope of this book, and so it is omitted. We have then the following theorem.

20.5.1 Theorem Suppose that M and N are functions of two variables x and y defined on an open disk $B((x_0, y_0); r)$ in R^2, and M_y and N_x are continuous on B. Then the vector

$$M(x, y)\mathbf{i} + N(x, y)\mathbf{j}$$

is a gradient on B if and only if

$$M_y(x, y) = N_x(x, y)$$

at all points in B.

● ILLUSTRATION 3: (a) We apply Theorem 20.5.1 to the vector in the right member of Eq. (2) in Illustration 1. Let $M(x, y) = y^2 + 2x + 4$ and $N(x, y) =$

$2xy + 4y - 5$. Then

$$M_y(x, y) = 2y \quad \text{and} \quad N_x(x, y) = 2y$$

Thus, $M_y(x, y) = N_x(x, y)$, and therefore the vector is a gradient.

(b) If we apply Theorem 20.5.1 to the vector in the right member of Eq. (11) in Illustration 2, with $M(x, y) = 3y$ and $N(x, y) = -2x$, we obtain

$$M_y(x, y) = 3 \quad \text{and} \quad N_x(x, y) = -2$$

Thus, $M_y(x, y) \neq N_x(x, y)$, and so the vector is not a gradient.   ●

EXAMPLE 2:   Determine if the following vector is a gradient $\nabla f(x, y)$, and if it is, then find $f(x, y)$:

$$(e^{-y} - 2x)\mathbf{i} - (xe^{-y} + \sin y)\mathbf{j}$$

SOLUTION: We apply Theorem 20.5.1. Let $M(x, y) = e^{-y} - 2x$ and $N(x, y) = -xe^{-y} - \sin y$. Then

$$M_y(x, y) = -e^{-y} \quad \text{and} \quad N_x(x, y) = -e^{-y}$$

Therefore, $M_y(x, y) = N_x(x, y)$, and so the given vector is a gradient $\nabla f(x, y)$. Furthermore,

$$f_x(x, y) = e^{-y} - 2x \tag{20}$$

and

$$f_y(x, y) = -xe^{-y} - \sin y \tag{21}$$

Integrating both members of Eq. (20) with respect to x, we obtain

$$f(x, y) = xe^{-y} - x^2 + g(y) \tag{22}$$

where $g(y)$ is independent of x. We now partially differentiate both members of Eq. (22) with respect to y, and we have

$$f_y(x, y) = -xe^{-y} + g'(y) \tag{23}$$

We equate the right members of Eqs. (23) and (21) and get

$$-xe^{-y} + g'(y) = -xe^{-y} - \sin y$$

$$g'(y) = -\sin y$$

$$g(y) = \cos y + C$$

We substitute this expression for $g(y)$ into Eq. (22) and we have

$$f(x, y) = xe^{-y} - x^2 + \cos y + C$$

We can extend Theorem 20.5.1 to functions of three variables.

20.5.2 Theorem   Let M, N, and R be functions of three variables x, y, and z defined on an open ball $B((x_0, y_0, z_0); r)$ in R^3, and M_y, M_z, N_x, N_z, R_x, and R_y are continuous on B. Then the vector $M(x, y, z)\mathbf{i} + N(x, y, z)\mathbf{j} + R(x, y, z)\mathbf{k}$ is a gradient on B if and only if $M_y(x, y, z) = N_x(x, y, z)$, $M_z(x, y, z) = R_x(x, y, z)$, and $N_z(x, y, z) = R_y(x, y, z)$.

The proof of the "only if" part of Theorem 20.5.2 is similar to the proof of the "only if" part of Theorem 20.5.1 and is left as an exercise (see Exercise 23). The proof of the "if" part is beyond the scope of this book.

EXAMPLE 3: Determine if the following vector is a gradient $\nabla f(x, y, z)$, and if it is then find $f(x, y, z)$:

$(e^x \sin z + 2yz)\mathbf{i} + (2xz + 2y)\mathbf{j}$
$+ (e^x \cos z + 2xy + 3z^2)\mathbf{k}$

SOLUTION: We apply Theorem 20.5.2. Let $M(x, y, z) = e^x \sin z + 2yz$, $N(x, y, z) = 2xz + 2y$, and $R(x, y, z) = e^x \cos z + 2xy + 3z^2$. Then

$$M_y(x, y, z) = 2z \qquad\qquad M_z(x, y, z) = e^x \cos z + 2y$$

$$N_x(x, y, z) = 2z \qquad\qquad N_z(x, y, z) = 2x$$

$$R_x(x, y, z) = e^x \cos z + 2y \qquad R_y(x, y, z) = 2x$$

Therefore, $M_y(x, y, z) = N_x(x, y, z)$, $M_z(x, y, z) = R_x(x, y, z)$, and $N_z(x, y, z) = R_y(x, y, z)$. Thus, the given vector is a gradient $\nabla f(x, y, z)$. Furthermore,

$$f_x(x, y, z) = e^x \sin z + 2yz \tag{24}$$

$$f_y(x, y, z) = 2xz + 2y \tag{25}$$

$$f_z(x, y, z) = e^x \cos z + 2xy + 3z^2 \tag{26}$$

Integrating both members of Eq. (24) with respect to x, we have

$$f(x, y, z) = e^x \sin z + 2xyz + g(y, z) \tag{27}$$

where $g(y, z)$ is independent of x. We partial differentiate both members of Eq. (27) with respect to y and obtain

$$f_y(x, y, z) = 2xz + g_y(y, z) \tag{28}$$

Equating the right members of Eqs. (28) and (25), we have

$$2xz + g_y(y, z) = 2xz + 2y$$

$$g_y(y, z) = 2y$$

We now integrate both members of this equation with respect to y, and get

$$g(y, z) = y^2 + h(z) \tag{29}$$

where h is independent of x and y. Substituting from Eq. (29) into Eq. (27), we obtain

$$f(x, y, z) = e^x \sin z + 2xyz + y^2 + h(z) \tag{30}$$

We now partial differentiate with respect to z both members of Eq. (30). We get

$$f_z(x, y, z) = e^x \cos z + 2xy + h'(z) \tag{31}$$

Equating the right members of Eqs. (31) and (26), we have

$$e^x \cos z + 2xy + h'(z) = e^x \cos z + 2xy + 3z^2$$

$$h'(z) = 3z^2$$

$$h(z) = z^3 + C \tag{32}$$

We substitute from Eq. (32) into Eq. (30), and we obtain

$$f(x, y, z) = e^x \sin z + 2xyz + y^2 + z^3 + C$$

Exercises 20.5

In the following exercises, determine if the vector is a gradient. If it is, find a function having the given gradient

1. $4x\mathbf{i} - 3y\mathbf{j}$

2. $y^2\mathbf{i} + 3x^2\mathbf{j}$

3. $(6x - 5y)\mathbf{i} - (5x - 6y^2)\mathbf{j}$

4. $(4y^2 + 6xy - 2)\mathbf{i} + (3x^2 + 8xy + 1)\mathbf{j}$

5. $(6x^2y^2 - 14xy + 3)\mathbf{i} + (4x^3y - 7x^2 - 8)\mathbf{j}$

6. $3(2x^2 + 6xy)\mathbf{i} + 3(3x^2 + 8y)\mathbf{j}$

7. $(2xy + y^2 + 1)\mathbf{i} + (x^2 + 2xy + x)\mathbf{j}$

8. $\dfrac{2x - 1}{y}\mathbf{i} + \dfrac{x - x^2}{y^2}\mathbf{j}$

9. $\left(\dfrac{1}{x^2} + \dfrac{1}{y^2}\right)\mathbf{i} + \left(\dfrac{1 - 2x}{y^3}\right)\mathbf{j}$

10. $(2x + \ln y)\mathbf{i} + \left(y^2 + \dfrac{x}{y}\right)\mathbf{j}$

11. $(2x \cos y - 1)\mathbf{i} - x^2 \sin y\mathbf{j}$

12. $(\sin 2x - \tan y)\mathbf{i} - x \sec^2 y\mathbf{j}$

13. $(e^y - 2xy)\mathbf{i} + (xe^y - x^2)\mathbf{j}$

14. $4x^3\mathbf{i} + 9y^2\mathbf{j} - 2z\mathbf{k}$

15. $(2y - 5z)\mathbf{i} + (2x + 8z)\mathbf{j} - (5x - 8y)\mathbf{k}$

16. $(2xy + 7z^3)\mathbf{i} + (x^2 + 2y^2 - 3z)\mathbf{j} + (21xz^2 - 4y)\mathbf{k}$

17. $(4xy + 3yz - 2)\mathbf{i} + (2x^2 + 3xz - 5z^2)\mathbf{j} + (3xy - 10yz + 1)\mathbf{k}$

18. $(2y + z)\mathbf{i} + (2x - 3z + 4yz)\mathbf{j} + (x - 3y + 2y^2)\mathbf{k}$

19. $z \tan y\mathbf{i} + xz \sec^2 y\mathbf{j} + x \tan y\mathbf{k}$

20. $e^z \cos x\mathbf{i} + z \sin y\mathbf{j} + (e^z \sin x - \cos y)\mathbf{k}$

21. $e^x(e^z - \ln y)\mathbf{i} + (e^y \ln z - e^x y^{-1})\mathbf{j} + (e^{x+z} + e^y z^{-1})\mathbf{k}$

22. $\dfrac{1}{y + z}\mathbf{i} - \dfrac{x - z}{(y + z)^2}\mathbf{j} - \dfrac{x + y}{(y + z)^2}\mathbf{k}$

23. Prove the "only if" part of Theorem 20.5.2.

20.6 LINE INTEGRALS

In Chapter 7 we used the concept of area to motivate the definition of the definite integral. To motivate the definition of an integral of a vector-valued function, we use the physical concept of work.

We have seen that if a constant force $\mathbf{F}$ moves an object along a straight line, then the work done is the product of the component of $\mathbf{F}$ along the line of motion times the displacement. We showed in Section 17.3 that if the constant force $\mathbf{F}$ moves an object from a point A to a point B, then if W is the measure of the work done,

$$W = \mathbf{F} \cdot \mathbf{V}(\overrightarrow{AB}) \tag{1}$$

Suppose now that the force vector is not constant and instead of the motion being along a straight line, it is along a curve. Let the force that is exerted on the object at the point (x, y) in some open disk B in R^2 be given by the force vector

$$\mathbf{F}(x, y) = M(x, y)\mathbf{i} + N(x, y)\mathbf{j}$$

where M and N are continuous on B. The vector-valued function $\mathbf{F}$ is called a *force field* on B. Let C be a curve lying in B and having the vector equation

$$\mathbf{R}(t) = f(t)\mathbf{i} + g(t)\mathbf{j} \qquad a \leq t \leq b$$

We require that C be smooth, that is, that f' and g' be continuous on $[a, b]$. We wish to define the work done by the variable force $\mathbf{F}$ in moving the object along C from the point $(f(a), g(a))$ to $(f(b), g(b))$. At a point $(f(t), g(t))$ on C, the force vector is

$$\mathbf{F}(f(t), g(t)) = M(f(t), g(t))\mathbf{i} + N(f(t), g(t))\mathbf{j} \qquad (2)$$

Let Δ be a partition of the interval $[a, b]$:

$$a = t_0 < t_1 < t_2 < \cdots < t_{n-1} < t_n = b$$

On C let P_i be the point $(x_i, y_i) = (f(t_i), g(t_i))$. Refer to Figure 20.6.1. The vector $\mathbf{V}(\overrightarrow{P_{i-1}P_i}) = \mathbf{R}(t_i) - \mathbf{R}(t_{i-1})$; therefore,

$$\mathbf{V}(\overrightarrow{P_{i-1}P_i}) = f(t_i)\mathbf{i} + g(t_i)\mathbf{j} - [f(t_{i-1})\mathbf{i} + g(t_{i-1})\mathbf{j}]$$

or, equivalently,

$$\mathbf{V}(\overrightarrow{P_{i-1}P_i}) = [f(t_i) - f(t_{i-1})]\mathbf{i} + [g(t_i) - g(t_{i-1})]\mathbf{j} \qquad (3)$$

Because f' and g' are continuous on $[a, b]$, it follows from the mean-value theorem (4.7.2) that there are numbers c_i and d_i in the open interval (t_{i-1}, t_i) such that

$$f(t_i) - f(t_{i-1}) = f'(c_i)(t_i - t_{i-1}) \qquad (4)$$

and

$$g(t_i) - g(t_{i-1}) = g'(d_i)(t_i - t_{i-1}) \qquad (5)$$

Letting $\Delta_i t = t_i - t_{i-1}$ and substituting from Eqs. (4) and (5) into Eq. (3), we obtain

$$\mathbf{V}(\overrightarrow{P_{i-1}P_i}) = [f'(c_i)\mathbf{i} + g'(d_i)\mathbf{j}]\,\Delta_i t \qquad (6)$$

For each i, consider the vector

$$\mathbf{F}_i = M(f(c_i), g(c_i))\mathbf{i} + N(f(d_i), g(d_i))\mathbf{j} \qquad (7)$$

Each of the vectors $\mathbf{F}_i$ $(i = 1, 2, \ldots, n)$ is an approximation to the force vector $\mathbf{F}(f(t), g(t))$, given by Eq. (2), along the arc of C from P_{i-1} to P_i. Observe that even though c_i and d_i are in general different numbers in the open interval (t_{i-1}, t_i), the values of the vectors $\mathbf{F}(f(t), g(t))$ are close to

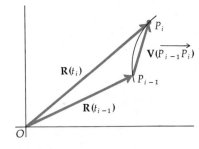

Figure 20.6.1

the vector $\mathbf{F}_i$. Furthermore, we approximate the arc of C from P_{i-1} to P_i by the line segment $\overrightarrow{P_{i-1}P_i}$. Thus, we apply formula (1) and obtain an approximation for the work done by the vector $\mathbf{F}(f(t), g(t))$ in moving an object along the arc of C from P_{i-1} to P_i. Denoting this approximation by $\Delta_i W$, we have from formula (1), and Eqs. (7) and (6),

$$\Delta_i W = [M(f(c_i), g(c_i))\mathbf{i} + N(f(d_i), g(d_i))\mathbf{j}] \cdot [f'(c_i)\mathbf{i} + g'(d_i)\mathbf{j}] \, \Delta_i t$$

or, equivalently,

$$\Delta_i W = [M(f(c_i), g(c_i))f'(c_i)] \, \Delta_i t + [N(f(d_i), g(d_i))g'(d_i)] \, \Delta_i t$$

An approximation of the work done by $F(f(t), g(t))$ along C is $\displaystyle\sum_{i=1}^{n} \Delta_i W$ or, equivalently,

$$\sum_{i=1}^{n} [M(f(c_i), g(c_i))f'(c_i)] \, \Delta_i t + \sum_{i=1}^{n} [N(f(d_i), g(d_i))g'(d_i)] \, \Delta_i t$$

Each of these sums is a Riemann sum. The first summation is a Riemann sum for the function having function values $M(f(t), g(t))f'(t)$ and the second summation is a Riemann sum for the function having function values $N(f(t), g(t))g'(t)$. If we let $n \to +\infty$, these two sums approach the definite integral:

$$\int_a^b [M(f(t), g(t))f'(t) + N(f(t), g(t))g'(t)] \, dt$$

We therefore have the following definition.

20.6.1 Definition   Let C be a curve lying in an open disk B in R^2 for which a vector equation of C is $\mathbf{R}(t) = f(t)\mathbf{i} + g(t)\mathbf{j}$, where f' and g' are continuous on $[a, b]$. Furthermore, let a force field on B be defined by $\mathbf{F}(x, y) = M(x, y)\mathbf{i} + N(x, y)\mathbf{j}$, where M and N are continuous on B. Then if W is the measure of the work done by $\mathbf{F}$ in moving an object along C from $(f(a), g(a))$ to $(f(b), g(b))$,

$$W = \int_a^b [M(f(t), g(t))f'(t) + N(f(t), g(t))g'(t)] \, dt \tag{8}$$

or, equivalently, by using vector notation,

$$W = \int_a^b \langle M(f(t), g(t)), N(f(t), g(t)) \rangle \cdot \langle f'(t), g'(t) \rangle \, dt \tag{9}$$

or, equivalently,

$$W = \int_a^b \mathbf{F}(f(t), g(t)) \cdot \mathbf{R}'(t) \, dt \tag{10}$$

EXAMPLE 1: Suppose an object moves along the parabola $y = x^2$ from the point $(-1, 1)$ to the point $(2, 4)$. Find the total work done if the motion is caused by the force field $\mathbf{F}(x, y) = (x^2 + y^2)\mathbf{i} + 3x^2 y\mathbf{j}$. Assume the arc is measured in inches and the force is measured in pounds.

SOLUTION: Parametric equations of the parabola are

$$x = t \quad \text{and} \quad y = t^2 \qquad -1 \le t \le 2$$

Thus, a vector equation of the parabola is

$$\mathbf{R}(t) = t\mathbf{i} + t^2\mathbf{j}$$

Because $f(t) = t$, $g(t) = t^2$, and $\mathbf{F}(x, y) = \langle x^2 + y^2, 3x^2 y \rangle$, then

$$\mathbf{F}(f(t), g(t)) = \mathbf{F}(t, t^2) = \langle t^2 + t^4, 3t^4 \rangle$$

If W in.-lb is the work done, then from formula (10) we have

$$W = \int_{-1}^{2} \mathbf{F}(t, t^2) \cdot \mathbf{R}'(t) \, dt$$

$$= \int_{-1}^{2} \langle t^2 + t^4, 3t^4 \rangle \cdot \langle 1, 2t \rangle \, dt$$

$$= \int_{-1}^{2} (t^2 + t^4 + 6t^5) \, dt$$

$$= \frac{t^3}{3} + \frac{t^5}{5} + t^6 \Big]_{-1}^{2}$$

$$= \tfrac{8}{3} + \tfrac{32}{5} + 64 - (-\tfrac{1}{3} - \tfrac{1}{5} + 1)$$

$$= \tfrac{363}{5}$$

Therefore, the work done is $\tfrac{363}{5}$ in.-lb.

The integral in Eq. (8) is called a "line integral." A common notation for the line integral of Eq. (8) is

$$\int_C M(x, y) \, dx + N(x, y) \, dy$$

This notation is suggested by the fact that because parametric equations of C are $x = f(t)$ and $y = g(t)$, then $dx = f'(t) \, dt$ and $dy = g'(t) \, dt$. We have the following formal definition.

20.6.2 Definition   Let M and N be functions of two variables x and y such that they are continuous on an open disk B in R^2. Let C be a curve lying in B and having parametric equations

$$x = f(t) \qquad y = g(t) \qquad a \le t \le b$$

such that f' and g' are continuous on $[a, b]$. Then the *line integral* of $M(x, y) \, dx + N(x, y) \, dy$ over C is given by

$$\int_C M(x, y)\ dx + N(x, y)\ dy$$

$$= \int_a [M(f(t), g(t))f'(t) + N(f(t), g(t))g'(t)]\ dt$$

or, equivalently, by using vector notation,

$$\int_C M(x, y)\ dx + N(x, y)\ dy$$

$$= \int_a^b \langle M(f(t), g(t)), N(f(t), g(t)) \rangle \cdot \langle f'(t), g'(t) \rangle\ dt$$

• ILLUSTRATION 1: In Example 1, W is given by the line integral

$$\int_C (x^2 + y^2)\ dx + 3x^2 y\ dy$$

where C is the arc of the parabola $y = x^2$ from $(-1, 1)$ to $(2, 4)$.   •

If an equation of C is of the form $y = F(x)$, then x may be used as a parameter in place of t. Similarly, if an equation of C is of the form $x = G(y)$, then y may be used as a parameter in place of t.

• ILLUSTRATION 2: In Example 1 and Illustration 1, the equation of C is $y = x^2$, which is of the form $y = F(x)$. Therefore, we can use x as a parameter instead of t. Thus, in the integral of Illustration 1 we can replace y by x^2 and dy by $2x\ dx$, and we have

$$W = \int_{-1}^{2} (x^2 + x^4)\ dx + 3x^2 x^2 (2x\ dx)$$

$$= \int_{-1}^{2} (x^2 + x^4 + 6x^5)\ dx$$

This integral is the same as the third one appearing in the solution of Example 1, except that the variable is x instead of t.   •

If the curve C in the definition of the line integral is the closed interval $[a, b]$ on the x axis, then $y = 0$ and $dy = 0$. Thus,

$$\int_C M(x, y)\ dx + N(x, y)\ dy = \int_a^b M(x, 0)\ dx$$

Therefore, in such a case, the line integral reduces to a definite integral.

In the definition of a line integral we required that the functions f and g in the parametric equations defining C be such that f' and g' are continuous. Such a curve C is said to be smooth. If the curve C consists of a finite number of arcs of smooth curves, then C is said to be *sectionally*

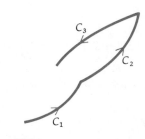

Figure 20.6.2

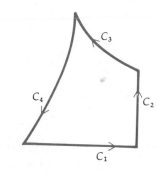

Figure 20.6.3

smooth. Figures 20.6.2 and 20.6.3 show two sectionally smooth curves. We can extend the concept of a line integral to include curves that are sectionally smooth.

20.6.3 Definition   Let the curve C consist of smooth arcs $C_1, C_2, \ldots, C_n$. Then the *line integral* of $M(x, y)\,dx + N(x, y)\,dy$ over C is defined by

$$\int_C M(x, y)\,dx + N(x, y)\,dy = \sum_{i=1}^{n} \left(\int_{C_i} M(x, y)\,dx + N(x, y)\,dy \right)$$

EXAMPLE 2:   Evaluate the line integral

$$\int_C 4xy\,dx + (2x^2 - 3xy)\,dy$$

over the curve C consisting of the line segment from $(-3, -2)$ to $(1, 0)$ and the first quadrant arc of the circle $x^2 + y^2 = 1$ from $(1, 0)$ to $(0, 1)$, traversed in the counterclockwise direction.

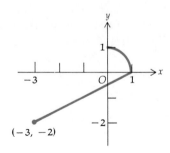

Figure 20.6.4

SOLUTION: Figure 20.6.4 shows the curve C composed of arcs C_1 and C_2. The arc C_1 is the line segment. An equation of the line through $(-3, -2)$ and $(1, 0)$ is $x - 2y = 1$. Therefore, C_1 can be represented parametrically by

$$x = 1 + 2t \qquad y = t \qquad -2 \leq t \leq 0$$

The arc C_2, which is the first quadrant arc of the circle $x^2 + y^2 = 1$, can be represented parametrically by

$$x = \cos t \qquad y = \sin t \qquad 0 \leq t \leq \tfrac{1}{2}\pi$$

Applying Definition 20.6.2 for each of the arcs C_1 and C_2, we have

$$\int_{C_1} 4xy\,dx + (2x^2 - 3xy)\,dy$$

$$= \int_{-2}^{0} 4(1 + 2t)t(2\,dt) + [2(1 + 2t)^2 - 3(1 + 2t)t]\,dt$$

$$= \int_{-2}^{0} (8t + 16t^2 + 2 + 8t + 8t^2 - 3t - 6t^2)\,dt$$

$$= \int_{-2}^{0} (18t^2 + 13t + 2)\,dt$$

$$= 6t^3 + \tfrac{13}{2}t^2 + 2t \Big]_{-2}^{0}$$

$$= -(-48 + 26 - 4)$$

$$= 26$$

and

$$\int_{C_2} 4xy\,dx + (2x^2 - 3xy)\,dy$$

$$= \int_{0}^{\pi/2} 4\cos t \sin t\,(-\sin t\,dt) + [2\cos^2 t - 3\cos t \sin t](\cos t\,dt)$$

$$= \int_{0}^{\pi/2} (-4\cos t \sin^2 t + 2\cos^3 t - 3\cos^2 t \sin t)\,dt$$

$$= \int_0^{\pi/2} [-4 \cos t \sin^2 t + 2 \cos t\, (1 - \sin^2 t) - 3 \cos^2 t \sin t]\, dt$$

$$= \int_0^{\pi/2} (2 \cos t - 6 \cos t \sin^2 t - 3 \cos^2 t \sin t)\, dt$$

$$= 2 \sin t - 2 \sin^3 t + \cos^3 t \Big]_0^{\pi/2}$$

$$= 2 - 2 - 1$$

$$= -1$$

Therefore, from Definition 20.6.3,

$$\int_C 4xy\ dx + (2x^2 - 3xy)\ dy = 26 + (-1)$$

$$= 25$$

The concept of a line integral can be extended to three dimensions.

20.6.4 Definition   Let M, N, and R be functions of three variables, x, y, and z such that they are continuous on an open disc B in R^3. Let C be a curve, lying in B, and having parametric equations

$$x = f(t) \qquad y = g(t) \qquad z = h(t) \qquad a \leq t \leq b$$

such that f', g', and h' are continuous on $[a, b]$. Then the *line integral* of $M(x, y, z)\ dx + N(x, y, z)\ dy + R(x, y, z)\ dz$ over C is given by

$$\int_C M(x, y, z)\ dx + N(x, y, z)\ dy + R(x, y, z)\ dz$$
$$= \int_a^b [M(f(t), g(t), h(t))f'(t) + N(f(t), g(t), h(t))g'(t) + R(f(t), g(t), h(t))h'(t)]\, dt$$

or, equivalently, by using vector notation

$$\int_C M(x, y, z)\ dx + N(x, y, z)\ dy + R(x, y, z)\ dz$$
$$= \int_a^b \langle M(f(t), g(t), h(t)), N(f(t), g(t), h(t)), R(f(t), g(t), h(t)) \rangle \cdot \langle f'(t), g'(t), h'(t) \rangle\, dt$$

We can define the work done by a force field in moving an object along a curve in R^3 as a line integral of the form of that in Definition 20.6.4.

EXAMPLE 3:   An object traverses the twisted cubic

$$R(t) = t\mathbf{i} + t^2\mathbf{j} + t^3\mathbf{k} \qquad 0 \leq t \leq 1$$

SOLUTION: Because $f(t) = t$, $g(t) = t^2$, $h(t) = t^3$, $M(x, y, z) = e^x$, $N(x, y, z) = xe^z$, and $R(x, y, z) = x \sin \pi y^2$, then $M(f(t), g(t), h(t)) = e^t$, $N(f(t), g(t), h(t)) = te^{t^3}$, and $R(f(t), g(t), h(t)) = t \sin \pi t^4$. Thus, if W in.-lb is the work done, we have from the line integral of Definition 20.6.4,

Find the total work done if the motion is caused by the force field $\mathbf{F}(x, y, z) = e^x\mathbf{i} + xe^z\mathbf{j} + x \sin \pi y^2\mathbf{k}$. Assume that the arc is measured in inches and the force is measured in pounds.

$$W = \int_0^1 [(e^t)(dt) + (te^{t^3})(2t\ dt) + (t \sin \pi t^4)(3t^2\ dt)]$$

$$= \int_0^1 (e^t + 2t^2e^{t^3} + 3t^3 \sin \pi t^4)\ dt$$

$$= e^t + \frac{2}{3} e^{t^3} - \frac{3}{4\pi} \cos \pi t^4 \Big]_0^1$$

$$= e + \frac{2}{3} e - \frac{3}{4\pi} \cos \pi - 1 - \frac{2}{3} + \frac{3}{4\pi} \cos 0$$

$$= \frac{5}{3} e + \frac{3}{2\pi} - \frac{5}{3}$$

Therefore, the work done is $\left[\frac{5}{3}(e-1) + \frac{3}{2\pi}\right]$ in.-lb.

Exercises 20.6

In Exercises 1 through 20, evaluate the line integral over the given curve.

1. $\int_C (x^2 + xy)\ dx + (y^2 - xy)\ dy$; C: the line $y = x$ from the origin to the point $(2, 2)$.

2. The line integral of Exercise 1; C: the parabola $x^2 = 2y$ from the origin to the point $(2, 2)$.

3. The line integral of Exercise 1; C: the x axis from the origin to $(2, 0)$ and then the line $x = 2$ from $(2, 0)$ to $(2, 2)$.

4. $\int_C yx^2\ dx + (x + y)\ dy$; C: the line $y = -x$ from the origin to the point $(1, -1)$.

5. The line integral of Exercise 4; C: the curve $y = -x^3$ from the origin to the point $(1, -1)$.

6. The line integral of Exercise 4; C: the y axis from the origin to $(0, -1)$ and then the line $y = -1$ from $(0, -1)$ to $(1, -1)$.

7. $\int_C y\ dx + x\ dy$; C: $\mathbf{R}(t) = t\mathbf{i} + t^2\mathbf{j}, 0 \le t \le 1$.

8. $\int_C (x - 2y)\ dx + xy\ dy$; C: $\mathbf{R}(t) = 3 \cos t\mathbf{i} + 2 \sin t\mathbf{j}, 0 \le t \le \frac{1}{2}\pi$

9. $\int_C (x - y)\ dx + (y + x)\ dy$; C: the entire circle $x^2 + y^2 = 4$.

10. $\int_C xy\ dx - y^2\ dy$; C: $\mathbf{R}(t) = t^2\mathbf{i} + t^3\mathbf{j}$, from the point $(1, 1)$ to the point $(4, -8)$.

11. $\int_C (xy + x^2)\ dx + x^2\ dy$; C: the parabola $y = 2x^2$ from the origin to the point $(1, 2)$.

12. $\int_C y \sin x\ dx - \cos x\ dy$; C: the line segment from $(\frac{1}{2}\pi, 0)$ to $(\pi, 1)$.

13. $\int_C (x + y)\ dx + (y + z)\ dy + (x + z)\ dz$; C: the line segment from the origin to the point $(1, 2, 4)$.

14. $\int_C (xy - z)\ dx + e^x\ dy + y\ dz$; C: the line segment from $(1, 0, 0)$ to $(3, 4, 8)$.

15. The line integral of Exercise 14; C: $\mathbf{R}(t) = (t + 1)\mathbf{i} + t^2\mathbf{j} + t^3\mathbf{k}$, $0 \le t \le 2$.

16. $\int_C y^2\ dx + z^2\ dy + x^2\ dz$; C: $\mathbf{R}(t) = (t - 1)\mathbf{i} + (t + 1)\mathbf{j} + t^2\mathbf{k}$, $0 \le t \le 1$.

17. $\int_C z\ dx + x\ dy + y\ dz$; C: the circular helix $\mathbf{R}(t) = a \cos t\mathbf{i} + a \sin t\mathbf{j} + t\mathbf{k}$; $0 \le t \le 2\pi$.

18. $\int_C 2xy\ dx + (6y^2 - xz)\ dy + 10z\ dz$; C: the twisted cubic $\mathbf{R}(t) = t\mathbf{i} + t^2\mathbf{j} + t^3\mathbf{k}$, $0 \le t \le 1$.

19. The line integral of Exercise 18; C: the line segment from the origin to the point $(0, 0, 1)$; then the line segment from $(0, 0, 1)$ to $(0, 1, 1)$; then the line segment from $(0, 1, 1)$ to $(1, 1, 1)$.

20. The line integral of Exercise 18; C: the line segment from the origin to the point $(1, 1, 1)$.

In Exercises 21 through 34, find the total work done in moving an object along the given arc C if the motion is caused by the given force field. Assume the arc is measured in inches and the force is measured in pounds.

21. $\mathbf{F}(x, y) = 2xy\mathbf{i} + (x^2 + y^2)\mathbf{j}$; C: the line segment from the origin to the point $(1, 1)$.

22. The force field of Exercise 21; C: the arc of the parabola $y^2 = x$ from the origin to the point $(1, 1)$.

23. $\mathbf{F}(x, y) = (y - x)\mathbf{i} + x^2 y\mathbf{j}$; C: the line segment from the point $(1, 1)$ to $(2, 4)$.

24. The force field of Exercise 23; C: the arc of the parabola $y = x^2$ from the point $(1, 1)$ to $(2, 4)$.

25. The force field of Exercise 23; C: the line segment from $(1, 1)$ to $(2, 2)$ and then the line segment from $(2, 2)$ to $(2, 4)$.

26. $\mathbf{F}(x, y) = -x^2 y\mathbf{i} + 2y\mathbf{j}$; C: the line segment from $(a, 0)$ to $(0, a)$.

27. The force field of Exercise 26; C: $\mathbf{R}(t) = a \cos t\mathbf{i} + a \sin t\mathbf{j}$, $0 \le t \le \frac{1}{2}\pi$.

28. The force field of Exercise 26; C: the line segment from $(a, 0)$ to (a, a) and then the line segment from (a, a) to $(0, a)$.

29. $\mathbf{F}(x, y, z) = (y + z)\mathbf{i} + (x + z)\mathbf{j} + (x + y)\mathbf{k}$; C: the line segment from the origin to the point $(1, 1, 1)$.

30. $\mathbf{F}(x, y, z) = z^2\mathbf{i} + y^2\mathbf{j} + xz\mathbf{k}$; C: the line segment from the origin to the point $(4, 0, 3)$.

31. $\mathbf{F}(x, y, z) = e^x\mathbf{i} + e^y\mathbf{j} + e^z\mathbf{k}$; C: $\mathbf{R}(t) = t\mathbf{i} + t^2\mathbf{j} + t^3\mathbf{k}$, $0 \le t \le 2$.

32. $\mathbf{F}(x, y, z) = (xyz + x)\mathbf{i} + (x^2 z + y)\mathbf{j} + (x^2 y + z)\mathbf{k}$; C: the arc of Exercise 31.

33. The force field of Exercise 32; C: the line segment from the origin to the point $(1, 0, 0)$; then the line segment from $(1, 0, 0)$ to $(1, 1, 0)$; then the line segment from $(1, 1, 0)$ to $(1, 1, 1)$.

34. $\mathbf{F}(x, y, z) = x\mathbf{i} + y\mathbf{j} + (yz - x)\mathbf{k}$; C: $\mathbf{R}(t) = 2t\mathbf{i} + t^2\mathbf{j} + 4t^3\mathbf{k}$, $0 \le t \le 1$.

20.7 LINE INTEGRALS INDEPENDENT OF THE PATH

We learned in Sec. 20.6 that the value of a line integral is determined by the integrand and a curve C between two points P_1 and P_2. However, under certain conditions the value of a line integral depends only on the integrand and the points P_1 and P_2 and not on the path from P_1 to P_2. Such a line integral is said to be independent of the path.

• ILLUSTRATION 1: Suppose a force field

$$\mathbf{F}(x, y) = (y^2 + 2x + 4)\mathbf{i} + (2xy + 4y - 5)\mathbf{j}$$

moves an object from the origin to the point $(1, 1)$. We show that the total work done is the same if the path is along (a) the line segment from the origin to $(1, 1)$; (b) the segment of the parabola $y = x^2$ from the origin to $(1, 1)$; and (c) the segment of the curve $x = y^3$ from the origin to $(1, 1)$.

If W in.-lb is the work done, then

$$W = \int_C (y^2 + 2x + 4)\ dx + (2xy + 4y - 5)\ dy \tag{1}$$

(a) An equation of C is $y = x$. We use x as the parameter and let $y = x$ and $dy = dx$ in Eq. (1). We have then

$$W = \int_0^1 (x^2 + 2x + 4)\ dx + (2x^2 + 4x - 5)\ dx$$

$$= \int_0^1 (3x^2 + 6x - 1)\ dx$$

$$= x^3 + 3x^2 - x \Big]_0^1$$

$$= 3$$

(b) An equation of C is $y = x^2$. Again taking x as the parameter and in Eq. (1) letting $y = x^2$ and $dy = 2x\ dx$, we have

$$W = \int_0^1 (x^4 + 2x + 4)\ dx + (2x^3 + 4x^2 - 5)2x\ dx$$

$$= \int_0^1 (5x^4 + 8x^3 - 8x + 4)\ dx$$

$$= x^5 + 2x^4 - 4x^2 + 4x \Big]_0^1$$

$$= 3$$

(c) An equation of C is $x = y^3$. We take y as the parameter and in Eq. (1) we let $x = y^3$ and $dx = 3y^2\ dy$. We have

$$W = \int_0^1 (y^2 + 2y^3 + 4)3y^2\ dy + (2y^4 + 4y - 5)\ dy$$

$$= \int_0^1 (6y^5 + 5y^4 + 12y^2 + 4y - 5)\ dy$$

$$= y^6 + y^5 + 4y^3 + 2y^2 - 5y \Big]_0^1$$

$$= 3$$

Thus, in parts (a), (b), and (c) the work done is 3 in.-lb.   •

In Illustration 1, we see that the value of the line integral is the same over three different paths from (0, 0) to (1, 1). Actually the value of the line integral is the same over any sectionally smooth curve from the origin to (1, 1), and so this line integral is independent of the path. (This fact is proved in Illustration 2, which follows Theorem 20.7.1.)

We now state and prove Theorem 20.7.1, which not only gives conditions for which the value of a line integral is independent of the path but also gives a formula for finding the value of such a line integral.

20.7.1 Theorem   Suppose that M and N are functions of two variables x and y defined on an open disk $B((x_0, y_0); r)$ in R^2, M_y and N_x are continuous on B, and

$$\nabla \phi(x, y) = M(x, y)\mathbf{i} + N(x, y)\mathbf{j}$$

Suppose that C is any sectionally smooth curve in B from the point (x_1, y_1) to the point (x_2, y_2). Then the line integral

$$\int_C M(x, y)\ dx + N(x, y)\ dy$$

is independent of the path C and

$$\int_C M(x, y)\ dx + N(x, y)\ dy = \phi(x_2, y_2) - \phi(x_1, y_1)$$

PROOF: We give the proof if C is smooth. If C is only sectionally smooth, then we consider each piece separately and the following proof applies to each smooth piece.

Let a vector equation of C be

$$\mathbf{R}(t) = f(t)\mathbf{i} + g(t)\mathbf{j} \qquad t_1 \le t \le t_2$$

where $(x_1, y_1) = (f(t_1), g(t_1))$ and $(x_2, y_2) = (f(t_2), g(t_2))$. Then from the definition of a line integral,

$$\int_C M(x, y)\ dx + N(x, y)\ dy = \int_{t_1}^{t_2} \nabla \phi(f(t), g(t)) \cdot \mathbf{R}'(t)\ dt \qquad (2)$$

We proceed to evaluate the definite integral in the right member of Eq. (2).

Because $\nabla \phi(x, y) = M(x, y)\mathbf{i} + N(x, y)\mathbf{j}$, then $\phi_x(x, y) = M(x, y)$ and $\phi_y(x, y) = N(x, y)$. Therefore,

$$d\phi(x, y) = M(x, y)\ dx + N(x, y)\ dy$$

for all points (x, y) in B. Then if $(f(t), g(t))$ is a point on C,

$$d\phi(f(t), g(t)) = [M(f(t), g(t))f'(t) + N(f(t), g(t))g'(t)]\ dt$$

or, equivalently,

$$d\phi(f(t), g(t)) = [\nabla\phi(f(t), g(t)) \cdot \mathbf{R}'(t)] \, dt \tag{3}$$

for $t_1 \le t \le t_2$. Consider the function G of the single variable t for which

$$\phi(f(t), g(t)) = G(t) \qquad t_1 \le t \le t_2 \tag{4}$$

Then

$$d\phi(f(t), g(t)) = G'(t) \, dt \tag{5}$$

From Eqs. (3) and (5) it follows that

$$\nabla\phi(f(t), g(t)) \cdot \mathbf{R}'(t) \, dt = G'(t) \, dt$$

Hence,

$$\int_{t_1}^{t_2} \nabla\phi(f(t), g(t)) \cdot \mathbf{R}'(t) \, dt = \int_{t_1}^{t_2} G'(t) \, dt$$

But from the fundamental theorem of the calculus (Theorem 7.6.2) the right member of this equation is $G(t_2) - G(t_1)$. Furthermore, from Eq. (4), $G(t_2) - G(t_1) = \phi(f(t_2), g(t_2)) - \phi(f(t_1), g(t_1))$. Therefore, we have

$$\int_{t_1}^{t_2} \nabla\phi(f(t), g(t)) \cdot \mathbf{R}'(t) \, dt = \phi(f(t_2), g(t_2)) - \phi(f(t_1), g(t_1)) \tag{6}$$

From Eqs. (2) and (6) and because $(f(t_2), g(t_2)) = (x_2, y_2)$ and $(f(t_1), g(t_1)) = (x_1, y_1)$, we obtain

$$\int_C M(x, y) \, dx + N(x, y) \, dy = \phi(x_2, y_2) - \phi(x_1, y_1)$$

which is what we wished to prove. ∎

Because of the resemblance of Theorem 20.7.1 to the fundamental theorem of the calculus, it is sometimes called the fundamental theorem for line integrals.

● ILLUSTRATION 2: We use Theorem 20.7.1 to evaluate the line integral in Illustration 1. The line integral is

$$\int_C (y^2 + 2x + 4) \, dx + (2xy + 4y - 5) \, dy$$

From Illustration 1, Sec. 20.5, it follows that if $\phi(x, y) = y^2x + x^2 + 4x + 2y^2 - 5y$, then

$$\nabla\phi(x, y) = (y^2 + 2x + 4)\mathbf{i} + (2xy + 4y - 5)\mathbf{j}$$

Thus, the value of the line integral is independent of the path, and C can be any sectionally smooth curve from $(0, 0)$ to $(1, 1)$. From Theorem 20.7.1, we have, then,

$$\int_C (y^2 + 2x + 4) \ dx + (2xy + 4y - 5) \ dy = \phi(1, 1) - \phi(0, 0)$$

$$= 3 - 0$$

$$= 3$$

This result agrees with that of Illustration 1.   •

If **F** is the vector-valued function defined by

$$\mathbf{F}(x, y) = M(x, y)\mathbf{i} + N(x, y)\mathbf{j} \tag{7}$$

and

$$\mathbf{F}(x, y) = \nabla\phi(x, y) \tag{8}$$

then **F** is called a *gradient field*, ϕ is called a *potential function*, and $\phi(x, y)$ is the potential of **F** at (x, y). Furthermore, if **F** is a force field satisfying Eq. (8), then **F** is said to be a *conservative* force field. Also, when a function **F**, defined by Eq. (7) has a potential function ϕ, then the expression $M(x, y) \ dx + N(x, y) \ dy$ is called an *exact differential*; this terminology is reasonable because $M(x, y) \ dx + N(x, y) \ dy = d\phi$.

• ILLUSTRATION 3: In Illustration 1, we have the force field

$$\mathbf{F}(x, y) = (y^2 + 2x + 4)\mathbf{i} + (2xy + 4y - 5)\mathbf{j}$$

In Illustration 2, we have the function ϕ such that

$$\phi(x, y) = y^2x + x^2 + 4x + 2y^2 - 5y$$

Because

$$\nabla\phi(x, y) = \mathbf{F}(x, y)$$

it follows that **F** is a conservative force field, and ϕ is a potential function of **F**. In particular, because $\phi(2, 1) = 11$, the potential of **F** at $(2, 1)$ is 11. Furthermore,

$$(y^2 + 2x + 4) \ dx + (2xy + 4y - 5) \ dy$$

is an exact differential and is equal to $d\phi$.   •

EXAMPLE 1: Evaluate the line integral

$$\int_C (e^{-y} - 2x) \ dx - (xe^{-y} + \sin y) \ dy$$

if C is the first quadrant arc of the circle $\mathbf{R}(t) = \pi \cos t\mathbf{i} + \pi \sin t\mathbf{j}$, and $0 \le t \le \frac{1}{2}\pi$.

SOLUTION: In Example 2, Sec. 20.5, we showed that

$$\nabla(xe^{-y} - x^2 + \cos y) = (e^{-y} - 2x)\mathbf{i} - (xe^{-y} + \sin y)\mathbf{j}$$

Therefore, we apply Theorem 20.7.1 with $\phi(x, y) = xe^{-y} - x^2 + \cos y$.

$$\int_C (e^{-y} - 2x) \ dx - (xe^{-y} + \sin y) \ dy = \phi(0, \pi) - \phi(\pi, 0)$$

$$= \cos \pi - (\pi - \pi^2 + 1)$$

$$= \pi^2 - \pi - 2$$

If the value of a line integral is independent of the path, it is not necessary to find a potential function ϕ. We show the procedure in the next example.

EXAMPLE 2:   Show that the value of the following line integral is independent of the path and evaluate it:

$$\int_C \frac{1}{y}\, dx - \frac{x}{y^2}\, dy$$

C is any sectionally smooth curve from the point $(5, -1)$ to the point $(9, -3)$.

SOLUTION: Let $M(x, y) = 1/y$ and $N(x, y) = -x/y^2$. Then

$$M_y(x, y) = -\frac{1}{y^2} \quad \text{and} \quad N_x(x, y) = -\frac{1}{y^2}$$

Because $M_y(x, y) = N_x(x, y)$, it follows from Theorem 20.5.1 that $(1/y)\mathbf{i} - (x/y^2)\mathbf{j}$ is a gradient, and therefore the value of the integral is independent of the path. We take for the path the line segment from $(5, -1)$ to $(9, -3)$. An equation of the line is $x + 2y = 3$. Thus, parametric equations of the line are

$$x = 3 + 2t \qquad y = -t \qquad 1 \le t \le 3$$

We compute the value of the line integral by applying Definition 20.6.2.

$$\int_C \frac{1}{y}\, dx - \frac{x}{y^2}\, dy = \int_1^3 \langle M((3 + 2t), -t), N((3 + 2t), -t)\rangle \cdot \langle 2, -1\rangle \, dt$$

$$= \int_1^3 \left\langle -\frac{1}{t}, -\frac{3 + 2t}{t^2}\right\rangle \cdot \langle 2, -1\rangle \, dt$$

$$= \int_1^3 \left(-\frac{2}{t} + \frac{3 + 2t}{t^2}\right) dt$$

$$= \int_1^3 \frac{3}{t^2}\, dt$$

$$= -\frac{3}{t}\Big]_1^3$$

$$= 2$$

The results of this section can be extended to functions of three variables. The statement of the following theorem and its proof are analogous to Theorem 20.7.1. The proof is left as an exercise (see Exercise 31).

20.7.2 Theorem   Suppose that M, N, and R are functions of three variables x, y, and z defined on an open ball $B((x_0, y_0, z_0); r)$ in R^3; M_y, M_z, N_x, N_z, R_x, and R_y are continuous on B; and

$$\nabla\phi(x, y, z) = M(x, y, z)\mathbf{i} + N(x, y, z)\mathbf{j} + R(x, y, z)\mathbf{k}$$

Suppose that C is any sectionally smooth curve in B from the point (x_1, y_1, z_1) to the point (x_2, y_2, z_2). Then the line integral

$$\int_C M(x, y, z) \, dx + N(x, y, z) \, dy + R(x, y, z) \, dz$$

is independent of the path C and

$$\int_C M(x, y, z) \, dx + N(x, y, z) \, dy + R(x, y, z) \, dz = \phi(x_2, y_2, z_2) - \phi(x_1, y_1, z_1)$$

● ILLUSTRATION 4: In Example 3, Sec. 20.5, we showed that the vector

$$(e^x \sin z + 2yz)\mathbf{i} + (2xz + 2y)\mathbf{j} + (e^x \cos z + 2xy + 3z^2)\mathbf{k}$$

is a gradient $\nabla f(x, y, z)$ and

$$f(x, y, z) = e^x \sin z + 2xyz + y^2 + z^3 + C$$

Therefore, if C is any sectionally smooth curve from $(0, 0, 0)$ to $(1, -2, \pi)$ then it follows from Theorem 20.7.2 that the line integral

$$\int_C (e^x \sin z + 2yz) \, dx + (2xz + 2y) \, dy + (e^x \cos z + 2xy + 3z^2) \, dz$$

is independent of the path and its value is

$$f(1, -2, \pi) - f(0, 0, 0) = (e \sin \pi - 4\pi + 4 + \pi^3) - 0$$
$$= \pi^3 - 4\pi + 4 \qquad ●$$

As with functions of two variables, if $\mathbf{F}(x, y, z) = \nabla \phi(x, y, z)$, then $\mathbf{F}$ is a gradient field, ϕ is a potential function, and $\phi(x, y, z)$ is the potential of $\mathbf{F}$ at (x, y, z). If $\mathbf{F}$ is a force field having a potential function, then $\mathbf{F}$ is a conservative force field. Also, if the function $\mathbf{F}$, defined by $\mathbf{F}(x, y, z) = M(x, y, z)\mathbf{i} + N(x, y, z)\mathbf{j} + R(x, y, z)\mathbf{k}$, has a potential function, then the expression $M(x, y, z) \, dx + N(x, y, z) \, dy + R(x, y, z) \, dz$ is an exact differential.

EXAMPLE 3: If $\mathbf{F}$ is the force field defined by $\mathbf{F}(x, y, z) = (z^2 + 1)\mathbf{i} + 2yz\mathbf{j} + (2xz + y^2)\mathbf{k}$ prove that $\mathbf{F}$ is conservative and find a potential function.

SOLUTION: To determine if $\mathbf{F}$ is conservative, we apply Theorem 20.5.2 to find out if $\mathbf{F}$ is a gradient. Let $M(x, y, z) = z^2 + 1$, $N(x, y, z) = 2yz$, and $R(x, y, z) = 2xz + y^2$. Then

$$M_y(x, y, z) = 0 \qquad M_z(x, y, z) = 2z \qquad N_x(x, y, z) = 0$$

$$N_z(x, y, z) = 2y \qquad R_x(x, y, z) = 2z \qquad R_y(x, y, z) = 2y$$

Therefore, $M_y(x, y, z) = N_x(x, y, z)$, $M_z(x, y, z) = R_x(x, y, z)$, and $N_z(x, y, z) = R_y(x, y, z)$. Thus, by Theorem 20.5.2, $\mathbf{F}$ is a gradient and hence a conservative force field. We now find a potential function ϕ such that $\mathbf{F}(x, y, z) = \nabla \phi(x, y, z)$; hence,

$$\phi_x(x, y, z) = z^2 + 1 \qquad \phi_y(x, y, z) = 2yz \qquad \phi_z(x, y, z) = 2xz + y^2 \quad (9)$$

Integrating with respect to x both members of the first of Eqs. (9), we have

$$\phi(x, y, z) = xz^2 + x + g(y, z) \qquad (10)$$

We now partial differentiate with respect to y both members of Eq. (10) and we obtain

$$\phi_y(x, y, z) = g_y(y, z) \tag{11}$$

Equating the right members of Eq. (11) and the second of Eqs. (9), we have

$$g_y(y, z) = 2yz$$

We now integrate with respect to y both members of this equation, and we get

$$g(y, z) = y^2 z + h(z) \tag{12}$$

Substituting from Eq. (12) into Eq. (10), we obtain

$$\phi(x, y, z) = xz^2 + x + y^2 z + h(z) \tag{13}$$

We partial differentiate with respect to z both members of Eq. (13) and get

$$\phi_z(x, y, z) = 2xz + y^2 + h'(z) \tag{14}$$

We equate the right members of Eq. (14) and the third of Eqs. (9) and we have

$$2xz + y^2 + h'(z) = 2xz + y^2$$

$$h'(z) = 0$$

$$h(z) = C \tag{15}$$

Substituting from Eq. (15) into Eq. (13), we obtain the required potential function ϕ such that

$$\phi(x, y, z) = xz^2 + x + y^2 z + C$$

Exercises 20.7

In Exercises 1 through 10, prove that the given force field is conservative and find a potential function.

1. $\mathbf{F}(x, y) = y\mathbf{i} + x\mathbf{j}$

2. $\mathbf{F}(x, y) = x\mathbf{i} + y\mathbf{j}$

3. $\mathbf{F}(x, y) = e^x \sin y\mathbf{i} + e^x \cos y\mathbf{j}$

4. $\mathbf{F}(x, y) = (\sin y \sinh x + \cos y \cosh x)\mathbf{i} + (\cos y \cosh x - \sin y \sinh x)\mathbf{j}$

5. $\mathbf{F}(x, y) = (2xy^2 - y^3)\mathbf{i} + (2x^2y - 3xy^2 + 2)\mathbf{j}$

6. $\mathbf{F}(x, y) = (3x^2 + 2y - y^2e^x)\mathbf{i} + (2x - 2ye^x)\mathbf{j}$

7. $\mathbf{F}(x, y, z) = (x^2 - y)\mathbf{i} - (x - 3z)\mathbf{j} + (z + 3y)\mathbf{k}$

8. $\mathbf{F}(x, y, z) = (2y^3 - 8xz^2)\mathbf{i} + (6xy^2 + 1)\mathbf{j} - (8x^2z + 3z^2)\mathbf{k}$

9. $\mathbf{F}(x, y, z) = (2x \cos y - 3)\mathbf{i} - (x^2 \sin y + z^2)\mathbf{j} - (2yz - 2)\mathbf{k}$

10. $\mathbf{F}(x, y, z) = (\tan y + 2xy \sec z)\mathbf{i} + (x \sec^2 y + x^2 \sec z)\mathbf{j} + \sec z(x^2y \tan z - \sec z)\mathbf{k}$

In Exercises 11 through 20, use the results of the indicated exercise to prove that the value of the given line integral is independent of the path. Then evaluate the line integral by applying either Theorem 20.7.1 or Theorem 20.7.2 and using the potential function found in the indicated exercise. In each exercise, C is any sectionally smooth curve from the point A to the point B.

11. $\displaystyle\int_C y\,dx + x\,dy$; A is $(1, 4)$ and B is $(3, 2)$; Exercise 1

12. $\displaystyle\int_C x\,dx + y\,dy$; A is $(-5, 2)$ and B is $(1, 3)$; Exercise 2

13. $\displaystyle\int_C e^x \sin y\,dx + e^x \cos y\,dy$; A is $(0, 0)$ and B is $(2, \tfrac{1}{2}\pi)$; Exercise 3

14. $\displaystyle\int_C (\sin y \sinh x + \cos y \cosh x)\,dx + (\cos y \cosh x - \sin y \sinh x)\,dy$; A is $(1, 0)$ and B is $(2, \pi)$; Exercise 4

15. $\displaystyle\int_C (2xy^2 - y^3)\,dx + (2x^2y - 3xy^2 + 2)\,dy$; A is $(-3, -1)$ and B is $(1, 2)$; Exercise 5

16. $\displaystyle\int_C (3x^2 + 2y - y^2e^x)\,dx + (2x - 2ye^x)\,dy$; A is $(0, 2)$ and B is $(1, -3)$; Exercise 6

17. $\displaystyle\int_C (x^2 - y)\,dx - (x - 3z)\,dy + (z + 3y)\,dz$; A is $(-3, 1, 2)$ and B is $(3, 0, 4)$; Exercise 7

18. $\displaystyle\int_C (2y^3 - 8xz^2)\,dx + (6xy^2 + 1)\,dy - (8x^2z + 3z^2)\,dz$; A is $(2, 0, 0)$ and B is $(3, 2, 1)$; Exercise 8

19. $\displaystyle\int_C (2x \cos y - 3)\,dx - (x^2 \sin y + z^2)\,dy - (2yz - 2)\,dz$; A is $(-1, 0, 3)$ and B is $(1, \pi, 0)$; Exercise 9

20. $\displaystyle\int_C (\tan y + 2xy \sec z)\,dx + (x \sec^2 y + x^2 \sec z)\,dy + \sec z(x^2y \tan z - \sec z)\,dz$; A is $(2, \tfrac{1}{4}\pi, 0)$ and B is $(3, \pi, \pi)$; Exercise 10

In Exercises 21 through 30, show that the value of the line integral is independent of the path and compute the value in any convenient manner. In each exercise, C is any sectionally smooth curve from the point A to the point B.

21. $\displaystyle\int_C (2y - x)\,dx + (y^2 + 2x)\,dy$; A is $(0, -1)$ and B is $(1, 2)$

22. $\displaystyle\int_C (\ln x + 2y)\,dx + (e^y + 2x)\,dy$; A is $(3, 1)$ and B is $(1, 3)$

23. $\displaystyle\int_C \tan y\,dx + x \sec^2 y\,dy$; A is $(-2, 0)$ and B is $(4, \tfrac{1}{4}\pi)$

24. $\displaystyle\int_C \sin y\,dx + (\sin y + x \cos y)\,dy$; A is $(-2, 0)$ and B is $(2, \tfrac{1}{6}\pi)$

25. $\displaystyle\int_C \frac{2y}{(xy + 1)^2}\,dx + \frac{2x}{(xy + 1)^2}\,dy$; A is $(0, 2)$ and B is $(1, 0)$

26. $\displaystyle\int_C \frac{x}{x^2 + y^2 + z^2}\,dx + \frac{y}{x^2 + y^2 + z^2}\,dy + \frac{z}{x^2 + y^2 + z^2}\,dz$; A is $(1, 0, 0)$ and B is $(1, 2, 3)$

27. $\displaystyle\int_C (y + z)\,dx + (x + z)\,dy + (x + y)\,dz$; A is $(0, 0, 0)$ and B is $(1, 1, 1)$

28. $\int_C (yz + x)\, dx + (xz + y)\, dy + (xy + z)\, dz$; A is $(0, 0, 0)$ and B is $(1, 1, 1)$

29. $\int_C (e^x \sin y + yz)\, dx + (e^x \cos y + z \sin y + xz)\, dy + (xy - \cos y)\, dz$; A is $(2, 0, 1)$ and B is $(0, \pi, 3)$

30. $\int_C (2x \ln yz - 5ye^x)\, dx - (5e^x - x^2y^{-1})\, dy + (x^2z^{-1} + 2z)\, dz$; A is $(2, 1, 1)$ and B is $(3, 1, e)$

31. Prove Theorem 20.7.2.

Review Exercises (Chapter 20)

In Exercises 1 and 2, find the value of the directional derivative at the particular point P_0 for the given function in the direction of **U**.

1. $f(x, y, z) = xy^2z - 3xyz + 2xz^2$; $\mathbf{U} = -\frac{2}{3}\mathbf{i} + \frac{2}{3}\mathbf{j} - \frac{1}{3}\mathbf{k}$; $P_0 = (2, 1, 1)$

2. $f(x, y) = \tan^{-1}\frac{y}{x}$; $\mathbf{U} = \frac{2}{\sqrt{13}}\mathbf{i} - \frac{3}{\sqrt{13}}\mathbf{j}$; $P_0 = (4, -4)$

In Exercises 3 and 4, find the rate of change of the function value in the direction of **U** at P.

3. $f(x, y) = \frac{1}{2}\ln (x^2 + y^2)$; $\mathbf{U} = \frac{1}{2}\mathbf{i} + \frac{\sqrt{3}}{2}\mathbf{j}$; $P = (1, 1)$

4. $f(x, y, z) = yz - y^2 - xz$; $\mathbf{U} = \frac{6}{7}\mathbf{i} + \frac{3}{7}\mathbf{j} + \frac{2}{7}\mathbf{k}$; $P = (1, 2, 3)$

In Exercises 5 and 6, determine if the vector is a gradient. If it is, then find a function having the given gradient.

5. $y(\cos x - z \sin x)\mathbf{i} + z(\cos x + \sin y)\mathbf{j} - (\cos y - y \cos x)\mathbf{k}$

6. $(e^x \tan y - \sec y)\mathbf{i} - \sec y(x \tan y - e^x \sec y)\mathbf{j}$

In Exercises 7 and 8, find an equation of the tangent plane and equations of the normal line to the given surface at the indicated point.

7. $z^2 + 2y + z = 8$; $(2, 1, 2)$

8. $z = x^2 + 2xy$; $(1, 3, 7)$

In Exercises 9 and 10, determine the relative extrema of f, if there are any.

9. $f(x, y) = x^3 + y^3 + 3xy$

10. $f(x, y) = 2x^2 - 3xy + 2y^2 + 10x - 11y$

In Exercises 11 and 12, evaluate the line integral over the given curve.

11. $\int_C (2x + 3y)\, dx + xy\, dy$; C: $\mathbf{R}(t) = 4 \sin t\mathbf{i} - \cos t\mathbf{j}$, $0 \le t \le \frac{1}{2}\pi$

12. $\int_C xe^y\, dx - xe^z\, dy + e^z\, dz$; C: $\mathbf{R}(t) = t\mathbf{i} + t^2\mathbf{j} + t^3\mathbf{k}$, $0 \le t \le 1$

In Exercises 13 and 14, find the total work done in moving an object along the given arc C if the motion is caused by the given force field. Assume the arc is measured in inches and the force is measured in pounds.

13. $\mathbf{F}(x, y, z) = (xy - z)\mathbf{i} + yj + z\mathbf{k}$; C: the line segment from the origin to the point $(4, 1, 2)$

14. $\mathbf{F}(x, y) = xy^2\mathbf{i} - x^2y\mathbf{j}$; C: the arc of the circle $x^2 + y^2 = 4$ from $(2, 0)$ to $(0, 2)$

In Exercises 15 and 16, prove that the value of the given line integral is independent of the path, and compute the value in any convenient manner. In each exercise C is any sectionally smooth curve from the point A to the point B.

15. $\displaystyle\int_C 2xe^y \, dx + x^2e^y \, dy$; A is $(1, 0)$ and B is $(3, 2)$

16. $\displaystyle\int_C z \sin y \, dx + xz \cos y \, dy + x \sin y \, dz$; A is $(0, 0, 0)$ and B is $(2, 3, \tfrac{1}{2}\pi)$

17. If $f(x, y, z) = 3xy^2 - 5xz^2 - 2xyz$, find the gradient of f at $(-1, 3, 2)$.

18. If $f(x, y, z) = \sinh(x + z) \cosh y$, find the rate of change of $f(x, y, z)$ with respect to distance in R^3 at the point $P(1, 1, 0)$ in the direction $\overrightarrow{PQ}$ if Q is the point $(-1, 0, 2)$.

19. Find the dimensions of the rectangular parallelepiped of greatest volume that can be inscribed in the ellipsoid $x^2 + 9y^2 + z^2 = 9$. Assume that the edges are parallel to the coordinate axes.

20. Find equations of the tangent line to the curve of intersection of the surface $z = 3x^2 + y^2 + 1$ with the plane $x = 2$ at the point $(2, -1, 14)$.

21. The temperature is T degrees at any point on a heated circular plate and

$$T = \frac{44}{x^2 + y^2 + 9}$$

where distance is measured in inches from the origin at the center of the plate. (a) Find the rate of change of the temperature at the point $(3, 2)$ in the direction of the vector $\cos\tfrac{1}{8}\pi\mathbf{i} + \sin\tfrac{1}{8}\pi\mathbf{j}$. (b) Find the direction and magnitude of the greatest rate of change of T at the point $(3, 2)$.

22. The temperature is T degrees at any point (x, y) of the curve $4x^2 + 12y^2 = 1$ and $T = 4x^2 + 24y^2 - 2x$. Find the points on the curve where the temperature is the greatest and where it is the least. Also find the temperature at these points.

23. A monopolist produces two commodities whose demand equations are

$$x = 16 - 3p - 2q \quad \text{and} \quad y = 11 - 2p - 2q$$

where $100x$ is the quantity of the first commodity demanded if the price is p dollars per unit and $100y$ is the quantity of the second commodity demanded if the price is q dollars per unit. Show that the two commodities are complementary. If the cost of production of each unit of the first commodity is \$1 and the cost of production of each unit of the second commodity is \$3, find the quantities demanded and the price of each commodity in order to have the greatest profit.

24. Find the value of the line integral

$$\int_C \frac{-y}{x^2 + y^2} \, dx + \frac{x}{x^2 + y^2} \, dy$$

if C is the arc of the circle $x^2 + y^2 = 4$ from $(\sqrt{2}, \sqrt{2})$ to $(-2, 0)$.

25. Given the force field $\mathbf{F}$ such that

$$\mathbf{F}(x, y, z) = z^2 \sec^2 x\mathbf{i} + 2ye^{3z}\mathbf{j} + (3y^2e^{3z} + 2z \tan x)\mathbf{k}$$

prove that $\mathbf{F}$ is conservative and find a potential function.

26. A piece of wire L ft long is cut into three pieces. One piece is bent into the shape of a circle, a second piece is bent into the shape of a square, and the third piece is bent into the shape of an equilateral triangle. How should the wire be cut so that (a) the combined area of the three figures is as small as possible and (b) the combined area of the three figures is as large as possible?

27. Use the method of Lagrange multipliers to find the critical points of the function f for which $f(x, y, z) = y + xz - 2x^2 - y^2 - z^2$ subject to the constraint $z = 35 - x - y$. Determine if the function has a relative maximum or a relative minimum value at any critical point.

28. In parts (a), (b), and (c) demand equations of two related commodities are given. In each part, determine if the commodities are complementary, substitutes, or neither: (a) $x = -4p + 2q + 6$, $y = 5p - q + 10$; (b) $x = 6 - 3p - 2q$, $y = 4 + 2p - q$; (c) $x = -7q - p + 7$, $y = 18 - 3q - 9p$.

29. Determine the relative dimensions of a rectangular box, without a top and having a specific surface area, if the volume is to be a maximum.

21

Multiple integration

21.1 THE DOUBLE INTEGRAL

The definite integral of a function of a single variable can be extended to a function of several variables. We call an integral of a function of a single variable a *single integral* to distinguish it from a multiple integral, which involves a function of several variables. The physical and geometric applications of multiple integrals are analogous to those given in Chapter 8 for single integrals.

In the discussion of a single integral we required that the function be defined on a closed interval in R^1. For the double integral of a function of two variables, we require that the function be defined on a closed region in R^2. By a closed region we mean that the region includes its boundary. In this chapter, when we refer to a region, it is assumed to be closed. The simplest kind of closed region in R^2 is a closed rectangle, which we now proceed to define. Consider two distinct points $A(a_1, a_2)$ and $B(b_1, b_2)$ such that $a_1 \leq b_1$ and $a_2 \leq b_2$. These two points determine a rectangle having sides parallel to the coordinate axes. Refer to Fig. 21.1.1. The two points, together with the points (b_1, a_2) and (a_1, b_2), are called the *vertices* of the rectangle. The line segments joining consecutive vertices are called the *edges* of the rectangle. The set of all points interior to the rectangle is called an *open rectangle*, and the set of all points in the open rectangle, together with the points on the edges of the rectangle, is called a *closed rectangle*.

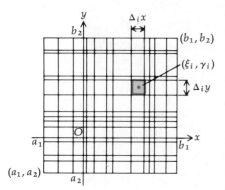

Figure 21.1.1

Let the closed rectangular region of Fig. 21.1.1 be denoted by R and let f be a function defined on R. The region R can be considered as a *region of integration*. Our first step is to define a *partition*, Δ, of R. We draw lines parallel to the coordinate axes and obtain a network of rectangular subregions which cover R. The *norm* of this partition, denoted by $\|\Delta\|$, is determined by the length of the longest diagonal of a rectangular subregion of the partition. We number the subregions in some arbitrary way and let the total be n. We denote the width of the ith subregion by $\Delta_i x$ units and its height by $\Delta_i y$ units. Then if $\Delta_i A$ square units is the area of the ith rectangular subregion,

$$\Delta_i A = \Delta_i x \, \Delta_i y$$

Let (ξ_i, γ_i) be an arbitrary point in the ith subregion and $f(\xi_i, \gamma_i)$ be the function value there. Consider the product $f(\xi_i, \gamma_i) \, \Delta_i A$. Associated with each of the n subregions is such a product, and their sum is

$$\sum_{i=1}^{n} f(\xi_i, \gamma_i) \, \Delta_i A \tag{1}$$

There are many sums of the form (1) because the norm of the partition can be any positive number and each point (ξ_i, γ_i) can be any point in the ith subregion. If all such sums can be made arbitrarily close to one number L by taking partitions with sufficiently small norms, then L is defined to be the limit of these sums as the norm of the partition of R approaches zero. We have the following definition.

21.1.1 Definition Let f be a function defined on a closed rectangular region R. The number

L is said to be the *limit* of sums of the form $\sum_{i=1}^{n} f(\xi_i, \gamma_i) \, \Delta_i A$ if L satisfies the property that for any $\epsilon > 0$, there exists a $\delta > 0$ such that

$$\left| \sum_{i=1}^{n} f(\xi_i, \gamma_i) \, \Delta_i A - L \right| < \epsilon$$

for every partition Δ for which $\|\Delta\| < \delta$ and for all possible selections of the point (ξ_i, γ_i) in the ith rectangle, $i = 1, 2, \ldots, n$. If such a number L exists, we write

$$\lim_{\|\Delta\| \to 0} \sum_{i=1}^{n} f(\xi_i, \gamma_i) \, \Delta_i A = L$$

If there is a number L satisfying Definition 21.1.1, it can be shown that it is unique. The proof is similar to the proof of the theorem (2.1.2) regarding the uniqueness of the limit of a function.

21.1.2 Definition   A function f of two variables is said to be *integrable* on a rectangular region R if f is defined on R and the number L of Definition 21.1.1 exists. This number L is called the *double integral* of f on R, and we write

$$\lim_{\|\Delta\| \to 0} \sum_{i=1}^{n} f(\xi_i, \gamma_i) \, \Delta_i A = \iint_R f(x, y) \, dA \tag{2}$$

Other symbols for the double integral in (2) are

$$\iint_R f(x, y) \, dx \, dy \quad \text{and} \quad \iint_R f(x, y) \, dy \, dx$$

The following theorem, which is stated without proof, gives us a condition under which a function of two variables is integrable.

21.1.3 Theorem   If a function f of two variables is continuous on a closed rectangular region R, then f is integrable on R.

The approximation of the value of a double integral by using Definition 21.1.3 is shown in the following example.

EXAMPLE 1:   Find an approximate value of the double integral

$$\iint_R (2x^2 - 3y) \, dA$$

where R is the rectangular region having vertices $(-1, 1)$ and $(2, 3)$. Take a partition of R formed by the lines $x = 0$, $x = 1$,

SOLUTION: Refer to Fig. 21.1.2, which shows the region R partitioned into six subregions which are squares having sides one unit in length. So for each i, $\Delta_i A = 1$. In each of the subregions the point (ξ_i, γ_i) is at the center of the square. Therefore, an approximation to the given double integral is given by

$$\iint_R (2x^2 - 3y) \, dA \approx f(-\tfrac{1}{2}, \tfrac{3}{2}) \cdot 1 + f(\tfrac{1}{2}, \tfrac{3}{2}) \cdot 1 + f(\tfrac{3}{2}, \tfrac{3}{2}) \cdot 1$$
$$+ f(\tfrac{3}{2}, \tfrac{5}{2}) \cdot 1 + f(\tfrac{1}{2}, \tfrac{5}{2}) \cdot 1 + f(-\tfrac{1}{2}, \tfrac{5}{2}) \cdot 1$$

and $y = 2$, and take (ξ_i, γ_i) at the center of the ith subregion.

$$= -4 \cdot 1 - 4 \cdot 1 + 0 \cdot 1 - 3 \cdot 1 - 7 \cdot 1 - 7 \cdot 1$$
$$= -25$$

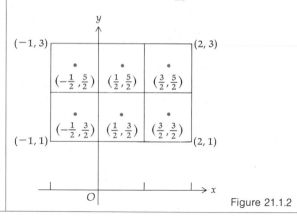

Figure 21.1.2

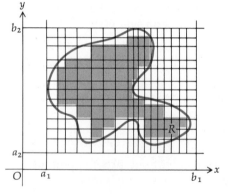

Figure 21.1.3

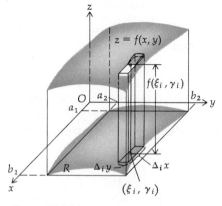

Figure 21.1.4

The exact value of the double integral in Example 1 is -24, as will be shown in Example 1 of Sec. 21.2.

We now consider the double integral of a function over a more general region. In Definition 8.10.2 we defined a smooth function as one that has a continuous derivative, and a smooth curve is the graph of a smooth function. Let R be a closed region whose boundary consists of a finite number of arcs of smooth curves that are joined together to form a closed curve. As we did with a rectangular region, we draw lines parallel to the coordinate axes, which gives us a rectangular partition of the region R. We discard the subregions which contain points not in R and consider only those which lie entirely in R (these are shaded in Fig. 21.1.3). Letting the number of these shaded subregions be n, we proceed in a manner analogous to the procedure we used for a rectangular region. Definitions 21.1.1 and 21.1.2 apply when the region R is the more general one described above. You should intuitively realize that as the norm of the partition approaches zero, n increases without bound, and the area of the region omitted (i.e., the discarded rectangles) approaches zero. Actually, in advanced calculus it can be proved that if a function is integrable on a region R, the limit of the approximating sums of the form (1) is the same no matter how we subdivide R, so long as each subregion has a shape to which an area can be assigned.

Just as the integral of a function of a single variable is interpreted geometrically as the measure of the area of a plane region, the double integral can be interpreted geometrically as the measure of the volume of a three-dimensional solid. Suppose that the function f is continuous on a closed region R in R^2. Furthermore, for simplicity in this discussion, assume that $f(x, y)$ is nonnegative on R. The graph of the equation $z = f(x, y)$ is a surface lying above the xy plane as shown in Fig. 21.1.4. The figure shows a particular rectangular subregion of R, having dimensions of measures $\Delta_i x$ and $\Delta_i y$. The figure also shows a rectangular solid having this subregion as a base and $f(\xi_i, \gamma_i)$ as the measure of the altitude where (ξ_i, γ_i) is a point in the ith subregion. The volume of the rectangular solid is determined by

$$\Delta_i V = f(\xi_i, \gamma_i)\ \Delta_i A = f(\xi_i, \gamma_i)\ \Delta_i x\ \Delta_i y \tag{3}$$

The number given in (3) is the measure of the volume of the thin rectangular solid shown in Fig. 21.1.4; thus, the sum given in (1) is the sum of the measures of the volumes of n such solids. This sum approximates the measure of the volume of the three-dimensional solid shown in Fig. 21.1.4 which is bounded above by the graph of f and below by the region R in the xy plane. The sum in (1) also approximates the number given by the double integral

$$\int_R\!\!\int f(x, y)\ dA$$

It can be proved that the volume of the three-dimensional solid of Fig. 21.1.4 is the value of the double integral. We state this in the following theorem for which a formal proof is not given.

21.1.4 Theorem   Let f be a function of two variables that is continuous on a closed region R in the xy plane and $f(x, y) \geq 0$ for all (x, y) in R. If $V(S)$ is the measure of the volume of the solid S having the region R as its base and having an altitude of measure $f(x, y)$ at the point (x, y) in R, then

$$V(S) = \lim_{\|\Delta\| \to 0} \sum_{i=1}^{n} f(\xi_i, \gamma_i)\ \Delta_i A = \int_R\!\!\int f(x, y)\ dA$$

EXAMPLE 2:   Approximate the volume of the solid bounded by the surface

$$f(x, y) = 4 - \tfrac{1}{9}x^2 - \tfrac{1}{16}y^2$$

the planes $x = 3$ and $y = 2$, and the three coordinate planes. To find an approximate value of the double integral take a partition of the region in the xy plane by drawing the lines $x = 1$, $x = 2$, and $y = 1$, and take (ξ_i, γ_i) at the center of the ith subregion.

SOLUTION: The solid is shown in Fig. 21.1.5. The rectangular region R is the rectangle in the xy plane bounded by the coordinate axes and the lines $x = 3$ and $y = 2$. From Theorem 21.1.4, if V cubic units is the volume of the solid,

$$V = \int_R\!\!\int (4 - \tfrac{1}{9}x^2 - \tfrac{1}{16}y^2)\ dA$$

Figure 21.1.5 shows R partitioned into six subregions which are squares having sides of length one unit. Therefore, for each i, $\Delta_i A = 1$. The point (ξ_i, γ_i) in each subregion is at the center of the square. Then an approximation of V is given by an approximation of the double integral, and we have

$$V \approx f(\tfrac{1}{2}, \tfrac{1}{2}) \cdot 1 + f(\tfrac{3}{2}, \tfrac{1}{2}) \cdot 1 + f(\tfrac{5}{2}, \tfrac{1}{2}) \cdot 1 + f(\tfrac{1}{2}, \tfrac{3}{2}) \cdot 1 + f(\tfrac{3}{2}, \tfrac{3}{2}) \cdot 1 + f(\tfrac{5}{2}, \tfrac{3}{2}) \cdot 1$$

$$= (4 - \tfrac{25}{576}) + (4 - \tfrac{17}{64}) + (4 - \tfrac{409}{576}) + (4 - \tfrac{97}{576}) + (4 - \tfrac{25}{64}) + (4 - \tfrac{481}{576})$$

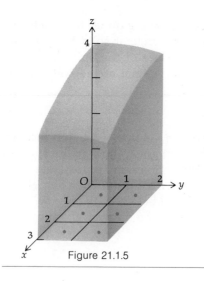

Figure 21.1.5

$$= 24 - \tfrac{695}{288}$$

$$\approx 21.59$$

Thus, the volume is approximately 21.59 cubic units.

The exact value of the volume in Example 2 is shown to be 21.5 cubic units in Example 2 of Sec. 21.2.

Analogous to properties of the definite integral of a function of a single variable are several properties of the double integral, and the most important ones are given in the following theorems.

21.1.5 Theorem   If c is a constant and the function f is integrable on a closed region R, then cf is integrable on R and

$$\int\!\!\int_R cf(x, y)\, dA = c \int\!\!\int_R f(x, y)\, dA$$

21.1.6 Theorem   If the functions f and g are integrable on a closed region R, then the function $f + g$ is integrable on R and

$$\int\!\!\int_R [f(x, y) + g(x, y)]\, dA = \int\!\!\int_R f(x, y)\, dA + \int\!\!\int_R g(x, y)\, dA$$

The result of Theorem 21.1.6 can be extended to any finite number of functions which are integrable. The proofs of Theorems 21.1.5 and 21.1.6 follow directly from the definition of a double integral. These proofs are left as exercises (see Exercises 13 and 14).

21.1.7 Theorem   If the functions f and g are integrable on the closed region R and $f(x, y) \geq g(x, y)$ for all (x, y) in R, then

$$\int\!\!\int_R f(x, y)\, dA \geq \int\!\!\int_R g(x, y)\, dA$$

Theorem 21.1.7 is analogous to Theorem 7.4.8 for the definite integral of a function of a single variable. The proof is similar and is left as an exercise (see Exercise 15).

21.1.8 Theorem   Let the function f be integrable on a closed region R, and suppose that m and M are two numbers such that $m \leq f(x, y) \leq M$ for all (x, y) in R. Then if A is the measure of the area of region R, we have

$$mA \leq \int\int_R f(x, y) \, dA \leq MA$$

The proof of Theorem 21.1.8 is left as an exercise (see Exercise 16). The proof is similar to that of Theorem 7.5.2 and is based on Theorem 21.1.7.

21.1.9 Theorem   Suppose that the function f is continuous on the closed region R and that region R is composed of the two subregions R_1 and R_2 which have no points in common except for points on parts of their boundaries. Then

$$\int\int_R f(x, y) \, dA = \int\int_{R_1} f(x, y) \, dA + \int\int_{R_2} f(x, y) \, dA$$

The proof of Theorem 21.1.9 is also left as an exercise and depends on the definition of a double integral and limit theorems (see Exercise 17).

Exercises 21.1

In Exercises 1 through 6, find an approximate value of the given double integral where R is the rectangular region having the vertices P and Q, Δ is a regular partition of R, and (ξ_i, γ_i) is the midpoint of each subregion.

1. $\int\int_R (x^2 + y) \, dA$; $P(0, 0)$; $Q(4, 2)$; Δ: $x_1 = 0$, $x_2 = 1$, $x_3 = 2$, $x_4 = 3$, $y_1 = 0$, $y_2 = 1$.

2. $\int\int_R (2 - x - y) \, dA$; $P(0, 0)$; $Q(6, 4)$; Δ: $x_1 = 0$, $x_2 = 2$, $x_3 = 4$, $y_1 = 0$, $y_2 = 2$.

3. $\int\int_R (xy + 3y^2) \, dA$; $P(-2, 0)$; $Q(4, 6)$; Δ: $x_1 = -2$, $x_2 = 0$, $x_3 = 2$, $y_1 = 0$, $y_2 = 2$, $y_3 = 4$.

4. $\int\int_R (xy + 3y^2) \, dA$; $P(0, -2)$; $Q(6, 4)$; Δ: $x_1 = 0$, $x_2 = 2$, $x_3 = 4$, $y_1 = -2$, $y_2 = 0$, $y_3 = 2$.

5. $\int\int_R (x^2 y - 2xy^2) \, dA$; $P(-3, -2)$; $Q(1, 6)$; Δ: $x_1 = -3$, $x_2 = -1$, $y_1 = -2$, $y_2 = 0$, $y_3 = 2$, $y_4 = 4$.

6. $\int\int_R (x^2 y - 2xy^2) \, dA$; $P(-3, -2)$; $Q(1, 6)$; Δ: $x_1 = -3$, $x_2 = -2$, $x_3 = -1$, $x_4 = 0$, $y_1 = -2$, $y_2 = -1$, $y_3 = 0$, $y_4 = 1$, $y_5 = 2$, $y_6 = 3$, $y_7 = 4$, $y_8 = 5$.

In Exercises 7 through 10, find an approximate value of the given double integral where R is the rectangular region having the vertices P and Q, Δ is a regular partition of R, and (ξ_i, γ_i) is an arbitrary point in each subregion.

7. The double integral, P, Q, and Δ are the same as in Exercise 1; $(\xi_1, \gamma_1) = (\frac{1}{4}, \frac{1}{2})$; $(\xi_2, \gamma_2) = (\frac{7}{4}, 0)$; $(\xi_3, \gamma_3) = (\frac{5}{2}, \frac{1}{4})$, $(\xi_4, \gamma_4) = (4, 1)$; $(\xi_5, \gamma_5) = (\frac{3}{4}, \frac{7}{4})$; $(\xi_6, \gamma_6) = (\frac{5}{4}, \frac{3}{2})$; $(\xi_7, \gamma_7) = (\frac{5}{2}, 2)$; $(\xi_8, \gamma_8) = (3, 1)$.

8. The double integral, P, Q, and Δ are the same as in Exercise 2; $(\xi_1, \gamma_1) = (\frac{1}{2}, \frac{3}{2})$; $(\xi_2, \gamma_2) = (3, 1)$; $(\xi_3, \gamma_3) = (\frac{11}{2}, \frac{1}{2})$; $(\xi_4, \gamma_4) = (2, 2)$; $(\xi_5, \gamma_5) = (2, 2)$; $(\xi_6, \gamma_6) = (5, 3)$.

9. The double integral, P, Q, and Δ are the same as in Exercise 3; $(\xi_1, \gamma_1) = (-\frac{1}{2}, \frac{1}{2})$; $(\xi_2, \gamma_2) = (1, \frac{3}{2})$; $(\xi_3, \gamma_3) = (\frac{5}{2}, 2)$; $(\xi_4, \gamma_4) = (-\frac{3}{2}, \frac{7}{2})$; $(\xi_5, \gamma_5) = (0, 3)$; $(\xi_6, \gamma_6) = (4, 4)$; $(\xi_7, \gamma_7) = (-1, \frac{9}{2})$; $(\xi_8, \gamma_8) = (1, \frac{9}{2})$; $(\xi_9, \gamma_9) = (3, \frac{9}{2})$.

10. The double integral, P, Q, and Δ are the same as in Exercise 3; $(\xi_1, \gamma_1) = (-2, 0)$; $(\xi_2, \gamma_2) = (0, 0)$; $(\xi_3, \gamma_3) = (2, 0)$; $(\xi_4, \gamma_4) = (-2, 2)$; $(\xi_5, \gamma_5) = (0, 2)$; $(\xi_6, \gamma_6) = (2, 2)$; $(\xi_7, \gamma_7) = (-2, 4)$; $(\xi_8, \gamma_8) = (0, 4)$; $(\xi_9, \gamma_9) = (2, 4)$.

11. Approximate the volume of the solid in the first octant bounded by the sphere $x^2 + y^2 + z^2 = 64$, the planes $x = 3$ and $y = 3$, and the three coordinate planes. To find an approximate value of the double integral take a partition of the region in the xy plane by drawing the lines $x = 1$, $x = 2$, $y = 1$, and $y = 2$, and take (ξ_i, γ_i) at the center of the ith subregion.

12. Approximate the volume of the solid bounded by the surface $100z = 300 - 25x^2 - 4y^2$, the planes $x = -1, x = 3, y = -3$, and $y = 5$, and the xy plane. To find an approximate value of the double integral take a partition of the region in the xy plane by drawing the lines $x = 1, y = -1, y = 1$, and $y = 3$, and take (ξ_i, γ_i) at the center of the ith subregion.

13. Prove Theorem 21.1.5.

14. Prove Theorem 21.1.6.

15. Prove Theorem 21.1.7.

16. Prove Theorem 21.1.8.

17. Prove Theorem 21.1.9.

21.2 EVALUATION OF DOUBLE INTEGRALS AND ITERATED INTEGRALS

For functions of a single variable, the fundamental theorem of calculus provides a method for evaluating a definite integral by finding an anti-derivative (or indefinite integral) of the integrand. We have a corresponding method for evaluating a double integral which involves performing successive single integrations. A rigorous development of this method belongs to a course in advanced calculus. Our discussion is an intuitive one, and we use the geometric interpretation of the double integral as the measure of a volume. We first develop the method for the double integral on a rectangular region.

Let f be a given function which is integrable on a closed rectangular region R in the xy plane bounded by the lines $x = a_1$, $x = b_1$, $y = a_2$, and $y = b_2$. We assume that $f(x, y) \geq 0$ for all (x, y) in R. Refer to Fig. 21.2.1, which shows a sketch of the graph of the equation $z = f(x, y)$ when (x, y) is in R. The number that represents the value of the double integral

$$\iint_R f(x, y)\, dA$$

is the measure of the volume of the solid between the surface and the region R. We find this number by the method of parallel plane sections, which we discussed in Sec. 8.4.

Let y be a number in $[a_2, b_2]$. Consider the plane which is parallel to the xz plane through the point $(0, y, 0)$. Let $A(y)$ be the measure of the area of the plane region of intersection of this plane with the solid. By the method of parallel plane sections, as discussed in Sec. 8.4, we express the measure of the volume of the solid by

$$\int_{a_2}^{b_2} A(y)\, dy$$

Because the volume of the solid also is determined by the double integral,

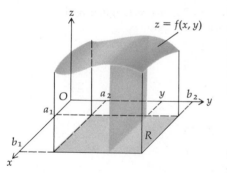

Figure 21.2.1

we have

$$\iint_R f(x, y) \, dA = \int_{a_2}^{b_2} A(y) \, dy \tag{1}$$

By using Eq. (1) we can find the value of the double integral of the function f on R by evaluating a single integral of $A(y)$. We now must find $A(y)$ when y is given. Because $A(y)$ is the measure of the area of a plane region, we can find it by integration. In Fig. 21.2.1, notice that the upper boundary of the plane region is the graph of the equation $z = f(x, y)$ when x is in $[a_1, b_1]$. Therefore, $A(y) = \int_{a_1}^{b_1} f(x, y) \, dx$. If we substitute from this equation into Eq. (1), we obtain

$$\iint_R f(x, y) \, dA = \int_{a_2}^{b_2} \left[\int_{a_1}^{b_1} f(x, y) \, dx \right] dy \tag{2}$$

The integral on the right side of Eq. (2) is called an *iterated integral.* Usually the brackets are omitted when writing an iterated integral. So we write Eq. (2) as

$$\iint_R f(x, y) \, dA = \int_{a_2}^{b_2} \int_{a_1}^{b_1} f(x, y) \, dx \, dy \tag{3}$$

When evaluating the "inner integral" in Eq. (3), remember that x is the variable of integration and y is considered a constant. This is analogous to considering y as a constant when finding the partial derivative of $f(x, y)$ with respect to x.

By considering plane sections parallel to the yz plane, we can develop the following formula, which interchanges the order of integration.

$$\iint_R f(x, y) \, dA = \int_{a_1}^{b_1} \int_{a_2}^{b_2} f(x, y) \, dy \, dx \tag{4}$$

A sufficient condition for formulas (3) and (4) to be valid is that the function be continuous on the rectangular region R.

EXAMPLE 1: Evaluate the double integral

$$\iint_R (2x^2 - 3y) \, dA$$

if R is the region consisting of all points (x, y) for which $-1 \le x \le 2$ and $1 \le y \le 3$.

SOLUTION: $a_1 = -1, b_1 = 2, a_2 = 1$, and $b_2 = 3$. So we have from formula (3)

$$\iint_R (2x^2 - 3y) \, dA = \int_1^3 \int_{-1}^2 (2x^2 - 3y) \, dx \, dy$$

$$= \int_1^3 \left[\int_{-1}^2 (2x^2 - 3y) \, dx \right] dy$$

$$= \int_1^3 \left[\tfrac{2}{3}x^3 - 3xy \right]_{-1}^2 dy$$

$$= \int_1^3 (6 - 9y) \, dy$$

$$= -24$$

In Example 1 of Sec. 21.1 we found an approximate value of the double integral in the above example to be -25.

EXAMPLE 2:   Find the volume of the solid bounded by the surface

$$f(x, y) = 4 - \tfrac{1}{9}x^2 - \tfrac{1}{16}y^2$$

the planes $x = 3$ and $y = 2$, and the three coordinate planes.

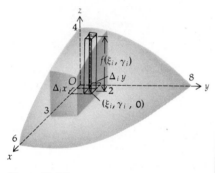

Figure 21.2.2

SOLUTION: Figure 21.2.2 shows the graph of the equation $z = f(x, y)$ in the first octant and the given solid. If V cubic units is the volume of the solid, we have from Theorem 21.1.4

$$V = \lim_{||\Delta|| \to 0} \sum_{i=1}^{n} f(\xi_i, \gamma_i)\, \Delta_i A = \iint_R f(x, y)\, dA$$

$$= \int_0^3 \int_0^2 (4 - \tfrac{1}{9}x^2 - \tfrac{1}{16}y^2)\, dy\, dx$$

$$= \int_0^3 \left[4y - \tfrac{1}{9}x^2 y - \tfrac{1}{48}y^3 \right]_0^2 dx$$

$$= \int_0^3 (\tfrac{47}{6} - \tfrac{2}{9}x^2)\, dx$$

$$= \tfrac{47}{6}x - \tfrac{2}{27}x^3 \Big]_0^3$$

$$= 21.5$$

The volume is therefore 21.5 cubic units.

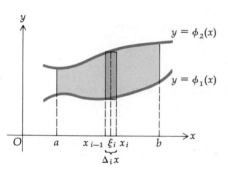

Figure 21.2.3

In Example 2 of Sec. 21.1 an approximate value of the volume in Example 2 was found to be 21.59 cubic units.

Suppose now that R is a region in the xy plane which is bounded by the lines $x = a$ and $x = b$, where $a < b$, and by the curves $y = \phi_1(x)$ and $y = \phi_2(x)$, where ϕ_1 and ϕ_2 are two functions which are continuous on the closed interval $[a, b]$; furthermore, $\phi_1(x) \leq \phi_2(x)$ whenever $a \leq x \leq b$ (see Fig. 21.2.3). Let Δ be a partition of the interval $[a, b]$ defined by Δ: $a = x_0 < x_1 < \cdots < x_n = b$. Consider the region R of Fig. 21.2.3 to be divided into vertical strips with widths of measure $\Delta_i x$. A particular strip is shown in the figure. The intersection of the surface $z = f(x, y)$ and a plane $x = \xi_i$, where $x_{i-1} \leq \xi_i \leq x_i$, is a curve. A segment of this curve is over the ith vertical strip. The region under this curve segment and above the xy plane is shown in Fig. 21.2.4, and the measure of the area of this region is given by

$$\int_{\phi_1(\xi_i)}^{\phi_2(\xi_i)} f(\xi_i, y)\, dy$$

The measure of the volume of the solid bounded above by the surface $z = f(x, y)$ and below by the ith vertical strip is approximately equal to

$$\left[\int_{\phi_1(\xi_i)}^{\phi_2(\xi_i)} f(\xi_i, y)\, dy \right] \Delta_i x$$

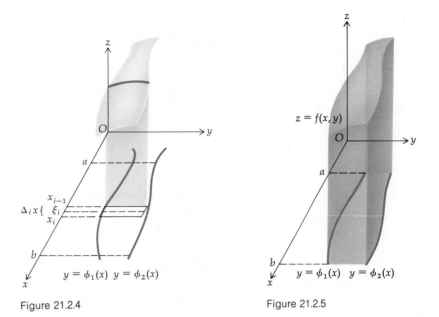

Figure 21.2.4   Figure 21.2.5

If we take the limit, as the norm of Δ approaches zero, of the sum of these measures of volume for n vertical strips of R from $x = a$ to $x = b$, we obtain the measure of the volume of the solid bounded above by the surface $z = f(x, y)$ and below by the region R in the xy plane. (See Fig. 21.2.5.) This is the double integral of f on R; that is,

$$\lim_{||\Delta|| \to 0} \sum_{i=1}^{n} \left[\int_{\phi_1(\xi)}^{\phi_2(\xi)} f(\xi_i, y) \, dy \right] \Delta_i x = \int_a^b \int_{\phi_1(x)}^{\phi_2(x)} f(x, y) \, dy \, dx$$

$$= \int\!\!\int_R f(x, y) \, dy \, dx$$

(5)

Sufficient conditions for formula (5) to be valid are that f be continuous on the closed region R and that ϕ_1 and ϕ_2 be smooth functions.

EXAMPLE 3: Express as both a double integral and an iterated integral the measure of the volume of the solid above the xy plane bounded by the elliptic paraboloid $z = x^2 + 4y^2$ and the cylinder $x^2 + 4y^2 = 4$. Evaluate the iterated integral to find the volume of the solid.

SOLUTION: The solid is shown in Fig. 21.2.6. Using properties of symmetry, we find the volume of the portion of the solid in the first octant which is one-fourth of the required volume. Then the region R in the xy plane is that bounded by the x and y axes and the ellipse $x^2 + 4y^2 = 4$. This region is shown in Fig. 21.2.7, which also shows the ith subregion of a rectangular partition of R, where (ξ_i, γ_i) is any point in this ith subregion. If V cubic units is the volume of the given solid, then by Theorem 21.1.4 we have

$$V = 4 \lim_{||\Delta|| \to 0} \sum_{i=1}^{n} (\xi_i^2 + 4\gamma_i^2) \, \Delta_i A = 4 \int\!\!\int_R (x^2 + 4y^2) \, dA$$

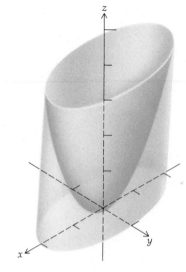

Figure 21.2.6

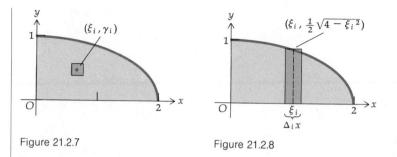

Figure 21.2.7

Figure 21.2.8

To express the measure of the volume as an iterated integral we divide the region R into n vertical strips. Figure 21.2.8 shows the region R and the ith vertical strip having width of $\Delta_i x$ units and length of $\frac{1}{2}\sqrt{4 - \xi_i^2}$ units, where $x_{i-1} \le \xi_i \le x_i$. Using formula (5) we have

$$V = 4 \lim_{\|\Delta\| \to 0} \sum_{i=1}^{n} \left[\int_0^{\sqrt{4 - \xi_i^2}/2} (\xi_i^2 + 4y^2) \, dy \right] \Delta_i x$$

$$= 4 \int_0^2 \int_0^{\sqrt{4 - x^2}/2} (x^2 + 4y^2) \, dy \, dx$$

Evaluating the iterated integral, we have

$$V = 4 \int_0^2 \left[x^2 y + \tfrac{4}{3} y^3 \right]_0^{\sqrt{4 - x^2}/2} dx$$

$$= 4 \int_0^2 \left[\tfrac{1}{2} x^2 \sqrt{4 - x^2} + \tfrac{1}{6}(4 - x^2)^{3/2} \right] dx$$

$$= \tfrac{4}{3} \int_0^2 (x^2 + 2) \sqrt{4 - x^2} \, dx$$

$$= -\tfrac{1}{3} x (4 - x^2)^{3/2} + 2x \sqrt{4 - x^2} + 8 \sin^{-1} \tfrac{1}{2} x \Big]_0^2$$

$$= 4\pi$$

Therefore, the volume is 4π cubic units.

If the region R is bounded by the curves $x = \lambda_1(y)$ and $x = \lambda_2(y)$ and the lines $y = c$ and $y = d$, where $c < d$, and λ_1 and λ_2 are two functions which are continuous on the closed interval $[c, d]$ for which $\lambda_1(y) \le \lambda_2(y)$ whenever $c \le y \le d$, then consider a partition Δ of the interval $[c, d]$ and divide the region into horizontal strips, the measures of whose widths are $\Delta_i y$. See Fig. 21.2.9, which shows the ith horizontal strip. The intersection of the surface $z = f(x, y)$ and a plane $y = \gamma_i$, where $y_{i-1} \le \gamma_i \le y_i$, is a curve, and a segment of this curve is over the ith horizontal strip. Then, as in the derivation of formula (5), the measure of the volume of the solid bounded above by the surface $z = f(x, y)$ and below by the ith

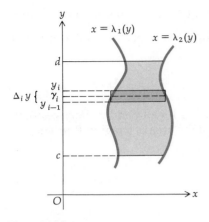

Figure 21.2.9

vertical strip is approximately equal to

$$\left[\int_{\lambda_1(\gamma_i)}^{\lambda_2(\gamma_i)} f(x, \gamma_i) \, dx \right] \Delta_i y$$

Taking the limit, as $\|\Delta\|$ approaches zero, of the sum of these measures of volume for n horizontal strips of R from $y = c$ to $y = d$, we obtain the measure of the volume of the solid bounded above by the surface $z = f(x, y)$ and below by the region R in the xy plane. This measure of volume is the double integral of f on R. Hence, we have

$$\lim_{\|\Delta\|\to 0} \sum_{i=1}^{n} \left[\int_{\lambda_1(\gamma_i)}^{\lambda_2(\gamma_i)} f(x, \gamma_i) \, dx \right] \Delta_i y = \int_c^d \int_{\lambda_1(y)}^{\lambda_2(y)} f(x, y) \, dx \, dy$$

$$= \iint_R f(x, y) \, dx \, dy \qquad (6)$$

Sufficient conditions for formula (6) to be valid are that λ_1 and λ_2 be smooth functions and f be continuous on R. In applying both formula (5) and formula (6) sometimes it may be necessary to subdivide a region R into subregions on which these sufficient conditions hold.

EXAMPLE 4: Express the volume of the solid of Example 3 by an iterated integral in which the order of integration is the reverse of that of Example 3. Compute the volume.

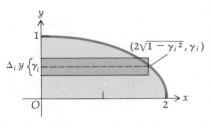

Figure 21.2.10

SOLUTION: Again we find the volume of the solid in the first octant and multiply the result by 4. Figure 21.2.10 shows the region R in the xy plane and the ith horizontal strip whose width has a measure of $\Delta_i y$, and whose length has a measure of $2\sqrt{1 - \gamma_i^2}$. Then by formula (6) we have

$$V = 4 \lim_{\|\Delta\|\to 0} \sum_{i=1}^{n} \left[\int_0^{2\sqrt{1-\gamma_i^2}} (x^2 + 4\gamma_i^2) \, dx \right] \Delta_i y$$

$$= 4 \int_0^1 \int_0^{2\sqrt{1-y^2}} (x^2 + 4y^2) \, dx \, dy$$

$$= 4 \int_0^1 \left[\tfrac{1}{3}x^3 + 4y^2x \right]_0^{2\sqrt{1-y^2}} dy$$

$$= 4 \int_0^1 \left[\tfrac{8}{3}(1 - y^2)^{3/2} + 8y^2 \sqrt{1 - y^2} \right] dy$$

$$= \tfrac{32}{3} \int_0^1 (2y^2 + 1) \sqrt{1 - y^2} \, dy$$

$$= -\tfrac{16}{3} y(1 - y^2)^{3/2} + 8y \sqrt{1 - y^2} + 8 \sin^{-1} y \Big]_0^1$$

$$= 4\pi$$

Hence, the volume is 4π cubic units, which agrees with the answer of Example 3.

From the solutions of Examples 3 and 4 we see that the double integral $\iint_R (x^2 + 4y^2) \, dA$ can be evaluated by either of the iterated integrals

$$\int_0^2 \int_0^{\sqrt{4-x^2}/2} (x^2 + 4y^2) \, dy \, dx \quad \text{or} \quad \int_0^1 \int_0^{2\sqrt{1-y^2}} (x^2 + 4y^2) \, dx \, dy$$

If in either formula (5) or (6), $f(x, y) = 1$ for all x and y, then we obtain a formula that expresses the measure A of the area of a region R as a double integral. We have

$$A = \int_R \int dy \, dx = \int_R \int dx \, dy \qquad (7)$$

EXAMPLE 5:   Find by double integration the area of the region in the xy plane bounded by the curves $y = x^2$ and $y = 4x - x^2$.

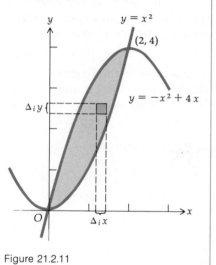

Figure 21.2.11

SOLUTION: The region is shown in Fig. 21.2.11. Applying formula (7), we have

$$A = \int_R \int dy \, dx = \int_0^2 \int_{x^2}^{4x-x^2} dy \, dx$$

$$= \int_0^2 (4x - x^2 - x^2) \, dx = 2x^2 - \tfrac{2}{3}x^3 \Big]_0^2$$

$$= \tfrac{8}{3}$$

Hence, the area of the region is $\tfrac{8}{3}$ square units.

Exercises 21.2

In Exercises 1 through 8, evaluate the given iterated integral.

1. $\displaystyle\int_1^2 \int_0^{2x} xy^3 \, dy \, dx$

2. $\displaystyle\int_0^4 \int_0^y dx \, dy$

3. $\displaystyle\int_0^1 \int_0^{y^2} e^{x/y} \, dx \, dy$

4. $\displaystyle\int_{-1}^1 \int_1^{e^x} \frac{1}{xy} \, dy \, dx$

5. $\displaystyle\int_0^1 \int_{y^2}^y \sqrt{\frac{y}{x}} \, dx \, dy$

6. $\displaystyle\int_0^1 \int_{x^2}^x \sqrt{\frac{y}{x}} \, dy \, dx$

7. $\displaystyle\int_0^1 \int_0^1 |x - y| \, dy \, dx$

8. $\displaystyle\int_0^\pi \int_0^{y^2} \sin \frac{x}{y} \, dx \, dy$

In Exercises 9 through 14, find the exact value of the double integral.

9. The double integral is the same as in Exercise 1 in Exercises 21.1.

10. The double integral is the same as in Exercise 4 in Exercises 21.1.

11. $\displaystyle\iint_R \sin x \, dA$; R is the region bounded by the lines $y = 2x$, $y = \frac{1}{2}x$, and $x = \pi$.

12. $\displaystyle\iint_R \cos(x + y) \, dA$; R is the region bounded by the lines $y = x$ and $x = \pi$, and the x axis.

13. $\displaystyle\iint_R x^2\sqrt{9 - y^2} \, dA$; R is the region bounded by the circle $x^2 + y^2 = 9$.

14. $\displaystyle\iint_R \frac{y^2}{x^2} \, dA$; R is the region bounded by the lines $y = x$ and $y = 2$, and the hyperbola $xy = 1$.

15. Find the volume of the solid under the plane $z = 4x$ and above the circle $x^2 + y^2 = 16$ in the xy plane. Draw a sketch of the solid.

16. Find the volume of the solid bounded by the planes $x = y + 2z + 1$, $x = 0$, $y = 0$, $z = 0$, and $3y + z - 3 = 0$. Draw a sketch of the solid.

17. Find the volume of the solid in the first octant bounded by the two cylinders $x^2 + y^2 = 4$ and $x^2 + z^2 = 4$. Draw a sketch of the solid.

18. Find the volume of the solid in the first octant bounded by the paraboloid $z = 9 - x^2 - 3y^2$. Draw a sketch of the solid.

19. Find the volume of the solid in the first octant bounded by the surfaces $x + z^2 = 1$, $x = y$, and $x = y^2$. Draw a sketch of the solid.

20. Find by double integration the volume of the portion of the solid bounded by the sphere $x^2 + y^2 + z^2 = 16$ which lies in the first octant. Draw a sketch of the solid.

In Exercises 21 through 24, use double integrals to find the area of the region bounded by the given curves in the xy plane. Draw a sketch of the region.

21. $y = x^3$ and $y = x^2$ 22. $y^2 = 4x$ and $x^2 = 4y$ 23. $y = x^2 - 9$ and $y = 9 - x^2$ 24. $x^2 + y^2 = 16$ and $y^2 = 6x$

25. Express as an iterated integral the measure of the volume of the solid bounded by the ellipsoid

$$\frac{x^2}{a^2} + \frac{y^2}{b^2} + \frac{z^2}{c^2} = 1$$

26. Given the iterated integral

$$\int_0^a \int_0^x \sqrt{a^2 - x^2} \, dy \, dx$$

(a) Draw a sketch of the solid the measure of whose volume is represented by the given iterated integral; (b) evaluate the iterated integral; (c) write the iterated integral which gives the measure of the volume of the same solid with the order of integration reversed.

27. Given the iterated integral

$$\frac{2}{3} \int_0^a \int_0^{\sqrt{a^2 - x^2}} (2x + y) \, dy \, dx$$

The instructions are the same as for Exercise 26.

28. Use double integration to find the area of the region in the first quadrant bounded by the parabola $y^2 = 4x$, the circle $x^2 + y^2 = 5$, and the x axis by two methods: (a) Integrate first with respect to x; (b) integrate first with respect to y. Compare the two methods of solution.

29. Find, by two methods, the volume of the solid below the plane $3x + 8y + 6z = 24$ and above the region in the xy plane bounded by the parabola $y^2 = 2x$, the line $2x + 3y = 10$, and the x axis: (a) Integrate first with respect to x; (b) integrate first with respect to y. Compare the two methods of solution.

In Exercises 30 and 31, the iterated integral cannot be evaluated exactly in terms of elementary functions by the given order of integration. Reverse the order of integration and perform the computation.

30. $\int_0^1 \int_y^1 e^{x^2} \, dx \, dy$

31. $\int_0^1 \int_x^1 \frac{\sin y}{y} \, dy \, dx$

32. Use double integration to find the volume of the solid common to two right-circular cylinders of radius r units, whose axes intersect at right angles. (See Exercise 8 in Exercises 8.4.)

21.3 CENTER OF MASS AND MOMENTS OF INERTIA

In Chapter 8 we used single integrals to find the center of mass of a homogeneous lamina. In using single integrals we can consider only laminae of constant area density (except in special cases); however, with double integrals we can find the center of mass of either a homogeneous or a nonhomogeneous lamina.

Suppose that we are given a lamina which has the shape of a closed region R in the xy plane. Let $\rho(x, y)$ be the measure of the area density of the lamina at any point (x, y) of R where ρ is continuous on R. To find the total mass of the lamina we proceed as follows. Let Δ be a partition of R into n rectangles. If (ξ_i, γ_i) is any point in the ith rectangle having an area of measure $\Delta_i A$, then an approximation to the measure of the mass of the ith rectangle is given by $\rho(\xi_i, \gamma_i) \Delta_i A$, and the measure of the total mass of the lamina is approximated by

$$\sum_{i=1}^n \rho(\xi_i, \gamma_i) \Delta_i A$$

Taking the limit of the above sum as the norm of Δ approaches zero, we express the measure M of the mass of the lamina by

$$M = \lim_{\|\Delta\| \to 0} \sum_{i=1}^n \rho(\xi_i, \gamma_i) \Delta_i A = \int\int_R \rho(x, y) \, dA \quad (1)$$

The measure of the moment of mass of the ith rectangle with respect to the x axis is approximated by $\gamma_i \rho(\xi_i, \gamma_i) \Delta_i A$. The sum of the measures of the moments of mass of the n rectangles with respect to the x axis is then approximated by the sum of n such terms. The measure M_x of the moment of mass with respect to the x axis of the entire lamina is given by

$$M_x = \lim_{\|\Delta\| \to 0} \sum_{i=1}^n \gamma_i \rho(\xi_i, \gamma_i) \Delta_i A = \int\int_R y\rho(x, y) \, dA \quad (2)$$

Analogously, the measure M_y of its moment of mass with respect to the y axis is given by

$$M_y = \lim_{||\Delta|| \to 0} \sum_{i=1}^{n} \xi_i \rho(\xi_i, \gamma_i) \, \Delta_i A = \int\int_R x\rho(x, y) \, dA \qquad (3)$$

The center of mass of the lamina is denoted by the point $(\bar{x}, \bar{y})$ and

$$\bar{x} = \frac{M_y}{M} \quad \text{and} \quad \bar{y} = \frac{M_x}{M}$$

EXAMPLE 1:   A lamina in the shape of an isosceles right triangle has an area density which varies as the square of the distance from the vertex of the right angle. If mass is measured in slugs and distance is measured in feet, find the mass and the center of mass of the lamina.

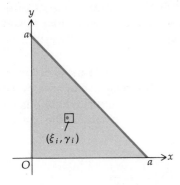

Figure 21.3.1

SOLUTION: Choose the coordinate axes so that the vertex of the right triangle is at the origin and the sides of length a ft of the triangle are along the coordinate axes (see Fig. 21.3.1). Let $\rho(x, y)$ be the number of slugs/ft² in the area density of the lamina at the point (x, y). Then $\rho(x, y) = k(x^2 + y^2)$ where k is a constant. Therefore, if M slugs is the mass of the lamina, we have from formula (1)

$$M = \lim_{||\Delta|| \to 0} \sum_{i=1}^{n} k(\xi_i^2 + \gamma_i^2) \, \Delta_i A$$

$$= k \int\int_R (x^2 + y^2) \, dA$$

$$= \int_0^a \int_0^{a-x} (x^2 + y^2) \, dy \, dx$$

$$= k \int_0^a \left[yx^2 + \tfrac{1}{3}y^3 \right]_0^{a-x} dx$$

$$= k \int_0^a (\tfrac{1}{3}a^3 - a^2x + 2ax^2 - \tfrac{4}{3}x^3) \, dx$$

$$= k(\tfrac{1}{3}a^4 - \tfrac{1}{2}a^4 + \tfrac{2}{3}a^4 - \tfrac{1}{3}a^4)$$

$$= \tfrac{1}{6}ka^4$$

To find the center of mass, we observe that because of symmetry it must lie on the line $y = x$. Therefore, if we find $\bar{x}$, we also have $\bar{y}$. Using formula (3), we have

$$M_y = \lim_{||\Delta|| \to 0} \sum_{i=1}^{n} k\xi_i(\xi_i^2 + \gamma_i^2) \, \Delta_i A$$

$$= k \int\int_R x(x^2 + y^2) \, dA$$

$$= k \int_0^a \int_0^{a-x} x(x^2 + y^2) \, dy \, dx$$

$$= k \int_0^a \left[x^3y + \tfrac{1}{3}xy^3 \right]_0^{a-x} dx$$

$$= k \int_0^a \left(\tfrac{1}{3}a^3 x - a^2 x^2 + 2ax^3 - \tfrac{4}{3}x^4 \right) \, dx$$

$$= k \left(\tfrac{1}{6}a^5 - \tfrac{1}{3}a^5 + \tfrac{1}{2}a^5 - \tfrac{4}{15}a^5 \right)$$

$$= \tfrac{1}{15} ka^5$$

Because $M\bar{x} = M_y$, we have $M\bar{x} = \tfrac{1}{15}ka^5$; and because $M = \tfrac{1}{6}ka^4$, we get $\bar{x} = \tfrac{2}{5}a$. Therefore, the center of mass is at the point $(\tfrac{2}{5}a, \tfrac{2}{5}a)$.

21.3.1 Definition   The *moment of inertia* of a particle, whose mass is m slugs, about an axis is defined to be mr^2 slug-ft^2, where r ft is the perpendicular distance from the particle to the axis.

If we have a system of n particles, the moment of inertia of the system is defined as the sum of the moments of inertia of all the particles. That is, if the ith particle has a mass of m_i slugs and is at a distance of r_i ft from the axis, then I slug-ft^2 is the moment of inertia of the system where

$$I = \sum_{i=1}^{n} m_i r_i^2 \tag{4}$$

Extending this concept of moment of inertia to a continuous distribution of mass in a plane such as rods or laminae by processes similar to those previously used, we have the following definition.

21.3.2 Definition   Suppose that we are given a continuous distribution of mass occupying a region R in the xy plane, and suppose that the measure of area density of this distribution at the point (x, y) is $\rho(x, y)$ slugs/ft^2, where ρ is continuous on R. Then the moment of inertia I_x slug-ft^2 about the x axis of this distribution of mass is determined by

$$I_x = \lim_{\|\Delta\| \to 0} \sum_{i=1}^{n} \gamma_i^2 \rho(\xi_i, \gamma_i) \, \Delta_i A = \iint_R y^2 \rho(x, y) \, dA \tag{5}$$

Similarly, the measure I_y of the moment of inertia about the y axis is given by

$$I_y = \lim_{\|\Delta\| \to 0} \sum_{i=1}^{n} \xi_i^2 \rho(\xi_i, \gamma_i) \, \Delta_i A = \iint_R x^2 \rho(x, y) \, dA \tag{6}$$

and the measure I_0 of the moment of inertia about the origin, or the z axis, is given by

$$I_0 = \lim_{\|\Delta\| \to 0} \sum_{i=1}^{n} (\xi_i^2 + \gamma_i^2) \rho(\xi_i, \gamma_i) \, \Delta_i A = \iint_R (x^2 + y^2) \rho(x, y) \, dA \tag{7}$$

The number I_0 of formula (7) is the measure of what is called the *polar moment of inertia*.

EXAMPLE 2:   A homogeneous straight wire has a constant linear density of ρ slugs/ft. Find the moment of inertia of the wire about an axis perpendicular to the wire and passing through one end.

SOLUTION: Let the wire be of length a ft, and suppose that it extends along the x axis from the origin. We find its moment of inertia about the y axis. Divide the wire into n segments; the length of the ith segment is $\Delta_i x$ ft. The mass of the ith segment is then $\rho \Delta_i x$ slugs. Assume that the mass of the ith segment is concentrated at a single point ξ_i, where $x_{i-1} \le \xi_i \le x_i$. The moment of inertia of the ith segment about the y axis lies between $\rho x_{i-1}^2 \Delta_i x$ slug-ft^2 and $\rho x_i^2 \Delta_i x$ slug-ft^2 and is approximated by $\rho \xi_i^2 \Delta_i x$ slug-ft^2, where $x_{i-1} \le \xi_i \le x_i$. If the moment of inertia of the wire about the y axis is I_y slug-ft^2, then

$$I_y = \lim_{||\Delta|| \to 0} \sum_{i=1}^{n} \rho \xi_i^2 \, \Delta_i x = \int_0^a \rho x^2 \, dx = \tfrac{1}{3}\rho a^3$$

Therefore, the moment of inertia is $\tfrac{1}{3}\rho a^3$ slug-ft^2.

EXAMPLE 3:   A homogeneous rectangular lamina has constant area density of ρ slugs/ft^2. Find the moment of inertia of the lamina about one corner.

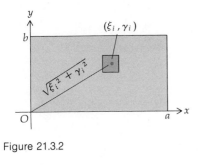

Figure 21.3.2

SOLUTION: Suppose that the lamina is bounded by the lines $x = a$, $y = b$, the x axis, and the y axis. See Fig. 21.3.2. If I_0 slug-ft^2 is the moment of inertia about the origin, then

$$I_0 = \lim_{||\Delta|| \to 0} \sum_{i=1}^{n} \rho(\xi_i^2 + \gamma_i^2) \, \Delta_i A$$

$$= \int\!\!\int_R \rho(x^2 + y^2) \, dA$$

$$= \rho \int_0^b \int_0^a (x^2 + y^2) \, dx \, dy$$

$$= \rho \int_0^b \left[\tfrac{1}{3}x^3 + xy^2 \right]_0^a dy$$

$$= \rho \int_0^b (\tfrac{1}{3}a^3 + ay^2) \, dy$$

$$= \tfrac{1}{3}\rho ab(a^2 + b^2)$$

The moment of inertia is therefore $\tfrac{1}{3}\rho ab(a^2 + b^2)$ slug-ft^2.

It is possible to find the distance from any axis L at which the mass of a lamina can be concentrated without affecting the moment of inertia of the lamina about L. The measure of this distance, denoted by r, is called the "radius of gyration" of the lamina about L. That is, if the mass M slugs of a lamina is concentrated at a point r ft from L, the moment of inertia of the lamina about L is the same as that of a particle of mass M slugs at a distance of r ft from L; this moment of inertia is Mr^2 slug-ft^2. Thus, we have the following definition.

21.3.3 Definition   If I is the measure of the moment of inertia about an axis L of a distribution of mass in a plane and M is the measure of the total mass of the distribution, then the *radius of gyration* of the distribution about L has measure r, where

$$r^2 = \frac{I}{M}$$

EXAMPLE 4: Suppose that a lamina is in the shape of a semi-circle and the measure of the area density of the lamina at any point is proportional to the measure of the distance of the point from the diameter. If mass is measured in slugs and distance is measured in feet, find the radius of gyration of the lamina about the x axis.

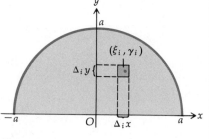

Figure 21.3.3

SOLUTION: Choose the x and y axes so that the semicircle is the top half of the circle $x^2 + y^2 = a^2$. See Fig. 21.3.3. The area density of the lamina at the point (x, y) is then ky slugs/ft^2. So if M slugs is the mass of the lamina, we have

$$M = \lim_{||\Delta|| \to 0} \sum_{i=1}^{n} k\gamma_i \, \Delta_i A$$

$$= \int\int_R ky \, dA$$

$$= \int_0^a \int_{-\sqrt{a^2-y^2}}^{\sqrt{a^2-y^2}} ky \, dx \, dy$$

$$= k \int_0^a \left[yx \right]_{-\sqrt{a^2-y^2}}^{\sqrt{a^2-y^2}} dy$$

$$= 2k \int_0^a y \sqrt{a^2 - y^2} \, dy$$

$$= -\tfrac{2}{3}k(a^2 - y^2)^{3/2} \Big]_0^a$$

$$= \tfrac{2}{3}ka^3$$

If I_x slug-ft^2 is the moment of inertia of the lamina about the x axis, then

$$I_x = \lim_{||\Delta|| \to 0} \sum_{i=1}^{n} \gamma_i^2 (k\gamma_i) \, \Delta_i A$$

$$= \int\int_R ky^3 \, dy \, dx$$

$$= \int_{-a}^a \int_0^{\sqrt{a^2-x^2}} ky^3 \, dy \, dx$$

$$= k \int_{-a}^a \left[\tfrac{1}{4}y^4 \right]_0^{\sqrt{a^2-x^2}} dx$$

$$= \tfrac{1}{4}k \int_{-a}^a (a^4 - 2a^2x^2 + x^4) \, dx$$

$$= \tfrac{1}{4}k(2a^5 - \tfrac{4}{3}a^5 + \tfrac{2}{5}a^5)$$

$$= \tfrac{4}{15}ka^5$$

Therefore, if r ft is the radius of gyration

$$r^2 = \frac{\frac{4}{15}ka^5}{\frac{2}{3}ka^3} = \frac{2}{5}a^2$$

and so $r = \frac{1}{5}\sqrt{10}a$. The radius of gyration is therefore $\frac{1}{5}\sqrt{10}a$ ft.

Exercises 21.3

In Exercises 1 through 10, find the mass and center of mass of the given lamina if the area density is as indicated. Mass is measured in slugs and distance is measured in feet.

1. A lamina in the shape of the rectangular region bounded by the lines $x = 3$ and $y = 2$, and the coordinate axes. The area density at any point is xy^2 slugs/ft².

2. A lamina in the shape of the region in the first quadrant bounded by the parabola $y = x^2$, the line $y = 1$, and the y axis. The area density at any point is $(x + y)$ slugs/ft².

3. A lamina in the shape of the region bounded by the parabola $x^2 = 8y$, the line $y = 2$, and the y axis. The area density varies as the distance from the line $y = -1$.

4. A lamina in the shape of the region bounded by the curve $y = e^x$, the line $x = 1$, and the coordinate axes. The area density varies as the distance from the x axis.

5. A lamina in the shape of the region in the first quadrant bounded by the circle $x^2 + y^2 = a^2$ and the coordinate axes. The area density varies as the sum of the distances from the two straight edges.

6. A lamina in the shape of the region bounded by the triangle whose sides are segments of the coordinate axes and the line $3x + 2y = 18$. The area density varies as the product of the distances from the coordinate axes.

7. A lamina in the shape of the region bounded by the curve $y = \sin x$ and the x axis from $x = 0$ to $x = \pi$. The area density varies as the distance from the x axis.

8. A lamina in the shape of the region bounded by the curve $y = \sqrt{x}$ and the line $y = x$. The area density varies as the distance from the y axis.

9. A lamina in the shape of the region in the first quadrant bounded by the circle $x^2 + y^2 = 4$ and the line $x + y = 2$. The area density at any point is xy slugs/ft².

10. A lamina in the shape of the region bounded by the circle $x^2 + y^2 = 1$ and the lines $x = 1$ and $y = 1$. The area density at any point is xy slugs/ft².

In Exercises 11 through 16, find the moment of inertia of the given homogeneous lamina about the indicated axis if the area density is ρ slugs/ft², and distance is measured in feet.

11. A lamina in the shape of the region bounded by $4y = 3x$, $x = 4$, and the x axis; about the x axis.

12. The lamina of Exercise 11; about the line $x = 4$.

13. A lamina in the shape of the region bounded by a circle of radius a units; about its center.

14. A lamina in the shape of the region bounded by the parabola $x^2 = 4 - 4y$ and the x axis; about the x axis.

15. The lamina of Exercise 14; about the origin.

16. A lamina in the shape of the region bounded by a triangle of sides of lengths a ft, b ft, and c ft; about the side of length a ft.

In Exercises 17 through 20, find for the given lamina each of the following: (a) the moment of inertia about the x axis; (b) the moment of inertia about the y axis; (c) the radius of gyration about the x axis; (d) the polar moment of inertia.

17. The lamina of Exercise 1.   18. The lamina of Exercise 2.   19. The lamina of Exercise 7.   20. The lamina of Exercise 8.

21. A homogeneous lamina of area density ρ slugs/ft^2 is in the shape of the region bounded by an isosceles triangle having a base of length b ft and an altitude of length h ft. Find the radius of gyration of the lamina about its line of symmetry.

22. A lamina is in the shape of the region enclosed by the parabola $y = 2x - x^2$ and the x axis. Find the moment of inertia of the lamina about the line $y = 4$ if the area density varies as its distance from the line $y = 4$. Mass is measured in slugs and distance is measured in feet.

21.4 THE DOUBLE INTEGRAL IN POLAR COORDINATES

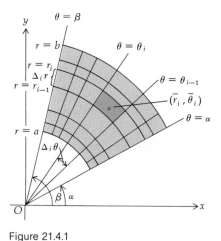

Figure 21.4.1

We now show how the double integral of a function on a closed region in the polar coordinate plane can be defined. We begin by considering the simplest kind of region. Let R be the region bounded by the rays $\theta = \alpha$ and $\theta = \beta$ and by the circles $r = a$ and $r = b$. Then let Δ be a *partition* of this region which is obtained by drawing rays through the pole and circles having centers at the pole. This is shown in Fig. 21.4.1. We obtain a network of subregions which we call "curved" rectangles. The norm $\|\Delta\|$ of the partition is the length of the longest of the diagonals of the "curved" rectangles. Let the number of subregions be n, and let $\Delta_i A$ be the measure of area of the ith "curved" rectangle. Because the area of the ith subregion is the difference of the areas of two circular sectors, we have

$$\Delta_i A = \tfrac{1}{2}r_i^2(\theta_i - \theta_{i-1}) - \tfrac{1}{2}r_{i-1}^2(\theta_i - \theta_{i-1})$$

$$= \tfrac{1}{2}(r_i - r_{i-1})(r_i + r_{i-1})(\theta_i - \theta_{i-1})$$

Letting $\bar{r}_i = \tfrac{1}{2}(r_i + r_{i-1})$, $\Delta_i r = r_i - r_{i-1}$, and $\Delta_i \theta = \theta_i - \theta_{i-1}$, we have

$$\Delta_i A = r_i\, \Delta_i r\, \Delta_i \theta$$

Take the point $(\bar{r}_i, \bar{\theta}_i)$ in the ith subregion, where $\theta_{i-1} \le \bar{\theta}_i \le \theta_i$, and form the sum

$$\sum_{i=1}^{n} f(\bar{r}_i, \bar{\theta}_i)\, \Delta_i A = \sum_{i=1}^{n} f(\bar{r}_i, \bar{\theta}_i)\bar{r}_i\, \Delta_i r\, \Delta_i \theta \tag{1}$$

It can be shown that if f is continuous on the region R, then the limit of the sum in (1), as $\|\Delta\|$ approaches zero, exists and that this limit will be the double integral of f on R. We write either

$$\lim_{\|\Delta\|\to 0} \sum_{i=1}^{n} f(\bar{r}_i, \bar{\theta}_i)\, \Delta_i A = \iint_{R} f(r, \theta)\, dA \tag{2}$$

or

$$\lim_{\|\Delta\|\to 0} \sum_{i=1}^{n} f(\bar{r}_i, \bar{\theta}_i)\bar{r}_i\, \Delta_i r\, \Delta_i \theta = \iint_{R} f(r, \theta)r\, dr\, d\theta \tag{3}$$

Observe that in polar coordinates, $dA = r\, dr\, d\theta$.

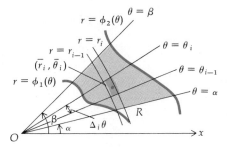

Figure 21.4.2

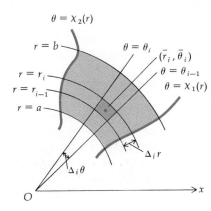

Figure 21.4.3

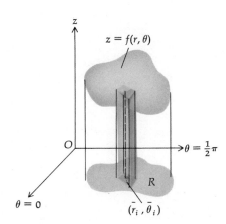

Figure 21.4.4

The double integral can be shown to be equal to an iterated integral having one of two possible forms:

$$\iint_R f(r, \theta)\,dA = \int_\alpha^\beta \int_a^b f(r, \theta)r\,dr\,d\theta = \int_a^b \int_\alpha^\beta f(r, \theta)\,r\,d\theta\,dr \qquad (4)$$

We can define the double integral of a continuous function f of two variables on closed regions of the polar coordinate plane other than the one previously considered. For example, consider the region R bounded by $r = \phi_1(\theta)$ and $r = \phi_2(\theta)$, where ϕ_1 and ϕ_2 are smooth functions, and by the lines $\theta = \alpha$ and $\theta = \beta$. See Fig. 21.4.2. In the figure, $\phi_1(\theta) \leq \phi_2(\theta)$ for all θ in the closed interval $[\alpha, \beta]$. Then it can be shown that the double integral of f on R exists and equals an iterated integral, and we have

$$\iint_R f(r, \theta)\,dA = \int_\alpha^\beta \int_{\phi_1(\theta)}^{\phi_2(\theta)} f(r, \theta)r\,dr\,d\theta \qquad (5)$$

If the region R is bounded by the curves $\theta = \chi_1(r)$ and $\theta = \chi_2(r)$, where χ_1 and χ_2 are smooth functions, and by the circles $r = a$ and $r = b$, as shown in Fig. 21.4.3, where $\chi_1(r) \leq \chi_2(r)$ for all r in the closed interval $[a, b]$, then

$$\iint_R f(r, \theta)\,dA = \int_a^b \int_{\chi_1(r)}^{\chi_2(r)} f(r, \theta)r\,d\theta\,dr \qquad (6)$$

We can interpret the double integral of a function on a closed region in the polar coordinate plane as the measure of the volume of a solid by using cylindrical coordinates. Figure 21.4.4 shows a solid having as its base a region R in the polar coordinate plane and bounded above by the surface $z = f(r, \theta)$ where f is continuous on R and $f(x, y) \geq 0$ on R. Take a partition of R giving a network of n "curved" rectangles. Construct the n solids for which the ith solid has as its base the ith "curved" rectangle and as the measure of its altitude $f(\bar{r}_i, \bar{\theta}_i)$ where $(\bar{r}_i, \bar{\theta}_i)$ is in the ith subregion. Figure 21.4.4 shows the ith solid. The measure of the volume of the ith solid is

$$f(\bar{r}_i, \bar{\theta}_i)\,\Delta_i A = f(\bar{r}_i, \bar{\theta}_i)\bar{r}_i\,\Delta_i r\,\Delta_i \theta$$

The sum of the measures of the volumes of the n solids is

$$\sum_{i=1}^n f(\bar{r}_i, \bar{\theta}_i)\bar{r}_i\,\Delta_i r\,\Delta_i \theta$$

If V is the measure of the volume of the given solid, then

$$V = \lim_{\|\Delta\| \to 0} \sum_{i=1}^n f(\bar{r}_i, \bar{\theta}_i)\bar{r}_i\,\Delta_i r\,\Delta_i \theta = \iint_R f(r, \theta)r\,dr\,d\theta \qquad (7)$$

EXAMPLE 1: Find the volume of the solid in the first octant

SOLUTION: The solid and the ith element are shown in Fig. 21.4.5. Using formula (7) with $f(r, \theta) = r$, we have, where V cubic units is the volume bounded by the cone $z = r$ and the cylinder $r = 3 \sin \theta$.

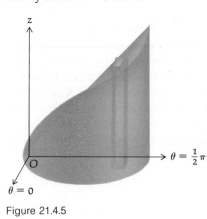

Figure 21.4.5

of the given solid,

$$V = \lim_{||\Delta|| \to 0} \sum_{i=1}^{n} \bar{r}_i \cdot \bar{r}_i \, \Delta_i r \, \Delta_i \theta$$

$$= \int_R \int r^2 \, dr \, d\theta$$

$$= \int_0^{\pi/2} \int_0^{3 \sin \theta} r^2 \, dr \, d\theta$$

$$= \int_0^{\pi/2} \left[\tfrac{1}{3} r^3 \right]_0^{3 \sin \theta} d\theta$$

$$= 9 \int_0^{\pi/2} \sin^3 \theta \, d\theta$$

$$= -9 \cos \theta + 3 \cos^3 \theta \Big]_0^{\pi/2}$$

$$= 6$$

The volume is therefore 6 cubic units.

EXAMPLE 2:   Find the mass of the lamina in the shape of the region inside the semicircle $r = a \cos \theta$, $0 \le \theta \le \tfrac{1}{2}\pi$, and whose measure of area density at any point is proportional to the measure of its distance from the pole. The mass is measured in slugs and distance is measured in feet.

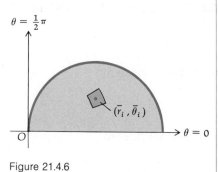

Figure 21.4.6

SOLUTION: Figure 21.4.6 shows a sketch of the lamina and the ith "curved" rectangle. The area density at the point (r, θ) is kr slugs/ft^2, where k is a constant. If M slugs is the mass of the lamina, then

$$M = \lim_{||\Delta|| \to 0} \sum_{i=1}^{n} (k\bar{r}_i) \bar{r}_i \, \Delta_i r \, \Delta_i \theta$$

$$= \int_R \int kr^2 \, dr \, d\theta$$

$$= k \int_0^{\pi/2} \int_0^{a \cos \theta} r^2 \, dr \, d\theta$$

$$= \tfrac{1}{3} k a^3 \int_0^{\pi/2} \cos^3 \theta \, d\theta$$

$$= \tfrac{1}{3} k a^3 \left[\sin \theta - \tfrac{1}{3} \sin^3 \theta \right]_0^{\pi/2}$$

$$= \tfrac{2}{9} k a^3$$

Therefore, the mass is $\tfrac{2}{9} k a^3$ slugs.

EXAMPLE 3:   Find the center of mass of the lamina in Example 2.

SOLUTION: Let the cartesian coordinates of the center of mass of the lamina be $\bar{x}$ and $\bar{y}$, where, as is customary, the x axis is along the polar axis and the y axis along the $\tfrac{1}{2}\pi$ axis. Let the cartesian coordinate representation of the point $(\bar{r}_i, \bar{\theta}_i)$ be $(\bar{x}_i, \bar{y}_i)$. Then if M_x slug-ft is the moment of mass of the lamina with respect to the x axis,

$$M_x = \lim_{\|\Delta\| \to 0} \sum_{i=1}^{n} \bar{y}_i (k\bar{r}_i) \bar{r}_i \, \Delta_i r \, \Delta_i \theta$$

Replacing $\bar{y}_i$ by $\bar{r}_i \sin \bar{\theta}_i$, we get

$$M_x = \lim_{\|\Delta\| \to 0} \sum_{i=1}^{n} k\bar{r}_i^3 \sin \bar{\theta}_i \, \Delta_i r \, \Delta_i \theta$$

$$= \int_R \int kr^3 \sin \theta \, dr \, d\theta$$

$$= k \int_0^{\pi/2} \int_0^{a \cos \theta} r^3 \sin \theta \, dr \, d\theta$$

$$= \tfrac{1}{4} ka^4 \int_0^{\pi/2} \cos^4 \theta \sin \theta \, d\theta$$

$$= -\tfrac{1}{20} ka^4 \cos^5 \theta \Big]_0^{\pi/2}$$

$$= \tfrac{1}{20} ka^4$$

If M_y slug-ft is the moment of mass of the lamina with respect to the y axis, then

$$M_y = \lim_{\|\Delta\| \to 0} \sum_{i=1}^{n} \bar{x}_i (k\bar{r}_i) \bar{r}_i \, \Delta_i r \, \Delta_i \theta$$

Replacing $\bar{x}_i$ by $\bar{r}_i \cos \bar{\theta}_i$, we have

$$M_y = \lim_{\|\Delta\| \to 0} \sum_{i=1}^{n} k\bar{r}_i^3 \cos \bar{\theta}_i \, \Delta_i r \, \Delta_i \theta$$

$$= \int_R \int kr^3 \cos \theta \, dr \, d\theta$$

$$= k \int_0^{\pi/2} \int_0^{a \cos \theta} r^3 \cos \theta \, dr \, d\theta$$

$$= \tfrac{1}{4} ka^4 \int_0^{\pi/2} \cos^5 \theta \, d\theta$$

$$= \tfrac{1}{4} ka^4 \left[\sin \theta - \tfrac{2}{3} \sin^3 \theta + \tfrac{1}{5} \sin^5 \theta \right]_0^{\pi/2}$$

$$= \tfrac{2}{15} ka^4$$

Therefore,

$$\bar{x} = \frac{M_y}{M} = \frac{\tfrac{2}{15} ka^4}{\tfrac{2}{9} ka^3} = \frac{3}{5} a$$

and

$$\bar{y} = \frac{M_x}{M} = \frac{\frac{1}{20}ka^4}{\frac{2}{9}ka^3} = \frac{9}{40}a$$

Hence, the center of mass is at the point $(\frac{3}{5}a, \frac{9}{40}a)$.

The area of a region in the polar plane can be found by double integration. The following example illustrates the method.

EXAMPLE 4: Find by double integration the area of the region enclosed by one leaf of the rose $r = \sin 3\theta$.

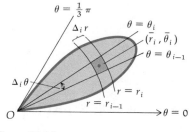

Figure 21.4.7

SOLUTION: Figure 21.4.7 shows the region and the ith "curved" rectangle. If A square units is the area of the region, then

$$A = \lim_{||\Delta|| \to 0} \sum_{i=1}^{n} \Delta_i A$$

$$= \lim_{||\Delta|| \to 0} \sum_{i=1}^{n} \bar{r}_i \, \Delta_i r \, \Delta_i \theta$$

$$= \int\int_R r \, dr \, d\theta$$

$$= \int_0^{\pi/3} \int_0^{\sin 3\theta} r \, dr \, d\theta$$

$$= \frac{1}{2} \int_0^{\pi/3} \sin^2 3\theta \, d\theta$$

$$= \frac{1}{4}\theta - \frac{1}{24}\sin 6\theta \Big]_0^{\pi/3}$$

$$= \frac{1}{12}\pi$$

Hence, the area is $\frac{1}{12}\pi$ square units.

Sometimes it is easier to evaluate a double integral by using polar coordinates instead of cartesian coordinates. Such a situation is shown in the following example.

EXAMPLE 5: Evaluate the double integral

$$\int\int_R e^{-(x^2+y^2)} \, dA$$

where the region R is in the first quadrant and bounded by the circle $x^2 + y^2 = a^2$ and the coordinate axes.

SOLUTION: Because $x^2 + y^2 = r^2$, and $dA = r \, dr \, d\theta$, we have

$$\int\int_R e^{-(x^2+y^2)} \, dA = \int\int_R e^{-r^2} r \, dr \, d\theta$$

$$= \int_0^{\pi/2} \int_0^a e^{-r^2} r \, dr \, d\theta$$

$$= -\frac{1}{2} \int_0^{\pi/2} \left[e^{-r^2} \right]_0^a d\theta$$

$$= -\frac{1}{2} \int_0^{\pi/2} (e^{-a^2} - 1) \, d\theta$$

$$= \frac{1}{4}\pi(1 - e^{-a^2})$$

Exercises 21.4

In Exercises 1 through 6, use double integrals to find the area of the given region.

1. The region inside the cardioid $r = 2(1 + \sin \theta)$.   2. One leaf of the rose $r = a \cos 2\theta$.

3. The region inside the cardioid $r = a(1 + \cos \theta)$ and outside the circle $r = a$.

4. The region inside the circle $r = 1$ and outside the lemniscate $r^2 = \cos 2\theta$.

5. The region inside the large loop of the limaçon $r = 2 - 4 \sin \theta$ and outside the small loop.

6. The region inside the limaçon $r = 3 - \cos \theta$ and outside the circle $r = 5 \cos \theta$.

In Exercises 7 through 12, find the volume of the given solid.

7. The solid bounded by the ellipsoid $z^2 + 9r^2 = 9$.

8. The solid cut out of the sphere $z^2 + r^2 = 4$ by the cylinder $r = 1$.

9. The solid cut out of the sphere $z^2 + r^2 = 16$ by the cylinder $r = 4 \cos \theta$.

10. The solid above the polar plane bounded by the cone $z = 2r$ and the cylinder $r = 1 - \cos \theta$.

11. The solid bounded by the paraboloid $z = 4 - r^2$, the cylinder $r = 1$, and the polar plane.

12. The solid above the paraboloid $z = r^2$ and below the plane $z = 2r \sin \theta$.

In Exercises 13 through 19, find the mass and center of mass of the given lamina if the area density is as indicated. Mass is measured in slugs and distance is measured in feet.

13. A lamina in the shape of the region of Exercise 1. The area density varies as the distance from the pole.

14. A lamina in the shape of the region of Exercise 2. The area density varies as the distance from the pole.

15. A lamina in the shape of the region inside the limaçon $r = 2 - \cos \theta$. The area density varies as the distance from the pole.

16. A lamina in the shape of the region bounded by the limaçon $r = 2 + \cos \theta$, $0 \le \theta \le \pi$, and the polar axis. The area density at any point is $k \sin \theta$ slugs/ft².

17. The lamina of Exercise 16. The area density at any point is $kr \sin \theta$ slugs/ft².

18. A lamina in the shape of the region of Exercise 6. The area density varies as the distance from the pole.

19. A lamina in the shape of the region of Exercise 5. The area density varies as the distance from the pole.

In Exercises 20 through 24, find the moment of inertia of the given lamina about the indicated axis or point if the area density is as indicated. Mass is measured in slugs and distance is measured in feet.

20. A lamina in the shape of the region enclosed by the circle $r = \sin \theta$; about the $\frac{1}{2}\pi$ axis. The area density at any point is k slugs/ft².

21. The lamina of Exercise 20; about the polar axis. The area density at any point is k slugs/ft².

22. A lamina in the shape of the region bounded by the cardioid $r = a(1 - \cos \theta)$; about the pole. The area density at any point is k slugs/ft².

23. A lamina in the shape of the region bounded by the cardioid $r = a(1 + \cos \theta)$ and the circle $r = 2a \cos \theta$; about the pole. The area density at any point is k slugs/ft².

24. A lamina in the shape of the region enclosed by the lemniscate $r^2 = a^2 \cos 2\theta$; about the polar axis. The area density varies as the distance from the pole.

25. A homogeneous lamina is in the shape of the region enclosed by one loop of the lemniscate $r^2 = \cos 2\theta$. Find the radius of gyration of the lamina about an axis perpendicular to the polar plane at the pole.

26. A lamina is in the shape of the region enclosed by the circle $r = 4$, and the area density varies as the distance from the pole. Find the radius of gyration of the lamina about an axis perpendicular to the polar plane at the pole.

27. Evaluate by polar coordinates the double integral

$$\iint_R e^{x^2+y^2}\, dA$$

where R is the region bounded by the circles $x^2 + y^2 = 1$ and $x^2 + y^2 = 9$.

28. Evaluate by polar coordinates the double integral

$$\iint_R \frac{x}{\sqrt{x^2 + y^2}}\, dA$$

where R is the region in the first quadrant bounded by the circle $x^2 + y^2 = 1$ and the coordinate axes.

29. In advanced calculus, improper double integrals are discussed, and $\displaystyle\int_0^{+\infty}\int_0^{+\infty} f(x, y)\, dx\, dy$ is defined to be

$$\lim_{h \to +\infty} \int_0^h \int_0^h f(x, y)\, dx\, dy$$

Use this definition to prove that $\displaystyle\int_0^{+\infty} e^{-x^2}\, dx = \tfrac{1}{2}\sqrt{\pi}$ by doing the following: (a) Show that the double integral in Example 5 can be expressed as $\left[\int_0^a e^{-x^2}\, dx\right]^2$; (b) because $\left[\int_0^{+\infty} e^{-x^2}\, dx\right]^2 = \lim_{a \to +\infty} \left[\int_0^a e^{-x^2}\, dx\right]^2$ use the result of Example 5 to obtain the desired result.

21.5 AREA OF A SURFACE

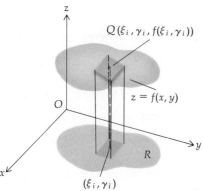

Figure 21.5.1

The double integral can be used to determine the area of the portion of the surface $z = f(x, y)$ that lies over a closed region R in the xy plane. To show this we must first define what we mean by the measure of this area and then obtain a formula for computing it. We assume that f and its first partial derivatives are continuous on R and suppose further that $f(x, y) > 0$ on R. Let Δ be a partition of R into n rectangular subregions. The ith rectangle has dimensions of measures $\Delta_i x$ and $\Delta_i y$ and an area of measure $\Delta_i A$. Let (ξ_i, γ_i) be any point in the ith rectangle, and at the point $Q(\xi_i, \gamma_i, f(\xi_i, \gamma_i))$ on the surface consider the tangent plane to the surface. Project vertically upward the ith rectangle onto the tangent plane and let $\Delta_i \sigma$ be the measure of the area of this projection. Figure 21.5.1 shows the region R, the portion of the surface above R, the ith rectangular subregion of R, and the projection of the ith rectangle onto the tangent plane to the surface at Q. The number $\Delta_i \sigma$ is an approximation to the measure of the area of the piece of the surface that lies above the ith rectangle. Because we have n such pieces, the summation

$$\sum_{i=1}^{n} \Delta_i \sigma$$

is an approximation to the measure σ of the area of the portion of the surface that lies above R. This leads to defining σ as follows:

$$\sigma = \lim_{\|\Delta\| \to 0} \sum_{i=1}^{n} \Delta_i \sigma \tag{1}$$

We now need to obtain a formula for computing the limit in Eq. (1). To do this we find a formula for computing $\Delta_i\sigma$ as the measure of the area of a parallelogram. For simplicity in computation we take the point (ξ_i, γ_i) in the ith rectangle at the corner (x_{i-1}, y_{i-1}). Let $\mathbf{A}$ and $\mathbf{B}$ be vectors having as representations the directed line segments having initial points at Q and forming the two adjacent sides of the parallelogram whose area has measure $\Delta_i\sigma$. See Fig. 21.5.2. Then $\Delta_i\sigma = |\mathbf{A} \times \mathbf{B}|$. Because

$$\mathbf{A} = \Delta_i x \mathbf{i} + f_x(\xi_i, \gamma_i)\, \Delta_i x \mathbf{k}$$

and

$$\mathbf{B} = \Delta_i y \mathbf{j} + f_y(\xi_i, \gamma_i)\, \Delta_i y \mathbf{k}$$

it follows that

$$\mathbf{A} \times \mathbf{B} = \begin{vmatrix} \mathbf{i} & \mathbf{j} & \mathbf{k} \\ \Delta_i x & 0 & f_x(\xi_i, \gamma_i)\, \Delta_i x \\ 0 & \Delta_i y & f_y(\xi_i, \gamma_i)\, \Delta_i y \end{vmatrix}$$

$$= -\Delta_i x\, \Delta_i y f_x(\xi_i, \gamma_i)\mathbf{i} - \Delta_i x\, \Delta_i y f_y(\xi_i, \gamma_i)\mathbf{j} + \Delta_i x\, \Delta_i y \mathbf{k}$$

Therefore,

$$\Delta_i\sigma = |\mathbf{A} \times \mathbf{B}| = \sqrt{f_x{}^2(\xi_i, \gamma_i) + f_y{}^2(\xi_i, \gamma_i) + 1}\; \Delta_i x\, \Delta_i y \tag{2}$$

Substituting from Eq. (2) into Eq. (1), we get

$$\sigma = \lim_{\|\Delta\| \to 0} \sum_{i=1}^{n} \sqrt{f_x{}^2(\xi_i, \gamma_i) + f_y{}^2(\xi_i, \gamma_i) + 1}\; \Delta_i x\, \Delta_i y$$

This limit is a double integral which exists on R because of the continuity of f_x and f_y on R. We have, then, the following theorem.

21.5.1 Theorem   Suppose that f and its first partial derivatives are continuous on the closed region R in the xy plane. Then if σ is the measure of the area of the surface $z = f(x, y)$ which lies over R,

$$\sigma = \iint_R \sqrt{f_x{}^2(x, y) + f_y{}^2(x, y) + 1}\; dx\, dy \tag{3}$$

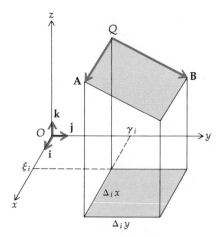

Figure 21.5.2

EXAMPLE 1: Find the area of the surface that is cut from the cylinder $x^2 + z^2 = 16$ by the planes $x = 0$, $x = 2$, $y = 0$, and $y = 3$.

SOLUTION: The given surface is shown in Fig. 21.5.3. The region R is the rectangle in the first quadrant of the xy plane bounded by the lines $x = 2$ and $y = 3$. The surface has the equation $x^2 + z^2 = 16$. Solving for z, we get $z = \sqrt{16 - x^2}$. Hence, $f(x, y) = \sqrt{16 - x^2}$. So if σ is the measure of the area of the surface, we have from Theorem 21.5.1

$$\sigma = \iint_R \sqrt{f_x{}^2(x, y) + f_y{}^2(x, y) + 1}\; dx\, dy$$

$$= \int_0^3 \int_0^2 \sqrt{\left(\frac{-x}{\sqrt{16 - x^2}}\right)^2 + 0 + 1}\; dx\, dy$$

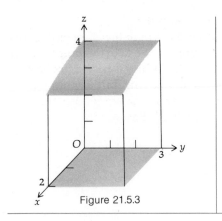

Figure 21.5.3

$$= \int_0^3 \int_0^2 \frac{4}{\sqrt{16 - x^2}} \, dx \, dy$$

$$= 4 \int_0^3 \left[\sin^{-1} \tfrac{1}{4}x \right]_0^2 dy$$

$$= 4 \int_0^3 \tfrac{1}{6}\pi \, dy$$

$$= 2\pi$$

The surface area is therefore 2π square units.

EXAMPLE 2: Find the area of the paraboloid $z = x^2 + y^2$ below the plane $z = 4$.

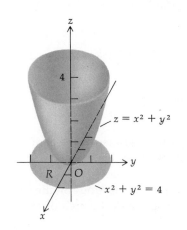

Figure 21.5.4

SOLUTION: Figure 21.5.4 shows the given surface. From the equation of the paraboloid we see that $f(x, y) = x^2 + y^2$. The closed region in the xy plane bounded by the circle $x^2 + y^2 = 4$ is the region R. If σ square units is the required surface area, we have from Theorem 21.5.1

$$\sigma = \iint_R \sqrt{f_x^2(x, y) + f_y^2(x, y) + 1} \, dx \, dy$$

$$= \iint_R \sqrt{4(x^2 + y^2) + 1} \, dx \, dy$$

Because the integrand contains the terms $4(x^2 + y^2)$, the evaluation of the double integral is simplified by using polar coordinates. Then $x^2 + y^2 = r^2$, and $dx \, dy = dA = r \, dr \, d\theta$. Furthermore, the limits for r are from 0 to 2 and the limits for θ are from 0 to 2π. We have then

$$\sigma = \iint_R \sqrt{4r^2 + 1} \, r \, dr \, d\theta$$

$$= \int_0^{2\pi} \int_0^2 \sqrt{4r^2 + 1} \, r \, dr \, d\theta$$

$$= \int_0^{2\pi} \left[\tfrac{1}{12}(4r^2 + 1)^{3/2} \right]_0^2 d\theta$$

$$= \tfrac{1}{6}\pi(17\sqrt{17} - 1)$$

Hence, the area of the paraboloid below the given plane is $\tfrac{1}{6}\pi(17\sqrt{17} - 1)$ square units.

EXAMPLE 3: Find the area of the top half of the sphere $x^2 + y^2 + z^2 = a^2$.

SOLUTION: The hemisphere is shown in Fig. 21.5.5. Solving the equation of the sphere for z and setting this equal to $f(x, y)$, we get

$$f(x, y) = \sqrt{a^2 - x^2 - y^2}$$

Because $f_x(x, y) = -x/\sqrt{a^2 - x^2 - y^2}$, and $f_y(x, y) = -y/\sqrt{a^2 - x^2 - y^2}$,

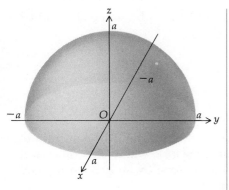

Figure 21.5.5

we note that f_x and f_y are not defined on the circle $x^2 + y^2 = a^2$ which is the boundary of the region R in the xy plane. Furthermore, the double integral obtained from Eq. (3) is

$$\int\int_R \frac{a}{\sqrt{a^2 - x^2 - y^2}} \, dx \, dy$$

which is improper because the integrand has an infinite discontinuity at each point of the boundary of R. We can take care of this situation by considering the region R' as that bounded by the circle $x^2 + y^2 = b^2$, where $b < a$, and then take the limit as $b \to a^-$. Furthermore, the computation is simplified if the double integral is evaluated by an iterated integral using polar coordinates. Then we have

$$\sigma = \lim_{b \to a^-} \int_0^b \int_0^{2\pi} \frac{a}{\sqrt{a^2 - r^2}} \, r \, d\theta \, dr$$

$$= 2\pi a \lim_{b \to a^-} \int_0^b \frac{r}{\sqrt{a^2 - r^2}} \, dr$$

$$= 2\pi a \lim_{b \to a^-} \left[-\sqrt{a^2 - r^2} \right]_0^b$$

$$= 2\pi a \lim_{b \to a^-} \left[-\sqrt{a^2 - b^2} + a \right]$$

$$= 2\pi a^2$$

The area of the hemisphere is therefore $2\pi a^2$ square units.

Consider now the curve $y = F(x)$ with $a \leq x \leq b$, F positive on $[a, b]$ and F' continuous on $[a, b]$. If this curve is rotated about the x axis, we obtain a surface of revolution. From Sec. 18.7 an equation of this surface is

$$y^2 + z^2 = [F(x)]^2 \tag{4}$$

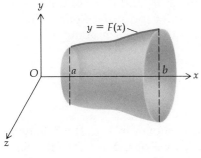

Figure 21.5.6

Figure 21.5.6 shows the surface of revolution. In the figure we have taken the xy plane in the plane of the paper; however, we still have a right-handed system. We wish to obtain a formula for finding the measure of the area of this surface of revolution by using Theorem 21.5.1 From properties of symmetry, the measure of the area of the surface above the xz plane and in front of the xy plane is one-fourth of the measure of the area of the entire surface. Solving Eq. (4) for z (neglecting the negative square root because $z \geq 0$), we get $f(x, y) = \sqrt{[F(x)]^2 - y^2}$. The region R in the xy plane is that bounded by the x axis, the curve $y = F(x)$, and the lines $x = a$ and $x = b$. Computing the partial derivatives of f, we obtain

$$f_x(x, y) = \frac{F(x)F'(x)}{\sqrt{[F(x)]^2 - y^2}} \qquad f_y(x, y) = \frac{-y}{\sqrt{[F(x)]^2 - y^2}}$$

We see that $f_x(x, y)$ and $f_y(x, y)$ do not exist on part of the boundary of

R (when $y = -F(x)$ and when $y = F(x)$). The double integral obtained from Eq. (3) is

$$\iint_R \sqrt{\frac{[F(x)]^2[F'(x)]^2}{[F(x)]^2 - y^2} + \frac{y^2}{[F(x)]^2 - y^2} + 1} \; dy \; dx$$

$$= \iint_R \frac{F(x)\sqrt{[F'(x)]^2 + 1}}{\sqrt{[F(x)]^2 - y^2}} \; dy \; dx$$

This double integral is improper because the integrand has an infinite discontinuity at each point of the boundary of R where $y = -F(x)$ and $y = F(x)$. Hence, we evaluate the double integral by an iterated integral for which the inner integral is improper.

$$\sigma = 4 \int_a^b \left[F(x)\sqrt{F'(x)^2 + 1} \int_0^{F(x)} \frac{dy}{\sqrt{[F(x)]^2 - y^2}} \right] dx \qquad (5)$$

where

$$\int_0^{F(x)} \frac{dy}{\sqrt{[F(x)]^2 - y^2}} = \lim_{\epsilon \to 0^+} \int_0^{F(x)-\epsilon} \frac{dy}{\sqrt{[F(x)]^2 - y^2}}$$

$$= \lim_{\epsilon \to 0^+} \left[\sin^{-1} \frac{y}{F(x)} \right]_0^{F(x)-\epsilon}$$

$$= \lim_{\epsilon \to 0^+} \sin^{-1} \left(1 - \frac{\epsilon}{F(x)} \right)$$

$$= \tfrac{1}{2}\pi$$

Therefore, from Eq. (5) we have

$$\sigma = 2\pi \int_a^b F(x)\sqrt{[F'(x)]^2 + 1} \; dx$$

We state this result as a theorem, where F is replaced by f.

21.5.2 Theorem   Suppose that the function f is positive on $[a, b]$ and f' is continuous on $[a, b]$. Then if σ is the measure of the area of the surface of revolution obtained by revolving the curve $y = f(x)$, with $a \le x \le b$, about the x axis,

$$\sigma = 2\pi \int_a^b f(x)\sqrt{[f'(x)]^2 + 1} \; dx$$

EXAMPLE 4:   Find the area of the paraboloid of revolution generated by revolving the top half of the parabola $y^2 = 4px$, with $0 \le x \le h$, about the x axis.

SOLUTION: The paraboloid of revolution is shown in Fig. 21.5.7. Solving the equation of the parabola for y ($y \ge 0$), we obtain $y = 2p^{1/2}x^{1/2}$. So if σ square units is the area of the surface, from Theorem 21.5.2, with $f(x) = 2p^{1/2}x^{1/2}$, we have

$$\sigma = 2\pi \int_0^h 2p^{1/2}x^{1/2} \sqrt{\frac{p}{x} + 1} \; dx$$

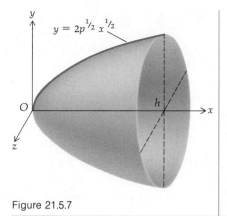

$y = 2p^{1/2} x^{1/2}$

Figure 21.5.7

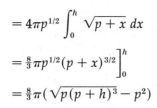

$$= 4\pi p^{1/2} \int_0^h \sqrt{p + x}\, dx$$

$$= \tfrac{8}{3}\pi p^{1/2}(p + x)^{3/2}\Big]_0^h$$

$$= \tfrac{8}{3}\pi (\sqrt{p(p + h)^3} - p^2)$$

The area of the paraboloid of revolution is therefore $\tfrac{8}{3}\pi(\sqrt{p(p + h)^3} - p^2)$ square units.

Exercises 21.5

1. Find the area of the surface which is cut from the plane $2x + y + z = 4$ by the planes $x = 0$, $x = 1$, $y = 0$, and $y = 1$.

2. Find the area of the portion of the surface of the plane $36x + 16y + 9z = 144$ which is cut by the coordinate planes.

3. Find the area of the surface in the first octant which is cut from the cylinder $x^2 + y^2 = 9$ by the plane $x = z$.

4. Find the area of the surface in the first octant which is cut from the cone $x^2 + y^2 = z^2$ by the plane $x + y = 4$.

5. Find the area of the portion of the surface of the sphere $x^2 + y^2 + z^2 = 4x$ which is cut out by one nappe of the cone $y^2 + z^2 = x^2$.

6. Find the area of the portion of the surface of the sphere $x^2 + y^2 + z^2 = 36$ which lies within the cylinder $x^2 + y^2 = 9$.

7. Find the area of the portion of the surface of the sphere $x^2 + y^2 + z^2 = 4z$ which lies within the paraboloid $x^2 + y^2 = 3z$.

8. For the sphere and paraboloid of Exercise 7, find the area of the portion of the surface of the paraboloid which lies within the sphere.

9. The line segment from the origin to the point (a, b) is revolved about the x axis. Find the area of the surface of the cone generated.

10. Derive the formula for the area of the surface of a sphere by revolving a semicircle about its diameter.

11. Find the area of the surface of revolution obtained by revolving the arc of the catenary $y = a \cosh(x/a)$ from $x = 0$ to $x = a$ about the y axis.

12. Find the area of the surface of revolution obtained by revolving the catenary of Exercise 11 about the x axis.

13. The loop of the curve $18y^2 = x(6 - x)^2$ is revolved about the x axis. Find the area of the surface of revolution generated.

14. Find the area of the surface of revolution generated by revolving the arc of the curve $y = \ln x$ from $x = 1$ to $x = 2$ about the y axis.

15. Find the area of the portion of the plane $x = z$ which lies between the planes $y = 0$ and $y = 6$ and within the hyperboloid $9x^2 - 4y^2 + 16z^2 = 144$.

16. Find the area of the surface cut from the hyperbolic paraboloid $y^2 - x^2 = 6z$ by the cylinder $x^2 + y^2 = 36$.

21.6 THE TRIPLE INTEGRAL

The extension of the double integral to the triple integral is analogous to the extension of the single integral to the double integral. The simplest type of region in R^3 is a rectangular parallelepiped which is bounded by six planes: $x = a_1$, $x = a_2$, $y = b_1$, $y = b_2$, $z = c_1$, and $z = c_2$, with $a_1 < a_2$, $b_1 < b_2$, and $c_1 < c_2$. Let f be a function of three variables and suppose that f is continuous on such a region S. A partition of this region is formed by dividing S into rectangular boxes by drawing planes parallel to the coordinate planes. Denote such a partition by Δ and suppose that n is the number of boxes. Let $\Delta_i V$ be the measure of the volume of the ith box. Choose an arbitrary point (ξ_i, γ_i, μ_i) in the ith box. Form the sum

$$\sum_{i=1}^{n} f(\xi_i, \gamma_i, \mu_i) \, \Delta_i V \qquad (1)$$

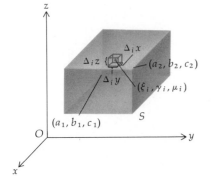

Figure 21.6.1

Refer to Fig. 21.6.1, which shows the rectangular parallelepiped together with the ith box. The *norm* $\|\Delta\|$ of the partition is the length of the longest diagonal of the boxes. The sums of the form (1) will approach a limit as the norm of the partition approaches zero for any choices of the points (ξ_i, γ_i, μ_i) if f is continuous on S. Then we call this limit the *triple integral* of f on R and write

$$\lim_{\|\Delta\| \to 0} \sum_{i=1}^{n} f(\xi_i, \gamma_i, \mu_i) \, \Delta_i V = \iiint_{S} f(x, y, z) \, dV$$

Analogous to a double integral being equal to a twice-iterated integral, the triple integral is equal to a thrice-iterated integral. When S is the rectangular parallelepiped described above, and f is continuous on S, we have

$$\iiint_{S} f(x, y, z) \, dV = \int_{a_1}^{a_2} \int_{b_1}^{b_2} \int_{c_1}^{c_2} f(x, y, z) \, dz \, dy \, dx$$

EXAMPLE 1: Evaluate the triple integral

$$\iiint_{S} xy \sin yz \, dV$$

if S is the rectangular parallelepiped bounded by the planes $x = \pi$, $y = \frac{1}{2}\pi$, $z = \frac{1}{3}\pi$, and the coordinate planes.

SOLUTION:

$$\iiint_{S} xy \sin yz \, dV = \int_{0}^{\pi} \int_{0}^{\pi/2} \int_{0}^{\pi/3} xy \sin yz \, dz \, dy \, dx$$

$$= \int_{0}^{\pi} \int_{0}^{\pi/2} \left[-x \cos yz \right]_{0}^{\pi/3} dy \, dx$$

$$= \int_{0}^{\pi} \int_{0}^{\pi/2} x(1 - \cos \tfrac{1}{3}\pi y) \, dy \, dx$$

$$= \int_{0}^{\pi} x \left(y - \frac{3}{\pi} \sin \frac{1}{3} \pi y \right) \Big]_{0}^{\pi/2} dx$$

$$= \int_{0}^{\pi} x \left(\frac{\pi}{2} - \frac{3}{\pi} \sin \frac{\pi^2}{6} \right) dx$$

$$= \frac{x^2}{2} \left(\frac{\pi}{2} - \frac{3}{\pi} \sin \frac{\pi^2}{6} \right) \Big]_0^\pi$$

$$= \frac{\pi}{4} \left(\pi^2 - 6 \sin \frac{\pi^2}{6} \right)$$

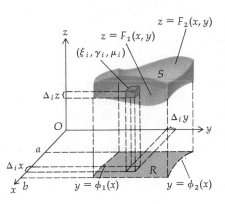

Figure 21.6.2

We now discuss how to define the triple integral of a continuous function of three variables on a region in R^3 other than a rectangular parallelepiped. Let S be the closed three-dimensional region which is bounded by the planes $x = a$ and $x = b$, the cylinders $y = \phi_1(x)$ and $y = \phi_2(x)$, and the surfaces $z = F_1(x, y)$ and $z = F_2(x, y)$, where the functions ϕ_1, ϕ_2, F_1, and F_2 are smooth (i.e., they have continuous derivatives or partial derivatives). See Fig. 21.6.2. Construct planes parallel to the coordinate planes, thereby forming a set of rectangular parallelepipeds that completely cover S. The parallelepipeds which are entirely inside S or on the boundary of S form a *partition* Δ of S. Choose some system of numbering so that they are numbered from 1 to n. The norm $\|\Delta\|$ of this partition of S is the length of the longest diagonal of any parallelepiped belonging to the partition. Let the measure of the volume of the ith parallelepiped be $\Delta_i V$. Let f be a function of three variables which is continuous on S and let (ξ_i, γ_i, μ_i) be an arbitrary point in the ith parallelepiped. Form the sum

$$\sum_{i=1}^n f(\xi_i, \gamma_i, \mu_i) \, \Delta_i V \qquad (2)$$

If the sums of form (2) have a limit as $\|\Delta\|$ approaches zero, and if this limit is independent of the choice of the partitioning planes and the choices of the arbitrary points (ξ_i, γ_i, μ_i) in each parallelepiped, then this limit is called the *triple integral* of f on S, and we write

$$\lim_{\|\Delta\| \to 0} \sum_{i=1}^n f(\xi_i, \gamma_i, \mu_i) \, \Delta_i V = \iiint_S f(x, y, z) \, dV \qquad (3)$$

It can be proved in advanced calculus that a sufficient condition for the limit in (3) to exist is that f be continuous on S. Furthermore, under the condition imposed upon the functions ϕ_1, ϕ_2, F_1, and F_2 that they be smooth, it can also be proved that the triple integral can be evaluated by the iterated integral

$$\int_a^b \int_{\phi_1(x)}^{\phi_2(x)} \int_{F_1(x,y)}^{F_2(x,y)} f(x, y, z) \, dz \, dy \, dx$$

Just as the double integral can be interpreted as the measure of the area of a plane region when $f(x, y) = 1$ on R^1, the triple integral can be interpreted as the measure of the volume of a three-dimensional region. If

$f(x, y, z) = 1$ on S, then Eq. (3) becomes

$$\lim_{||\Delta|| \to 0} \sum_{i=1}^{n} \Delta_i V = \iiint_S dV$$

and the triple integral is the measure of the volume of the region S.

EXAMPLE 2: Find by triple integration the volume of the solid of Example 3 in Sec. 21.2.

SOLUTION: If V cubic units is the volume of the solid, then

$$V = \lim_{||\Delta|| \to 0} \sum_{i=1}^{n} \Delta_i V = \iiint_S dV \tag{4}$$

where S is the region bounded by the solid. The z limits are from 0 (the value of z on the xy plane) to $x^2 + 4y^2$ (the value of z on the elliptic paraboloid). The y limits for one-fourth of the volume are from 0 (the value of y on the xz plane) to $\frac{1}{2}\sqrt{4 - x^2}$ (the value of y on the cylinder). The x limits for the first octant are from 0 to 2. We evaluate the triple integral in (4) by an iterated integral and obtain

$$V = 4 \int_0^2 \int_0^{\sqrt{4-x^2}/2} \int_0^{x^2+4y^2} dz \, dy \, dx$$

Hence,

$$V = 4 \int_0^2 \int_0^{\sqrt{4-x^2}/2} (x^2 + 4y^2) \, dy \, dx \tag{5}$$

The right side of Eq. (5) is the same twice-iterated integral that we obtained in Example 3 in Sec. 21.2, and so the remainder of the solution is the same.

EXAMPLE 3: Find the volume of the solid bounded by the cylinder $x^2 + y^2 = 25$, the plane $x + y + z = 8$ and the xy plane.

SOLUTION: The solid is shown in Fig. 21.6.3. The z limits for the iterated integral are from 0 to $8 - x - y$ (the value of z on the plane). The y limits are obtained from the boundary region in the xy plane which is the circle $x^2 + y^2 = 25$. Hence, the y limits are from $-\sqrt{25 - x^2}$ to $\sqrt{25 - x^2}$. The x limits are from -5 to 5. If V cubic units is the required volume, we have

$$V = \lim_{||\Delta|| \to 0} \sum_{i=1}^{n} \Delta_i V = \iiint_S dV$$

$$= \int_{-5}^{5} \int_{-\sqrt{25-x^2}}^{\sqrt{25-x^2}} \int_0^{8-x-y} dz \, dy \, dx$$

$$= \int_{-5}^{5} \int_{-\sqrt{25-x^2}}^{\sqrt{25-x^2}} (8 - x - y) \, dy \, dx$$

$$= \int_{-5}^{5} \left[(8 - x)y - \tfrac{1}{2}y^2 \right]_{-\sqrt{25-x^2}}^{\sqrt{25-x^2}} dx$$

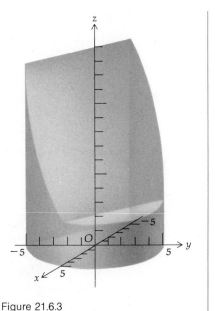

Figure 21.6.3

$$= 2 \int_{-5}^{5} (8 - x) \sqrt{25 - x^2} \, dx$$

$$= 16 \int_{-5}^{5} \sqrt{25 - x^2} \, dx + \int_{-5}^{5} \sqrt{25 - x^2}(-2x) \, dx$$

$$= 16 \left(\tfrac{1}{2} x \sqrt{25 - x^2} + \tfrac{25}{2} \sin^{-1} \tfrac{1}{5} x \right) + \tfrac{2}{3}(25 - x^2)^{3/2} \bigg]_{-5}^{5}$$

$$= 200\pi$$

The volume is therefore 200π cubic units.

EXAMPLE 4:   Find the mass of the solid above the xy plane bounded by the cone $9x^2 + z^2 = y^2$ and the plane $y = 9$ if the measure of the volume density at any point (x, y, z) in the solid is proportional to the measure of the distance of the point from the xy plane.

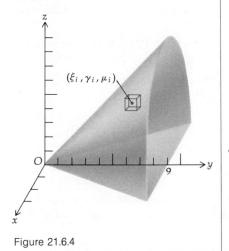

Figure 21.6.4

SOLUTION: Figure 21.6.4 shows the solid. Let M slugs be the mass of the solid, and let the distance be measured in feet. Then the volume density at any point (x, y, z) in the solid is kz slugs/ft³, where k is a constant. Then if (ξ_i, γ_i, μ_i) is any point in the ith rectangular parallelepiped of the partition, we have

$$M = \lim_{\|\Delta\| \to 0} \sum_{i=1}^{n} k\mu_i \, \Delta_i V = \iiint\limits_{S} kz \, dV$$

$$= 2k \int_{0}^{9} \int_{0}^{y/3} \int_{0}^{\sqrt{y^2 - 9x^2}} z \, dz \, dx \, dy$$

$$= 2k \int_{0}^{9} \int_{0}^{y/3} \left[\tfrac{1}{2} z^2 \right]_{0}^{\sqrt{y^2 - 9x^2}} dx \, dy$$

$$= k \int_{0}^{9} \int_{0}^{y/3} (y^2 - 9x^2) \, dx \, dy$$

$$= \tfrac{2}{9} k \int_{0}^{9} y^3 \, dy = \tfrac{729}{2} k$$

The mass is therefore $\tfrac{729}{2} k$ slugs.

Exercises 21.6

In Exercises 1 through 4, evaluate the iterated integral.

1. $\displaystyle\int_0^1\int_0^{1-x}\int_{2y}^{1+y^2} x\, dz\, dy\, dx$
2. $\displaystyle\int_1^2\int_y^{y^2}\int_0^{\ln x} ye^z\, dz\, dx\, dy$
3. $\displaystyle\int_0^{\pi/2}\int_z^{\pi/2}\int_0^{xz} \cos\frac{y}{z}\, dy\, dx\, dz$
4. $\displaystyle\int_1^2\int_0^y\int_0^{\sqrt{3}z} \frac{z}{x^2+z^2}\, dx\, dz\, dy$

In Exercises 5 through 10, evaluate the triple integral.

5. $\displaystyle\iiint_S y\, dV$ if S is the region bounded by the tetrahedron formed by the plane $12x + 20y + 15z = 60$ and the coordinate planes.

6. $\displaystyle\iiint_S (x^2 + z^2)\, dV$ if S is the same region as in Exercise 5.

7. $\displaystyle\iiint_S z\, dV$ if S is the region bounded by the tetrahedron having vertices $(0, 0, 0)$, $(1, 1, 0)$, $(1, 0, 0)$, and $(1, 0, 1)$.

8. $\displaystyle\iiint_S yz\, dV$ if S is the same region as in Exercise 7.

9. $\displaystyle\iiint_S (xz + 3z)\, dV$ if S is the region bounded by the cylinder $x^2 + z^2 = 9$ and the planes $x + y = 3$, $z = 0$, and $y = 0$, above the xy plane.

10. $\displaystyle\iiint_S xyz\, dV$, if S is the region bounded by the cylinders $x^2 + y^2 = 4$ and $x^2 + z^2 = 4$.

In Exercises 11 through 21, use triple integration.

11. Find the volume of the solid in the first octant bounded below by the xy plane, above by the plane $z = y$, and laterally by the cylinder $y^2 = x$ and the plane $x = 1$.

12. Find the volume of the solid in the first octant bounded by the cylinder $x^2 + z^2 = 16$, the plane $x + y = 2$, and the three coordinate planes.

13. Find the volume of the solid in the first octant bounded by the cylinders $x^2 + y^2 = 4$ and $x^2 + 2z = 4$, and the three coordinate planes.

14. Find the volume of the solid bounded by the elliptic cone $4x^2 + 9y^2 - 36z^2 = 0$ and the plane $z = 1$.

15. Find the volume of the solid above the elliptic paraboloid $3x^2 + y^2 = z$ and below the cylinder $x^2 + z = 4$.

16. Find the volume of the solid enclosed by the sphere $x^2 + y^2 + z^2 = a^2$.

17. Find the volume of the solid enclosed by the ellipsoid

$$\frac{x^2}{a^2} + \frac{y^2}{b^2} + \frac{z^2}{c^2} = 1$$

18. Find the mass of the solid enclosed by the tetrahedron formed by the plane $100x + 25y + 16z = 400$ and the coordinate planes if the volume density varies as the distance from the yz plane. The volume density is measured in slugs/ft³.

19. Find the mass of the solid bounded by the cylinders $x = z^2$ and $y = x^2$, and the planes $x = 1$, $y = 0$, and $z = 0$. The volume density varies as the product of the distances from the three coordinate planes, and it is measured in slugs/ft³.

20. Find the mass of the solid bounded by the surface $z = 4 - 4x^2 - y^2$ and the xy plane. The volume density at any point of the solid is ρ slugs/ft^3 and $\rho = 3z|x|$.

21. Find the mass of the solid bounded by the surface $z = xy$, and the planes $x = 1$, $y = 1$, and $z = 0$. The volume density at any point of the solid is ρ slugs/ft^3 and $\rho = 3\sqrt{x^2 + y^2}$.

21.7 THE TRIPLE INTEGRAL IN CYLINDRICAL AND SPHERICAL COORDINATES

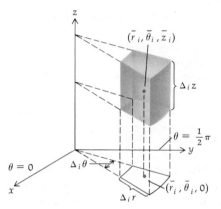

Figure 21.7.1

If a region S in R^3 has an axis of symmetry, triple integrals on S are easier to evaluate if cylindrical coordinates are used. If there is symmetry with respect to a point, it is often convenient to choose that point as the origin and to use spherical coordinates. In this section we discuss the triple integral in these coordinates and apply them to physical problems.

To define the triple integral in cylindrical coordinates we construct a partition of the region S by drawing planes through the z axis, planes perpendicular to the z axis, and right-circular cylinders having the z axis as axis. A typical subregion is shown in Fig. 21.7.1. The elements of the constructed partition lie entirely in S. We call this partition a *cylindrical partition*. The measure of the length of the longest "diagonal" of any of the subregions is the *norm* of the partition. Let n be the number of subregions of the partition and $\Delta_i V$ be the measure of the volume of the ith subregion. The measure of the area of the base is $\bar{r}_i \Delta_i r \Delta_i \theta$, where $\bar{r}_i = \frac{1}{2}(r_i + r_{i-1})$. Hence, if $\Delta_i z$ is the measure of the altitude of the ith subregion,

$$\Delta_i V = \bar{r}_i \Delta_i r \Delta_i \theta \Delta_i z$$

Let f be a function of r, θ, and z, and suppose that f is continuous on S. Choose a point $(\bar{r}_i, \bar{\theta}_i, \bar{z}_i)$ in the ith subregion such that $\theta_{i-1} \leq \bar{\theta}_i \leq \theta_i$ and $z_{i-1} \leq \bar{z}_i \leq z_i$. Form the sum

$$\sum_{i=1}^{n} f(\bar{r}_i, \bar{\theta}_i, \bar{z}_i) \, \Delta_i V = \sum_{i=1}^{n} f(\bar{r}_i, \bar{\theta}_i, \bar{z}_i) \bar{r}_i \, \Delta_i r \, \Delta_i \theta \, \Delta_i z \qquad (1)$$

As the norm of Δ approaches zero, it can be shown, under suitable conditions on S, that the limit of the sums of form (1) exist. This limit is called the *triple integral in cylindrical coordinates* of the function f on S, and we write

$$\lim_{\|\Delta\| \to 0} \sum_{i=1}^{n} f(\bar{r}_i, \bar{\theta}_i, \bar{z}_i) \, \Delta_i V = \iiint\limits_{S} f(r, \theta, z) \, dV \qquad (2)$$

or

$$\lim_{\|\Delta\| \to 0} \sum_{i=1}^{n} f(\bar{r}_i, \bar{\theta}_i, \bar{z}_i) \bar{r}_i \, \Delta_i r \, \Delta_i \theta \, \Delta_i z = \iiint\limits_{S} f(r, \theta, z) r \, dr \, d\theta \, dz \qquad (3)$$

Note that in cylindrical coordinates, $dV = r \, dr \, d\theta \, dz$. We can evaluate the triple integral in (2) and (3) by an iterated integral. For instance, suppose that the region S in R^3 is bounded by the planes $\theta = \alpha$ and

$\theta = \beta$, with $\alpha < \beta$, by the cylinders $r = \lambda_1(\theta)$ and $r = \lambda_2(\theta)$, where λ_1 and λ_2 are smooth on $[\alpha, \beta]$ and $\lambda_1(\theta) \le \lambda_2(\theta)$ for $\alpha \le \theta \le \beta$, and by the surfaces $z = F_1(r, \theta)$ and $z = F_2(r, \theta)$, where F_1 and F_2 are functions of two variables that are smooth on some region R in the polar plane bounded by the curves $r = \lambda_1(\theta)$, $r = \lambda_2(\theta)$, $\theta = \alpha$, and $\theta = \beta$. Furthermore, suppose that $F_1(r, \theta) \le F_2(r, \theta)$ for every point (r, θ) in R. Then the triple integral can be evaluated by an iterated integral by the formula

$$\iiint\limits_S f(r, \theta, z)r \, dr \, d\theta \, dz = \int_\alpha^\beta \int_{\lambda_1(\theta)}^{\lambda_2(\theta)} \int_{F_1(r,\theta)}^{F_2(r,\theta)} f(r, \theta, z)r \, dz \, dr \, d\theta \qquad (4)$$

There are five other iterated integrals that can be used to evaluate the triple integral in (4) because there are six possible permutations of the three variables r, θ, and z.

Triple integrals and cylindrical coordinates are especially useful in finding the moment of inertia of a solid with respect to the z axis because the distance from the z axis to a point in the solid is determined by the coordinate r.

EXAMPLE 1: A homogeneous solid in the shape of a right-circular cylinder has a radius of 2 ft and an altitude of 4 ft. Find the moment of inertia of the solid with respect to its axis.

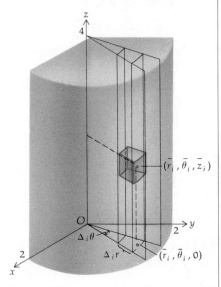

Figure 21.7.2

SOLUTION: Choose the coordinate planes so that the xy plane is the plane of the base of the solid and the z axis is the axis of the solid. Figure 21.7.2 shows the portion of the solid in the first octant together with the ith subregion of a cylindrical partition. Using cylindrical coordinates and taking the point $(\bar{r}_i, \bar{\theta}_i, \bar{z}_i)$ in the ith subregion with k slugs/ft^3 as the volume density at any point, then if I_z slug-ft^2 is the moment of inertia of the solid with respect to the z axis, we have

$$I_z = \lim_{\|\Delta\| \to 0} \sum_{i=1}^n \bar{r}_i^2 k \, \Delta_i V = \iiint\limits_S kr^2 \, dV$$

There are six different possible orders of integration. Figure 21.7.2 shows the order $dz \, dr \, d\theta$. Using this order, we have

$$I_z = \iiint\limits_S kr^2 \, dz \, r \, dr \, d\theta = 4k \int_0^{\pi/2} \int_0^2 \int_0^4 r^3 \, dz \, dr \, d\theta$$

In the first integration, the blocks are summed from $z = 0$ to $z = 4$; the blocks become a column. In the second integration, the columns are summed from $r = 0$ to $r = 2$; the columns become a wedge-shaped slice of the cylinder. In the third integration, the wedge-shaped slice is rotated from $\theta = 0$ to $\theta = \frac{1}{2}\pi$; this sweeps the wedge about the entire three-dimensional region in the first octant. We multiply by 4 to obtain the entire volume. Performing the integration, we obtain

$$I_z = 16k \int_0^{\pi/2} \int_0^2 r^3 \, dr \, d\theta = 64k \int_0^{\pi/2} d\theta = 32k\pi$$

Hence, the moment of inertia is $32k\pi$ slug-ft^2.

EXAMPLE 2: Solve Example 1 by taking the order of integration as (a) $dr\,dz\,d\theta$; (b) $d\theta\,dr\,dz$.

SOLUTION: (a) Figure 21.7.3 represents the order $dr\,dz\,d\theta$. It shows the block summed from $r = 0$ to $r = 2$ to give a wedge-shaped sector. We then sum from $z = 0$ to $z = 4$ to give a wedge-shaped slice. The slice is rotated from $\theta = 0$ to $\theta = \frac{1}{2}\pi$ to cover the first octant. We have, then,

$$I_z = 4k \int_0^{\pi/2} \int_0^4 \int_0^2 r^3\,dr\,dz\,d\theta = 32k\pi$$

(b) Figure 21.7.4 represents the order $d\theta\,dr\,dz$. It shows the blocks summed from $\theta = 0$ to $\theta = \frac{1}{2}\pi$ to give a hollow ring inside the cylinder. These hollow rings are summed from $r = 0$ to $r = 2$ to give a horizontal slice of the cylinder. The horizontal slices are summed from $z = 0$ to $z = 4$. Therefore, we have

$$I_z = 4k \int_0^4 \int_0^2 \int_0^{\pi/2} r^3\,d\theta\,dr\,dz = 32k\pi$$

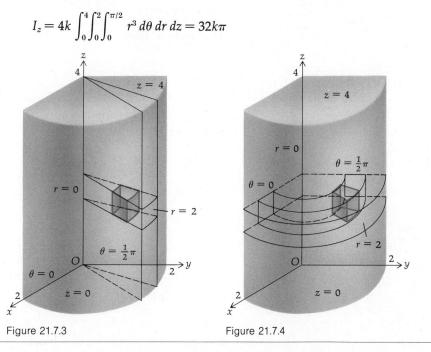

Figure 21.7.3   Figure 21.7.4

EXAMPLE 3: Find the mass of a solid hemisphere of radius a ft if the volume density at any point is proportional to the distance of the point from the axis of the solid.

SOLUTION: If we choose the coordinate planes so that the origin is at the center of the sphere and the z axis is the axis of the solid, then an equation of the hemispherical surface above the xy plane is $z = \sqrt{a^2 - x^2 - y^2}$. Figure 21.7.5 shows this surface and the solid together with the ith subregion of a cylindrical partition. An equation of the hemisphere in cylindrical coordinates is $z = \sqrt{a^2 - r^2}$. If $(\bar{r}_i, \bar{\theta}_i, \bar{z}_i)$ is a point in the ith subregion, the volume density at this point is $k\bar{r}_i$ slugs/ft³, where k is a constant; and if M slugs is the mass of the solid, then

$$M = \lim_{\|\Delta\| \to 0} \sum_{i=1}^n k\bar{r}_i\,\Delta_i V$$

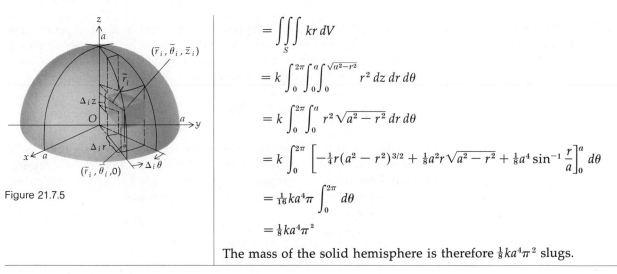

Figure 21.7.5

$$= \iiint_S kr \, dV$$

$$= k \int_0^{2\pi} \int_0^a \int_0^{\sqrt{a^2-r^2}} r^2 \, dz \, dr \, d\theta$$

$$= k \int_0^{2\pi} \int_0^a r^2 \sqrt{a^2 - r^2} \, dr \, d\theta$$

$$= k \int_0^{2\pi} \left[-\tfrac{1}{4} r(a^2 - r^2)^{3/2} + \tfrac{1}{8} a^2 r \sqrt{a^2 - r^2} + \tfrac{1}{8} a^4 \sin^{-1} \frac{r}{a} \right]_0^a d\theta$$

$$= \tfrac{1}{16} k a^4 \pi \int_0^{2\pi} d\theta$$

$$= \tfrac{1}{8} k a^4 \pi^2$$

The mass of the solid hemisphere is therefore $\tfrac{1}{8} k a^4 \pi^2$ slugs.

EXAMPLE 4: Find the center of mass of the solid of Example 3.

SOLUTION: Let the cartesian-coordinate representation of the center of mass be $(\bar{x}, \bar{y}, \bar{z})$. Because of symmetry, $\bar{x} = \bar{y} = 0$. We need to calculate $\bar{z}$. If M_{xy} slug-ft is the moment of mass of the solid with respect to the xy plane, we have

$$M_{xy} = \lim_{\|\Delta\| \to 0} \sum_{i=1}^n \bar{z}_i (k \bar{r}_i) \, \Delta_i V$$

$$= \iiint_S kzr \, dV$$

$$= k \int_0^{2\pi} \int_0^a \int_0^{\sqrt{a^2-r^2}} zr^2 \, dz \, dr \, d\theta$$

$$= \tfrac{1}{2} k \int_0^{2\pi} \int_0^a (a^2 - r^2) r^2 \, dr \, d\theta$$

$$= \tfrac{1}{15} k a^5 \int_0^{2\pi} d\theta$$

$$= \tfrac{2}{15} k a^5 \pi$$

Because $M\bar{z} = M_{xy}$, we get

$$\bar{z} = \frac{M_{xy}}{M} = \frac{\tfrac{2}{15} k a^5 \pi}{\tfrac{1}{8} k a^4 \pi^2} = \frac{16}{15\pi} a$$

The center of mass is therefore on the axis of the solid at a distance of $16a/15\pi$ ft from the plane of the base.

We now proceed to define the triple integral in spherical coordinates.

A spherical partition of the three-dimensional region S is formed by planes containing the z axis, spheres with centers at the origin, and circular cones having vertices at the origin and the z axis as the axis. A typical subregion of the partition is shown in Fig. 21.7.6. If $\Delta_i V$ is the measure of the volume of the ith subregion, and $(\bar{\rho}_i, \bar{\theta}_i, \bar{\phi}_i)$ is a point in it, we can get an approximation to $\Delta_i V$ by considering the region as if it were a rectangular parallelepiped and taking the product of the measures of the three dimensions. These measures are $\bar{\rho}_i \sin \bar{\phi}_i \, \Delta_i\theta$, $\bar{\rho}_i \, \Delta_i\phi$, and $\Delta_i\rho$. Figures 21.7.7 and 21.7.8 show how the first two measures are obtained, and Figure 21.7.6 shows the dimension of measure $\Delta_i\rho$. Hence,

$$\Delta_i V = \bar{\rho}_i{}^2 \sin \bar{\phi}_i \, \Delta_i\rho \, \Delta_i\theta \, \Delta_i\phi$$

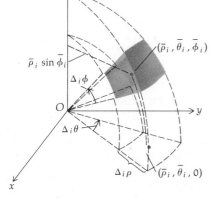

Figure 21.7.6

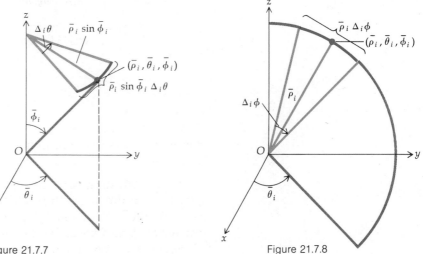

Figure 21.7.7

Figure 21.7.8

The *triple integral in spherical coordinates* of a function f on S is given by

$$\lim_{||\Delta|| \to 0} \sum_{i=1}^{n} f(\bar{\rho}_i, \bar{\theta}_i, \bar{\phi}_i) \, \Delta_i V = \iiint\limits_{S} f(\rho, \theta, \phi) \, dV \qquad (5)$$

or

$$\lim_{||\Delta|| \to 0} \sum_{i=1}^{n} f(\bar{\rho}_i, \bar{\theta}_i, \bar{\phi}_i) \bar{\rho}_i{}^2 \sin \bar{\phi}_i \, \Delta_i\rho \, \Delta_i\theta \, \Delta_i\phi$$

$$= \iiint\limits_{S} f(\rho, \theta, \phi) \rho^2 \sin \phi \, d\rho \, d\theta \, d\phi \qquad (6)$$

Observe that in spherical coordinates, $dV = \rho^2 \sin \phi \, dp \, d\theta \, d\phi$. The triple integrals in (5) or (6) can be evaluated by an iterated integral. Spherical coordinates are especially useful in some problems involving spheres, as illustrated in the following example.

EXAMPLE 5: Find the mass of the solid hemisphere of Example 3 if the volume density at any point is proportional to the distance of the point from the center of the base.

SOLUTION: If $(\bar{\rho}_i, \bar{\theta}_i, \bar{\phi}_i)$ is a point in the ith subregion of a spherical partition, the volume density at this point is $k\bar{\rho}_i$ slugs/ft³, where k is a constant. If M slugs is the mass of the solid, then

$$M = \lim_{\|\Delta\| \to 0} \sum_{i=1}^{n} k\bar{\rho}_i \, \Delta_i V$$

$$= \iiint_S k\rho \, dV$$

$$= 4k \int_0^{\pi/2} \int_0^{\pi/2} \int_0^a \rho^3 \sin\phi \, d\rho \, d\phi \, d\theta$$

$$= a^4 k \int_0^{\pi/2} \int_0^{\pi/2} \sin\phi \, d\phi \, d\theta$$

$$= a^4 k \int_0^{\pi/2} \left[-\cos\phi \right]_0^{\pi/2} d\theta$$

$$= a^4 k \int_0^{\pi/2} d\theta$$

$$= \tfrac{1}{2} a^4 k \pi$$

Hence, the mass of the solid hemisphere is $\tfrac{1}{2}a^4 k\pi$ slugs.

It is interesting to compare the solution of Example 5 which uses spherical coordinates with what is entailed when using cartesian coordinates. By the latter method, a partition of S is formed by dividing S into rectangular boxes by drawing planes parallel to the coordinate planes. If (ξ_i, γ_i, μ_i) is any point in the ith subregion, and because $\rho = \sqrt{x^2 + y^2 + z^2}$, then

$$M = \lim_{\|\Delta\| \to 0} \sum_{i=1}^{n} k\sqrt{\xi_i^2 + \gamma_i^2 + \mu_i^2} \, \Delta_i V$$

$$= \iiint_S k\sqrt{x^2 + y^2 + z^2} \, dV$$

$$= 4k \int_0^a \int_0^{\sqrt{a^2 - z^2}} \int_0^{\sqrt{a^2 - y^2 - z^2}} \sqrt{x^2 + y^2 + z^2} \, dx \, dy \, dz$$

The computation involved in evaluating this integral is obviously much more complicated than that using spherical coordinates.

EXAMPLE 6: A homogeneous solid is bounded above by the sphere $\rho = a$ and below by the cone $\phi = \alpha$, where $0 < \alpha < \tfrac{1}{2}\pi$.

SOLUTION: The solid is shown in Fig. 21.7.9. Let k slugs/ft³ be the constant volume density at any point of the solid. Form a spherical partition of the solid and let $(\bar{\rho}_i, \bar{\theta}_i, \bar{\phi}_i)$ be a point in the ith subregion. The measure of the distance of the point $(\bar{\rho}_i, \bar{\theta}_i, \bar{\phi}_i)$ from the z axis is $\bar{\rho}_i \sin\bar{\phi}_i$. Hence,

Find the moment of inertia of the solid about the z axis.

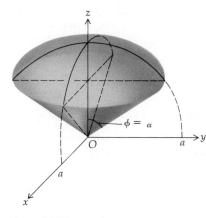

Figure 21.7.9

if I_z slug-ft² is the moment of inertia of the given solid about the z axis, then

$$I_z = \lim_{||\Delta|| \to 0} \sum_{i=1}^{n} (\bar{\rho}_i \sin \bar{\phi}_i)^2 k \, \Delta_i V$$

$$= \iiint_S k\rho^2 \sin^2 \phi \, dV$$

$$= k \int_0^\alpha \int_0^{2\pi} \int_0^a (\rho^2 \sin^2 \phi)\rho^2 \sin \phi \, d\rho \, d\theta \, d\phi$$

$$= \tfrac{1}{5}ka^5 \int_0^\alpha \int_0^{2\pi} \sin^3 \phi \, d\theta \, d\phi$$

$$= \tfrac{2}{5}ka^5\pi \int_0^\alpha \sin^3 \phi \, d\phi$$

$$= \tfrac{2}{5}ka^5\pi \left[-\cos \phi + \tfrac{1}{3} \cos^3 \phi \right]_0^\alpha$$

$$= \tfrac{2}{15}ka^5\pi (\cos^3 \alpha - 3 \cos \alpha + 2)$$

The moment of inertia of the solid about the z axis is therefore

$$\tfrac{2}{15}ka^5\pi (\cos^3 \alpha - 3 \cos \alpha + 2) \text{ slug-ft}^2$$

Exercises 21.7

In Exercises 1 through 4, evaluate the iterated integral.

1. $\int_0^{\pi/4} \int_0^a \int_0^{r \cos \theta} r \sec^3 \theta \, dz \, dr \, d\theta$

2. $\int_0^{\pi/4} \int_{2 \sin \theta}^{2 \cos \theta} \int_0^{r \sin \theta} r^2 \cos \theta \, dz \, dr \, d\theta$

3. $\int_0^{\pi/4} \int_0^{2a \cos \phi} \int_0^{2\pi} \rho^2 \sin \phi \, d\theta \, d\rho \, d\phi$

4. $\int_{\pi/4}^{\pi/2} \int_{\pi/4}^{\phi} \int_0^{a \csc \theta} \rho^3 \sin^2 \theta \sin \phi \, d\rho \, d\theta \, d\phi$

5. Find the volume of the solid enclosed by the sphere $x^2 + y^2 + z^2 = a^2$ by using (a) cylindrical coordinates and (b) spherical coordinates.

6. If S is the solid in the first octant bounded by the sphere $x^2 + y^2 + z^2 = 16$ and the coordinate planes, evaluate the triple integral $\iiint_S xyz \, dV$ by three methods: (a) using spherical coordinates; (b) using rectangular coordinates; (c) using cylindrical coordinates.

In Exercises 7 through 10, use cylindrical coordinates.

7. Find the mass of the solid bounded by a sphere of radius a ft if the volume density varies as the square of the distance from the center. The volume density is measured in slugs/ft³.

8. Find the mass of the solid in the first octant inside the cylinder $x^2 + y^2 = 4x$ and under the sphere $x^2 + y^2 + z^2 = 16$. The volume density varies as the distance from the xy plane, and it is measured in slugs/ft³.

9. Find the moment of inertia with respect to the z axis of the homogeneous solid bounded by the cylinder $r = 5$, the cone $z = r$, and the xy plane. The volume density at any point is k slugs/ft^3.

10. Find the moment of inertia of the solid bounded by a right-circular cylinder of altitude h ft and radius a ft, with respect to the axis of the cylinder. The volume density varies as the distance from the axis of the cylinder, and it is measured in slugs/ft^3.

In Exercises 11 through 14, use spherical coordinates.

11. Find the center of mass of the solid bounded by the hemisphere of Example 5. The volume density is the same as that in Example 5.

12. Find the moment of inertia with respect to the z axis of the homogeneous solid bounded by the sphere $x^2 + y^2 + z^2 = 4$. The volume density at any point is k slugs/ft^3.

13. Find the moment of inertia with respect to the z axis of the homogeneous solid inside the cylinder $x^2 + y^2 - 2x = 0$, below the cone $x^2 + y^2 = z^2$, and above the xy plane. The volume density at any point is k slugs/ft^3.

14. Find the mass of a spherical solid of radius a ft if the volume density at each point is proportional to the distance of the point from the center of the sphere. The volume density is measured in slugs/ft^3.

In Exercises 15 through 18, use the coordinate system that you decide is best for the problem.

15. Find the center of mass of the solid inside the paraboloid $x^2 + y^2 = z$ and outside the cone $x^2 + y^2 = z^2$. The constant volume density is k slugs/ft^3.

16. Find the moment of inertia with respect to the z axis of the homogeneous solid of Exercise 15.

17. Find the moment of inertia about a diameter of the solid between two concentric spheres having radii a ft and $2a$ ft. The volume density varies inversely as the square of the distance from the center, and it is measured in slugs/ft^3.

18. Find the mass of the solid of Exercise 17. The volume density is the same as that in Exercise 17.

In Exercises 19 through 22, evaluate the iterated integral by using either cylindrical or spherical coordinates.

19. $\displaystyle\int_0^4 \int_0^3 \int_0^{\sqrt{9-x^2}} \sqrt{x^2 + y^2}\, dy\, dx\, dz$

20. $\displaystyle\int_0^2 \int_0^{\sqrt{4-y^2}} \int_0^{\sqrt{4-x^2-y^2}} \frac{1}{x^2 + y^2 + z^2}\, dz\, dx\, dy$

21. $\displaystyle\int_0^1 \int_0^{\sqrt{1-y^2}} \int_{\sqrt{x^2+y^2}}^{\sqrt{2-x^2-y^2}} z^2\, dz\, dx\, dy$

22. $\displaystyle\int_0^1 \int_0^{\sqrt{1-x^2}} \int_0^{\sqrt{1-x^2-y^2}} \frac{z}{\sqrt{x^2 + y^2}}\, dz\, dy\, dx$

Review Exercises (Chapter 21)

In Exercises 1 through 8, evaluate the given iterated integral.

1. $\displaystyle\int_0^1 \int_x^{\sqrt{x}} x^2 y\, dy\, dx$

2. $\displaystyle\int_{-2}^2 \int_{-\sqrt{4-y^2}}^{\sqrt{4-y^2}} xy\, dx\, dy$

3. $\displaystyle\int_0^{\pi/2} \int_0^{2\sin\theta} r\cos^2\theta\, dr\, d\theta$

4. $\displaystyle\int_0^\pi \int_0^{3(1+\cos\theta)} r^2 \sin\theta\, dr\, d\theta$

5. $\displaystyle\int_0^1 \int_0^z \int_0^{y+z} e^x e^y e^z\, dx\, dy\, dz$

6. $\displaystyle\int_1^2 \int_0^x \int_0^{\sqrt{3}y} \frac{y}{y^2 + z^2}\, dz\, dy\, dx$

7. $\displaystyle\int_0^{\pi/2} \int_{\pi/6}^{\pi/2} \int_0^2 \rho^3 \sin\phi \cos\phi\, d\rho\, d\phi\, d\theta$

8. $\displaystyle\int_0^a \int_0^{\pi/2} \int_0^{\sqrt{a^2-z^2}} zre^{-r^2}\, dr\, d\theta\, dz$

In Exercises 9 through 12, evaluate the multiple integral.

9. $\displaystyle\iint_R xy\, dA$; R is the region in the first quadrant bounded by the circle $x^2 + y^2 = 1$ and the coordinate axes.

10. $\displaystyle\iint_R (x+y)\, dA$; R is the region bounded by the curve $y = \cos x$ and the x axis from $x = -\frac{1}{2}\pi$ to $x = \frac{1}{2}\pi$.

11. $\displaystyle\iiint_S z^2\, dV$; S is the region bounded by the cylinders $x^2 + z = 1$ and $y^2 + z = 1$, and the xy plane.

12. $\displaystyle\iiint_S y\cos(x+z)\, dV$; S is the region bounded by the cylinder $x = y^2$, and the planes $x + z = \frac{1}{2}\pi$, $y = 0$, and $z = 0$.

13. Evaluate by polar coordinates the double integral

$$\iint_R \frac{1}{x^2 + y^2}\, dA$$

where R is the region in the first quadrant bounded by the two circles $x^2 + y^2 = 1$ and $x^2 + y^2 = 4$.

14. Evaluate by polar coordinates the iterated integral $\displaystyle\int_0^1 \int_{\sqrt{3}y}^{\sqrt{4-y^2}} \ln(x^2 + y^2)\, dx\, dy$.

In Exercises 15 and 16, evaluate the iterated integral by reversing the order of integration.

15. $\displaystyle\int_0^1 \int_x^1 \sin y^2\, dy\, dx$

16. $\displaystyle\int_0^1 \int_0^{\cos^{-1}y} e^{\sin x}\, dx\, dy$

In Exercises 17 and 18, evaluate the iterated integral by changing to either cylindrical or spherical coordinates.

17. $\displaystyle\int_0^3 \int_0^{\sqrt{9-x^2}} \int_0^2 \frac{1}{\sqrt{x^2 + y^2}}\, dz\, dy\, dx$

18. $\displaystyle\int_0^2 \int_0^{\sqrt{4-x^2}} \int_0^{\sqrt{4-x^2-y^2}} z\sqrt{4 - x^2 - y^2}\, dz\, dy\, dx$

19. Use double integration to find the area of the region in the first quadrant bounded by the parabolas $x^2 = 4y$ and $x^2 = 8 - 4y$ by two methods: (a) Integrate first with respect to x; (b) integrate first with respect to y.

20. Use double integration to find the volume of the solid above the xy plane bounded by the cylinder $x^2 + y^2 = 16$ and the plane $z = 2y$ by two methods: (a) Integrate first with respect to x; (b) integrate first with respect to y.

21. Find the volume of the solid bounded by the surfaces $x^2 = 4y$, $y^2 = 4x$, and $x^2 = z - y$.

22. Find the mass of the lamina in the shape of the region bounded by the parabola $y = x^2$ and the line $x - y + 2 = 0$ if the area density at any point is x^2y^2 slugs/ft^2.

23. Find the area of the surface of the cylinder $x^2 + y^2 = 9$ lying in the first octant and between the planes $x = z$ and $3x = z$.

24. Find the area of the surface of the part of the cylinder $x^2 + y^2 = a^2$ that lies inside the cylinder $y^2 + z^2 = a^2$.

25. Use double integration to find the area of the region inside the circle $r = 1$ and to the right of the parabola $r(1 + \cos\theta) = 1$.

26. Find the mass of the lamina in the shape of the region exterior to the limaçon $r = 3 - \cos\theta$ and interior to the circle $r = 5\cos\theta$ if the area density at any point is $2|\sin\theta|$ slugs/ft^2.

27. Find the center of mass of the rectangular lamina bounded by the lines $x = 3$ and $y = 2$ and the coordinate axes if the area density at any point is xy^2 slugs/ft^2.

28. Find the center of mass of the lamina in the shape of the region bounded by the parabolas $x^2 = 4 + 4y$ and $x^2 = 4 - 8y$ if the area density at any point is kx^2 slugs/ft^2.

29. Find the mass of the lamina in the shape of the region bounded by the polar axis and the curve $r = \cos 2\theta$, where $0 \le \theta \le \frac{1}{4}\pi$. The area density at any point is $r\theta$ slugs/ft^2.

30. Find the moment of inertia about the x axis of the lamina in the shape of the region bounded by the circle $x^2 + y^2 = a^2$ if the area density at any point is $k\sqrt{x^2 + y^2}$ slugs/ft^2.

31. Find the moment of inertia about the x axis of the lamina in the shape of the region bounded by the curve $y = e^x$, the line $x = 2$, and the coordinate axes if the area density at any point is xy slugs/ft².

32. Find the moment of inertia of the lamina of Exercise 31 about the y axis.

33. Find the moment of inertia with respect to the $\frac{1}{2}\pi$ axis of the homogeneous lamina in the shape of the region bounded by the curve $r^2 = 4 \cos 2\theta$ if the area density at any point is k slugs/ft².

34. Find the mass of the lamina of Exercise 33.

35. Find the polar moment of inertia and the corresponding radius of gyration of the lamina of Exercise 33.

36. Find the moment of inertia about the y axis of the lamina in the shape of the region bounded by the parabola $y = x - x^2$ and the line $x + y = 0$ if the area density at any point is $(x + y)$ slugs/ft².

37. Find the mass of the solid bounded by the spheres $x^2 + y^2 + z^2 = 4$ and $x^2 + y^2 + z^2 = 9$ if the volume density at any point is $k \sqrt{x^2 + y^2 + z^2}$ slugs/ft³.

38. Find the moment of inertia about the z axis of the solid of Exercise 37.

39. The homogeneous solid bounded by the cone $z^2 = 4x^2 + 4y^2$ between the planes $z = 0$ and $z = 4$ has a volume density at any point of k slugs/ft³. Find the moment of inertia about the z axis for this solid.

40. Find the center of mass of the solid bounded by the sphere $x^2 + y^2 + z^2 - 6z = 0$ and the cone $x^2 + y^2 = z^2$, and above the cone, if the volume density at any point is kz slugs/ft³.

Appendix

Table 1   *Powers and roots*

n	n^2	$\sqrt{n}$	n^3	$\sqrt[3]{n}$	n	n^2	$\sqrt{n}$	n^3	$\sqrt[3]{n}$
1	1	1.000	1	1.000	51	2,601	7.141	132,651	3.708
2	4	1.414	8	1.260	52	2,704	7.211	140,608	3.732
3	9	1.732	27	1.442	53	2,809	7.280	148,877	3.756
4	16	2.000	64	1.587	54	2,916	7.348	157,464	3.780
5	25	2.236	125	1.710	55	3,025	7.416	166,375	3.803
6	36	2.449	216	1.817	56	3,136	7.483	175,616	3.826
7	49	2.646	343	1.913	57	3,249	7.550	185,193	3.848
8	64	2.828	512	2.000	58	3,364	7.616	195,112	3.871
9	81	3.000	729	2.080	59	3,481	7.681	205,379	3.893
10	100	3.162	1,000	2.154	60	3,600	7.746	216,000	3.915
11	121	3.317	1,331	2.224	61	3,721	7.810	226,981	3.936
12	144	3.464	1,728	2.289	62	3,844	7.874	238,328	3.958
13	169	3.606	2,197	2.351	63	3,969	7.937	250,047	3.979
14	196	3.742	2,744	2.410	64	4,096	8.000	262,144	4.000
15	225	3.873	3,375	2.466	65	4,225	8.062	274,625	4.021
16	256	4.000	4,096	2.520	66	4,356	8.124	287,496	4.041
17	289	4.123	4,913	2.571	67	4,489	8.185	300,763	4.062
18	324	4.243	5,832	2.621	68	4,624	8.246	314,432	4.082
19	361	4.359	6,859	2.668	69	4,761	8.307	328,509	4.102
20	400	4.472	8,000	2.714	70	4,900	8.367	343,000	4.121
21	441	4.583	9,261	2.759	71	5,041	8.426	357,911	4.141
22	484	4.690	10,648	2.802	72	5,184	8.485	373,248	4.160
23	529	4.796	12,167	2.844	73	5,329	8.544	389,017	4.179
24	576	4.899	13,824	2.884	74	5,476	8.602	405,224	4.198
25	625	5.000	15,625	2.924	75	5,625	8.660	421,875	4.217
26	676	5.099	17,576	2.962	76	5,776	8.718	438,976	4.236
27	729	5.196	19,683	3.000	77	5,929	8.775	456,533	4.254
28	784	5.291	21,952	3.037	78	6,084	8.832	474,552	4.273
29	841	5.385	24,389	3.072	79	6,241	8.888	493,039	4.291
30	900	5.477	27,000	3.107	80	6,400	8.944	512,000	4.309
31	961	5.568	29,791	3.141	81	6,561	9.000	531,441	4.327
32	1,024	5.657	32,768	3.175	82	6,724	9.055	551,368	4.344
33	1,089	5.745	35,937	3.208	83	6,889	9.110	571,787	4.362
34	1,156	5.831	39,304	3.240	84	7,056	9.165	592,704	4.380
35	1,225	5.916	42,875	3.271	85	7,225	9.220	614,125	4.397
36	1,296	6.000	46,656	3.302	86	7,396	9.274	636,056	4.414
37	1,369	6.083	50,653	3.332	87	7,569	9.327	658,503	4.431
38	1,444	6.164	54,872	3.362	88	7,744	9.381	681,472	4.448
39	1,521	6.245	59,319	3.391	89	7,921	9.434	704,969	4.465
40	1,600	6.325	64,000	3.420	90	8,100	9.487	729,000	4.481
41	1,681	6.403	68,921	3.448	91	8,281	9.539	753,571	4.498
42	1,764	6.481	74,088	3.476	92	8,464	9.592	778,688	4.514
43	1,849	6.557	79,507	3.503	93	8,649	9.643	804,357	4.531
44	1,936	6.633	85,184	3.530	94	8,836	9.695	830,584	4.547
45	2,025	6.708	91,125	3.557	95	9,025	9.747	857,375	4.563
46	2,116	6.782	97,336	3.583	96	9,216	9.798	884,736	4.579
47	2,209	6.856	103,823	3.609	97	9,409	9.849	912,673	4.595
48	2,304	6.928	110,592	3.634	98	9,604	9.899	941,192	4.610
49	2,401	7.000	117,649	3.659	99	9,801	9.950	970,299	4.626
50	2,500	7.071	125,000	3.684	100	10,000	10.000	1,000,000	4.642

Table 2 Natural logarithms

N	0	1	2	3	4	5	6	7	8	9
1.0	0000	0100	0198	0296	0392	0488	0583	0677	0770	0862
1.1	0953	1044	1133	1222	1310	1398	1484	1570	1655	1740
1.2	1823	1906	1989	2070	2151	2231	2311	2390	2469	2546
1.3	2624	2700	2776	2852	2927	3001	3075	3148	3221	3293
1.4	3365	3436	3507	3577	3646	3716	3784	3853	3920	3988
1.5	4055	4121	4187	4253	4318	4383	4447	4511	4574	4637
1.6	4700	4762	4824	4886	4947	5008	5068	5128	5188	5247
1.7	5306	5365	5423	5481	5539	5596	5653	5710	5766	5822
1.8	5878	5933	5988	6043	6098	6152	6206	6259	6313	6366
1.9	6419	6471	6523	6575	6627	6678	6729	6780	6831	6881
2.0	6931	6981	7031	7080	7129	7178	7227	7275	7324	7372
2.1	7419	7467	7514	7561	7608	7655	7701	7747	7793	7839
2.2	7885	7930	7975	8020	8065	8109	8154	8198	8242	8286
2.3	8329	8372	8416	8459	8502	8544	8587	8629	8671	8713
2.4	8755	8796	8838	8879	8920	8961	9002	9042	9083	9123
2.5	9163	9203	9243	9282	9322	9361	9400	9439	9478	9517
2.6	9555	9594	9632	9670	9708	9746	9783	9821	9858	9895
2.7	9933	9969	*0006	*0043	*0080	*0116	*0152	*0188	*0225	*0260
2.8	1.0296	0332	0367	0403	0438	0473	0508	0543	0578	0613
2.9	0647	0682	0716	0750	0784	0818	0852	0886	0919	0953
3.0	1.0986	1019	1053	1086	1119	1151	1184	1217	1249	1282
3.1	1314	1346	1378	1410	1442	1474	1506	1537	1569	1600
3.2	1632	1663	1694	1725	1756	1787	1817	1848	1878	1909
3.3	1939	1969	2000	2030	2060	2090	2119	2149	2179	2208
3.4	2238	2267	2296	2326	2355	2384	2413	2442	2470	2499
3.5	1.2528	2556	2585	2613	2641	2669	2698	2726	2754	2782
3.6	2809	2837	2865	2892	2920	2947	2975	3002	3029	3056
3.7	3083	3110	3137	3164	3191	3218	3244	3271	3297	3324
3.8	3350	3376	3403	3429	3455	3481	3507	3533	3558	3584
3.9	3610	3635	3661	3686	3712	3737	3762	3788	3813	3838
4.0	1.3863	3888	3913	3938	3962	3987	4012	4036	4061	4085
4.1	4110	4134	4159	4183	4207	4231	4255	4279	4303	4327
4.2	4351	4375	4398	4422	4446	4469	4493	4516	4540	4563
4.3	4586	4609	4633	4656	4679	4702	4725	4748	4770	4793
4.4	4816	4839	4861	4884	4907	4929	4951	4974	4996	5019
4.5	1.5041	5063	5085	5107	5129	5151	5173	5195	5217	5239
4.6	5261	5282	5304	5326	5347	5369	5390	5412	5433	5454
4.7	5476	5497	5518	5539	5560	5581	5602	5623	5644	5665
4.8	5686	5707	5728	5748	5769	5790	5810	5831	5851	5872
4.9	5892	5913	5933	5953	5974	5994	6014	6034	6054	6074
5.0	1.6094	6114	6134	6154	6174	6194	6214	6233	6253	6273
5.1	6292	6312	6332	6351	6371	6390	6409	6429	6448	6467
5.2	6487	6506	6525	6544	6563	6582	6601	6620	6639	6658
5.3	6677	6696	6715	6734	6752	6771	6790	6808	6827	6845
5.4	6864	6882	6901	6919	6938	6956	6974	6993	7011	7029

Table 2   (Continued)

N	0	1	2	3	4	5	6	7	8	9
5.5	1.7047	7066	7084	7102	7120	7138	7156	7174	7192	7210
5.6	7228	7246	7263	7281	7299	7317	7334	7352	7370	7387
5.7	7405	7422	7440	7457	7475	7492	7509	7527	7544	7561
5.8	7579	7596	7613	7630	7647	7664	7681	7699	7716	7733
5.9	7750	7766	7783	7800	7817	7834	7851	7867	7884	7901
6.0	1.7918	7934	7951	7967	7984	8001	8017	8034	8050	8066
6.1	8083	8099	8116	8132	8148	8165	8181	8197	8213	8229
6.2	8245	8262	8278	8294	8310	8326	8342	8358	8374	8390
6.3	8405	8421	8437	8453	8469	8485	8500	8516	8532	8547
6.4	8563	8579	8594	8610	8625	8641	8656	8672	8687	8703
6.5	1.8718	8733	8749	8764	8779	8795	8810	8825	8840	8856
6.6	8871	8886	8901	8916	8931	8946	8961	8976	8991	9006
6.7	9021	9036	9051	9066	9081	9095	9110	9125	9140	9155
6.8	9169	9184	9199	9213	9228	9242	9257	9272	9286	9301
6.9	9315	9330	9344	9359	9373	9387	9402	9416	9430	9445
7.0	1.9459	9473	9488	9502	9516	9530	9544	9559	9573	9587
7.1	9601	9615	9629	9643	9657	9671	9685	9699	9713	9727
7.2	9741	9755	9769	9782	9796	9810	9824	9838	9851	9865
7.3	9879	9892	9906	9920	9933	9947	9961	9974	9988	*0001
7.4	2.0015	0028	0042	0055	0069	0082	0096	0109	0122	0136
7.5	2.0149	0162	0176	0189	0202	0215	0229	0242	0255	0268
7.6	0281	0295	0308	0321	0334	0347	0360	0373	0386	0399
7.7	0412	0425	0438	0451	0464	0477	0490	0503	0516	0528
7.8	0541	0554	0567	0580	0592	0605	0618	0630	0643	0656
7.9	0669	0681	0694	0707	0719	0732	0744	0757	0769	0782
8.0	2.0794	0807	0819	0832	0844	0857	0869	0882	0894	0906
8.1	0919	0931	0943	0956	0968	0980	0992	1005	1017	1029
8.2	1041	1054	1066	1078	1090	1102	1114	1126	1138	1150
8.3	1163	1175	1187	1199	1211	1223	1235	1247	1258	1270
8.4	1282	1294	1306	1318	1330	1342	1353	1365	1377	1389
8.5	2.1401	1412	1424	1436	1448	1459	1471	1483	1494	1506
8.6	1518	1529	1541	1552	1564	1576	1587	1599	1610	1622
8.7	1633	1645	1656	1668	1679	1691	1702	1713	1725	1736
8.8	1748	1759	1770	1782	1793	1804	1815	1827	1838	1849
8.9	1861	1872	1883	1894	1905	1917	1928	1939	1950	1961
9.0	2.1972	1983	1994	2006	2017	2028	2039	2050	2061	2072
9.1	2083	2094	2105	2116	2127	2138	2148	2159	2170	2181
9.2	2192	2203	2214	2225	2235	2246	2257	2268	2279	2289
9.3	2300	2311	2322	2332	2343	2354	2364	2375	2386	2396
9.4	2407	2418	2428	2439	2450	2460	2471	2481	2492	2502
9.5	2.2513	2523	2534	2544	2555	2565	2576	2586	2597	2607
9.6	2618	2628	2638	2649	2659	2670	2680	2690	2701	2711
9.7	2721	2732	2742	2752	2762	2773	2783	2793	2803	2814
9.8	2824	2834	2844	2854	2865	2875	2885	2895	2905	2915
9.9	2925	2935	2946	2956	2966	2976	2986	2996	3006	3016

Use ln 10 = 2.30259 to find logarithms of numbers greater than 10 or less than 1. *Example:*
ln 220 = ln 2.2 + 2 ln 10 = 0.7885 + 2(2.30259) = 5.3937.

Table 3 *Exponential functions*

x	e^x	$\log_{10}(e^x)$	e^{-x}	x	e^x	$\log_{10}(e^x)$	e^{-x}
0.00	1.0000	0.00000	1.000000	**0.50**	1.6487	0.21715	0.606531
0.01	1.0101	.00434	0.990050	0.51	1.6653	.22149	.600496
0.02	1.0202	.00869	.980199	0.52	1.6820	.22583	.594521
0.03	1.0305	.01303	.970446	0.53	1.6989	.23018	.588605
0.04	1.0408	.01737	.960789	0.54	1.7160	.23452	.582748
0.05	1.0513	0.02171	0.951229	**0.55**	1.7333	0.23886	0.576950
0.06	1.0618	.02606	.941765	0.56	1.7507	.24320	.571209
0.07	1.0725	.03040	.932394	0.57	1.7683	.24755	.565525
0.08	1.0833	.03474	.923116	0.58	1.7860	.25189	.559898
0.09	1.0942	.03909	.913931	0.59	1.8040	.35623	.554327
0.10	1.1052	0.04343	0.904837	**0.60**	1.8221	0.26058	0.548812
0.11	1.1163	.04777	.895834	0.61	1.8404	.26492	.543351
0.12	1.1275	.05212	.886920	0.62	1.8589	.26926	.537944
0.13	1.1388	.05646	.878095	0.63	1.8776	.27361	.532592
0.14	1.1503	.06080	.869358	0.64	1.8965	.27795	.527292
0.15	1.1618	0.06514	0.860708	**0.65**	1.9155	0.28229	0.522046
0.16	1.1735	.06949	.852144	0.66	1.9348	.28663	.516851
0.17	1.1853	.07383	.843665	0.67	1.9542	.29098	.511709
0.18	1.1972	.07817	.835270	0.68	1.9739	.29532	.506617
0.19	1.2092	.08252	.826959	0.69	1.9937	.29966	.501576
0.20	1.2214	0.08686	0.818731	**0.70**	2.0138	0.30401	0.496585
0.21	1.2337	.09120	.810584	0.71	2.0340	.30835	.491644
0.22	1.2461	.09554	.802519	0.72	2.0544	.31269	.486752
0.23	1.2586	.09989	.794534	0.73	2.0751	.31703	.481909
0.24	1.2712	.10423	.786628	0.74	2.0959	.32138	.477114
0.25	1.2840	0.10857	0.778801	**0.75**	2.1170	0.32572	0.472367
0.26	1.2969	.11292	.771052	0.76	2.1383	.33006	.467666
0.27	1.3100	.11726	.763379	0.77	2.1598	.33441	.463013
0.28	1.3231	.12160	.755784	0.78	2.1815	.33875	.458406
0.29	1.3364	.12595	.748264	0.79	2.2034	.34309	.453845
0.30	1.3499	0.13029	0.740818	**0.80**	2.2255	0.34744	0.449329
0.31	1.3634	.13463	.733447	0.81	2.2479	.35178	.444858
0.32	1.3771	.13897	.726149	0.82	2.2705	.35612	.440432
0.33	1.3910	.14332	.718924	0.83	2.2933	.36046	.436049
0.34	1.4049	.14766	.711770	0.84	2.3164	.36481	.431711
0.35	1.4191	0.15200	0.704688	**0.85**	2.3396	0.36915	0.427415
0.36	1.4333	.15635	.697676	0.86	2.3632	.37349	.423162
0.37	1.4477	.16069	.690734	0.87	2.3869	.37784	.418952
0.38	1.4623	.16503	.683861	0.88	2.4109	.38218	.414783
0.39	1.4770	.16937	.677057	0.89	2.4351	.38652	.410656
0.40	1.4918	0.17372	0.670320	**0.90**	2.4596	0.39087	0.406570
0.41	1.5068	.17806	.663650	0.91	2.4843	.39521	.402524
0.42	1.5220	.18240	.657047	0.92	2.5093	.39955	.398519
0.43	1.5373	.18675	.650509	0.93	2.5345	.40389	.394554
0.44	1.5527	.19109	.644036	0.94	2.5600	.40824	.390628
0.45	1.5683	0.19543	0.637628	**0.95**	2.5857	0.41258	0.386741
0.46	1.5841	.19978	.631284	0.96	2.6117	.41692	.382893
0.47	1.6000	.20412	.625002	0.97	2.6379	.42127	.379083
0.48	1.6161	.20846	.618783	0.98	2.6645	.42561	.375311
0.49	1.6323	.21280	.612626	0.99	2.6912	.42995	.371577
0.50	1.6487	0.21715	0.606531	**1.00**	2.7183	0.43429	0.367879

Table 3   (Continued)

x	e^x	$\log_{10}(e^x)$	e^{-x}	x	e^x	$\log_{10}(e^x)$	e^{-x}
1.00	2.7183	0.43429	0.367879	**1.50**	4.4817	0.65144	0.223130
1.01	2.7456	.43864	.364219	1.51	4.5267	.65578	.220910
1.02	2.7732	.44298	.360595	1.52	4.5722	.66013	.218712
1.03	2.8011	.44732	.357007	1.53	4.6182	.66447	.216536
1.04	2.8292	.45167	.353455	1.54	4.6646	.66881	.214381
1.05	2.8577	0.45601	0.349938	**1.55**	4.7115	0.67316	0.212248
1.06	2.8864	.46035	.346456	1.56	4.7588	.67750	.210136
1.07	2.9154	.46470	.343009	1.57	4.8066	.68184	.208045
1.08	2.9447	.46904	.339596	1.58	4.8550	.68619	.205975
1.09	2.9743	.47338	.336216	1.59	4.9037	.69053	.203926
1.10	3.0042	0.47772	0.332871	**1.60**	4.9530	0.69487	0.201897
1.11	3.0344	.48207	.329559	1.61	5.0028	.69921	.199888
1.12	3.0649	.48641	.326280	1.62	5.0531	.70356	.197899
1.13	3.0957	.49075	.323033	1.63	5.1039	.70790	.195930
1.14	3.1268	.49510	.319819	1.64	5.1552	.71224	.193980
1.15	3.1582	0.49944	0.316637	**1.65**	5.2070	0.71659	0.192050
1.16	3.1899	.50378	.313486	1.66	5.2593	.72093	.190139
1.17	3.2220	.50812	.310367	1.67	5.3122	.72527	.188247
1.18	3.2544	.51247	.307279	1.68	5.3656	.72961	.186374
1.19	3.2871	.51681	.304221	1.69	5.4195	.73396	.184520
1.20	3.3201	0.52115	0.301194	**1.70**	5.4739	0.73830	0.182684
1.21	3.3535	.52550	.298197	1.71	5.5290	.74264	.180866
1.22	3.3872	.52984	.295230	1.72	5.5845	.74699	.179066
1.23	3.4212	.53418	.292293	1.73	5.6407	.75133	.177284
1.24	3.4556	.53853	.289384	1.74	5.6973	.75567	.175520
1.25	3.4903	0.54287	0.286505	**1.75**	5.7546	0.76002	0.173774
1.26	3.5254	.54721	.283654	1.76	5.8124	.76436	.172045
1.27	3.5609	.55155	.280832	1.77	5.8709	.76870	.170333
1.28	3.5966	.55590	.278037	1.78	5.9299	.77304	.168638
1.29	3.6328	.56024	.275271	1.79	5.9895	.77739	.166960
1.30	3.6693	0.56458	0.272532	**1.80**	6.0496	0.78173	0.165299
1.31	3.7062	.56893	.269820	1.81	6.1104	.78607	.163654
1.32	3.7434	.57327	.267135	1.82	6.1719	.79042	.162026
1.33	3.7810	.57761	.264477	1.83	6.2339	.79476	.160414
1.34	3.8190	.58195	.261846	1.84	6.2965	.79910	.158817
1.35	3.8574	0.58630	0.259240	**1.85**	6.3598	0.80344	0.157237
1.36	3.8962	.59064	.256661	1.86	6.4237	.80779	.155673
1.37	3.9354	.59498	.254107	1.87	6.4483	.81213	.154124
1.38	3.9749	.59933	.251579	1.88	6.5535	.81647	.152590
1.39	4.0149	.60367	.249075	1.89	6.6194	.82082	.151072
1.40	4.0552	0.60801	0.246597	**1.90**	6.6859	0.82516	0.149569
1.41	4.0960	.61236	.244143	1.91	6.7531	.82950	.148080
1.42	4.1371	.61670	.241714	1.92	6.8210	.83385	.146607
1.43	4.1787	.62104	.239309	1.93	6.8895	.83819	.145148
1.44	4.2207	.62538	.236928	1.94	6.9588	.84253	.143704
1.45	4.2631	0.62973	0.234570	**1.95**	7.0287	0.84687	0.142274
1.46	4.3060	.63407	.232236	1.96	7.0993	.85122	.140858
1.47	4.3492	.63841	.229925	1.97	7.1707	.85556	.139457
1.48	4.3929	.64276	.227638	1.98	7.2427	.85990	.138069
1.49	4.4371	.64710	.225373	1.99	7.3155	.86425	.136695
1.50	4.4817	0.65144	0.223130	**2.00**	7.3891	0.86859	0.135335

Table 3 (*Continued*)

x	e^x	$\log_{10}(e^x)$	e^{-x}	x	e^x	$\log_{10}(e^x)$	e^{-x}
2.00	7.3891	0.86859	0.135335	**2.50**	12.182	1.08574	0.082085
2.01	7.4633	.87293	.133989	2.51	12.305	1.09008	.081268
2.02	7.5383	.87727	.132655	2.52	12.429	1.09442	.080460
2.03	7.6141	.88162	.131336	2.53	12.554	1.09877	.079659
2.04	7.6906	.88596	.130029	2.54	12.680	1.10311	.078866
2.05	7.7679	0.89030	0.128735	**2.55**	12.807	1.10745	0.078082
2.06	7.8460	.89465	.127454	2.56	12.936	1.11179	.077305
2.07	7.9248	.89899	.126186	2.57	13.066	1.11614	.076536
2.08	8.0045	.90333	.124930	2.58	13.197	1.12048	.075774
2.09	8.0849	.90756	.123687	2.59	13.330	1.12482	.075020
2.10	8.1662	0.91202	0.122456	**2.60**	13.464	1.12917	0.074274
2.11	8.2482	.91636	.121238	2.61	13.599	1.13351	.073535
2.12	8.3311	.92070	.120032	2.62	13.736	1.13785	.072803
2.13	8.4149	.92505	.118837	2.63	13.874	1.14219	.072078
2.14	8.4994	.92939	.117655	2.64	14.013	1.14654	.071361
2.15	8.5849	0.93373	0.116484	**2.65**	14.154	1.15088	0.070651
2.16	8.6711	.93808	.115325	2.66	14.296	1.15522	.069948
2.17	8.7583	.94242	.114178	2.67	14.440	1.15957	.069252
2.18	8.8463	.94676	.113042	2.68	14.585	1.16391	.068563
2.19	8.9352	.95110	.111917	2.69	14.732	1.16825	.067881
2.20	9.0250	0.95545	0.110803	**2.70**	14.880	1.17260	0.067206
2.21	9.1157	.95979	.109701	2.71	15.029	1.17694	.066537
2.22	9.2073	.96413	.108609	2.72	15.180	1.18128	.065875
2.23	9.2999	.96848	.107528	2.73	15.333	1.18562	.065219
2.24	9.3933	.97282	.106459	2.74	15.487	1.18997	.064570
2.25	9.4877	0.97716	0.105399	**2.75**	15.643	1.19431	0.063928
2.26	9.5831	.98151	.104350	2.76	15.800	1.19865	.063292
2.27	9.6794	.98585	.103312	2.77	15.959	1.20300	.062662
2.28	9.7767	.99019	.102284	2.78	16.119	1.20734	.062039
2.29	9.8749	.99453	.101266	2.79	16.281	1.21168	.061421
2.30	9.9742	0.99888	0.100259	**2.80**	16.445	1.21602	0.060810
2.31	10.074	1.00322	.099261	2.81	16.610	1.22037	.060205
2.32	10.176	1.00756	.098274	2.82	16.777	1.22471	.059606
2.33	10.278	1.01191	.097296	2.83	16.945	1.22905	.059013
2.34	10.381	1.01625	.096328	2.84	17.116	1.23340	.058426
2.35	10.486	1.02059	0.095369	**2.85**	17.288	1.23774	0.057844
2.36	10.591	1.02493	.094420	2.86	17.462	1.24208	.057269
2.37	10.697	1.02928	.093481	2.87	17.637	1.24643	.056699
2.38	10.805	1.03362	.092551	2.88	17.814	1.25077	.056135
2.39	10.913	1.03796	.091630	2.89	17.993	1.25511	.055576
2.40	11.023	1.04231	0.090718	**2.90**	18.174	1.25945	0.055023
2.41	11.134	1.04665	.089815	2.91	18.357	1.26380	.054476
2.42	11.246	1.05099	.088922	2.92	18.541	1.26814	.053934
2.43	11.359	1.05534	.088037	2.93	18.728	1.27248	.053397
2.44	11.473	1.05968	.087161	2.94	18.916	1.27683	.052866
2.45	11.588	1.06402	0.086294	**2.95**	19.106	1.28117	0.052340
2.46	11.705	1.06836	.085435	2.96	19.298	1.28551	.051819
2.47	11.822	1.07271	.084585	2.97	19.492	1.28985	.051303
2.48	11.941	1.07705	.083743	2.98	19.688	1.29420	.050793
2.49	12.061	1.08139	.082910	2.99	19.886	1.29854	.050287
2.50	12.182	1.08574	0.082085	**3.00**	20.086	1.30288	0.049787

Table 3 (*Continued*)

x	e^x	$\log_{10}(e^x)$	e^{-x}	x	e^x	$\log_{10}(e^x)$	e^{-x}
3.00	20.086	1.30288	0.049787	**3.50**	33.115	1.52003	0.030197
3.01	20.287	1.30723	.049292	3.51	33.448	1.52437	.029897
3.02	20.491	1.31157	.048801	3.52	33.784	1.52872	.029599
3.03	20.697	1.31591	.048316	3.53	34.124	1.53306	.029305
3.04	20.905	1.32026	.047835	3.54	34.467	1.53740	.029013
3.05	21.115	1.32460	0.047359	**3.55**	34.813	1.54175	0.028725
3.06	21.328	1.32894	.046888	3.56	35.163	1.54609	.028439
3.07	21.542	1.33328	.046421	3.57	35.517	1.55043	.028156
3.08	21.758	1.33763	.045959	3.58	35.874	1.55477	.027876
3.09	21.977	1.34197	.045502	3.59	36.234	1.55912	.027598
3.10	22.198	1.34631	0.045049	**3.60**	36.598	1.56346	0.027324
3.11	22.421	1.35066	.044601	3.61	36.966	1.56780	.027052
3.12	22.646	1.35500	.044157	3.62	37.338	1.57215	.026783
3.13	22.874	1.35934	.043718	3.63	37.713	1.57649	.026516
3.14	23.104	1.36368	.043283	3.64	38.092	1.58083	.026252
3.15	23.336	1.36803	0.042852	**3.65**	38.475	1.58517	0.025991
3.16	23.571	1.37237	.042426	3.66	38.861	1.58952	.025733
3.17	23.807	1.36671	.042004	3.67	39.252	1.59386	.025476
3.18	24.047	1.38106	.041586	3.68	39.646	1.59820	.025223
3.19	24.288	1.38540	.041172	3.69	40.045	1.60255	.024972
3.20	24.533	1.38974	0.040764	**3.70**	40.447	1.60689	0.024724
3.21	24.779	1.39409	.040357	3.71	40.854	1.61123	.024478
3.22	25.028	1.39843	.039955	3.72	41.264	1.61558	.024234
3.23	25.280	1.40277	.039557	3.73	41.679	1.61992	.023993
3.24	25.534	1.40711	.039164	3.74	42.098	1.62426	.023754
3.25	25.790	1.41146	0.038774	**3.75**	42.521	1.62860	0.023518
3.26	26.050	1.41580	.038388	3.76	42.948	1.63295	.023284
3.27	26.311	1.42014	.038006	3.77	43.380	1.63729	.023052
3.28	26.576	1.42449	.037628	3.78	43.816	1.64163	.022823
3.29	26.843	1.42883	.037254	3.79	44.256	1.64598	.022596
3.30	27.113	1.44317	0.036883	**3.80**	44.701	1.65032	0.022371
3.31	27.385	1.43751	.036516	3.81	45.150	1.65466	.022148
3.32	27.660	1.44186	.036153	3.82	45.604	1.65900	.021928
3.33	27.938	1.44620	.035793	3.83	46.063	1.66335	.021710
3.34	28.219	1.45054	.035437	3.84	46.525	1.66769	.021494
3.35	28.503	1.45489	0.035084	**3.85**	46.993	1.67203	0.021280
3.36	28.789	1.45923	.034735	3.86	47.465	1.67638	.021068
3.37	29.079	1.46357	.034390	3.87	47.942	1.68072	.020858
3.38	29.371	1.46792	.034047	3.88	48.424	1.68506	.020651
3.39	29.666	1.47226	.033709	3.89	48.911	1.68941	.020445
3.40	29.964	1.47660	0.033373	**3.90**	49.402	1.69375	0.020242
3.41	30.265	1.48094	.033041	3.91	49.899	1.69809	.020041
3.42	30.569	1.48529	.032712	3.92	50.400	1.70243	.019840
3.43	30.877	1.48963	.032387	3.93	50.907	1.70678	.019644
3.44	31.187	1.49397	.032065	3.94	51.419	1.71112	.019448
3.45	31.500	1.49832	0.031746	**3.95**	51.935	1.71546	0.019255
3.46	31.817	1.50266	.031430	3.96	52.457	1.71981	.019063
3.47	32.137	1.50700	.031117	3.97	52.985	1.72415	.018873
3.48	32.460	1.51134	.030807	3.98	53.517	1.72849	.018686
3.49	32.786	1.51569	.030501	3.99	54.055	1.73283	.018500
3.50	33.115	1.52003	0.030197	**4.00**	54.598	1.73718	0.018316

Table 3 (*Continued*)

x	e^x	$\log_{10}(e^x)$	e^{-x}	x	e^x	$\log_{10}(e^x)$	e^{-x}
4.00	54.598	1.73718	0.018316	**4.50**	90.017	1.95433	0.011109
4.01	55.147	1.74152	.018133	4.51	90.922	1.95867	.010998
4.02	55.701	1.74586	.017953	4.52	91.836	1.96301	.010889
4.03	56.261	1.75021	.017774	4.53	92.759	1.96735	.010781
4.04	56.826	1.75455	.017597	4.54	93.691	1.97170	.010673
4.05	57.397	1.75889	0.017422	**4.55**	94.632	1.97604	0.010567
4.06	57.974	1.76324	.017249	4.56	95.583	1.98038	.010462
4.07	58.577	1.76758	.017077	4.57	96.544	1.98473	.010358
4.08	59.145	1.77192	.016907	4.58	97.514	1.98907	.010255
4.09	59.740	1.77626	.016739	4.59	98.494	1.99341	.010153
4.10	60.340	1.78061	0.016573	**4.60**	99.484	1.99775	0.010052
4.11	60.947	1.78495	.016408	4.61	100.48	2.00210	.009952
4.12	61.559	1.78929	.016245	4.62	101.49	2.00644	.009853
4.13	62.178	1.79364	.016083	4.63	102.51	2.01078	.009755
4.14	62.803	1.79798	.015923	4.64	103.54	2.01513	.009658
4.15	63.434	1.80232	0.015764	**4.65**	104.58	2.01947	0.009562
4.16	64.072	1.80667	.015608	4.66	105.64	2.02381	.009466
4.17	64.715	1.81101	.015452	4.67	106.70	2.02816	.009372
4.18	65.366	1.81535	.015299	4.68	107.77	2.03250	.009279
4.19	66.023	1.81969	.015146	4.69	108.85	2.03684	.009187
4.20	66.686	1.82404	0.014996	**4.70**	109.95	2.04118	0.009095
4.21	67.357	1.82838	.014846	4.71	111.05	2.04553	.009005
4.22	68.033	1.83272	.014699	4.72	112.17	2.04987	.008915
4.23	68.717	1.83707	.014552	4.73	113.30	2.05421	.008826
4.24	69.408	1.84141	.014408	4.74	114.43	2.05856	.008739
4.25	70.105	1.84575	0.014264	**4.75**	115.58	2.06290	0.008652
4.26	70.810	1.85009	.014122	4.76	116.75	2.06724	.008566
4.27	71.522	1.85444	.013982	4.77	117.92	2.07158	.008480
4.28	72.240	1.85878	.013843	4.78	119.10	2.07593	.008396
4.29	72.966	1.86312	.013705	4.79	120.30	2.08027	.008312
4.30	73.700	1.86747	0.013569	**4.80**	121.51	2.08461	0.008230
4.31	74.440	1.87181	.013434	4.81	122.73	2.08896	.008148
4.32	75.189	1.87615	.013300	4.82	123.97	2.09330	.008067
4.33	75.944	1.88050	.013168	4.83	125.21	2.09764	.007987
4.34	76.708	1.88484	.013037	4.84	126.47	2.10199	.007907
4.35	77.478	1.88918	0.012907	**4.85**	127.74	2.10633	0.007828
4.36	78.257	1.89352	.012778	4.86	129.02	2.11067	.007750
4.37	79.044	1.89787	.012651	4.87	130.32	2.11501	.007673
4.38	79.838	1.90221	.012525	4.88	131.63	2.11936	.007597
4.39	80.640	1.90655	.012401	4.89	132.95	2.12370	.007521
4.40	81.451	1.91090	0.012277	**4.90**	134.29	2.12804	0.007477
4.41	82.269	1.91524	.012155	4.91	135.64	2.13239	.007372
4.42	83.096	1.91958	.012034	4.92	137.00	2.13673	.007299
4.43	83.931	1.92392	.011914	4.93	138.38	2.14107	.007227
4.44	84.775	1.92827	.011796	4.94	139.77	2.14541	.007155
4.45	85.627	1.93261	0.011679	**4.95**	141.17	2.14976	0.007083
4.46	86.488	1.93695	.011562	4.96	142.59	2.15410	.007013
4.47	87.357	1.94130	.011447	4.97	144.03	2.15844	.006943
4.48	88.235	1.94564	.011333	4.98	145.47	2.16279	.006874
4.49	89.121	1.94998	.011221	4.99	146.94	2.16713	.006806
4.50	90.017	1.95433	0.011109	**5.00**	148.41	2.17147	0.006738

Table 3 (*Continued*)

x	e^x	$\log_{10}(e^x)$	e^{-x}	x	e^x	$\log_{10}(e^x)$	e^{-x}
5.00	148.41	2.17147	0.006738	**5.50**	244.69	2.38862	0.0040868
5.01	149.90	2.17582	.006671	5.55	257.24	2.41033	.0038875
5.02	151.41	2.18016	.006605	5.60	270.43	2.43205	.0036979
5.03	152.93	2.18450	.006539	5.65	284.29	2.45376	.0035175
5.04	154.47	2.18884	.006474	5.70	298.87	2.47548	.0033460
5.05	156.02	2.19319	0.006409	**5.75**	314.19	2.49719	0.0031828
5.06	157.59	2.19753	.006346	5.80	330.30	2.51891	.0030276
5.07	159.17	2.20187	.006282	5.85	347.23	2.54062	.0028799
5.08	160.77	2.20622	.006220	5.90	365.04	2.56234	.0027394
5.09	162.39	2.21056	.006158	5.95	383.75	2.58405	.0026058
5.10	164.02	2.21490	0.006097	**6.00**	403.43	2.60577	0.0024788
5.11	165.67	2.21924	.006036	6.05	424.11	2.62748	.0023579
5.12	167.34	2.22359	.005976	6.10	445.86	2.64920	.0022429
5.13	169.02	2.22793	.005917	6.15	468.72	2.67091	.0021335
5.14	170.72	2.23227	.005858	6.20	492.75	2.69263	.0020294
5.15	172.43	2.23662	0.005799	**6.25**	518.01	2.71434	0.0019305
5.16	174.16	2.24096	.005742	6.30	544.57	2.73606	.0018363
5.17	175.91	2.24530	.005685	6.35	572.49	2.75777	.0017467
5.18	177.68	2.24965	.005628	6.40	601.85	2.77948	.0016616
5.19	179.47	2.25399	.005572	6.45	632.70	2.80120	.0015805
5.20	181.27	2.25833	0.005517	**6.50**	665.14	2.82291	0.0015034
5.21	183.09	2.26267	.005462	6.55	699.24	2.84463	.0014301
5.22	184.93	2.26702	.005407	6.60	735.10	2.86634	.0013604
5.23	186.79	2.27136	.005354	6.65	772.78	2.88806	.0012940
5.24	188.67	2.27570	.005300	6.70	812.41	2.90977	.0012309
5.25	190.57	2.28005	0.005248	**6.75**	854.06	2.93149	0.0011709
5.26	192.48	2.28439	.005195	6.80	897.85	2.95320	.0011138
5.27	194.42	2.28873	.005144	6.85	943.88	2.97492	.0010595
5.28	196.37	2.29307	.005092	6.90	992.27	2.99663	.0010078
5.29	198.34	2.29742	.005042	6.95	1043.1	3.01835	.0009586
5.30	200.34	2.30176	0.004992	**7.00**	1096.6	3.04006	0.0009119
5.31	202.35	2.30610	.004942	7.05	1152.9	3.06178	.0008674
5.32	204.38	2.31045	.004893	7.10	1212.0	3.08349	.0008251
5.33	206.44	2.31479	.004844	7.15	1274.1	3.10521	.0007849
5.34	208.51	2.31913	.004796	7.20	1339.4	3.12692	.0007466
5.35	210.61	2.32348	0.004748	**7.25**	1408.1	3.14863	0.0007102
5.36	212.72	2.32782	.004701	7.30	1480.3	3.17035	.0006755
5.37	214.86	2.33216	.004654	7.35	1556.2	3.19206	.0006426
5.38	217.02	2.33650	.004608	7.40	1636.0	3.21378	.0006113
5.39	219.20	2.34085	.004562	7.45	1719.9	3.23549	.0005814
5.40	221.41	2.34519	0.004517	**7.50**	1808.0	3.25721	0.0005531
5.41	223.63	2.34953	.004472	7.55	1900.7	3.27892	.0005261
5.42	225.88	2.35388	.004427	7.60	1998.2	3.30064	.0005005
5.43	228.15	2.35822	.004383	7.65	2100.6	3.32235	.0004760
5.44	230.44	2.36256	.004339	7.70	2208.3	3.34407	.0004528
5.45	232.76	2.36690	0.004296	**7.75**	2321.6	3.36578	0.0004307
5.46	235.10	2.37125	.004254	7.80	2440.6	3.38750	.0004097
5.47	237.46	2.37559	.004211	7.85	2565.7	3.40921	.0003898
5.48	239.85	2.37993	.004169	7.90	2697.3	3.43093	.0003707
5.49	242.26	2.38428	.004128	7.95	2835.6	3.45264	.0003527
5.50	244.69	2.38862	0.004087	**8.00**	2981.0	3.47436	0.0003355

Table 3 (*Continued*)

x	e^x	$\log_{10}(e^x)$	e^{-x}	x	e^x	$\log_{10}(e^x)$	e^{-x}
8.00	2981.0	3.47436	0.0003355	**9.00**	8103.1	3.90865	0.0001234
8.05	3133.8	3.49607	.0003191	9.05	8518.5	3.93037	.0001174
8.10	3294.5	3.51779	.0003035	9.10	8955.3	3.95208	.0001117
8.15	3463.4	3.53950	.0002887	9.15	9414.4	3.97379	.0001062
8.20	3641.0	3.56121	.0002747	9.20	9897.1	3.99551	.0001010
8.25	3827.6	3.58293	0.0002613	**9.25**	10405	4.01722	0.0000961
8.30	4023.9	3.60464	.0002485	9.30	10938	4.03894	.0000914
8.35	4230.2	3.62636	.0002364	9.35	11499	4.06065	.0000870
8.40	4447.1	3.64807	.0002249	9.40	12088	4.08237	.0000827
8.45	4675.1	3.66979	.0002139	9.45	12708	4.10408	.0000787
8.50	4914.8	3.69150	0.0002036	**9.50**	13360	4.12580	0.0000749
8.55	5166.8	3.71322	.0001935	9.55	14045	4.14751	.0000712
8.60	5431.7	3.73493	.0001841	9.60	14765	4.16923	.0000677
8.65	5710.0	3.75665	.0001751	9.65	15522	4.19094	.0000644
8.70	6002.9	3.77836	.0001666	9.70	16318	4.21266	.0000613
8.75	6310.7	3.80008	0.0001585	**9.75**	17154	4.23437	0.0000583
8.80	6634.2	3.82179	.0001507	9.80	18034	4.25609	.0000555
8.85	6974.4	3.84351	.0001434	9.85	18958	4.27780	.0000527
8.90	7332.0	3.86522	.0001364	9.90	19930	4.29952	.0000502
8.95	7707.9	3.88694	.0001297	9.95	20952	4.32123	0.0000477
9.00	8103.1	3.90865	0.0001234	**10.00**	22026	4.34294	0.0000454

Table 4   *Hyperbolic functions*

x	sinh x	cosh x	tanh x
0	.00000	1.0000	.00000
0.1	.10017	1.0050	.09967
0.2	.20134	1.0201	.19738
0.3	.30452	1.0453	.29131
0.4	.41075	1.0811	.37995
0.5	.52110	1.1276	.46212
0.6	.63665	1.1855	.53705
0.7	.75858	1.2552	.60437
0.8	.88811	1.3374	.66404
0.9	1.0265	1.4331	.71630
1.0	1.1752	1.5431	.76159
1.1	1.3356	1.6685	.80050
1.2	1.5095	1.8107	.83365
1.3	1.6984	1.9709	.86172
1.4	1.9043	2.1509	.88535
1.5	2.1293	2.3524	.90515
1.6	2.3756	2.5775	.92167
1.7	2.6456	2.8283	.93541
1.8	2.9422	3.1075	.94681
1.9	3.2682	3.4177	.95624
2.0	3.6269	3.7622	.96403
2.1	4.0219	4.1443	.97045
2.2	4.4571	4.5679	.97574
2.3	4.9370	5.0372	.98010
2.4	5.4662	5.5569	.98367
2.5	6.0502	6.1323	.98661
2.6	6.6947	6.7690	.98903
2.7	7.4063	7.4735	.99101
2.8	8.1919	8.2527	.99263
2.9	9.0596	9.1146	.99396
3.0	10.018	10.068	.99505
3.1	11.076	11.122	.99595
3.2	12.246	12.287	.99668
3.3	13.538	13.575	.99728
3.4	14.965	14.999	.99777
3.5	16.543	16.573	.99818
3.6	18.285	18.313	.99851
3.7	20.211	20.236	.99878
3.8	22.339	22.362	.99900
3.9	24.691	24.711	.99918
4.0	27.290	27.308	.99933
4.1	30.162	30.178	.99945
4.2	33.336	33.351	.99955
4.3	36.843	36.857	.99963
4.4	40.719	40.732	.99970
4.5	45.003	45.014	.99975
4.6	49.737	49.747	.99980
4.7	54.969	54.978	.99983
4.8	60.751	60.759	.99986
4.9	67.141	67.149	.99989
5.0	74.203	74.210	.99991

Table 5 Trigonometric functions

Degrees	Radians	Sin	Cos	Tan	Cot		
0	0.0000	0.0000	1.0000	0.0000		1.5708	90
1	0.0175	0.0175	0.9998	0.0175	57.290	1.5533	89
2	0.0349	0.0349	0.9994	0.0349	28.636	1.5359	88
3	0.0524	0.0523	0.9986	0.0524	19.081	1.5184	87
4	0.0698	0.0698	0.9976	0.0699	14.301	1.5010	86
5	0.0873	0.0872	0.9962	0.0875	11.430	1.4835	85
6	0.1047	0.1045	0.9945	0.1051	9.5144	1.4661	84
7	0.1222	0.1219	0.9925	0.1228	8.1443	1.4486	83
8	0.1396	0.1392	0.9903	0.1405	7.1154	1.4312	82
9	0.1571	0.1564	0.9877	0.1584	6.3138	1.4137	81
10	0.1745	0.1736	0.9848	0.1763	5.6713	1.3963	80
11	0.1920	0.1908	0.9816	0.1944	5.1446	1.3788	79
12	0.2094	0.2079	0.9781	0.2126	4.7046	1.3614	78
13	0.2269	0.2250	0.9744	0.2309	4.3315	1.3439	77
14	0.2443	0.2419	0.9703	0.2493	4.0108	1.3265	76
15	0.2618	0.2588	0.9659	0.2679	3.7321	1.3090	75
16	0.2793	0.2756	0.9613	0.2867	3.4874	1.2915	74
17	0.2967	0.2924	0.9563	0.3057	3.2709	1.2741	73
18	0.3142	0.3090	0.9511	0.3249	3.0777	1.2566	72
19	0.3316	0.3256	0.9455	0.3443	2.9042	1.2392	71
20	0.3491	0.3420	0.9397	0.3640	2.7475	1.2217	70
21	0.3665	0.3584	0.9336	0.3839	2.6051	1.2043	69
22	0.3840	0.3746	0.9272	0.4040	2.4751	1.1868	68
23	0.4014	0.3907	0.9205	0.4245	2.3559	1.1694	67
24	0.4189	0.4067	0.9135	0.4452	2.2460	1.1519	66
25	0.4363	0.4226	0.9063	0.4663	2.1445	1.1345	65
26	0.4538	0.4384	0.8988	0.4877	2.0503	1.1170	64
27	0.4712	0.4540	0.8910	0.5095	1.9626	1.0996	63
28	0.4887	0.4695	0.8829	0.5317	1.8807	1.0821	62
29	0.5061	0.4848	0.8746	0.5543	1.8040	1.0647	61
30	0.5236	0.5000	0.8660	0.5774	1.7321	1.0472	60
31	0.5411	0.5150	0.8572	0.6009	1.6643	1.0297	59
32	0.5585	0.5299	0.8480	0.6249	1.6003	1.0123	58
33	0.5760	0.5446	0.8387	0.6494	1.5399	0.9948	57
34	0.5934	0.5592	0.8290	0.6745	1.4826	0.9774	56
35	0.6109	0.5736	0.8192	0.7002	1.4281	0.9599	55
36	0.6283	0.5878	0.8090	0.7265	1.3764	0.9425	54
37	0.6458	0.6018	0.7986	0.7536	1.3270	0.9250	53
38	0.6632	0.6157	0.7880	0.7813	1.2799	0.9076	52
39	0.6807	0.6293	0.7771	0.8098	1.2349	0.8901	51
40	0.6981	0.6428	0.7660	0.8391	1.1918	0.8727	50
41	0.7156	0.6561	0.7547	0.8693	1.1504	0.8552	49
42	0.7330	0.6691	0.7431	0.9004	1.1106	0.8378	48
43	0.7505	0.6820	0.7314	0.9325	1.0724	0.8203	47
44	0.7679	0.6947	0.7193	0.9657	1.0355	0.8029	46
45	0.7854	0.7071	0.7170	1.0000	1.0000	0.7854	45
		Cos	Sin	Cot	Tan	Radians	Degrees

Table 6 *Common logarithms*

N	0	1	2	3	4	5	6	7	8	9
10	0000	0043	0086	0128	0170	0212	0253	0294	0334	0374
11	0414	0453	0492	0531	0569	0607	0645	0682	0719	0755
12	0792	0828	0864	0899	0934	0969	1004	1038	1072	1106
13	1139	1173	1206	1239	1271	1303	1335	1367	1399	1430
14	1461	1492	1523	1553	1584	1614	1644	1673	1703	1732
15	1761	1790	1818	1847	1875	1903	1931	1959	1987	2014
16	2041	2068	2095	2122	2148	2175	2201	2227	2253	2279
17	2304	2330	2355	2380	2405	2430	2455	2480	2504	2529
18	2553	2577	2601	2625	2648	2672	2695	2718	2742	2765
19	2788	2810	2833	2856	2878	2900	2923	2945	2967	2989
20	3010	3032	3054	3075	3096	3118	3139	3160	3181	3201
21	3222	3243	3263	3284	3304	3324	3345	3365	3385	3404
22	3424	3444	3464	3483	3502	3522	3541	3560	3579	3598
23	3617	3636	3655	3674	3692	3711	3729	3747	3766	3784
24	3802	3820	3838	3856	3874	3892	3909	3927	3945	3962
25	3979	3997	4014	4031	4048	4065	4082	4099	4116	4133
26	4150	4166	4183	4200	4216	4232	4249	4265	4281	4298
27	4314	4330	4346	4362	4378	4393	4409	4425	4440	4456
28	4472	4487	4502	4518	4533	4548	4564	4579	4594	4609
29	4624	4639	4654	4669	4683	4698	4713	4728	4742	4757
30	4771	4786	4800	4814	4829	4843	4857	4871	4886	4900
31	4914	4928	4942	4955	4969	4983	4997	5011	5024	5038
32	5051	5065	5079	5092	5105	5119	5132	5145	5159	5172
33	5185	5198	5211	5224	5237	5250	5263	5276	5289	5302
34	5315	5328	5340	5353	5366	5378	5391	5403	5416	5428
35	5441	5453	5465	5478	5490	5502	5514	5527	5539	5551
36	5563	5575	5587	5599	5611	5623	5635	5647	5658	5670
37	5682	5694	5705	5717	5729	5740	5752	5763	5775	5786
38	5798	5809	5821	5832	5843	5855	5866	5877	5888	5899
39	5911	5922	5933	5944	5955	5966	5977	5988	5999	6010
40	6021	6031	6042	6053	6064	6075	6085	6096	6107	6117
41	6128	6138	6149	6160	6170	6180	6191	6201	6212	6222
42	6232	6243	6253	6263	6274	6284	6294	6304	6314	6325
43	6335	6345	6355	6365	6375	6385	6395	6405	6415	6425
44	6435	6444	6454	6464	6474	6484	6493	6503	6513	6522
45	6532	6542	6551	6561	6571	6580	6590	6599	6609	6618
46	6628	6637	6646	6656	6665	6675	6684	6693	6702	6712
47	6721	6730	6739	6749	6758	6767	6776	6785	6794	6803
48	6812	6821	6830	6839	6848	6857	6866	6875	6884	6893
49	6902	6911	6920	6928	6937	6946	6955	6964	6972	6981
50	6990	6998	7007	7016	7024	7033	7042	7050	7059	7067
51	7076	7084	7093	7101	7110	7118	7126	7135	7143	7152
52	7160	7168	7177	7185	7193	7202	7210	7218	7226	7235
53	7243	7251	7259	7267	7275	7284	7292	7300	7308	7316
54	7324	7332	7340	7348	7356	7364	7372	7380	7388	7396

Table 6 (*Continued*)

N	0	1	2	3	4	5	6	7	8	9
55	7404	7412	7419	7427	7435	7443	7451	7459	7466	7474
56	7482	7490	7497	7505	7513	7520	7528	7536	7543	7551
57	7559	7566	7574	7582	7589	7597	7604	7612	7619	7627
58	7634	7642	7649	7657	7664	7672	7679	7686	7694	7701
59	7709	7716	7723	7731	7738	7745	7752	7760	7767	7774
60	7782	7789	7796	7803	7810	7818	7825	7832	7839	7846
61	7853	7860	7868	7875	7882	7889	7896	7903	7910	7917
62	7924	7931	7938	7945	7952	7959	7966	7973	7980	7987
63	7993	8000	8007	8014	8021	8028	8035	8041	8048	8055
64	8062	8069	8075	8082	8089	8096	8102	8109	8116	8122
65	8129	8136	8142	8149	8156	8162	8169	8176	8182	8189
66	8195	8202	8209	8215	8222	8228	8235	8241	8248	8254
67	8261	8267	8274	8280	8287	8293	8299	8306	8312	8319
68	8325	8331	8338	8344	8351	8357	8363	8370	8376	8382
69	8388	8395	8401	8407	8414	8420	8426	8432	8439	8445
70	8451	8457	8463	8470	8476	8482	8488	8494	8500	8506
71	8513	8519	8525	8531	8537	8543	8549	8555	8561	8567
72	8573	8579	8585	8591	8597	8603	8609	8615	8621	8627
73	8633	8639	8645	8651	8657	8663	8669	8675	8681	8686
74	8692	8698	8704	8710	8716	8722	8727	8733	8739	8745
75	8751	8756	8762	8768	8774	8779	8785	8791	8797	8802
76	8808	8814	8820	8825	8831	8837	8842	8848	8854	8859
77	8865	8871	8876	8882	8887	8893	8899	8904	8910	8915
78	8921	8927	8932	8938	8943	8949	8954	8960	8965	8971
79	8976	8982	8987	8993	8998	9004	9009	9015	9020	9025
80	9031	9036	9042	9047	9053	9058	9063	9069	9074	9079
81	9085	9090	9096	9101	9106	9112	9117	9122	9128	9133
82	9138	9143	9149	9154	9159	9165	9170	9175	9180	9186
83	9191	9196	9201	9206	9212	9217	9222	9227	9232	9238
84	9243	9248	9253	9258	9263	9269	9274	9279	9284	9289
85	9294	9299	9304	9309	9315	9320	9325	9330	9335	9340
86	9345	9350	9355	9360	9365	9370	9375	9380	9385	9390
87	9395	9400	9405	9410	9415	9420	9425	9430	9435	9440
88	9445	9450	9455	9460	9465	9469	9474	9479	9484	9489
89	9494	9499	9504	9509	9513	9518	9523	9528	9533	9538
90	9542	9547	9552	9557	9562	9566	9571	9576	9581	9586
91	9590	9595	9600	9605	9609	9614	9619	9624	9628	9633
92	9638	9643	9647	9652	9657	9661	9666	9671	9675	9680
93	9685	9689	9694	9699	9703	9708	9713	9717	9722	9727
94	9731	9736	9741	9745	9750	9754	9759	9763	9768	9773
95	9777	9782	9786	9791	9795	9800	9805	9809	9814	9818
96	9823	9827	9832	9836	9841	9845	9850	9854	9859	9863
97	9868	9872	9877	9881	9886	9890	9894	9899	9903	9908
98	9912	9917	9921	9926	9930	9934	9939	9943	9948	9952
99	9956	9961	9965	9969	9974	9978	9983	9987	9991	9996

Table 7   *The Greek alphabet*

α	alpha	ν	nu
β	beta	ξ	xi
γ	gamma	o	omicron
δ	delta	π	pi
ϵ	epsilon	ρ	rho
ζ	zeta	σ	sigma
η	eta	τ	tau
θ	theta	υ	upsilon
ι	iota	ϕ	phi
κ	kappa	χ	chi
λ	lambda	ψ	psi
μ	mu	ω	omega

Answers to odd-numbered exercises

Exercises 16.1 *(Page 666)*

5. $\frac{1}{2}$ 7. divergent   9. 0   11. 1   13. divergent   15. divergent   17. $e^{1/3}$ 19. 1

Exercises 16.2 *(Page 673)*

1. increasing   3. not monotonic   5. decreasing   7. not monotonic   9. increasing   11. decreasing

Exercises 16.3 *(Page 683)*

1. $s_n = \dfrac{n}{2n+1}; \dfrac{1}{2}$ 3. $s_n = \ln\left(\dfrac{1}{n+1}\right)$; divergent   5. $s_n = \dfrac{n(n+2)}{(n+1)^2}; 1$ 7. $\displaystyle\sum_{n=1}^{+\infty} \dfrac{2}{(3n-2)(3n+1)}; \dfrac{2}{3}$ 9. $\dfrac{1}{2} - \displaystyle\sum_{n=2}^{+\infty} \dfrac{1}{2^n}; 0$

13. divergent   15. 2   17. 1   19. $\dfrac{1}{e-1}$ 21. divergent   23. $\frac{3}{2}$ 25. divergent   27. $\frac{137}{111}$ 29. $\frac{47}{101}$

Exercises 16.4 *(Page 693)*

1. convergent   3. convergent   5. divergent   7. convergent   9. divergent   11. convergent   13. divergent
15. convergent   17. convergent

Exercises 16.5 *(Page 697)*

1. divergent   3. convergent   5. convergent   7. convergent   9. convergent   11. divergent

Exercises 16.6 *(Page 706)*

1. convergent   3. convergent   5. convergent   7. convergent   9. $|R_4| < \frac{1}{5}$ 11. $|R_4| < \frac{1}{81}$ 13. 0.113   15. 0.406
17. absolutely convergent   19. absolutely convergent   21. divergent   23. absolutely convergent   25. absolutely convergent
27. divergent

Exercises 16.7 *(Page 712)*

1. $(-\infty, +\infty)$ 3. $[-\frac{1}{2}, \frac{1}{2}]$ 5. 0   7. $(-9, 9]$ 9. $(0, 2]$ 11. $\left(-\dfrac{1}{e^2}, \dfrac{1}{e^2}\right)$ 13. $[-1, 1]$ 15. $(-e, e)$ 17. $[4, 6)$

19. $[-1, 1]$

Exercises 16.8 *(Page 721)*

1. (a) $r = 1$; $[-1, 1]$; (b) $\displaystyle\sum_{n=1}^{+\infty} \dfrac{x^{n-1}}{n}$; $r = 1$; (c) $[-1, 1)$ 3. (a) $r = 1$; $[-1, 1)$; (b) $\displaystyle\sum_{n=1}^{+\infty} \sqrt{n}\, x^{n-1}$; $r = 1$; (c) $(-1, 1)$ 5. (a) $r = +\infty$; $(-\infty, +\infty)$;

(b) $\displaystyle\sum_{n=1}^{+\infty} (-1)^{n-1} \dfrac{x^{2n-2}}{(2n-2)!}$; (c) $(-\infty, +\infty)$ 7. (a) $r = 3$; $[-2, 4)$; (b) $\displaystyle\sum_{n=1}^{+\infty} \dfrac{(x-1)^{n-1}}{3^n}$; $r = 3$; (c) $(-2, 4)$ 9. $\frac{1}{2} \displaystyle\sum_{n=2}^{+\infty} n(n-1)x^{n-2}$

11. $\displaystyle\sum_{n=0}^{+\infty} (-1)^n (n+1)x^n$ 13. 0.60653   15. (a) $\displaystyle\sum_{n=0}^{+\infty} \dfrac{x^{2n+1}}{(2n+1)!}$; (b) $\displaystyle\sum_{n=0}^{+\infty} \dfrac{x^{2n}}{(2n)!}$ 17. 2   19. (a) $\displaystyle\sum_{n=0}^{+\infty} (-1)^n \dfrac{x^{n+2}}{n!}$ 21. $\displaystyle\sum_{n=0}^{+\infty} \dfrac{x^n}{n!}$

Exercises 16.9 *(Page 728)*

1. 0.4854   3. 0.7468   5. 0.2483   7. 1.3179   9. 0.2450   11. $\displaystyle\sum_{n=0}^{+\infty} \dfrac{x^{2n+1}}{2n+1}$ 15. $\displaystyle\sum_{n=0}^{+\infty} \dfrac{(-1)^n x^{2n+1}}{(2n+1)!}$; $+\infty$

Exercises 16.10   *(Page 737)*

7. $\ln 2 + \sum\limits_{n=1}^{+\infty} (-1)^{n-1} \dfrac{(x-2)^n}{n2^n}$ 9. $\sum\limits_{n=1}^{+\infty} (-1)^{n-1} \dfrac{(x-1)^n}{n}$; $R=1$ 11. $2 + \frac{1}{4}(x-4) + 2\sum\limits_{n=2}^{+\infty} (-1)^{n-1} \dfrac{1 \cdot 3 \cdot 5 \cdot \ldots \cdot (2n-3)(x-4)^n}{2 \cdot 4 \cdot 6 \cdot \ldots \cdot (2n) \cdot 4^n}$;

$R=4$ 13. $\frac{1}{2} - \frac{1}{2}\sqrt{3}(x - \frac{1}{3}\pi) - \frac{1}{4}(x - \frac{1}{3}\pi)^2 + \frac{1}{12}\sqrt{3}(x - \frac{1}{3}\pi)^3 + \frac{1}{48}(x - \frac{1}{3}\pi)^4 - \cdots$; $R = +\infty$ 15. $\frac{1}{2}\sum\limits_{n=1}^{+\infty} \dfrac{(-1)^{n-1}(2x)^{2n}}{(2n)!}$

17. (a) $x + \frac{1}{3}x^3 + \frac{2}{15}x^5$; (b) $1 + x^2 + \frac{2}{3}x^4$; (c) $\frac{1}{2}x^2 + \frac{1}{12}x^4 + \frac{1}{45}x^6$ 19. 0.5299   21. 1.97435   23. -0.2231 25. 0.0415   27. 0.0048
29. 0.2398   31. $a_4 = 3$; $a_3 = -5$; $a_2 = 2$; $a_1 = -1$; $a_0 = 6$

Exercises 16.11   *(Page 742)*

1. $1 + \sum\limits_{n=1}^{+\infty} \dfrac{(-1)^n(-1) \cdot 1 \cdot 3 \cdot \ldots \cdot (2n-3)}{2^n n!} x^n$; 1   3. $\sum\limits_{n=0}^{+\infty} \dfrac{(-1)^n x^{2n}}{2^{2n+2}}$; 2   5. $1 + \sum\limits_{n=1}^{+\infty} \dfrac{(-1)^n \cdot 1 \cdot 3 \cdot 5 \cdot \ldots \cdot (2n-1)}{2^n n!} x^{n+2}$; 1

7. $x + \sum\limits_{n=1}^{+\infty} \dfrac{(-1)^n \cdot 1 \cdot 3 \cdot 5 \cdot \ldots \cdot (2n-1)}{2^n n!(2n+1)} x^{2n+1}$ 9. 4.8989   11. 5.010   13. 0.3361   15. 0.5082

Review Exercises for Chapter 16   *(Page 742)*

1. $1, \frac{3}{2}, \frac{9}{5}, 2; 3$ 3. $0, \frac{1}{3}, \frac{4}{5}, \frac{15}{17}; 1$ 5. $1, 3, 1, 3$; no limit   7. convergent; 3   9. divergent   11. convergent; $4 + 2\sqrt{3}$
13. convergent; $\frac{1}{8}$ 15. convergent   17. divergent   19. convergent   21. divergent   23. convergent   25. divergent
27. absolutely convergent   29. conditionally convergent   31. divergent   33. absolutely convergent   35. $[-1, 1)$
37. $[-3, 3]$ 39. $x = 3$ 41. $(-7, 5)$ 43. 0.1973   45. 5.0658   47. 0.9986   49. 0.0124   51. $\sum\limits_{n=0}^{+\infty} \dfrac{(\ln a)^n}{n!} x^n$; $(-\infty, +\infty)$

53. $\frac{3}{4}\sum\limits_{n=1}^{+\infty} (-1)^{n-1} \dfrac{(3^{2n} - 1)}{(2n+1)!} x^{2n+1}$; $(-\infty, +\infty)$ 55. $\sum\limits_{n=1}^{+\infty} (-1)^n \dfrac{(3x + \pi)^{2n-1}}{(2n-1)!}$

Exercises 17.1   *(Page 750)*

1. 5   3. 2   5. $\sqrt{11}$ 7. $\langle 2, -3 \rangle$ 9. $\langle -2, -7 \rangle$ 11. $\langle 5, 6 \rangle$ 13. $\langle -4, 3 \rangle$ 15. $\langle 12, -5 \rangle$ 17. $\langle -1, 9 \rangle$ 19. $\langle 1, -5 \rangle$
21. $\langle -2, 2 \rangle$ 23. $\langle 7, 3 \rangle$ 25. $\langle -9, -4 \rangle$ 27. $\langle \sqrt{2}, \sqrt{3} \rangle$ 29. (a) $\langle 1, -2 \rangle$; (b) $\langle 1, -2 \rangle$ 31. $\langle -2, 7 \rangle$ 33. $\sqrt{74}$ 35. $\sqrt{1061}$

Exercises 17.2   *(Page 755)*

1. $6\mathbf{i} + 2\mathbf{j}$ 3. $-14\mathbf{i} + 21\mathbf{j}$ 5. $2\sqrt{10}$ 7. $5\sqrt{5}$ 9. $\dfrac{11}{\sqrt{137}}\mathbf{i} + \dfrac{4}{\sqrt{137}}\mathbf{j}$ 11. $h = 2$, $k = 3$ 13. (a) $8[(\cos \frac{2}{3}\pi)\mathbf{i} + (\sin \frac{2}{3}\pi)\mathbf{j}]$;
(b) $-\frac{1}{2}\mathbf{i} + \frac{1}{2}\sqrt{3}\mathbf{j}$ 15. (a) $2[(\cos \frac{1}{2}\pi)\mathbf{i} + (\sin \frac{1}{2}\pi)\mathbf{j}]$; (b) $\mathbf{j}$

Exercises 17.3   *(Page 762)*

1. 10   3. -1 11. $\frac{1}{10}\sqrt{2}$ 13. $-\frac{16}{65}$ 15. $10, -\frac{2}{5}$ 17. (a) 0; (b) no k 19. $\dfrac{-240 + \sqrt{85683}}{407}$ 21. $-\frac{4}{17}\sqrt{17}\mathbf{i} + \frac{1}{17}\sqrt{17}\mathbf{j}$; $\frac{4}{17}\sqrt{17}\mathbf{i}$
$-\frac{1}{17}\sqrt{17}\mathbf{j}$ 23. $-\frac{112}{17}\mathbf{i} + \frac{96}{17}\mathbf{j}$ 25. $\frac{23}{50}\sqrt{50}$ 27. (a) 24 ft-lb; (b) $24\sqrt{3}$ ft-lb

Exercises 17.4   *(Page 770)*

1. $(-\infty, 0)$ and $(0, 4]$ 3. $[-1, 1]$ 5. all real numbers not in $(-4, 3)$ 7. $\frac{4}{3}t; \frac{4}{9}$ 9. $\dfrac{1 + \ln t}{te^t(2 + t)}; \dfrac{(2 + t) - (1 + \ln t)(2 + 4t + t^2)}{t^3 e^{2t}(2 + t)^3}$

11. $-\dfrac{b}{a}\cot t; -\dfrac{b}{a^2}\csc^3 t$ 13. $(y - 1)^2 = x$ 15. $25x^2 - 9y^2 = 225$ 17. $y = 1$; $x = -1$ 19. $2y + 5\sqrt{3}x = 20$ 21. $\dfrac{dy}{dx} = 0$;
$\dfrac{d^2y}{dx^2} = -\dfrac{1}{4a}$; $\dfrac{d^3y}{dx^3} = 0$ 25. $x^{2/3} + y^{2/3} = a^{2/3}$ 29. $3\pi a^2$

Exercises 17.5   *(Page 778)*

1. $4\mathbf{j}$ 3. $2\mathbf{i}$ 5. $\mathbf{R}'(t) = 2t\mathbf{i} + 2\mathbf{j}$; $\mathbf{R}''(t) = 2\mathbf{i}$ 7. $\mathbf{R}'(t) = 2e^{2t}\mathbf{i} + t^{-1}\mathbf{j}$; $\mathbf{R}''(t) = 4e^{2t}\mathbf{i} - t^{-2}\mathbf{j}$ 9. $\mathbf{R}'(t) = (1 + t^2)^{-1}\mathbf{i} + (\ln 2)2^t\mathbf{j}$;
$\mathbf{R}''(t) = -2t(1 + t^2)^{-2}\mathbf{i} + (\ln 2)^2 2^t\mathbf{j}$ 11. $(2t - 3)(2t^2 - 6t + 5)^{-1/2}$ 13. $20t$ 15. $8e^{4t} - 8e^{-4t}$ 19. $\ln|\sec t|\mathbf{i} - \ln|t|\mathbf{j} + \mathbf{C}$
21. $(t \ln t - t)\mathbf{i} + \frac{1}{3}t^3\mathbf{j} + \mathbf{C}$ 23. $\frac{1}{2}(-\pi + t - \frac{1}{2}\sin 2t)\mathbf{i} + (-\pi + t + \frac{1}{2}\sin 2t)\mathbf{j}$ 25. $x^2 + y^2 = 1$; 0

Exercises 17.6   (*Page 785*)

1. $1 + \frac{1}{2}\sqrt{2}\ln(1 + \sqrt{2})$ 3. $\frac{2}{27}[(40)^{3/2} - (13)^{3/2}]$ 5. $6a$ 7. $a[\ln \cosh 2 + \ln \cosh 1]$ 9. $2\pi a$ 11. $2\pi a$ 13. 12
15. $\frac{1}{2}a(\theta_1 - \frac{3}{2}\sin \frac{2}{3}\theta_1)$

Exercises 17.7   (*Page 791*)

1. (a) $2t\mathbf{i} + \mathbf{j}$; (b) $2\mathbf{i}$; (c) $\sqrt{37}$; (d) 2   3. (a) $\mathbf{i} + \tan t\mathbf{j}$; (b) $\sec^2 t\mathbf{j}$; (c) $\sqrt{2}$; (d) 2   5. (a) $\cos t\mathbf{i} + \sec^2 t\mathbf{j}$; (b) $-\sin t\mathbf{i} + 2\sec^2 t \tan t\mathbf{j}$;
(c) $\frac{1}{6}\sqrt{91}$; (d) $\frac{1}{18}\sqrt{849}$ 7. (a) $2\mathbf{i} + 6\mathbf{j}$; (b) $2\mathbf{j}$; (c) $2\sqrt{10}$; (d) 2   9. (a) $3\mathbf{j}$; (b) $-4\mathbf{i}$; (c) 3; (d) 4   11. (a) $\mathbf{i} + \sqrt{3}\mathbf{j}$; (b) $-\sqrt{3}\mathbf{i} + \mathbf{j}$; (c) 2; (d) 2
13. $\frac{2t - 3}{t - 1}\mathbf{i} + \frac{4 - 2t - t^2}{2}\mathbf{j}$ 15. (a) $\frac{390{,}625}{2}$ ft; (b) $\frac{390{,}625}{8}$ ft; (c) $1250\sqrt{2}\mathbf{i} - 1250\sqrt{2}\mathbf{j}$ 17. $(25 + \sqrt{631})$ sec; $(20{,}000\sqrt{3} + 800\sqrt{1893})$ ft
19. $40° 8'$ 21. 283 ft/sec

Exercises 17.8   (*Page 796*)

1. $\mathbf{T}(t) = \frac{t^2 - 1}{t^2 + 1}\mathbf{i} + \frac{2t}{t^2 + 1}\mathbf{j}$; $\mathbf{N}(t) = \frac{2t}{t^2 + 1}\mathbf{i} + \frac{1 - t^2}{t^2 + 1}\mathbf{j}$ 3. $\mathbf{T}(t) = \frac{e^{2t}}{\sqrt{e^{4t} + 1}}\mathbf{i} - \frac{1}{\sqrt{e^{4t} + 1}}\mathbf{j}$; $\mathbf{N}(t) = \frac{1}{\sqrt{e^{4t} + 1}}\mathbf{i} + \frac{e^{2t}}{\sqrt{e^{4t} + 1}}\mathbf{j}$
5. $\mathbf{T}(t) = -\sin kt\mathbf{i} + \cos kt\mathbf{j}$; $\mathbf{N}(t) = -\cos kt\mathbf{i} - \sin kt\mathbf{j}$ 7. $\mathbf{T}(t) = -(1 + \cot^4 t)^{-1/2}\mathbf{i} + (1 + \tan^4 t)^{-1/2}\mathbf{j}$;
$\mathbf{N}(t) = \frac{-\cos^2 t}{\sqrt{\sin^4 t + \cos^4 t}}\mathbf{i} - \frac{\sin^2 t}{\sqrt{\sin^4 t + \cos^4 t}}\mathbf{j}$ 9. $\frac{27}{185}\sqrt{37}$ 13. $x = 2 + \cos s$; $y = 3 + \sin s$ 15. $x = a\left(\frac{3a - 2s}{3a}\right)^{3/2}$
$y = a\left(\frac{2s}{3a}\right)^{3/2}$

Exercises 17.9   (*Page 803*)

1. $\frac{1}{8}\sqrt{2}$ 3. $\frac{1}{4}\sqrt{2}$ 5. $\frac{\sqrt{2}|1 - t^2|^3}{(1 + 6t^2 + t^4)^{3/2}}$; $\sqrt{2}$ 7. $\frac{1}{2}$ 9. $\frac{1}{4}\sqrt{2}$ 11. $\frac{4}{49}\sqrt{7}$ 13. $\frac{(2 - x^2)^{3/2}}{|x|}$ 15. $\frac{2(x + y)^{3/2}}{a^{1/2}}$ 17. $4|a \sin \frac{1}{2}t|$
21. $(3, 9)$ 23. $(-3, -1)$ 25. $\frac{23}{98}\sqrt{7}$ 27. $\frac{1}{16|a|}$ 31. $(0, -\frac{1}{2})$; 2   33. $\left(3x + 2p, -\frac{y^3}{4p^2}\right)$ 35. $\left(\frac{a^2 - b^2}{a}\cos^3 t, \frac{b^2 - a^2}{b}\sin^3 t\right)$

Exercises 17.10   (*Page 807*)

1. $\mathbf{V}(t) = 2\mathbf{i} + 2t\mathbf{j}$; $\mathbf{A}(t) = 2\mathbf{j}$; $\mathbf{T}(t) = \frac{1}{\sqrt{1 + t^2}}\mathbf{i} + \frac{t}{\sqrt{1 + t^2}}\mathbf{j}$; $\mathbf{N}(t) = \frac{-t}{\sqrt{1 + t^2}}\mathbf{i} + \frac{1}{\sqrt{1 + t^2}}\mathbf{j}$; $|\mathbf{V}(t)| = 2\sqrt{1 + t^2}$; $A_T(t) = \frac{2t}{\sqrt{1 + t^2}}$;
$A_N(t) = \frac{2}{\sqrt{1 + t^2}}$; $K(t) = \frac{1}{2(1 + t^2)^{3/2}}$; $\mathbf{V}(2) = 2\mathbf{i} + 4\mathbf{j}$; $\mathbf{T}(2) = \frac{1}{\sqrt{5}}\mathbf{i} + \frac{2}{\sqrt{5}}\mathbf{j}$; $\mathbf{A}(2) = 2\mathbf{j}$; $\mathbf{N}(2) = \frac{-2}{\sqrt{5}}\mathbf{i} + \frac{1}{\sqrt{5}}\mathbf{j}$; $|\mathbf{V}(2)| = 2\sqrt{5}$; $A_T(2) = \frac{4}{\sqrt{5}}$;
$A_N(2) = \frac{2}{\sqrt{5}}$; $K(2) = \frac{1}{10\sqrt{5}}$ 3. $\mathbf{V}(t) = -15 \sin 3t\mathbf{i} + 15 \cos 3t\mathbf{j}$; $\mathbf{A}(t) = -45 \cos 3t\mathbf{i} - 45 \sin 3t\mathbf{j}$; $\mathbf{T}(t) = -\sin 3t\mathbf{i} + \cos 3t\mathbf{j}$;
$\mathbf{N}(t) = -\cos 3t\mathbf{i} - \sin 3t\mathbf{j}$; $|\mathbf{V}(t)| = 15$; $A_T(t) = 0$; $A_N(t) = 45$; $K(t) = \frac{1}{5}$; $\mathbf{V}(\frac{1}{3}\pi) = -15\mathbf{j}$; $\mathbf{A}(\frac{1}{3}\pi) = 45\mathbf{i}$; $\mathbf{T}(\frac{1}{3}\pi) = -\mathbf{j}$; $\mathbf{N}(\frac{1}{3}\pi) = \mathbf{i}$; $|\mathbf{V}(\frac{1}{3}\pi)| = 15$
5. $\mathbf{V}(t) = e^t\mathbf{i} - e^{-t}\mathbf{j}$; $\mathbf{A}(t) = e^t\mathbf{i} + e^{-t}\mathbf{j}$; $\mathbf{T}(t) = \frac{e^{2t}}{\sqrt{e^{4t} + 1}}\mathbf{i} - \frac{1}{\sqrt{e^{4t} + 1}}\mathbf{j}$; $\mathbf{N}(t) = \frac{1}{\sqrt{e^{4t} + 1}}\mathbf{i} + \frac{e^{2t}}{\sqrt{e^{4t} + 1}}\mathbf{j}$; $|\mathbf{V}(t)| = \frac{\sqrt{e^{4t} + 1}}{e^t}$; $A_T(t) = \frac{e^{4t} - 1}{e^t\sqrt{e^{4t} + 1}}$;
$A_N(t) = \frac{2e^t}{\sqrt{e^{4t} + 1}}$; $K(t) = \frac{2e^{3t}}{(e^{4t} + 1)^{3/2}}$; $\mathbf{V}(0) = \mathbf{i} - \mathbf{j}$; $\mathbf{A}(0) = \mathbf{i} + \mathbf{j}$; $\mathbf{T}(0) = \frac{1}{\sqrt{2}}\mathbf{i} - \frac{1}{\sqrt{2}}\mathbf{j}$; $\mathbf{N}(0) = \frac{1}{\sqrt{2}}\mathbf{i} + \frac{1}{\sqrt{2}}\mathbf{j}$; $|\mathbf{V}(0)| = \sqrt{2}$; $A_T(0) = 0$;
$A_N(0) = \sqrt{2}$; $K(0) = \frac{1}{\sqrt{2}}$ 7. $\mathbf{R} = 2\mathbf{i} + 4\mathbf{j}$; if k = constant speed, $\mathbf{V} = \frac{k}{\sqrt{2}}\mathbf{i} + \frac{k}{\sqrt{2}}\mathbf{j}$; $\mathbf{A} = \frac{k^2}{16}\mathbf{i} - \frac{k^2}{16}\mathbf{j}$; $\mathbf{T} = \frac{1}{\sqrt{2}}\mathbf{i} + \frac{1}{\sqrt{2}}\mathbf{j}$; $\mathbf{N} = \frac{1}{\sqrt{2}}\mathbf{i} - \frac{1}{\sqrt{2}}\mathbf{j}$;
$A_T = 0$; $A_N = \frac{k^2\sqrt{2}}{16}$

Review Exercises for Chapter 17   (*Page 807*)

1. $-25\mathbf{i} + 63\mathbf{j}$ 3. $-22\mathbf{i} + 50\mathbf{j}$ 5. 92   7. $\frac{9}{\sqrt{106}}\mathbf{i} - \frac{5}{\sqrt{106}}\mathbf{j}$ 9. $h = -\frac{1}{2}$; $k = \frac{1}{2}$ 11. $\frac{-38}{\sqrt{50}}$ 13. (a) all real numbers in $[0, +\infty)$
except $t = 1$; (b) $\frac{1}{2}\mathbf{i} + \frac{1}{2}\mathbf{j}$; (c) $\frac{-1}{(t + 1)^2}\mathbf{i} + \frac{2t^{1/2} - t - 1}{2t^{1/2}(t - 1)^2}\mathbf{j}$ 15. $x = 12$; $y = 16$; $y = -16$ 17. $\frac{3}{2}\sqrt{37} + \frac{1}{4}\ln(6 + \sqrt{37})$ 23. $|at|$

25. $\dfrac{dy}{dx} = -\tan t;\ \dfrac{d^2y}{dx^2} = \dfrac{1}{3a}\sec^4 t\csc t$ 27. $A_T = \dfrac{-8+4t}{\sqrt{25-16t+4t^2}};\ A_N = \dfrac{6}{\sqrt{25-16t+4t^2}}$ 29. $\mathbf{T}(t) = \dfrac{e^t - e^{-t}}{e^t + e^{-t}}\mathbf{i} + \dfrac{2}{e^t + e^{-t}}\mathbf{j}$;

$\mathbf{N}(t) = \dfrac{2}{e^t + e^{-t}}\mathbf{i} + \dfrac{e^{-t}+e^t}{e^t + e^{-t}}\mathbf{j}$ 31. $x = 2(3s + 17\sqrt{17})^{2/3} - 34;\ y = \frac{1}{3}\{(3s + 17\sqrt{17})^{2/3} - 16\}^{3/2}$ 33. $h = \frac{1}{64}(v_0\sin\alpha)^2$

37. $\mathbf{V}(t) = 2\sinh 2t\mathbf{i} + 2\cosh 2t\mathbf{j};\ \mathbf{A}(t) = 4\cosh 2t\mathbf{i} + 4\sinh 2t\mathbf{j};\ |\mathbf{V}(t)| = 2\sqrt{\cosh 4t};\ A_T(t) = \dfrac{4\sinh 4t}{\sqrt{\cosh 4t}};\ A_N(t) = \dfrac{4}{\sqrt{\cosh 4t}}$

Exercises 18.1   (Page 817)

1. (b) $(7,2,0)$, $(0,0,3)$, $(0,2,0)$, $(0,2,3)$, $(7,0,3)$, $(7,0,0)$; (c) $\sqrt{62}$ 3. (b) $(2,1,2)$, $(-1,3,2)$, $(-1,1,5)$, $(2,3,2)$, $(-1,3,5)$, $(2,1,5)$; (c) $\sqrt{22}$ 5. (b) $3\sqrt{77}$; (c) $(0,0,0)$, $(15,18,12)$, $(15,0,0)$, $(15,18,0)$, $(0,18,0)$, $(0,18,12)$, $(0,0,12)$, $(15,0,12)$
7. (a) $\frac{13}{2}$; (b) $(\frac{5}{4},-1,2)$ 9. (a) $\frac{23}{2}$; (b) $(\frac{3}{2},\frac{1}{4},\frac{1}{2})$ 11. $(\pm 4\sqrt{6},4,2)$ 17. sphere with center at $(4,-2,-1)$ and $r = 5$ 19. the
point $(0,0,3)$ 21. the empty set   23. $x^2 + (y-1)^2 + (z+4)^2 = r^2,\ |r| > 0$

Exercises 18.2   (Page 824)

7. $\langle 21,-13,-2\rangle$ 9. $\langle -25,-26,5\rangle$ 11. $7\sqrt{59} - 5\sqrt{41}$ 13. $\langle -19,-16,-1\rangle$ 15. $\langle -6\sqrt{91},-8\sqrt{91},-2\sqrt{91}\rangle$ 17. $a = b = 0$
19. $\dfrac{4}{\sqrt{89}};\dfrac{3}{\sqrt{89}};\dfrac{8}{\sqrt{89}}$ 21. $-\dfrac{6}{\sqrt{86}};-\dfrac{1}{\sqrt{86}};-\dfrac{7}{\sqrt{86}}$ 23. $\langle\frac{13}{3},0,-\frac{4}{3}\rangle$ 25. $7(-\frac{6}{7}\mathbf{i}+\frac{2}{7}\mathbf{j}+\frac{3}{7}\mathbf{k})$ 27. $\sqrt{14}\left(-\dfrac{2}{\sqrt{14}}\mathbf{i}+\dfrac{1}{\sqrt{14}}\mathbf{j}-\dfrac{3}{\sqrt{14}}\mathbf{k}\right)$
29. $\cos^{-1}\dfrac{1}{\sqrt{3}}$ or $\cos^{-1}\left(-\dfrac{1}{\sqrt{3}}\right)$ 31. $\langle\frac{1}{9},\frac{8}{9},\frac{4}{9}\rangle$ 33. (c) $r = 8,\ s = -7,\ t = 5$

Exercises 18.3   (Page 828)

5. -44 7. -468 9. $\langle -84,198,124\rangle$ 11. $-\frac{13}{54}\sqrt{6}$ 13. (a) -3; (b) $\langle 2,1,-2\rangle$ 19. $\frac{1}{11}\sqrt{4422}$ 21. $\frac{7}{2}\sqrt{3}$ 23. $\frac{5}{3}\sqrt{6}$ ft-lb
25. $\frac{2}{5}$

Exercises 18.4   (Page 835)

1. $x + 2y - 3z + 1 = 0$ 3. $x - 3y - 4z - 3 = 0$ 5. $3x + 2y + 6z = 23$ 7. $\langle\frac{2}{3},-\frac{1}{3},\frac{2}{3}\rangle;\langle-\frac{2}{3},\frac{1}{3},-\frac{2}{3}\rangle$ 9. $\langle\frac{4}{13},\frac{3}{13},-\frac{12}{13}\rangle;\langle-\frac{4}{13},-\frac{3}{13},\frac{12}{13}\rangle$
11. $\left\langle\dfrac{3}{\sqrt{13}},0,\dfrac{2}{\sqrt{13}}\right\rangle;\left\langle-\dfrac{3}{\sqrt{13}},0,-\dfrac{2}{\sqrt{13}}\right\rangle$ 13. $5x - 3y + 7z + 14 = 0$ 15. $2x - y - z + 1 = 0$ 17. $4y - 3z - 1 = 0$ and $z = 1$
19. $-\frac{16}{45}$ 21. $\frac{16}{45}\sqrt{6}$ 23. $\frac{3}{2}$

Exercises 18.5   (Page 840)

1. $x = 1 + 4t,\ y = 2 - 3t,\ z = 1;\ \dfrac{x-1}{4} = \dfrac{y-2}{-3},\ z = 1$ 3. $x = 4 + t,\ y = -5 + 3t,\ z = 20 - 6t;\ \dfrac{x-4}{1} = \dfrac{y+5}{3} = \dfrac{z-20}{-6}$ 5. $\dfrac{x}{13} = \dfrac{y}{-12} = \dfrac{z}{-8}$
9. $8x - y - 66 = 0;\ 13x - 5z - 102 = 0;\ 13y - 40z + 42 = 0$ 11. $4x + y + 3 = 0;\ 3x - z + 4 = 0;\ 3y + 4z - 7 = 0$ 13. $\frac{5}{18}\sqrt{6}$
15. $4x + 7y - 3z + 7 = 0$ 17. $4x + 2y - 3z + 5 = 0$ 19. $\dfrac{x-3}{1} = \dfrac{y-6}{2} = \dfrac{z-4}{1}$ 21. $\frac{2}{5}\sqrt{70}$

Exercises 18.6   (Page 851)

1. $\langle 7,13,-11\rangle$ 3. -490 11. $\langle 9,-1,-23\rangle$ 19. $\frac{2}{3}\sqrt{2}$ 21. $\sqrt{89}$ 23. $9\sqrt{29}$ 27. $\dfrac{1}{\sqrt{3}}(\mathbf{i}+\mathbf{j}-\mathbf{k})$ 29. 20
31. $5x - 2y + 7z = 0$ 33. $\dfrac{38}{3\sqrt{78}}$

Exercises 18.7   (Page 857)

9. $x^2 + z^2 = 4y$ 11. $x^2 + 4y^2 + 4z^2 = 16$ 13. $y^2 + z^2 = \sin^2 x$ 15. $x^2 - z^2 = 4;\ z$ axis   17. $z = \sqrt{|y|};\ y$ axis

Exercises 18.8   (Page 864)

1. ellipsoid   3. elliptic hyperboloid of one sheet   5. elliptic cone   7. elliptic paraboloid   9. hyperbolic paraboloid
11. elliptic hyperboloid of two sheets   13. (a) $1 < |k| < \sqrt{2}$; (b) $|k| < 1$.   15. $\frac{96}{25}\pi$ 17. $\frac{4}{3}\pi abc$

Exercises 18.9   (*Page 871*)

1. $T(t) = (5 + 9t^4)^{-1/2}(i - 3t^2j - 2k)$ 3. $T(t) = \frac{1}{3}\sqrt{3}[(\cos t - \sin t)i + (\cos t + \sin t)j + k]$ 5. $\sqrt{21} + \frac{3}{2} + \frac{5}{4}\ln(4 + \sqrt{21})$

7. $\sqrt{3}(e^3 - 1)$ 11. $R(t) = ti + e^t j + te^t k$ 13. $T(1) = \frac{1}{14}\sqrt{14}i + \frac{1}{7}\sqrt{14}j + \frac{3}{14}\sqrt{14}k$; $N(1) = -\frac{11}{266}\sqrt{266}i - \frac{1}{133}\sqrt{266}j + \frac{9}{266}\sqrt{266}k$;

$B(1) = \dfrac{\sqrt{19}}{19}(3i - 3j + k); K(1) = \frac{1}{98}\sqrt{266}$ 15. $T(-1) = \frac{1}{3}(i + 2j - 2k); N(-1) = \frac{2}{15}\sqrt{5}i - \frac{1}{3}\sqrt{5}j - \frac{4}{15}\sqrt{5}k$;

$B(-1) = -\frac{2}{3}\sqrt{5}i - \frac{1}{3}\sqrt{5}k; K(-1) = \frac{2}{27}\sqrt{5}$ 17. $T(0) = \frac{1}{3}\sqrt{3}(i + j + k); N(0) = -\frac{1}{2}\sqrt{2}(i - j); B(0) = -\frac{1}{6}\sqrt{6}(i + j - 2k); K(0) = \frac{1}{3}\sqrt{2}$

19. $V(\frac{1}{2}\pi) = -ai + k; A(\frac{1}{2}\pi) = -aj; |V(\frac{1}{2}\pi)| = \sqrt{a^2 + 1}$ 21. $V(1) = 2e^2i - 2e^{-2}j + 3e^2k; A(1) = 4e^2i + 4e^{-2}j + 8e^2k$;

$|V(1)| = \sqrt{13e^4 + 4e^{-4}}$ 27. 2

Exercises 18.10   (*Page 876*)

1. (a) $(0, 3, 5)$; (b) $(-\frac{7}{2}, \frac{7}{2}\sqrt{3}, -4)$; (c) $(\cos 1, \sin 1, 1)$ 3. (a) $(\sqrt{6}, \sqrt{2}, 2\sqrt{2})$; (b) $(0, 2\sqrt{3}, 2)$; (c) $(\frac{1}{2}\sqrt{3}, \frac{3}{2}, -\sqrt{3})$

5. (a) $(2, \frac{2}{3}\pi, -2\sqrt{3})$; (b) $(0, \frac{3}{4}\pi, -\sqrt{2})$; (c) $(\sqrt{6}, \frac{1}{3}\pi, \sqrt{6})$ 7. ellipsoid; $r^2 + 4z^2 = 16$ 9. elliptic cone; $r^2 \cos 2\theta = 3z^2$ 11. sphere;

$\rho^2 - 9\rho \cos \phi = 0$ 13. right circular cylinder; $\rho^2 \sin^2 \phi = 9$ 15. (a) right circular cylinder; $x^2 + y^2 = 16$; (b) plane through z axis;

$y = x$ 17. $x^2 - y^2 = z^3$ 19. (a) sphere; $x^2 + y^2 + z^2 = 81$; (b) plane through z axis; $x = y$; (c) cone with vertex at origin, $z = \sqrt{x^2 + y^2}$

21. $x\sqrt{x^2 + y^2 + z^2} = 2y$ 25. $2\pi\sqrt{a^2 + 1}$

Review Exercises for Chapter 18   (*Page 878*)

3. the x axis   5. the circle in the xz plane with center at the origin and radius 2   7. the plane perpendicular to the xy plane and intersecting the xy plane in the line $y = x$ 9. the solid of revolution generated by revolving $y^2 = 9z$ about the z axis   11. the solid of revolution generated by revolving $y = x$ about the x axis   13. $i + 26j - 16k$ 15. -3 17. $7\sqrt{1270}$ 19. 16

21. $\langle 60, -40, 80\rangle$ 23. 295   25. $(x + 2)^2 + (y + 1)^2 + (z - 3)^2 = 17$ 27. 3   29. $\frac{47}{10}\sqrt{2}$ 31. $x - 6y - 10z + 23 = 0$ 33. 3

35. $\frac{1}{3}\sqrt{3}$ 37. $\dfrac{x}{4} = \dfrac{y}{-3} = \dfrac{z}{1}; x = 4t, y = -3t, z = t$ 39. 24   41. $V(\frac{1}{2}\pi) = -\frac{1}{2}\pi i + j + k; A(\frac{1}{2}\pi) = -2i - \frac{1}{2}\pi j; |V(\frac{1}{2}\pi)| = \frac{1}{2}\sqrt{8 + \pi^2}$

43. (a) $z = r^2(1 + \sin 2\theta) + 1$; (b) $r^2(25 \cos^2 \theta + 4 \sin^2 \theta) = 100$

Exercises 19.1   (*Page 887*)

1. (a) $-\dfrac{1}{7}$; (b) $\dfrac{x^2 + y^2}{x^2 - y^2}$; (c) $\dfrac{x^2 + 2xy + y^2}{x^2 - 2xy + y^2}$; (d) 0; (e) the set of all points (x, y) in R^2 except those on the line $x = y$; (f) $(-\infty, +\infty)$

3. domain: set of all points (x, y) in R^2 interior to and on the circumference of the circle $x^2 + y^2 = 25$ except those on the line $x = 0$; range: $(-\infty, +\infty)$ 5. domain: set of all points (x, y) in R^2 interior to the circle $x^2 + y^2 = 25$ and all points on the y axis except $(0, 5)$ and $(0, -5)$; range: $(-\infty, +\infty)$ 7. domain: set of all points (x, y) in R^2 except those on the line $x = y$; range: $(-\infty, +\infty)$

9. domain: set of all points (x, y) in R^2 except those on the x axis; range: $(-\infty, +\infty)$ 11. domain: set of all points (x, y) in R^2 for which $xy > 1$; range: $(-\infty, +\infty)$ 13. domain: set of all points (x, y, z) in R^3 for which $|x| \le 1$ and $|y| \le 1$; range: $(-\pi, 2\pi)$

15. domain: set of all points (x, y) in R^2; range: $[0, +\infty)$ 17. domain: set of all points (x, y) in R^2; range: $(-\infty, 16]$ 19. domain: set of all points (x, y) in R^2 for which $x + y^2 \le 10$; range: $[0, +\infty)$ 27. $h(x, y) = \sin^{-1}\sqrt{1 - x^2 - y^2}$; domain: set of all points (x, y) in R^2 interior to and on the circle $x^2 + y^2 = 1$ 29. (a) 2; (b) 6; (c) $\sqrt{x - y^2}$; (d) $|x - y|$; (e) $|x - y|$

Exercises 19.2   *Page 899*)

1. $\delta = \frac{1}{4}\epsilon$ 3. $\delta = \min(1, \frac{1}{6}\epsilon)$ 5. $\delta = \min(1, \frac{1}{8}\epsilon)$ 17. 0   19. 2   21. $\frac{1}{4}\pi$ 23. $\frac{1}{2}$ 25. limit exists and equals 0   27. limit does not exist   29. limit exists and equals 0

Exercises 19.3   (*Page 904*)

1. continuous at every point in R^2 3. continuous at every point $(x, y) \ne (0, 0)$ in R^2 5. continuous at every point in R^2 9. all points (x, y) in R^2 which are interior to the circle $x^2 + y^2 = 16$ 11. all points (x, y) in R^2 which are exterior to the ellipse $4x^2 + 9y^2 = 36$ 13. all points (x, y) in R^2 which are in either the first or third quadrant   15. all points (x, y) in R^2 for which $|xy| \ge 1$ 17. all points in R^2 19. removable; $f(0, 0) = 0$ 21. essential   23. continuous at every point (x, y, z) in R^3 for which $x^2 + y^2 + z^2 > 1$ 25. continuous at all points in R^3

Exercises 19.4 (*Page 912*)

1. 6   3. $3x - 2y$ 5. $\dfrac{x}{\sqrt{x^2 + y^2}}$ 7. $x^2 - 6xy + 2z$ 9. $xy + yt + zt$ 11. 4   13. $\dfrac{x}{\sqrt{x^2 + y^2}}$ 15. $-2 \sin 3\theta \sin 2\phi$

17. $\dfrac{e^{y/x}}{xy}\left(y \ln \dfrac{x^2}{y} - x\right)$ 19. $\dfrac{-z}{(x^2 + y^2 + z^2)^{3/2}}$ 21. $4xy + \dfrac{1}{z}$ 23. $xze^{xyz} + \dfrac{3xz^2}{z^4 + 9x^2y^2}$ 25. $-\ln \sin x; \ln \sin y$ 29. (a) 1;

(b) 1   31. (a) -2; (b) 0   33. 4   35. -4 deg/ft; -8 deg/ft   37. (a) $\dfrac{100}{i^2}\left[\dfrac{9i + 1}{(1 + i)^9} - 1\right]$; (b) $\dfrac{1}{0.0036}\left[\dfrac{1.54}{(1.06)^9} - 1\right] \approx -24.4$;

(c) $\dfrac{5000 \ln 1.06}{3(1.06)^t}$; (d) $-\dfrac{5000 \ln 1.06}{3(1.06)^8} \approx -61$

Exercises 19.5 (*Page 924*)

1. (a) 0.5411; (b) 0.54   3. (a) 0.2141; (b) 0.214   5. (a) $2(x_0y_0 - y_0)\ \Delta x + (x_0^2 - 2x_0)\ \Delta y + (y_0\ \Delta x + \Delta x\ \Delta y)\ \Delta x + 2(x_0\ \Delta x - \Delta x)\ \Delta y$;

(b) $\epsilon_1 = y_0\ \Delta x + \Delta x\ \Delta y$; $\epsilon_2 = 2(x_0\ \Delta x - \Delta x)$ 7. (a) $\dfrac{2x_0y_0\ \Delta x + y_0(\Delta x)^2 - x_0^2\ \Delta y}{y_0^2 + y_0\ \Delta y}$; (b) $\epsilon_1 = \dfrac{y_0^2\ \Delta x}{y_0^3 + y_0^2\ \Delta y}$; $\epsilon_2 = \dfrac{x_0^2\ \Delta y - 2x_0y_0\ \Delta x}{y_0^3 + y_0^2\ \Delta y}$

15. $\xi_1 = \frac{1}{3}\sqrt{156}$ 17. $\xi_2 = \sqrt{5} - 1$ 21. (a) $(y_0 - z_0)\ \Delta x + x_0\ \Delta y + (2z_0 - x_0)\ \Delta z - \Delta z\ \Delta x + \Delta x\ \Delta y + \Delta z\ \Delta z$; (b) $\epsilon_1 = -\Delta z$, $\epsilon_2 = \Delta x$,

$\epsilon_3 = \Delta z$ 25. 0.14 in.; 1.4%   27. $\frac{13}{1600}$; 0.325%   29. \$1200

31. $D_1 f(x, y) = \begin{cases} 2x \sin \dfrac{1}{\sqrt{x^2 + y^2}} - \dfrac{x}{\sqrt{x^2 + y^2}} \cos \dfrac{1}{\sqrt{x^2 + y^2}} & \text{if } (x, y) \neq (0, 0) \\ 0 & \text{if } xy = (0, 0) \end{cases}$

$D_2 f(x, y) = \begin{cases} 2y \sin \dfrac{1}{\sqrt{x^2 + y^2}} - \dfrac{y}{\sqrt{x^2 + y^2}} \cos \dfrac{1}{\sqrt{x^2 + y^2}} & \text{if } (x, y) \neq (0, 0) \\ 0 & \text{if } (x, y) = (0, 0) \end{cases}$

Exercises 19.6 (*Page 932*)

1. $\dfrac{\partial u}{\partial r}$: (a) $6x - 2y$; (b) $16r - 10s$; $\dfrac{\partial u}{\partial s}$: (a) $-2x - 4y$; (b) $-10r - 6s$ 3. $\dfrac{\partial u}{\partial r}$: (a) $\dfrac{2e^{y/x}}{x^2}(2x \sin t - y \cos t)$; (b) 0;

$\dfrac{\partial u}{\partial s}$: (a) $\dfrac{2re^{y/x}}{x^2}(y \sin t + 2x \cos t)$; (b) $2e^{2\tan t} \sec^2 t$ 5. $\dfrac{\partial u}{\partial r} = \dfrac{6re^s + s \cos rs}{\sqrt{1 - (3x + y)^2}}$; $\dfrac{\partial u}{\partial s} = \dfrac{3r^2e^s + r \cos rs}{\sqrt{1 - (3x + y)^2}}$ 7. $\dfrac{\partial u}{\partial r} = \dfrac{6s}{x^2} \sinh \dfrac{y}{x}(xe^r - ry)$;

$\dfrac{\partial u}{\partial s} = \dfrac{3}{x^2} \sinh \dfrac{y}{x}(2xe^r - yr^2) = 0$ 9. $\dfrac{\partial u}{\partial r} = 2x \sin \phi \cos \theta + 2y \sin \phi \sin \theta + 2z \cos \phi$; $\dfrac{\partial u}{\partial \phi} = 2xr \cos \phi \cos \theta + 2yr \cos \phi \sin \theta - 2zr \sin \phi$;

$\dfrac{\partial u}{\partial \theta} = -2xr \sin \phi \sin \theta + 2yr \sin \phi \cos \theta$ 11. (a) $e^x(\cos t - y \sin t) + e^y(x \cos t - \sin t)$; (b) $e^{\cos t}(\cos t - \sin^2 t) + e^{\sin t}(\cos^2 t - \sin t)$

13. (a) $\dfrac{x \sec^2 t - y \sin t + z \cos t}{\sqrt{x^2 + y^2 + z^2}}$; (b) $\tan t \sec t$ 15. $\dfrac{txe^t - y}{t(x^2 + y^2)}$ 17. $\dfrac{x + y + 2t + ty - tx}{t(y + t)^2}$ 19. $\dfrac{\partial z}{\partial x} = \dfrac{3y - 6x - 4z}{2z + 4x}$; $\dfrac{\partial z}{\partial y} = \dfrac{3x - 2y}{2z + 4x}$

21. $\dfrac{\partial z}{\partial x} = -\dfrac{z}{x}$; $\dfrac{\partial z}{\partial y} = \dfrac{xyz + 1}{3xy \tan 3xz - xy^2}$ 27. $\dfrac{\partial u}{\partial v} = \cos w \sinh v \dfrac{\partial u}{\partial x} + \sin w \cosh v \dfrac{\partial u}{\partial y}$; $\dfrac{\partial u}{\partial w} = -\sin w \cosh v \dfrac{\partial u}{\partial x} + \cos w \sinh v \dfrac{\partial u}{\partial y}$

29. decreasing at a rate of $\frac{8}{81}$ rad/sec   31. increasing at a rate of 16 in.^{3}/sec

Exercises 19.7 (*Page 939*)

1. (a) $\dfrac{2}{y} - \dfrac{6y}{x^4}$; (b) $\dfrac{2x^2}{y^3}$ 3. (a) $4e^{2x} \sin y$; (b) $-e^{2x} \sin y$ 5. (a) $2 \tan^{-1} \dfrac{y}{x} - \dfrac{2xy}{x^2 + y^2}$; (b) $2 \tan^{-1} \dfrac{y}{x} + \dfrac{2xy}{x^2 + y^2}$ 7. (a) $3y \cosh x$;

(b) $4x \sinh y$ 9. (a) 0; (b) e^y 11. (a) $12r + 4s$; (b) $4r - 30s$ 13. (a) $\dfrac{-320rst}{(r^2 + 4s^2 - 5t^2)^3}$; (b) $\dfrac{16r(5t^2 + 12s^2 - r^2)}{(r^2 + 4s^2 - 5t^2)^3}$ 21. neither exist

23. $f_{12}(0, 0) = -1$; $f_{21}(0, 0) = 1$ 27. $6se^{r-s}(2 + r) - 8e^{-2s}$ 29. $10 \cos^2 \theta + 8$ 31. $-10r \sin 2\theta$

Review Exercises for Chapter 19 (*Page 941*)

1. $\dfrac{2x}{3y^2}; \dfrac{y - 2x^2}{3y^3}; -\dfrac{4x}{3y^3}$ 3. $t^2 \cos st^2 + te^s$; $2st \cos st^2 + e^s$; $2t(\cos st^2 - st^2 \sin st^2) + e^s$ 5. $\dfrac{1}{uw^2}; -\dfrac{2}{uw^3}; \dfrac{2}{u^2w^3}$

7. (a) $\dfrac{\partial u}{\partial t} = \dfrac{6y(x+y)}{x^2+y^2} + 3\ln(x^2+y^2)$; $\dfrac{\partial u}{\partial s} = \dfrac{4y(x-y)}{x^2+y^2} - 2\ln(x^2+y^2)$; (b) $\dfrac{\partial u}{\partial t} = (3t-2s)\dfrac{18t}{4s^2+9t^2} + 3\ln(8s^2+18t^2)$;

$\dfrac{\partial u}{\partial s} = (3t-2s)\dfrac{8s}{4s^2+9t^2} - 2\ln(8s^2+18t^2)$ 9. (a) $3x\cos t - 4(y+2x)\sin t$; (b) $12\cos^2 t - 12\sin^2 t - 32\sin t\cos t$ $\dfrac{du}{dt}\Big]_{t=1/4\pi} = -16$

11. all (x,y) such that $|x| \geq \frac{1}{2}\sqrt{y}$; $[0, +\infty)$ 13. all (x,y) such that $|x| \geq |y|$; $[0, \frac{1}{2}\pi)$ 15. all (x,y,z) such that $z > 0$; $(-\infty, +\infty)$

17. all (x,y,z) except $y = \pm z$; $(-\infty, +\infty)$ 19. $\delta = \min(1, \frac{1}{35}\epsilon)$ 21. limit exists and equals 0   23. continuous at every

point in R^2 25. continuous at all points (x,y) in R^2 not on the lines $x = \pm 2y$ 27. continuous at all points (x,y)

in R^2 except $(x,y) = (2n+1, 2m+1)$, where n and m are any integers   31. 73 cents

Exercises 20.1   (Page 951)

1. $2\sqrt{2}x + 5\sqrt{2}y$ 3. $3x + \sqrt{2}y + 4z$ 5. -42 7. -2 9. $-3e^{\pi/4}\cos\frac{1}{12}\pi$ 11. (a) $(-4, -4)$; (b) $-2 - 2\sqrt{3}$

13. (a) $\langle -12, 2, 14 \rangle$; (b) $\frac{6}{7}$ 17. $\frac{3}{20}\pi + \frac{2}{5}$; $\frac{1}{4}\sqrt{\pi^2+4}$ 19. $-\frac{29}{11}$; $\sqrt{21}$ 21. $\theta = \tan^{-1}\dfrac{3}{3\pi+1}$ 23. (a) -1; (b) $-\mathbf{j}$; 2

25. (a) direction of $\dfrac{3}{\sqrt{10}}\mathbf{i} - \dfrac{1}{\sqrt{10}}\mathbf{j}$; (b) climbing at 60 ft per ft; (c) descending at $20\sqrt{2}$ ft per ft; (d) direction of $\dfrac{1}{\sqrt{10}}\mathbf{i} + \dfrac{3}{\sqrt{10}}\mathbf{j}$ or

$-\dfrac{1}{\sqrt{10}}\mathbf{i} - \dfrac{3}{\sqrt{10}}\mathbf{j}$

Exercises 20.2   (Page 956)

1. $2x - 2y + 3z = 17$; $\dfrac{x-2}{2} = \dfrac{y+2}{-2} = \dfrac{z-3}{3}$ 3. $4x + 8y + 3z + 22 = 0$; $\dfrac{x+2}{4} = \dfrac{y+4}{8} = \dfrac{z-6}{3}$ 5. $ex - y = 0$; $\dfrac{x-1}{-e} = \dfrac{y-e}{1}$, $z = 0$

7. $x - y - 3 = 0$; $\dfrac{x-6}{1} = \dfrac{y-3}{-1}$, $z = 3$ 9. $x + 2y + 2z - 8 = 0$; $\dfrac{x-4}{1} = \dfrac{y-1}{2} = \dfrac{z-1}{2}$ 11. $3x - 2y - 6z + 84 = 0$;

$\dfrac{x+8}{-3} = \dfrac{y-27}{2} = \dfrac{z-1}{6}$ 13. $\dfrac{x-2}{4} = \dfrac{y+2}{-1} = \dfrac{z}{20}$ 15. $x = 4$, $y = 16$ 17. surfaces are tangent

Exercises 20.3   (Page 966)

1. no relative extrema; $(1, -2)$ a saddle point   3. $\frac{3}{2}\sqrt{3}$, rel max at $(\frac{1}{3}\pi, \frac{1}{3}\pi)$; $-\frac{3}{2}\sqrt{3}$, rel min at $(\frac{5}{3}\pi, \frac{5}{3}\pi)$ 5. no relative extrema;

$(0, \frac{1}{2})$ and $(0, -\frac{1}{2})$ saddle points   7. $(\frac{3}{2}, -\frac{3}{2})$ 9. $(0, 0)$ and $(0, 4)$ 11. $(\frac{6}{7}, -\frac{4}{7}, \frac{2}{7})$ 17. $\frac{1}{3}N, \frac{1}{3}N, \frac{1}{3}N$ 19. $l:w:h = 1:1:\frac{1}{2}$

21. hottest at $(\pm\frac{1}{2}\sqrt{3}, -\frac{1}{2})$; coldest at $(0, \frac{1}{2})$ 23. $\left(0, \dfrac{1}{\sqrt{17}}, -\dfrac{4}{\sqrt{17}}\right)$ and $\left(0, -\dfrac{1}{\sqrt{17}}, \dfrac{4}{\sqrt{17}}\right)$; 1   25. 2 ft by 3 ft by $2\frac{2}{3}$ ft   27. $\frac{65}{4}$

Exercises 20.4   (Page 975)

1. $\dfrac{\partial x}{\partial p} = -1$; $\dfrac{\partial x}{\partial q} = -2$; $\dfrac{\partial y}{\partial p} = -2$; $\dfrac{\partial y}{\partial q} = -1$; complementary   3. $\dfrac{\partial x}{\partial p} = -3$; $\dfrac{\partial x}{\partial q} = 5$; $\dfrac{\partial y}{\partial p} = 2$; $\dfrac{\partial y}{\partial q} = -4$; substitutes   5. $\dfrac{\partial x}{\partial p} = -3$; $\dfrac{\partial x}{\partial q} = -2$;

$\dfrac{\partial y}{\partial p} = 1$; $\dfrac{\partial y}{\partial q} = -2$; neither   7. $\dfrac{\partial x}{\partial p} = -0.4p^{-1.4}q^{0.5}$; $\dfrac{\partial x}{\partial q} = 0.5p^{-0.4}q^{-0.5}$; $\dfrac{\partial y}{\partial p} = 0.4p^{-0.6}q^{-1.5}$; $\dfrac{\partial y}{\partial q} = -1.5p^{0.4}q^{-2.5}$; substitutes   9. $-qp^{-2}$; p^{-1};

$2pq^{-1}$; $-p^2q^{-2}$; substitutes   11. $x = qp^{-1}$, $y = p^2q^{-1}$ 13. 250 units of first sold at \$7.50 per unit and 300 units of second sold at

\$11.50 per sq unit   15. \$2000

Exercises 20.5   (Page 981)

1. $f(x, y) = 2x^2 - \frac{3}{2}y^2 + C$ 3. $f(x, y) = 3x^2 - 5xy + 2y^3 + C$ 5. $f(x, y) = 2x^3y^2 - 7x^2y + 3x - 8y + C$ 7. not a gradient

9. $f(x, y) = \dfrac{2x^2 - 2y^2 - x}{2xy^2} + C$ 11. $f(x, y) = x^2\cos y - x + C$ 13. $f(x, y) = xe^y - x^2y + C$ 15. $f(x, y, z) = 2xy - 5xz + 8yz + C$

17. $f(x, y, z) = 2x^2y + 3xyz - 5yz^2 - 2x + z + C$ 19. $f(x, y, z) = xz\tan y + C$ 21. $f(x, y, z) = e^{x+z} + e^y\ln z - e^x\ln y + C$

Exercises 20.6   (Page 988)

1. $\frac{16}{3}$ 3. $\frac{4}{3}$ 5. $-\frac{5}{12}$ 7. 1   9. 8π 11. $\frac{11}{6}$ 13. $\frac{35}{2}$ 15. $\frac{328}{15} + 2e(e^2+1)$ 17. 3π 19. 8   21. $\frac{1}{3}$ in.-lb

23. $20\frac{3}{4}$ in.-lb   25. $27\frac{3}{4}$ in.-lb   27. $\frac{1}{16}\pi a^4 + a^2$ in.-lb   29. 3 in.-lb   31. $(e^2 + e^4 + e^8 - 3)$ in.-lb   33. $2\frac{1}{2}$ in.-lb

Exercises 20.7   (*Page 996*)

1. $\varphi(x, y) = xy + C$ 3. $\varphi(x, y) = e^x \sin y + C$ 5. $\varphi(x, y) = x^2 y^2 - xy^3 + 2y + C$ 7. $\varphi(x, y, z) = \frac{1}{3} x^3 + \frac{1}{2} z^2 - xy + 3yz + C$
9. $\varphi(x, y, z) = x^2 \cos y - yz^2 - 3x + 2z + C$ 11. 2   13. e^2 15. -4 17. 15   19. -14 21. $\frac{13}{2}$ 23. 4   25. 0   27. 3
29. 4

Review Exercises for Chapter 20   (*Page 998*)

1. $-\frac{8}{3}$ 3. $\frac{1}{4}(1 + \sqrt{3})$ 5. not a gradient   7. $2y + 5z - 12 = 0$; $x = 2$, $\dfrac{y-1}{2} = \dfrac{z-2}{5}$

9. rel max at $(-1, -1)$ 11. $\frac{44}{3} - 3\pi$ 13. $\frac{23}{6}$ in.-lb   15. $9e^2 - 1$ 17. $-5i - 14j + 26k$

19. $2\sqrt{3} \times \dfrac{2\sqrt{3}}{3} \times 2\sqrt{3}$ 21. (a) $-\dfrac{3\sqrt{3}+2}{11}$ degrees per in.; (b) $\dfrac{2}{11}\sqrt{13}$ degrees per in. in the direction $-\dfrac{3}{\sqrt{13}}i - \dfrac{2}{\sqrt{13}}j$

23. 350 units of the first commodity sold at \$3 and 150 units of the second commodity sold at \$1.75   25. $\varphi(x, y, z) = y^2 e^{3z} + z^2 \tan x + C$
27. (9, 11, 15), rel max   29. square base and a depth which is one-half that of the length of a side of the base

Exercises 21.1   (*Page 1007*)

1. 50   3. 1368   5. 704   7. $\frac{203}{4}$ 9. 1376   11. 68.6

Exercises 21.2   (*Page 1014*)

1. 42   3. $\frac{1}{2}$ 5. $\frac{1}{8}$ 7. $\frac{1}{3}$ 9. $\frac{152}{3}$ 11. $\frac{3}{2}\pi$ 13. $\frac{864}{5}$ 15. $\frac{512}{3}$ cu units   17. $\frac{16}{3}$ cu units   19. $(\frac{1}{8}\pi - \frac{1}{15})$ cu units

21. $\frac{1}{12}$ sq units   23. 72 sq units   25. $\dfrac{c}{ab} \displaystyle\int_{-a}^{a} \int_{-(b/a)\sqrt{a^2-x^2}}^{(b/a)\sqrt{a^2-x^2}} \sqrt{a^2 b^2 - b^2 x^2 - a^2 y^2}\, dy\, dx$ 27. (b) $\frac{2}{3}a^3$; (c) $\dfrac{2}{3}\displaystyle\int_0^a \int_0^{\sqrt{a^2-y^2}} (2x + y)\, dx\, dy$

29. $\frac{337}{30}$ cu units   31. $1 - \cos 1$

Exercises 21.3   (*Page 1021*)

1. 12 slugs; $(2, \frac{3}{2})$ 3. $\frac{176}{15}k$ slugs; $(\frac{35}{22}, \frac{102}{77})$ 5. $\frac{2}{3}ka^3$ slugs; $(\frac{3}{32}a(2 + \pi), \frac{3}{32}a(2 + \pi))$ 7. $\dfrac{1}{4} k\pi$ slugs; $\left(\dfrac{\pi}{2}, \dfrac{16}{9\pi}\right)$ 9. $\frac{1}{3}$ slugs; $(\frac{6}{5}, \frac{6}{5})$

11. 9ρ slug-ft^2 13. $\frac{1}{2}\pi\rho a^4$ slug-ft^2 15. $\frac{96}{35}\rho$ slug-ft^2 17. (a) $\frac{144}{5}$ slug-ft^2; (b) 54 slug-ft^2; (c) $\frac{2}{5}\sqrt{15}$ ft; $\frac{144}{5}$ slug-ft^2
19. (a) $\frac{3}{32}\pi k$ slug-ft^2; (b) $\frac{1}{24}\pi(2\pi^2 - 3)k$ slug-ft^2; (c) $\frac{1}{4}\sqrt{6}$ ft; (d) $(\frac{1}{12}\pi^3 - \frac{1}{32}\pi)k$ slug-ft^2 21. $\frac{1}{12}b\sqrt{6}$ ft

Exercises 21.4   (*Page 1027*)

1. 6π sq units   3. $\frac{1}{4}a^2(8 + \pi)$ sq units   5. $(4\pi + 12\sqrt{3})$ sq units   7. 4π cu units   9. $\frac{128}{9}(3\pi - 4)$ cu units   11. $\frac{7}{2}\pi$ cu units
13. $\frac{40}{3}\pi k$ slugs; $(0, \frac{21}{10})$ 15. $\frac{2}{3}\pi k$ slugs; $(-\frac{57}{44}, 0)$ 17. $\frac{20}{3}k$ slugs; $(\frac{23}{25}, \frac{531}{1280}\pi)$ 19. $\frac{112}{3}\pi k$ slugs; $(0, -\frac{24}{7})$ 21. $\frac{5}{64}k\pi$ slug-ft^2
23. $\frac{11}{16}k\pi a^4$ slug-ft^2 25. $\frac{1}{4}\sqrt{2\pi}$ ft   27. $\pi e(e^8 - 1)$

Exercises 21.5   (*Page 1033*)

1. $\sqrt{6}$ sq units   3. 9 sq units   5. 8π sq units   7. 12π sq units   9. $\pi b\sqrt{a^2 + b^2}$ sq units   11. $2\pi a^2(1 - e^{-1})$ sq units
13. 12π sq units   15. $\frac{72}{5}[2 + \sqrt{2}\ln(1 + \sqrt{2})]$ sq units

Exercises 21.6   (*Page 1038*)

1. $\frac{1}{10}$ 3. $\frac{1}{2}\pi - 1$ 5. $\frac{15}{2}$ 7. $\frac{1}{24}$ 9. $\frac{648}{5}$ 11. $\frac{1}{4}$ cu units   13. $\frac{3}{2}\pi$ cu units   15. 4π cu units   17. $\frac{4}{3}\pi abc$ cu units
19. $\frac{1}{28}k$ slugs   21. $\frac{2}{5}(2\sqrt{2} - 1)$ slugs

Exercises 21.7   (*Page 1045*)

1. $\frac{1}{3}a^3$ 3. πa^3 5. $\frac{4}{3}\pi a^3$ 7. $\frac{4}{3}a^5\pi k$ slugs   9. $1250\pi k$ slug-ft^2 11. $(0, 0, \frac{2}{5}a)$ 13. $\frac{512}{75}k$ slug-ft^2 15. $(0, 0, \frac{1}{2})$
17. $\frac{56}{9}\pi a^3 k$ slug-ft^2 19. 18π 21. $\frac{1}{15}\pi(2\sqrt{2} - 1)$

Review Exercises for Chapter 21   (*Page 1046*)

1. $\frac{1}{40}$ 3. $\frac{1}{8}\pi$ 5. $\frac{1}{8}e^4 - \frac{3}{4}e^2 + e - \frac{3}{8}$ 7. $\frac{3}{4}\pi$ 9. $\frac{1}{8}$ 11. $\frac{1}{3}$ 13. $\frac{1}{2}\pi \ln 2$ 15. $\frac{1}{2}(1 - \cos 1)$ 17. 3π 19. $\frac{8}{3}$ sq units
21. $\frac{1104}{35}$ cu units   23. 18 sq units   25. $(\frac{1}{2}\pi - \frac{2}{3})$ sq units   27. $(2, \frac{3}{2})$ 29. $\frac{1}{108}(3\pi - 7)$ 31. $\frac{1}{64}(7e^8 + 1)$ slug-ft^2
33. $k(\pi + \frac{8}{3})$ slug-ft^2 35. $2k\pi$ slug-ft^2; $\frac{1}{2}\sqrt{2\pi}$ ft   37. $65k\pi$ slugs   39. $\frac{32}{5}\pi k$ slug-ft^2

Index

Absolute extrema of functions, 956–966
Absolute maximum value, of functions of two variables, 956
Absolute minimum value, of functions of two variables, 957
Absolutely convergent infinite series, 701
Acceleration, instantaneous, 786
  normal component of, 805
  tangential component of, 805
Acceleration vector, 786, 870
Accumulation point, 893
Addition, of vectors, 748, 820
Additive identity, existence of for vectors, 751, 822
Alternating series, 697
Alternating-series test, 698
Angle, between two planes, 832
  between two vectors, 757, 826
  direction of a vector, 818
Arc, of a curve in R^3, 868
  length of, 779–784
  as a parameter, 794–795
Area, of a surface, 1028–1033
Associative laws, for vectors, 751–752, 822
Axiom of completeness, 669–670
Axis, of surface of revolution, 855

Bases for vector space, 754, 824
Binomial series, 738–742
Binormal vector, 869
Bounded sequences, 667–673

Calculus, fundamental theorem of, of vector-valued functions, 772–778
Cartesian coordinates, rectangular, three-dimensional, 812
Cartesian equations, 764
  of a plane, 830
  in three-dimensional space, 865
Cauchy-Riemann equations, 941
Center, of curvature, 804
  of mass, 1016–1018
  of a sphere, 815
Center-radius form, of an equation of a sphere, 816
Central quadrics, 859
Chain rule, general, 926–932

Circle, of curvature, 800
  osculating, 800
Circular helix, 866
Closed ball, 889
Closed disk, 890
Closed rectangle, 1002
Commodities, complementary, 968
  substitute, 968
Common logarithms, table of, A-14–A-15
Commutative laws, for vectors, 751–752, 757, 822, 825
Comparison test, 685–687
Complementary commodities, 968
Completeness, axiom of, 669–670
Components of a vector, 746, 761, 818, 826
Composite function, 884
Conditionally convergent infinite series, 701
Cone, elliptic, 862
  right-circular, 857
Conservative force field, 993
Constant terms, infinite series of, 673–683
Constrained extrema, 963
Constraint, 963
Continuity, and differentiability, 916
  on an open ball, 903
  of a function of more than one variable, 900–904
  of a vector-valued function, 772
Continuous differentiability, 920
Continuous function, 881
Contour curve of a function, 886
Contour map, 886
Convergence, interval of, 711
  radius of, 711
Convergent infinite series, 675
Convergent sequence, 664, 670–672
Coordinates, cylindrical, 872–876
  and triple integrals, 1039–1042
  left-handed, 811
  and double integrals, 1022–1026
  rectangular cartesian, 812
  spherical, 872–876
  and triple integrals, 1043–1045
Cosines, direction, 819
Cost function, joint, 971
  marginal, 971
Critical point, 958
Cross product of vectors, 842–851
Cross section of a surface in a plane, 854

Curvature, 796–803, 868
  center of, 804
  circle of, 800
  radius of, 800
  vector, 799, 868
Curve(s), equipotential, 886
  generating, 855
  in R^3, 864–871
  smooth, sectionally, 985
Cycloid, 769
Cylinder, 852–854
  directrix of, 852
  elliptic, 853
  generator of, 852
  hyperbolic, 853
  parabolic, 853
  of revolution, 855
  ruling of, 852
  as a surface, 852
Cylindrical coordinates, 872–876
  and triple integrals, 1039–1042
Cylindrical partition, 1035

Decreasing sequence, 667
Del (∇), 947
Demand, marginal, 969–971
Demand surface, 968
Dependent variable(s), 883
Derivative(s), directional, 945–951
  ordinary, 908
  partial, 905–912
    applications of to economics, 967–975
    definition of, 905
    higher order, 934–939
  total, 931
  of vector-valued functions, 772, 866
  See also Differentiation
Difference, of vectors, 749, 821
Differentiability, 915
  and continuity, 916
  continuous, 920
  of vector-valued functions, 774
Differential(s), exact, 993
  total, 921–924
Differential equations, partial, 941
Differential geometry, 870
Differentiation, partial, 905
  of power series, 713–721
  See also Derivative(s)

Dimension of vector space, 754
Directed distance, 813
Directed line segment, 746
Direction of a vector, 747, 818
Direction angles, 818
Direction cosines, 819
Direction numbers, 837
Directional derivative, 945–951
Directrix, of a cylinder, 852
Discontinuity, essential, 901
    removable, 901
Discontinuous function, 900
Displacement vector, 761
Distance, between two points, 814
    directed, 813
    from a point to a line, 827
    from a point to a plane, 834–835
Distributive law, for vectors, 752, 757,
        822, 825, 844
Divergent infinite series, 675
Divergent sequence, 664
Domain of a function, 881
Dot product of vectors, 756–762, 825–828
Double integral, 1002–1007
    definition of, 1003
    evaluation of, 1008–1014
    in polar coordinates, 1022–1026

Economics, applications of partial deriva-
        tives to, 967–975
Edges of a rectangle, 1002
Elements of a sequence, 660
Ellipsoid, 858
    of revolution, 856
Elliptic cone, 862
Elliptic cylinder, 853
Elliptic hyperboloid, of one sheet, 858
    of two sheets, 859
Elliptic integral, 808
Elliptic paraboloid, 861
Epicycloid, 809
Equation(s), cartesian, 764, 865
    graph of, 815
    linear, 835
    parametric, 764, 837, 865
    of a plane, 830
    of a sphere, 816
    of a straight line in R^3, 836–840
        parametric, 837
        symmetric, 837
    vector, 764, 865
Equipotential curves, 886
Equipotential surfaces, 951
Essential discontinuity, 901
Exact differential, 993
Existence theorem, 671
    table of, A-5–A-11
Exponential functions, table of, A-5–A-11
Extrema, absolute, 956–966
    constrained, 963
    free, 963

of functions of two variables, 956–966
    relative, 957
Extreme value theorem, for functions of
        two variables, 957

Field(s), force, 982
    gradient, 993
Finite sequence, 660
Force field, 982
    conservative, 993
Free extrema, 963
Function(s), absolute extrema of, 956–966
    composite, 884
    continuity of, with more than one vari-
            able, 900–904
        on an open ball, 903
    continuously differentiable, 920
    contour curves of, 886
    definition of, 881
    derivate of, total, 931
    differentiability of, 913–920
    discontinuous, 900
    domain of, 881
    gradient of, 947–951, 976–981
    graph of, 885
    integrable, 1003
    level curves of, 886
    level surface of, 887
    limit of, with more than one variable,
            889–898
    maximum value of, 956–966
        absolute, 956
        relative, 957
    minimum value of, 956–966
        absolute, 957
        relative, 957
    of more than one variable, 881–887
        continuity of, 900–904
        limits of, 889–898
    of n variables, 881, 883, 963–966
    obtaining of from its gradient, 976–981
    polynomial, 884
    potential, 993
    range of, 881
    rational, 885
    relative extrema of, 957
    of several variables, differential calculus
            of, 881–943
    total differential of, 921–924
    of two variables, absolute maximum
            value of, 956
        absolute minimum value of, 957
        extrema of, 956–966
        extreme-value theorem for, 957
        relative maximum value of, 957
        relative minimum value of, 957
    vector-valued, 763, 778, 864
        calculus of, 772–778

Gas, ideal, law of, 910

Generating curve of a surface of revolu-
        tion, 855
Generator, of a cylinder, 852
Geometric series, 678–679
Geometry, differential, 870
Gradient field, 993
Gradient of a function, 947–951
    obtaining a function from, 976–981
Gradient vector, 947
Graph(s), of equations, 815
    of a function, 885
Greatest lower bound of a sequence, 669
Gyration, radius of, 1019

Harmonic series, 676–677
Helix, 866
    circular, 866
Higher-order partial derivatives, 934–939
Hyperbola, unit, 768
Hyperbolic cylinder, 853
Hyperbolic functions, table of, A-12
Hyperbolic paraboloid, 861
Hyperbolic radian, 768
Hyperboloid, of revolution, 856
Hyperharmonic series, 692
Hypocycloid, 771

Ideal gas law, 910
Increasing sequence, 667
Increment of function of two variables,
        914
Independent variables, 883
Independent vectors, 756, 824
Inertia, moment of, 1018–1021
    polar, 1018
Infinite sequence, 660
Infinite series, 660–744
    absolutely convergent, 701
    alternating, 697
    alternating-series test, 698
    binomial, 738–742
    comparison test, 685–687
    conditionally convergent, 701
    of constant terms, 673–683
    convergent, 675
    definition of, 673
    divergent, 675
    geometric, 678–679
    harmonic, 676–677
    hyperharmonic, 692
    integral test, 694–696
    limit comparison test, 687–690
    Maclaurin, 731
    p, 692
    partial sum of, 674
    of positive and negative terms, 697–706
    of positive terms, 684–693
    power series, 707–712
        differentiation of, 713–721
        integration of, 722–728
        interval of convergence of, 711

radius of convergence of, 711
ratio test, 703–706
remainder of, 699
sum of, 675
Taylor, 729–737
terms of, 673
Initial point, 746
Inner product, 756–762
Instantaneous acceleration, 786
Instantaneous velocity, 785
Integrable function, 1003
Integral(s), double, 1002–1007
  definition of, 1003
  evaluation of, 1008–1014
  in polar coordinates, 1022–1026
  elliptic, 808
  iterated, 1009
  line, 981–988
    independent of the path, 989–996
  multiple, 1002
  single, 1002
  test, 694–696
  triple, 1034–1037
    in cylindrical coordinates, 1039–1042
    definition of, 1034
  See also Integration
Integration, multiple, 1002–1045
  of power series, 722–728
  region of, 1002
  See also Integral(s)
Intercepts, of a plane, 831
Interval, of convergence of power series, 711
Isothermal surface, 951
Isothermals, 886
Iterated integrals, 1009

Joint-cost function, 971

Lagrange, Joseph, 963
Lagrange multipliers, 975
Laplace's equation, 940
Least upper bound of a sequence, 669
Left-handed system, 811
Length of arc, of curves, 779–784, 868
  as a parameter, 794–795
Level curve of a function, 886
Level surface of a function, 887
Limit(s), of functions of more than one
    variable, 889–898
  of a sequence, 662
  of a vector-valued function, 772, 866
Limit comparison test, 687–688
Line(s), equations of in R^3, 836–840
  normal, 954
  tangent, 955
Line integrals, 981–988
  independent of the path, 989–996
Line segment, directed, 746
  midpoint of, 815
Linear equation, 831

Lower bound of a sequence, 668
  greatest, 669

Maclaurin series, 731
Magnitude of a vector, 747, 818
Map, contour, 886
Marginal cost function, 971
Marginal demand, 969–971
Mass, center of, of a lamina, 1016–1018
  definition of, 1017
Maximum value of a function, 956–966
  of functions of two variables, 956
  of functions of two variables, 957
Midpoint of a line segment, 815
Minimum value of a function, 956–966
  absolute, of functions of two variables, 957
  relative, of functions of two variables, 957
Moment, of inertia, 1018–1021
  polar, 1018
Monotonic sequence, 663–673
Motion, plane, 785–791
Moving trihedral, 869
Multiple integral, 1002
Multiple integration, 1002–1045
Multiplication of vectors, 842
  cross-product, 842–851
  dot product, 756–762, 825–828
  scalar, 749–750, 751–755, 821
Muzzle speed, 788

n-dimensional number space, 881
Natural logarithms, table of, A-3–A-4
Noncentral quadrics, 861
Norm of partition, 1002, 1022, 1035
Normal component of acceleration, 805
Normal line, to a surface, 954
Normal vector, to a plane, 829
  to a surface, 953
  unit, 792, 869
Number space, n-dimensional, 881
  three-dimensional, 811–817
Numerical tables, A-2–A-15

Oblate spheroid, 858
Octants, 812
One-to-one correspondence, 746, 812
Open ball, 889
  continuity of a function on, 903
Open disk, 890
Open rectangle, 1002
Ordered n-tuple, 881
Ordered pair, 746, 882
Ordered triple, 811
Ordinary derivative, 908
Origin, 811
Orthogonal vectors, 759, 828
Osculating circle, 800

p series, 692

Pair, ordered, 746, 882
Parabolic cylinder, 853
Paraboloid, elliptic, 861
  hyperbolic, 861
  of revolution, 856
Parallel planes, 832
Parallel vectors, 758–759, 827–828
Parallelogram law, 749
Parameter, 764
Parametric equations, 763–770
  of a line, 837
  in R^3, 865
Partial derivatives, 905–912
  applications of to economics, 967–975
  higher-order, 934–939
Partial differential equations, 941
Partial differentiation, 905
Partial sum of an infinite series, 674
Partial sums, sequence of, 674
Partition, cylindrical, 1035
  norm of, 1002, 1022, 1035
Perfectly competitive market, 973
Perpendicular planes, 833
Perpendicular vectors, 759
Plane motion, 785–791
Plane(s), 829–835
  angle between, 832
  cartesian equations of, 830
  definition of, 829
  equation of, 829
  parallel, 832
  perpendicular, 833
  tangent, 953–956
  traces of, 831
Point, accumulation, 893
  critical, 958
  in n-dimensional number space, 881
  saddle, 958
  in three-dimensional number space, 811
Point-sphere, 816
  are length in, 784
  double integrals in, 1022–1026
Polar moment of inertia, 1018
Polynomial function, 884
Position representation, of a vector, 746, 818
Position vector, 764, 870
Potential function, 993
Power series, 707–712
  differentiation of, 713–722
  integration of, 722–728
  interval of convergence of, 711
  radius of convergence of, 711
Powers and roots, table of, A-2
Principal part of a function, 921
Product, of vector and a scalar, 750, 820
  cross, 842–851
  dot, 756–762, 825–828
  triple scalar, 847
Production function, 973

Projectile, motion of, 787–791
  muzzle speed of, 788
Projection, scalar, of vectors, 759–760, 826
Prolate spheroid, 858

Quadric surfaces, 858–864
  central, 859
  noncentral, 861

R^3 (three-dimensional number space),
    811–817
  curves in, 864–871
    graph of an equation in, 815
    lines in, 836–840
Radian, hyperbolic, 768
Radius, of convergence of a power series,
    711
  of curvature, 800
  of a sphere, 815
Radius vector, 764
Range of a function, 881
Ratio test, 703–706
Rational function, 885
Real vector space, 753–755
  basis of, 754
  dimension of, 754
Rectangle(s), closed, 1002
  edges of, 1002
  open, 1002
  vertices of, 1002
Rectangular cartesian coordinates, three-
    dimensional, 812
Region of integration, 1002
Relative extrema, 957
Relative maximum value, of a function, of
    functions of two variables, 957
Relative minimum value, of functions
    of two variables, 957
Remainder in infinite series, 699
Removable discontinuity, 901
Representation of a vector, 746
Revolution, cylinders of, 855
  ellipsoid of, 856
  hyperboloid of, 856
  paraboloid of, 856
  surfaces of, 854–857
Right-circular cone, 857
Right-handed system, 811
Ruling of a cylinder, 852

Saddle point, 958
Scalar, 749
Scalar multiplication of vectors, 749–750,
    751–755, 820
Scalar (dot) product, 756–762, 825–828
Scalar projection of vectors, 760, 826
Second derivative test for relative ex-
    trema, for functions of two vari-
    ables, 959–963
Sectionally smooth curve, 985

Sequence(s), 660–673
  bounded, 667–673
  convergent, 664, 670–672
  decreasing, 667
  definition of, 660
  divergent, 664
  elements of, 660
  finite, 660
  greatest lower bound of, 669
  increasing, 667
  infinite, 660
  least upper bound of, 669
  limit of, 662
  lower bound of, 668
  monotonic, 667–673
  of partial sums, 674
  strictly decreasing, 667
  strictly increasing, 667
  upper bound of, 668
Series. See Infinite series
Side condition, 963
Single integral, 1002
Smooth curve, 985
Speed, 786, 870
  muzzle, 788
Sphere, 815, 858
  center of, 815
  equation of, center-radius form of, 816
    general form of, 816
  point-, 816
  radius of, 815
Spherical coordinates, 872–876
  and triple integrals, 1039–1042
Spheroid, 858
  oblate, 858
  prolate, 858
Strictly decreasing sequence, 667
Strictly increasing sequence, 667
Substitute commodities, 968
Subtraction, of vectors, 749, 821
Sum, of infinite series, 675
  partial, sequence of, 674
  of vectors, 748–749, 820
Surface(s), 815, 852
  area of, 1028–1033
  demand, 968
  equipotential, 951
  isothermal, 951
  level, 887
  quadric, 858–864
  of revolution, 854–857
Symmetric equations of a line, 837

Tables, numerical, A-2–A-15
Tangent line, 955
Tangent plane, 953–956
Tangent vector, unit, 792, 869
Tangential component of acceleration, 805
Taylor series, 729–737
Terminal point, 746

Terms of infinite series, 673
Three-dimensional rectangular cartesian
    coordinates, 812
Three-dimensional number space (R^3),
    811–817
  cartesian equations in, 865
  vectors in, 818–824
Total differential of a function, 921–924
Total derivative, 931
Traces of a plane, 831
Tractrix, 771
Trigonometric functions, table of, A-13
Trihedral, moving, 869
Triple integral, 1034–1037
  in cylindrical coordinates, 1039–1042
  in spherical coordinates, 1043–1045
Triple scalar product of vectors, 847
Triple, ordered, 811
Twisted cubic, 866

Unit binormal vector, 869
Unit hyperbola, 768
Unit normal vector, 792, 869
Unit tangent vector, 792, 869
Unit vector, 754, 820
Upper bound of a sequence, 668
  least, 669

Variables, dependent, 883
  independent, 883
Vector(s), 746
  acceleration, 786, 870
    normal component of, 805
    tangential component of, 805
  addition of, 748–749, 751–755, 820
  analysis of, 746
  angle between, 757, 826
  associative laws for, 751–752, 822, 844
  commutative laws for, 751–752, 757,
    822, 825
  components of, 746, 761, 826
  cross product of, 842–851
  curvature, 799, 868
  difference of, 749, 821
  direction of, 747, 818
  direction angles of, 818
  direction cosines of, 819
  displacement, 761
  distributive laws for, 752, 757, 822, 825,
    844
  dot product of, 756–762, 825–828
  equation, 764, 865
  existence of additive identity for, 751,
    822
  existence of negative for, 751, 822
  existence of scalar multiplicative iden-
    tity for, 751, 822
  gradient, 947
  independent, 756, 824
  magnitude of, 747, 818

multiplication of, 749–750, 751–755, 756–762, 821, 842
negative of, 749, 820
normal, 829, 953
orthogonal, 759, 828
parallel, 758–759, 827–828
in the plane, 746–750
position, 764, 870
position representation of, 746, 818
product, 750, 842
   dot, 756–762
projection of onto another vector, 759–760, 826
quantities, 746
radius, 764
scalar multiplication of, 749–750, 751–755, 820
scalar (dot) product of, 756–762, 825–828

scalar projection of, 760, 826
space, 753–755
   basis for, 754, 824
   dimension of, 754
subtraction of, 749, 821
sum of, 748–749, 820
in three-dimensional space, 818–824
triple scalar product of, 847
unit, 754, 820
unit binormal, 869
unit normal, 792, 869
unit tangent, 792, 869
velocity, 785, 870
zero, 747, 818
Vector-valued function(s), 763–778, 864
calculus of, 772–778
continuity of, 772
derivatives of, 765–766, 773–778, 866–867

differentiability of, 774
graph of, 764
limits of, 772, 866
Velocity, instantaneous, 785
Velocity vector, 785, 870
Vertex, of a rectangle, 1002

Work, 761, 983

x coordinate, 812
x intercept, of a plane, 831

y coordinate, 812
y intercept, of a plane, 831

z coordinate, 812
z intercept, of a plane, 831
Zero vector, 747, 818

44. $\int \dfrac{u^2\,du}{\sqrt{a^2-u^2}} = -\dfrac{u}{2}\,\sqrt{a^2-u^2} + \dfrac{a^2}{2}\,\sin^{-1}\dfrac{u}{a} + C$

45. $\int \dfrac{du}{u\,\sqrt{a^2-u^2}} = -\dfrac{1}{a}\,\ln\left|\dfrac{a+\sqrt{a^2-u^2}}{u}\right| + C$

$ = -\dfrac{1}{a}\,\cosh^{-1}\dfrac{a}{u} + C$

46. $\int \dfrac{du}{u^2\,\sqrt{a^2-u^2}} = -\dfrac{\sqrt{a^2-u^2}}{a^2 u} + C$

47. $\int (a^2-u^2)^{3/2}\,du = -\dfrac{u}{8}\,(2u^2-5a^2)\,\sqrt{a^2-u^2} + \dfrac{3a^4}{8}\,\sin^{-1}\dfrac{u}{a} + C$

48. $\int \dfrac{du}{(a^2-u^2)^{3/2}} = \dfrac{u}{a^2\,\sqrt{a^2-u^2}} + C$

Forms Containing $2au - u^2$

49. $\int \sqrt{2au-u^2}\,du = \dfrac{u-a}{2}\,\sqrt{2au-u^2} + \dfrac{a^2}{2}\,\cos^{-1}\left(1-\dfrac{u}{a}\right) + C$

50. $\int u\,\sqrt{2au-u^2}\,du = \dfrac{2u^2-au-3a^2}{6}\,\sqrt{2au-u^2}$

$ + \dfrac{a^3}{2}\,\cos^{-1}\left(1-\dfrac{u}{a}\right) + C$

51. $\int \dfrac{\sqrt{2au-u^2}\,du}{u} = \sqrt{2au-u^2} + a\,\cos^{-1}\left(1-\dfrac{u}{a}\right) + C$

52. $\int \dfrac{\sqrt{2au-u^2}\,du}{u^2} = -\dfrac{2\,\sqrt{2au-u^2}}{u} - \cos^{-1}\left(1-\dfrac{u}{a}\right) + C$

53. $\int \dfrac{du}{\sqrt{2au-u^2}} = \cos^{-1}\left(1-\dfrac{u}{a}\right) + C$

54. $\int \dfrac{u\,du}{\sqrt{2au-u^2}} = -\sqrt{2au-u^2} + a\,\cos^{-1}\left(1-\dfrac{u}{a}\right) + C$

55. $\int \dfrac{u^2\,du}{\sqrt{2au-u^2}} = -\dfrac{(u+3a)}{2}\,\sqrt{2au-u^2} + \dfrac{3a^2}{2}\,\cos^{-1}\left(1-\dfrac{u}{a}\right) + C$

56. $\int \dfrac{du}{u\,\sqrt{2au-u^2}} = -\dfrac{\sqrt{2au-u^2}}{au} + C$

57. $\int \dfrac{du}{(2au-u^2)^{3/2}} = \dfrac{u-a}{a^2\,\sqrt{2au-u^2}} + C$

58. $\int \dfrac{u\,du}{(2au-u^2)^{3/2}} = \dfrac{u}{a\,\sqrt{2au-u^2}} + C$

Forms Containing Trigonometric Functions

59. $\int \sin u\,du = -\cos u + C$

60. $\int \cos u\,du = \sin u + C$

61. $\int \tan u\,du = \ln|\sec u| + C$

62. $\int \cot u\,du = \ln|\sin u| + C$

63. $\int \sec u\,du = \ln|\sec u + \tan u| + C$

$ = \ln|\tan(\tfrac{1}{4}\pi + \tfrac{1}{2}u)| + C$

64. $\int \csc u\,du = \ln|\csc u - \cot u| + C$

$ = \ln|\tan \tfrac{1}{2}u| + C$

65. $\int \sec^2 u\,du = \tan u + C$

66. $\int \csc^2 u\,du = -\cot u + C$

67. $\int \sec u\,\tan u\,du = \sec u + C$

68. $\int \csc u\,\cot u\,du = -\csc u + C$

69. $\int \sin^2 u\,du = \tfrac{1}{2}u - \tfrac{1}{4}\sin 2u + C$

70. $\int \cos^2 u\,du = \tfrac{1}{2}u + \tfrac{1}{4}\sin 2u + C$

71. $\int \tan^2 u\,du = \tan u - u + C$

72. $\int \cot^2 u\,du = -\cot u - u + C$

73. $\int \sin^n u\,du = -\dfrac{1}{n}\,\sin^{n-1} u\,\cos u + \dfrac{n-1}{n}\int \sin^{n-2} u\,du$

74. $\int \cos^n u\,du = \dfrac{1}{n}\,\cos^{n-1} u\,\sin u + \dfrac{n-1}{n}\int \cos^{n-2} u\,du$

75. $\int \tan^n u\,du = \dfrac{1}{n-1}\,\tan^{n-1} u - \int \tan^{n-2} u\,du$

76. $\int \cot^n u\,du = -\dfrac{1}{n-1}\,\cot^{n-1} u - \int \cot^{n-2} u\,du$

77. $\int \sec^n u\,du = \dfrac{1}{n-1}\,\sec^{n-2} u\,\tan u + \dfrac{n-2}{n-1}\int \sec^{n-2} u\,du$

78. $\int \csc^n u\,du = -\dfrac{1}{n-1}\,\csc^{n-2} u\,\cot u + \dfrac{n-2}{n-1}\int \csc^{n-2} u\,du$

79. $\int \sin mu\,\sin nu\,du = -\dfrac{\sin(m+n)u}{2(m+n)} + \dfrac{\sin(m-n)u}{2(m-n)} + C$

80. $\int \cos mu\,\cos nu\,du = \dfrac{\sin(m+n)u}{2(m+n)} + \dfrac{\sin(m-n)u}{2(m-n)} + C$

81. $\int \sin mu\,\cos nu\,du = -\dfrac{\cos(m+n)u}{2(m+n)} - \dfrac{\cos(m-n)u}{2(m-n)} + C$

82. $\int u\,\sin u\,du = \sin u - u\,\cos u + C$

83. $\int u\,\cos u\,du = \cos u + u\,\sin u + C$

84. $\int u^2\,\sin u\,du = 2u\,\sin u + (2-u^2)\,\cos u + C$